Practical Carpentry's easy-to-understand text and large clear illustrations make carpentry work as simple as A.B.C.

Practical
CARPENTRY

Edited By FLOYD M. MIX, President

Goodheart-Willcox Co., Inc.

and

ERNEST H. CIROU, Carpentry Department

Washburne Trade School, Chicago

HOMEWOOD, ILL.

THE GOODHEART-WILLCOX CO., Inc.

Publishers

INTRODUCTION

PRACTICAL CARPENTRY is an easy-to-understand cyclopedia of information on modern building methods.

Large, clear drawings show house construction details from foundation to roof; reduce the job of building a modern home, or garage, to simple steps. Information is given too, on farm building construction.

Special emphasis has been placed on proper techniques so the apprentice, and the student, may understand and become acquainted with generally accepted carpentry practices and the use of modern building materials.

Information in PRACTICAL CARPENTRY, if carefully applied, will enable the inexperienced builder to do many jobs he was afraid to tackle before; will make any experienced carpenter a better carpenter.

Floyd M. Mix
Ernest H. Cirou

ACKNOWLEDGMENTS

PRACTICAL CARPENTRY contains material secured from hundreds of different sources. The editors want to record here their deep appreciation of the individuals and organizations whose splendid cooperation has made this book possible.

To list all who have contributed to the collecting and presenting of the data would take more space than is available. Some of those furnishing material and helpful advice were:

Alsco, Inc.
Aluminum Window Mfrs. Assn.
Andersen Corp.
Asbestos Cement Products Assn.
Asphalt Roofing Industry Bureau
Bradley Lumber Co.
Carr, Adams & Collier Co.
Congoleum-Nairn, Inc.
Copper & Brass Research Corp.
P. & F. Corbin
Douglas Fir Plywood Assn.
Elastic Stop Nut Corp.
EZ-Way Sales, Inc.
Federal Housing Administration
Flintkote Co.
Forest Products Laboratory
Gate City Sash & Door Co.
Harbor Plywood Corp.
HomOgraf Co.
Kimberly-Clark Corp.
Libbey-Owens-Ford Glass Co.
Maple Flooring Mfrs. Assn.
Masonite Corp.
Metal Window Institute
Mississippi Glass Co.

Morgan Co.
Jay G. McKenna, Inc.
National Board Fire Underwriters
National Gypsum Co.
National Housing Agency
National Lumber Mfrs. Assn.
National Oak Flooring Mfrs. Assn.
National Woodwork Mfrs. Assn.
Pittsburgh Corning Corp.
Pittsburgh Plate Glass Co.
Portland Cement Assn.
Practical Builder
Red Cedar Shingle Bureau
Richey Mfg. Co.
Southern Pine Assn.
Timm Industries, Inc.
U. S. Department of Agriculture
U. S. Department of Commerce
U. S. Department of Interior
U. S. Gypsum Co.
United States Plywood Corp.
Wallace Mfg. Co.
West Coast Lumbermen's Assn.
Western Pine Assn.
Weyerhaeuser Sales Co.

CONTENTS

CONTENTS

CONTENTS

HomOgraf

HOUSE PARTS DICTIONARY

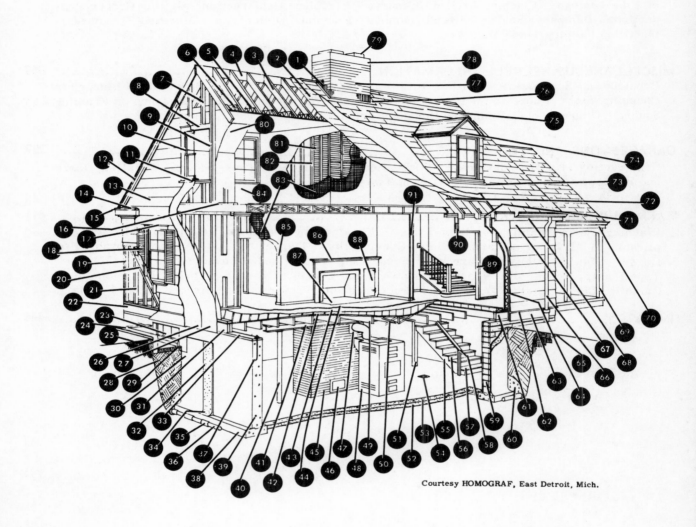

Courtesy HOMOGRAF, East Detroit, Mich.

1. FLASHING	24. WINDOW AREA-WAY	47. THIMBLE	69. PORCH POST
2. ROOF BOARDS	25. GRADE LINE	48. FURNACE	70. PORCH FRIEZE BOARD
3. RAFTERS	26. BUILDING PAPER	49. FLOOR JOISTS	71. TOP PLATES
4. RIDGE BOARD	27. SHEATHING	50. BRIDGING	72. RAFTERS
5. CEILING JOISTS	28. BACKFILL	51. POST OR COLUMN	73. FLASHING
6. CEILING INSULATION	29. AGGREGATE FILL	52. AGGREGATE FILL	74. DORMER
7. GABLE STUDS	30. WATERPROOFING	53. CONCRETE FLOOR SLAB	75. SHINGLES
8. WINDOW HEADER	31. JOIST HEADER	54. FLOOR DRAIN	76. FLASHING
9. ROUGH WINDOW OPENING	32. CEMENT PLASTER	55. STAIR STRINGER	77. MASONRY CHIMNEY
10. WINDOW SASH	33. BOND PLATE	56. STAIR RISER	78. CEMENT CAP
11. WINDOW SILL	34. CEMENT COVE	57. STAIR TREAD	79. CHIMNEY POT OR FLUE LINING
12. GABLE RAKE MOLDING	35. TARPAPER JOINT COVER	58. STAIR RAIL	80. ANGLED CEILING
13. BEVEL SIDING	36. DRAIN TILE	59. CEMENT BLOCK FOUNDATION WALL	81. MASONRY
14. CORNICE RETURN	37. ANCHOR BOLTS		82. FURRING STRIPS
15. GUTTER	38. CONCRETE FOOTING	60. AGGREGATE FILL	83. LATH
16. FLOOR PLATE	39. CONCRETE FOUNDATION WALL	61. JOIST TRIMMER	84. PLASTER
17. DRIP CAP MOLDING	40. PIPE COLUMN	62. DRIP CAP	85. PLASTER ARCH
18. SHUTTERS	41. STEEL BEAM	63. WEATHER BOARD	86. MANTLE
19. CORNER STUDS	42. WOOD SUB-FLOOR	64. WALL INSULATION	87. HEARTH
20. DIAGONAL BRACING	43. FLOORING FELT	65. EARTH	88. WOOD BOX
21. WALL STUDS	44. FINISH FLOORING	66. CONDUCTOR	89. CASED OPENING
22. JOIST TRIMMER	45. MASONRY CHIMNEY	67. FRIEZE BOARD	90. HEADER
23. BASEMENT SASH	46. ASH PIT CLEANOUT	68. FACIA OR CORNICE BOARD	91. PARTITION

Forms
Concrete Work

A house has comparatively few main parts—foundation; floor frame consisting of bearing posts, joists and girders; walls and partitions built of studding; and the roof. Other framing members are incidental to one of these parts.

The purpose of this book is to present in simple, non-technical form, examples of proved construction methods; information that will enable anyone who is handy with tools to build a home that is well designed, sturdy and one that will not require costly repairs at an early date.

LAYING OUT THE FOUNDATION

Our discussion will begin with laying out the building lines ready for the foundation. After the lot has been properly surveyed and permanent markers driven at the corners, we are ready to proceed with the building lines.

One of the best ways to do this job is by using batter boards and what is known as the right-triangle method. The right-triangle method of squaring up a foundation is based on the fact

that a triangle with sides 12, 16 and 20 ft. long, or of similar proportions, is a right triangle and the 90 degree angle, or right angle, is opposite the longest side. See drawing A-1.

USING BATTER BOARDS

Batter boards, Fig. A-2, are used to locate building lines during excavation and construction of the foundation. Right-angle batter boards for the corners are made by nailing two 1 x 2 or 1 x 4 in. boards to three 2 x 4 in. stakes to form a right angle. Straight batter boards are made by nailing one 1 x 2 strip to a couple of stakes.

Next, a base line, either one side or one end is established; corners are marked with stakes; and batter boards are installed.

Other temporary building lines are established and the balance of the batter boards erected. Next, lines should be run between batter boards as indicated in Fig. 1. When length A equals length B the corners are square, if the opposite sides are of equal length.

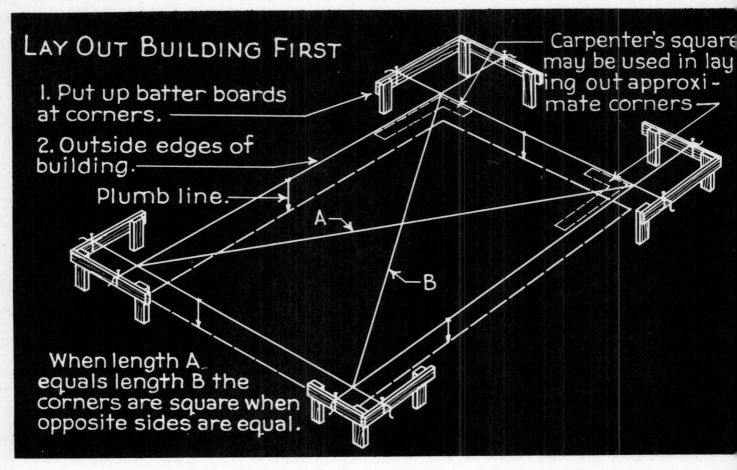

LAY OUT BUILDING FIRST

1. Put up batter boards at corners.

2. Outside edges of building.

Plumb line.

A

B

Carpenter's square may be used in laying out approximate corners

When length A equals length B the corners are square when opposite sides are equal.

A-1. Using batter boards and right-triangle method of locating building lines.

The batter boards should be on an approximate level with each other, but precise leveling is not necessary as the wall heights will be determined later.

MAKING A MITER BOX

A miter box will be found helpful in doing a good job of sawing lumber for the foundation and footing forms, so let's take time out and make one.

The ordinary miter box is a three-sided or trough-shaped box, having both ends open and with slits cut through the sides to guide the saw, Fig. A-3.

The most frequent cuts are 45 degree and square-end cuts. Dimensions of the lumber to be used are given by the drawing. The two side pieces should be screwed to the edges of the bottom piece to form a three-sided box, being careful to have the sides flush with the bottom. Holes should be drilled for screws, to prevent splitting the side pieces. Square a line between B and E, across the top of the box near the middle, marking the line on top of side pieces 1 and 2. Next, measure from point B along the outside edge of side 1, the distance G which should be the same as between the outside faces of the side pieces, and mark point A. From point A draw diagonal line shown as AE. This line will be on a 45 degree angle drawn from one outside face to another. Each end of the diagonal line AE should then be squared down the outside face of

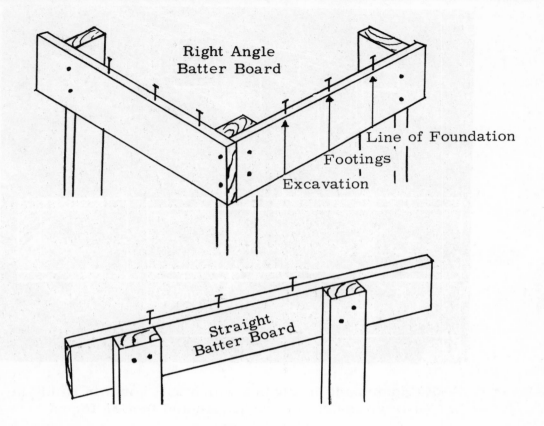

Right Angle
Batter Board

Line of Foundation

Footings

Excavation

Straight
Batter Board

A-2. Straight and right-angle batter boards are made by nailing 1 x 4 or 1 x 6 in. boards to 2 x 4 stakes, and providing lines for excavation, footings and foundation as shown.

each side, to form a perpendicular.

Proceed in the same manner to lay out a second diagonal line BD in the opposite direction, to form an X cut with diagonal A E. Before cutting through on the diagonal lines, be sure there are a couple of screws in each side between points A and B and D and E to securely fasten the short sides thus formed. Saw carefully through the two sides along the diagonal and down the perpendicular lines until the top face of the bottom piece is reached.

Near one end cut a third line CF across the miter box, at right angles to the sides and perpendicular to the bottom, for cutting off square ends.

Special cuts in the box should be made where many cuts of the same or unusual angle are required.

In use, the box is inserted in a vise or temporarily attached to a sawhorse or other base that will serve to hold it stationary.

FOUNDATIONS AND FOOTINGS

No matter how carefully a building may be framed, or how ruggedly it may be built, an inadequate foundation will result in uneven settling, cracking of plaster, ill fitting doors and numerous other difficulties.

A foundation should have sufficient ground bearing area to support the weight of the structure without settling,

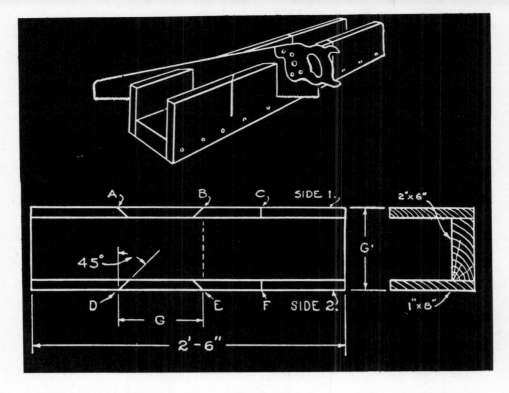

A-3. Homemade miter box which will come in handy in
sawing lumber for foundation and footing forms.

and be so constructed that it will protect the wood frame against moisture from the ground.

Particular attention should be given also to providing of adequate footings. The size of the footings needed varies according to soil conditions. When questionable soil conditions are encountered, such as soft or poorly drained soils, footings should be reinforced with steel bars. In all cases footings should meet local building code requirements.

In the absence of a code, the general practice is to build residential footings having a depth equal to the thickness of the foundation wall and a width equal to twice the wall thickness.

Footings which support cast-in-place concrete walls should be cast with a recess to form a keyed construction joint with the wall as illustrated in Fig. A-4.

When chimney footings are independent of other footings, they should have a minimum projection of 4 in. on each side in a single-story dwelling. For a two-story house, chimney footings should have a minimum thickness of 12 in. and a minimum projection of 6 in. on each side. Exact dimensions will vary somewhat according to the weight of the chimney and the nature of the soil. Where chimneys occur in outside walls or inside bearing walls, chimney footings should be constructed as part of the wall footing. Concrete for chimney and for the wall footings should be cast at the same time.

14

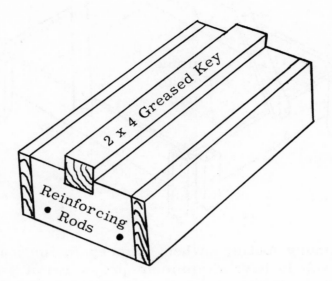

A-4. Footings which support cast-in-place concrete walls should be cast with a recess to form a keyed construction joint.

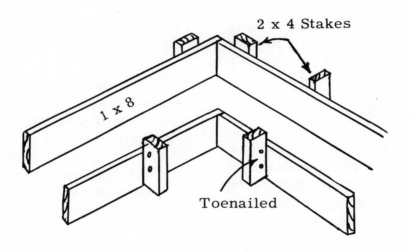

A-5. Constructing form for concrete footing.
Leveling is done with a carpenter's level.

FORMS FOR FOOTINGS AND CAST-IN-PLACE CONCRETE WALLS.

Foundation footings should be poured separately from the walls. A typical footing form is shown in drawing A-5. Drawing A-6 shows a practical way to construct forms for a chimney footing.

Leveling may be done with an ordinary carpenter's level. Greased two-by-fours with the edges slightly beveled should be set in the wet concrete forming keyways for wedges

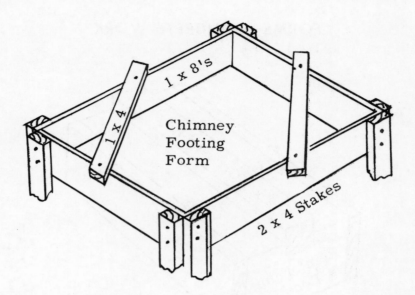

1 x 8's

1 x 4

Chimney Footing Form

2 x 4 Stakes

A-6. Form for chimney footing. When chimney footings are independent of other footings they should have a minimum projection of 4 in. on each side in a single-story dwelling. For a two-story house, chimney footings should be at least 12 in. thick and project a minimum of 6 in. on each side.

which lock the foundation and footing together, Fig. A-4. When the footing forms are in place we are ready for the concrete.

MAKING GOOD CONCRETE

Concrete is a mixture in which a paste of Portland cement and water binds materials known as aggregates (sand, crushed rock, etc.) into a rock-like mass as the paste hardens.

It costs very little more to make good quality concrete than poor concrete, and good concrete is far more economical in the long run because of its durability. A few simple rules, closely followed, assure concrete of good quality.

Each sack of Portland cement holds 94 lbs., equal to one cubic foot in volume. Cement should be a free-flowing powder. If it contains lumps that

cannot be pulverized easily between thumb and fingers it should not be used.

Fine aggregate consists of sand or other suitable fine materials graded from dust to 1/4 in. in size. Coarse aggregate consists of gravel, crushed stone or other suitable material graded from 1/4 in. to 3/4 in. or larger, depending on the job at hand. Coarse aggregates that are sound, hard and durable are best suited for making good concrete.

In specifying a concrete mix, the first number refers to the proportion of Portland cement, the second number the sand and the third the gravel or crushed stone.

In a 1: 2 1/2: 2 3/4 mix, for example, we would have 1 part Portland cement, 2 1/2 parts sand and 2 3/4 parts gravel. A shovel, wheelbarrow

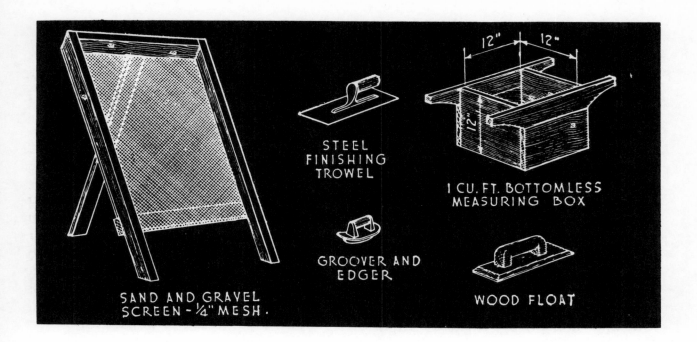

SAND AND GRAVEL SCREEN - ¼" MESH.

STEEL FINISHING TROWEL

GROOVER AND EDGER

1 CU. FT. BOTTOMLESS MEASURING BOX

WOOD FLOAT

Size of aggregate	Trial Mixes			
	Mixing water* per sack of cement	Portland cement	Aggregates	
			Sand	Gravel or crushed stone
	U.S. gal.	Sacks	Cu.ft.	Cu.ft.
Maximum size ¾ in.	5	1	2½	2¾
Maximum size 1 in.	5	1	2¼	3
Maximum size 1½ in.	5	1	2¼	3½

*Based on 6 gal. of water per sack of cement including water contained in damp sand.

A-7. Below. Recommended concrete mixes for basement footings, walls, floors and stairs. Above. Some of the tools and equipment needed for concrete jobs. A bottomless box holding 1 or 2 cubic feet makes a convenient measure for proportioning sand and gravel.

or bottomless measuring box, Fig. A-7, may be used for the measuring.

The table specifies 5 gal. of water per sack of cement (with damp sand) so we would use 1 1/4 gal. for 1/4 sack, 2 1/2 gal. for a half sack, etc.

Mixing water should be clean. A good rule is to use water that is suitable for drinking. The amount of water used per sack determines to a considerable extent the durability, water tightness and strength of the concrete.

In general the less mixing water used, the better the quality of the concrete so long as the mixture is plastic and workable. Some concrete jobs must be stronger and more water-tight than others; therefore, less mixing water is used in making concrete for such work. Six gallons of water to each sack of cement are recommended for basement footings, walls, floors and stairs.

Most fine aggregate contains some water which combines with Portland cement. Therefore, allowance must be made for this moisture in determining the amount of water to be added to the mix. Allowance has been made in the table, Fig. A-7, for the amount of water contained in average wet sand.

If the proportions suggested in Table A-7 do not make a workable mixture in the first trial batch, it may be necessary to vary the proportions of fine and coarse aggregates slightly from those given to obtain a smooth, plastic, workable mix. The amount of cement or water should not be varied from the quantities shown. If the trial proportion used results in a mix that is too wet, fine and coarse aggregates in small amounts should be added until the right degree of plasticity is obtained. If the mix is too stiff, the amounts of fine and coarse aggregates in the next batch should be cut down until the right consistency is obtained. In this way the best proportions for the job can be determined to insure good quality concrete.

MIXING CONCRETE

Concrete should be mixed thoroughly until it is uniform in appearance, with all ingredients evenly distributed. Machine-mixing is preferred and should continue for at least one minute after all the materials have been placed in the mixer. The concrete should be placed in the forms promptly, but in any case within 45 to 60 minutes after mixing. When delay in placing occurs, and the concrete has stiffened, it may be used if its workability is restored by remixing. Under no circumstances, however, should water be added.

PLACING CONCRETE

The method used to move concrete from the mixer to its final position will depend largely upon job conditions. Wheelbarrows are commonly used. Rubber-tired barrows are easier to wheel, and there is less jarring that might cause the coarse and fine particles to separate.

Concrete should be placed as nearly as practicable in its final position. To avoid segregation, it should not be placed in large quantities at a given point and allowed to run or be worked over a long distance.

In general, concrete for walls should be placed in the forms in horizontal layers of uniform thickness not exceeding 6 to 12 in. deep. As the concrete is placed, it is spaded or vibrated just enough to compact it thoroughly and produce a dense mass. Working the concrete next to the form tends to produce a smooth dense surface, free from honeycombing, along the form faces. A spade or thin board may be used for this purpose. Thus the large aggregates are forced away from the forms and any air that may have been entrapped along the form face is released.

Mechanical vibrators are most efficient in consolidating concrete, and permit use of stiffer mixes than when concrete is spaded by hand. However, vibrators create an increased pressure on the forms and this factor must be considered in their design. The vibrator should not be held in one location long enough to draw a pool of grout from the surrounding concrete.

As successive layers of concrete are placed in the wall, the water content of the mix should be decreased progressively to offset the water gain from the lower layers. If this is not done, the concrete becomes wetter than intended with consequent loss of durability and strength in the upper layer. Its nonuniformity will result in discoloration and formation of laitance (foamy scum which rises to top).

To avoid construction seams, it is desirable to complete a basement wall in one continuous operation. If work is stopped before a wall can be finished, the concrete should be leveled in the forms. Just before the concrete hardens, the top surface is roughened to remove laitance or scum and provide a good bonding surface for the next layer of concrete. Unless care is used in providing a good bond between successive layers of concrete, seams may develop and cause leakage.

Before depositing a new layer on the hardened concrete, the top surface should be coated with a cement-water paste mixed to a thick creamy consistency. This paste is applied in a thick brush coat just a few feet ahead of the concreting operations so that it does not have a chance to dry before the fresh concrete is placed.

In warm weather wall forms can usually be stripped after one or two days and in the cooler weather of spring or fall in from four to seven.

To remove all form marks and provide a smooth surface, all exposed inside and outside surfaces can be rubbed with a carborundum stone and a mixture of Portland cement and water.

CURING CONCRETE

To attain the desired durability, watertightness and strength, the concrete should be properly cured. Concrete will harden as long as temperatures are favorable and moisture is present to hydrate the cement.

Concrete should be kept damp during the entire curing period. In the case of walls, the concrete should be protected from loss of moisture as soon as forms are removed by coverings of burlap or other suitable absorbent material which can be kept saturated with water. For basement floors and footings the concrete is kept damp by covering with canvas, burlap, sand, dirt or straw, which are kept wet. Sometimes floors are kept damp by covering with watertight paper.

The length of time the concrete should remain damp depends on the temperature of the concrete and the type of cement used. For air temperatures of 70 degrees F. or more, the concrete should be kept moist for at least seven days with normal Portland cement or three days with high-early-strength Portland cement. For

How to Figure Quantities

QUANTITIES OF CEMENT, FINE AGGREGATE AND COARSE AGGREGATE REQUIRED FOR 1 CU.YD. OF COMPACT MORTAR OR CONCRETE

MIXTURES			QUANTITIES OF MATERIALS				
Cement	Fine Aggregate (sand)	Coarse Aggregate (gravel or stone)	Cement in sacks	Fine Aggregate		Coarse Aggregate	
				cu.ft.	cu.yd.	cu.ft.	cu.yd.
1	2	...	12	24	0.9	..	....
1	3	...	9	27	1.0	..	....
1	1	1¾	10	10	0.37	17	0.63
1	1¾	2	8	14	0.52	16	0.59
1	2¼	3	6¼	14	0.52	19	0.70
1	2¾	4	5	14	0.52	20	0.74

1 sack cement = 1 cu.ft.; 4 sacks = 1 bbl. If concrete aggregates are sold in your locality by weight, you may assume for estimating purposes that a ton contains approximately 22 cu.ft. of sand or crushed stone; or about 20 cu.ft. of gravel. For information on local aggregates consult your building material dealer.

MATERIALS REQUIRED FOR 100 SQ.FT. OF SURFACE FOR VARYING THICKNESSES OF CONCRETE OR MORTAR

Quantities may vary 10 per cent either way, depending upon character of aggregate used. No allowance made for waste.

Thickness of mortar or concrete (in.)	Amount of mortar or concrete (cu.yd.)	PROPORTIONS								
		1:2			1:3			1:1:1¾		
		Cement (sacks)	Fine Aggregate (cu.ft.)	Coarse Aggregate (cu.ft.)	Cement (sacks)	Fine Aggregate (cu.ft.)	Coarse Aggregate (cu.ft.)	Cement (sacks)	Fine Aggregate (cu.ft.)	Coarse Aggregate (cu.ft.)
⅜	0.115	1.4	2.8	....	1.0	3.0	....	....	....	....
½	0.15	1.8	3.6	....	1.3	4.0	....	....	....	....
¾	0.23	2.7	5.4	....	2.0	6.0	....	2.3	2.3	3.9
1	0.31	3.7	7.4	....	2.7	8.1	....	3.1	3.1	5.3
1¼	0.38	4.5	9.0	....	3.3	10.0	....	3.8	3.8	6.5
1½	0.46	5.4	10.8	....	4.0	12.0	....	4.6	4.6	7.8
1¾	0.54	6.4	12.8	....	4.7	14.1	....	5.4	5.4	9.2
2	0.62	7.3	14.6	....	5.4	16.2	....	6.2	6.2	10.5
		1:1¾:2			1:2¼:3			1:2¾:4		
3	0.92	7.5	12.9	14.7	5.8	12.9	17.5	4.6	12.9	18.4
4	1.24	10.0	17.3	19.9	7.8	17.3	23.6	6.2	17.3	24.8
5	1.56	....	....	....	9.8	21.7	29.6	7.8	21.8	31.2
6	1.85	....	....	....	11.5	26.0	35.2	9.3	26.0	37.0
8	2.46	....	....	....	15.4	34.4	46.8	12.3	34.4	49.3
10	3.08	....	....	....	19.3	43.2	58.5	15.4	43.2	61.6
12	3.70	....	....	....	23.1	51.8	70.4	18.5	51.8	74.0

temperatures between 50 and 70 degrees F. the concrete should be kept moist for at least twelve days with normal Portland cement; seven days with high-early-strength Portland cement. The time during which the forms are in place can be counted as part of the curing period.

When concreting is done at temperatures below 50 degrees F. protective measures to insure proper curing and hardening should be taken.

BASEMENT WALLS OF CAST-IN-PLACE CONCRETE

In well-drained locations, concrete that is properly proportioned, placed and cured will provide sufficient protection against moisture penetration. In poorly drained soils, the exterior surface of the basement wall should be given two continuous coatings of hot bituminous material applied with brush strokes at right angles to each other over a suitable priming coat, extending from 6 in. above the ground line down over the top of the footing. When severe ground water conditions are encountered, thicker walls and special reinforcement may be required.

At the time of placing the concrete for foundation walls, dowels should be provided and placed in the concrete for all connecting walls and areaways.

Anchor bolts should be placed in the top of cast-in-place concrete basement walls when they are to support frame construction. The usual practice is to use 1/2 x 8 in. bolts on 4 ft. centers for attaching wood sills. Bolts are set in cast-in-place walls at time concrete is placed.

REINFORCEMENT

Reinforcement is the term used to describe the steel rods or mesh that are placed in the concrete to increase its strength where subjected to forces tending to bend or pull it apart. Care should be taken to place the reinforcement in correct position and in the part of the concrete mass where it will be most effective.

FOUNDATION FORMS

Figs. A-8, A-9 and A-10 show conventional methods of erecting foundation forms structures using wood sheating or plywood, studs, wales and appropriate bracing. Fig. A-11 illustrates the use of prefabricated panels that are assembled on the job site. These panels are designed so that they can be readily removed from

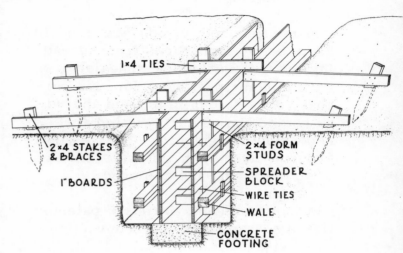

A-8. Suggested method of building form for foundation which is supported on footing.

one job and reassembled on subsequent work.

Forms shown in Figs. A-8, A-9 and A-10 are commonly assembled from 1 in. sheathing boards and are supported by two-by-four studs at 24 in. intervals. Such forms will withstand pressure without bulging from freshly placed concrete up to 3 ft. in depth. For placing concrete in depths greater than 3 ft. the studs should be placed at intervals closer than 24 in. or heavier sheathing used.

The desired smoothness of a wall frequently determines the choice of form materials. When a particularly smooth finish is wanted, plywood or form lining paper is frequently employed. Joints between form boards or panels should be tight to prevent loss of cement paste which will tend to weaken the concrete and result in honeycombing.

Wire ties or tierods are used to keep the two form faces from spreading apart. Soft black annealed iron wire is commonly used for this purpose. It is strong in tension and will withstand the severe twisting that is necessary in tightening. The tie wires are cut flush with the wall surface when the forms are removed.

In many instances tierods or patented ties are replacing the conventional

the forms the proper distance apart. These are cut to a length equal to the desired wall thickness and are placed between the forms before the ties are tightened. These spacers are removed as placed concrete reaches their level.

Some patented ties have weakened sections which allow the metal to be broken off about an inch and a half inside the wall face when the forms are removed. When the broken tie is removed, the resulting hole is patched with mortar, completely embedding

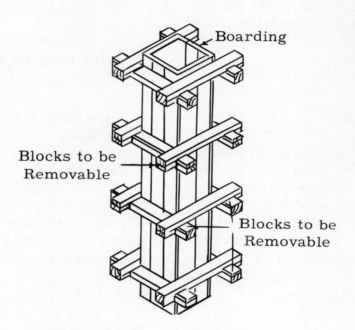

A-9. Form for pier.

wire ties. These are usually easier to install and their use saves considerable time.

When spreader attachments are not part of the ties, wood spacers should be used to keep the inside faces of

the remaining portion of the tie and providing a smooth surface.

To prevent the concrete from sticking to the forms, crude oil, soft soap, or whitewash should be painted on the form faces.

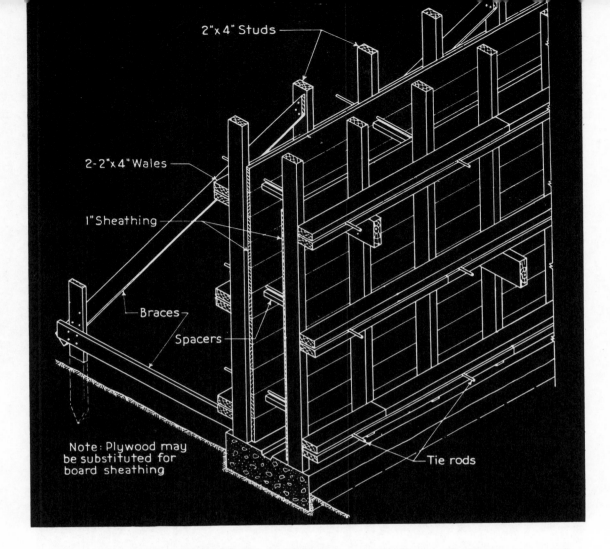

2"x4" Studs

2-2"x4" Wales

1" Sheathing

Braces

Spacers

Note: Plywood may
be substituted for
board sheathing

Tie rods

A-10. Built-in-place form using tierods to
keep the two form faces from spreading.

At the time the forms are being constructed, frames for window and door openings should be inserted, See Fig. A-12. The frames should be fastened securely to the forms to prevent leakage of mortar or displacement during concreting operations. In door openings wedge shaped nailing block may be provided for fastening of door framing, Fig. A-13.

Openings in the basement wall to accommodate the passage of utility connections may be formed by using metal or wood sleeves.

If precast concrete joists are to be used, pockets are usually built at the top of the basement wall, as in Fig. A-14. These pockets should be 1/4 to 1/2 in. larger on each side than the joist and spaced according to the floor framing plan. The pocket form should be beveled and oiled for easy removal.

All forms should be cleaned promptly after stripping, making the lumber available for sheathing, sub-flooring, etc.

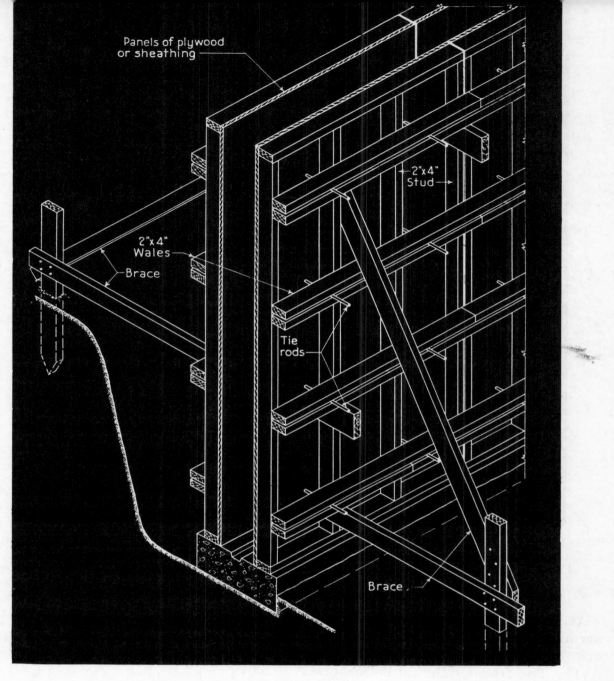

A-11. Form assembled from prefab panels. The panels are designed so they can be readily removed from one job and reassembled for use on subsequent work.

Fig. A-15 shows how to set anchor bolts. Placing is determined by local code requirements and plan specifications. Most plans specify bolts of 1/2 or 5/8 in. diameter, and approximately 8 in. in length. Bolts should be spaced no more than 12 in. from corners and on 4 ft. centers.

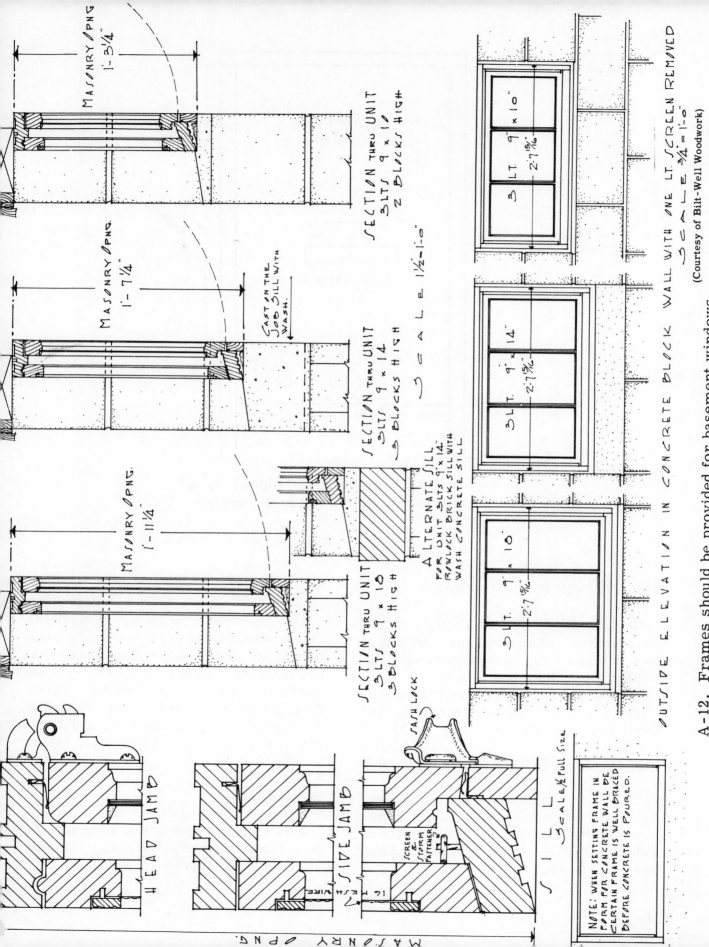

MASONRY OPNG.
1'-3¾"

SECTION THRU UNIT
3LTS 9" x 10"
2 BLOCKS HIGH

MASONRY OPNG.
1'-7¼"

CAST ON THE
JOB SILL WITH
WASH.

SECTION THRU UNIT
3LTS 9" x 14"
3 BLOCKS HIGH

SCALE 1½"=1'-0"

MASONRY OPNG.
1'-11¼"

SECTION THRU UNIT
3LTS 9" x 10"
3 BLOCKS HIGH

ALTERNATE SILL
FOR UNIT 3LTS 9"x 14"
ROWLOCK BRICK SILL WITH
WASH CONCRETE SILL

3 LT. 9" x 10"
2'-7¹⁵⁄₁₆"

3 LT. 9" x 14"
2'-7¹⁵⁄₁₆"

3 LT. 9" x 10"
2'-7¹⁵⁄₁₆"

OUTSIDE ELEVATION IN CONCRETE BLOCK WALL WITH ONE LT. SCREEN REMOVED
SCALE ¾"=1'-0"

(Courtesy of Bilt-Well Woodwork)

HEAD JAMB

SIDE JAMB

SASH LOCK

SCREEN & STORM FASTENER

16 MESH WIRE

SILL

SCALE ½ FULL SIZE

NOTE: WHEN SETTING FRAME IN
FORM FOR CONCRETE WALL BE
CERTAIN FRAME IS WELL BRACED
BEFORE CONCRETE IS POURED.

MASONRY OPNG.

A-12. Frames should be provided for basement windows
at the time the forms are being constructed.

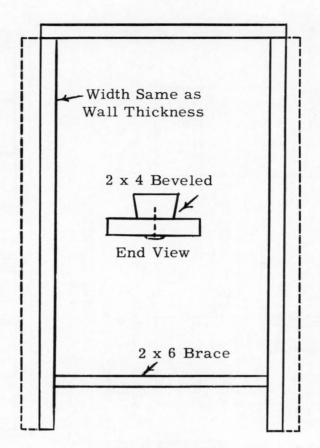

Width Same as
Wall Thickness

2 x 4 Beveled

End View

2 x 6 Brace

A-13. Placing nailing blocks into foundation for anchoring door framing.

PROVISIONS FOR DRAINAGE

Unless the house is being erected in a section of the country having a dry climate, or the subsoil is unusually well drained, a line of drain tile should be placed around the outside edge of the footing and other precautions taken as shown in Fig. A-16.

CONCRETE FLOOR ON THE GROUND

For residences without basements or for unexcavated portions under houses, concrete floors on ground provide an excellent type of construction. See Fig. A-17.

Basementless houses, regardless of the type of floor construction, should not be erected in low-lying areas that are damp or in danger of flooding from surface water. Surrounding ground level should slope away from the house with good drainage and should be at least 6 in. below the finished floor level.

SUBGRADE

It is important that the subgrade be well compacted to prevent any unequal settlement of the floor slab.

The entire subgrade should be rough-graded to an elevation slightly above the finished grade and then thoroughly compacted by tamping or rolling. The finished subgrade should be carefully checked for elevation and profile.

GRANULAR FILL

A coarse granular fill should be placed over the finished subgrade. The fill should be brought to the desired grade and then thoroughly compacted. This granular fill should be made of either coarse cinders, slag, gravel or crushed stone, preferably ranging from 1/2 in. to 1 in. in size. This fill is intended to serve both as an insulating material and as a protection against moisture from the ground. The fill material should be of uniform size particles, without fines, so as to insure a maximum volume of air space in the fill, If necessary, the material should be screened to remove the fines. The large volume of air space will add to the insulating qualities and reduce the capillary attraction for any subsoil moisture.

A line of drain tile should be placed around the outside edge of the exterior wall footings and connected to proper drains to minimize the possibility of ground moisture entering this granular fill. Such moisture would reduce its insulative value. Tile would be unnecessary, however, where the floor is to be located on relatively high ground or where the sub-soil is well drained or is in a section of the country having a dry climate.

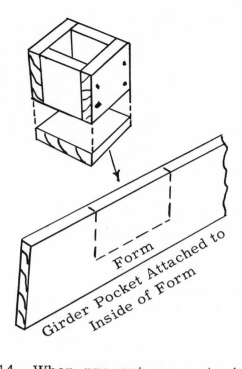

A-14. When precast concrete joists are to be used pockets are usually provided at the top of the basement wall. The pocket form should be beveled and the surface contacting the concrete oiled for easy removal.

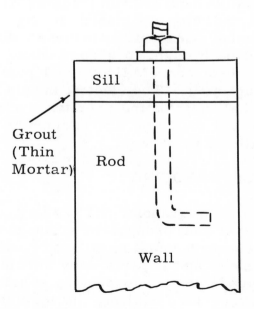

A-15. Setting anchor bolts. Spacing of bolts is determined by plan specifications and local code requirements.

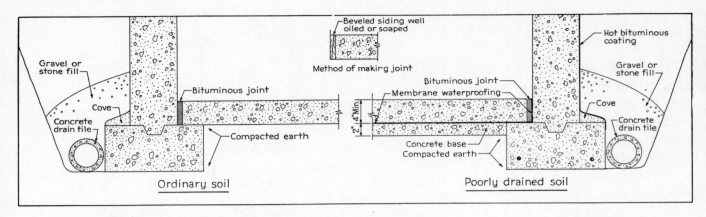

A-16. Some precautions which should be taken to assure a dry basement.

PROVISIONS FOR MECHANICAL TRADES

Where required, provisions can be made for embedding ducts for heating systems and supply and waste plumbing lines under the granular fill. Water service supply lines, if placed under the floor slab, should be installed in trenches of the same depth as those outside the building to prevent any possible damage from freezing in case the building is closed during cold weather. Connections to these utilities can be brought to a point above the finished concrete floor level prior to concreting. The electric supply line and all distributing lines for electricity and plumbing are carried in the walls or partitions.

DAMPPROOFING

After the granular fill has been compacted and brought to grade a stiff grout coat consisting of 1 part Portland cement and 3 parts sand should be placed over it to provide a smooth surface for installing the membrane dampproofing. The grout coat should be at least 1/2 in. thick and should be broomed or floated in place. The grouted surface when hardened and

dried and also the top of any bearing partition footings should be mopped with hot asphalt. As the mopping proceeds and before the asphalt has time to cool and harden, a layer of 15-lb. asphalt-saturated roofing felt should be placed on the mastic with edges of felt well lapped. Two layers of roofing felt are recommended with hot asphalt mopped between layers and also on top of the second felt. This membrane dampproofing should be continuous over the entire floor area and carried up on the inside of the foundation walls to a point 1 in. or more above the finished floor level. Workmen must be cautioned against puncturing the membrane when placing the concrete floor.

CONCRETE

Concrete for the floor slab and bearing partition footing should be made with durable, well-graded aggregate and should contain not more than 6 gal. of water for each sack of cement including the moisture contained in the aggregate. With average moist sand do not add more than 5 gal. of

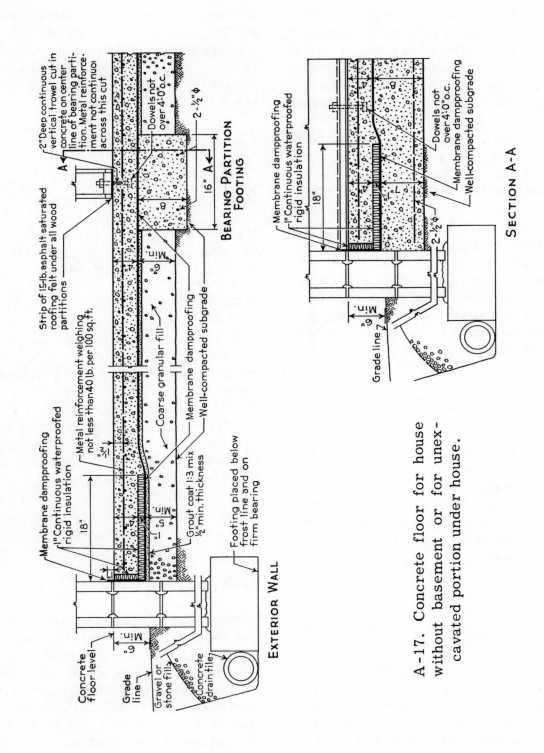

BEARING PARTITION FOOTING

2" Deep continuous vertical trowel cut in concrete on center line of bearing partition. Metal reinforcement not continual across this cut

Dowels not over 4'-0" o.c.

2 - ½" φ

16"

Strip of 15-lb. asphalt saturated roofing felt under all wood partitions

A

A

Metal reinforcement weighing not less than 40 lb. per 100 sq.ft.

Coarse granular fill

Membrane dampproofing

Well-compacted subgrade

Membrane dampproofing

1" Continuous waterproofed rigid insulation

18"

1 - ½"

6" Min.

Grout coat 1:3 mix ½" min. thickness

Footing placed below frost line and on firm bearing

1 - ½"

Min.

Concrete floor level

Grade line

Gravel or stone fill

Concrete drain tile

6" Min.

EXTERIOR WALL

SECTION A-A

Membrane dampproofing

1" Continuous rigid insulation

18"

T

L

2 - ½" φ

Dowels not over 4'-0" o.c.

Membrane dampproofing

Well-compacted subgrade

Grade line

6" Min.

A-17. Concrete floor for house without basement or for unex-cavated portion under house.

water for each sack of cement. The mix should consist of 1 part Portland cement to approximately 2 1/4 parts of fine aggregate well graded from 1/4 in. down, and 3 parts of coarse aggregate well graded in size from 1/4 in. up to 1 in. It should be a plastic mix which can be placed without honeycombing or developing excess water on the surface. If necessary, the proportion of fine and coarse aggregate should be adjusted to obtain a mix of desired workability. The concrete after placing should be thoroughly compacted by vibrating or by tamping and spading after which it should be screeded to proper grade. The subsequent steps in finishing the concrete surface will depend upon the floor finish specified.

KEEP CONCRETE MOIST

For an even true surface, the concrete, after being struck-off to proper grade, should be worked with a wood float in a manner which will compact the surface and leave no depressions or inequalities of any kind. After the concrete has hardened sufficiently to prevent fine material from working to the top (when the sheen or shiny film of water on the surface has disappeared) it should be steel-troweled, but excessive troweling should be avoided.

The concrete should be kept moist for at least two days except when the finished floor is to be exposed concrete. In this case at least five days of moist curing will be required. Moist burlap or canvas or a waterproof concrete curing paper may be used to cover the floor slab during this curing period. Curing should begin as soon as the concrete has hardened sufficiently to prevent damage, and if burlap or canvas is used, it should be sprinkled with water at sufficient intervals to keep it wet.

REINFORCEMENT

Metal reinforcement weighing not less than 40 lb. per 100 sq. ft. with equal cross-sectional area of the reinforcement in both directions should be placed in the concrete slab 1 1/2 in. from the top surface.

INSULATION

A 1 in. thick, continuous, waterproofed rigid insulation strip should be provided between the foundation walls and the edge of the floor slab. Recent studies by the National Bureau of Standards have indicated that this edge insulation is highly important. The granular fill and membrane dampproofing under the floor slab act as an insulating material and in most cases have sufficiently reduced the heat loss to the subgrade.

FLOOR FINISHES

Terrazzo, concrete tile, ceramic tile, asphalt tile, wood flooring, linoleum, small rugs or all-over carpeting are the coverings most widely used for concrete floors on ground. When linoleum, asphalt tile, or other similar resilient-type flooring material is to be applied, the concrete surface should be given a smooth steel-troweled finish. Where other types of floor covering are contemplated, it is recommended that the manufacturer's advice be obtained as to their suitability and the methods of application.

Some concrete floors are troweled smooth in their natural color and may be given a linseed oil treatment or waxed and polished.

Color can be added to concrete floors by incorporating pure mineral oxide pigments as the concrete is placed.

wide may be made of 1 x 8 in. boards; wider steps require 2 x 8 in. forms to prevent bending or bulging when the forms are filled with concrete. If one low riser is needed to complete a set of steps the low step, for safety's sake, should always be the bottom step. To make steps which afford maximum comfort in climbing, the riser form boards may be tilted in at the bottom about 1 in. This provides additional toe space on the treads.

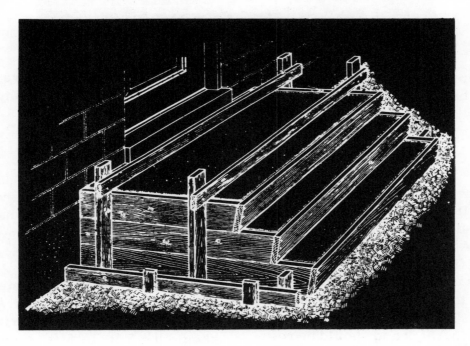

A-18. Building forms for concrete steps. Note that the riser form boards are tilted in at the bottom about 1 in. to provide additional toe space on the treads.

PERMANENT STEPS

Forms for concrete steps may be built as shown in Fig. A-18. Side forms are usually 1 in. boards backed up with 2 x 4 form studs braced and tied as indicated in the drawing. Riser forms for steps not more than 3 ft.

Edges of steps are rounded by finishing with an edging tool after the concrete has become quite stiff. Fig. A-19 on the next page shows forms and constructional details on some practical basement steps.

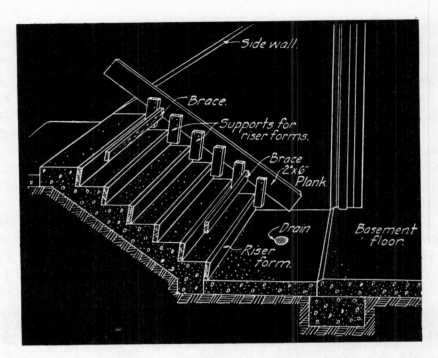

A-19. Forms for basement steps. Riser forms for steps not more than 3 ft. wide may be made of 1 x 8 in. boards; wider steps require using 2 x 8's.

CONCRETE PORCH FLOORS

Where the new concrete porch floor is to be 2 ft. or more above the general ground level, a slab built on a fill, Fig. A-20, makes an excellent floor. The fill of gravel, crushed rock or cinders which supports the floor should be tamped before placing the concrete. The concrete is usually built 4 to 5 in. thick and should be reinforced as shown as a protection against possible cracking due to uneven settlement. It is also important that the thickened edge of the slab be reinforced with two 1/2 in. diameter round reinforcing bars. This construction makes a reinforced concrete beam which spans the distance between supporting piers. The piers are made by filling 8 in. post holes with concrete. At laps the ends of the 1/2 in. bars should extend past each other about 2 ft. Porch floors should be sloped about 1/4 in. per foot toward the outer edge to provide good drainage.

CONCRETE WALKS

Construction of concrete walks is shown in Figs. A-21 and A-22. The most used, or most important walks, should be 3 ft. to 5 ft. wide; less important walks 2 ft. to 3 ft. wide. Walks are usually built 4 in. thick except where heavy vehicles are driven over them, in which case the thickness should be increased to 6 in.

One-course construction; that is, placement of the full 4 in. or 6 in. of concrete in one operation, is desirable. Expansion joints are provided at 4 to 5 ft. intervals along the walk by placing dividing strips at right angles to the side forms. Or, strips

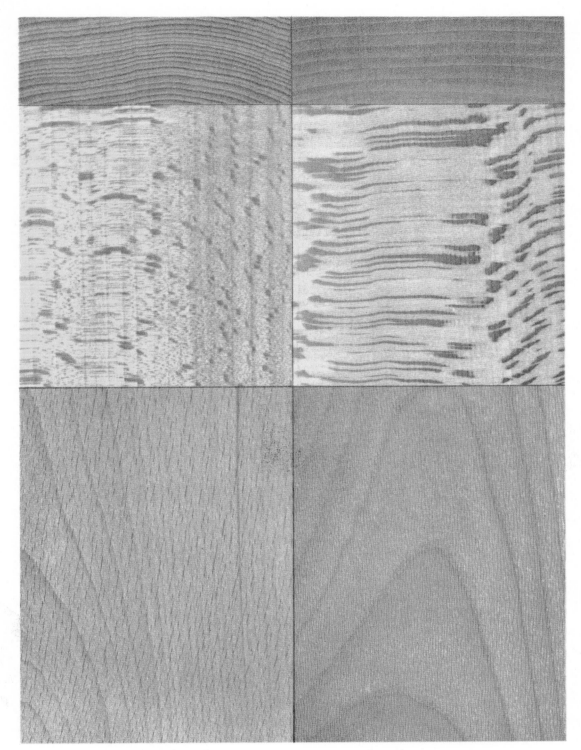

American beech   American sycamore

HARDWOODS (Broad-Leaved Species)

AMERICAN BEECH: A hard, heavy wood which ranks high in nail-withdrawal resistance, but has a tendency to split when nails are driven into it. Beech is not easily worked with hand tools, but machines smoothly with power tools. Heartwood is white with reddish tinge to reddish brown. Pores are not visible without magnification, but wood rays (strips of cells extending radially within the tree) can be seen on all surfaces. Average weight 45 lbs. to cubic foot.

AMERICAN SYCAMORE: Moderately hard, strong and stiff. Ranks high in ability to withstand splitting. Not durable when exposed to conditions favorable to decay. Reddish brown or flesh brown in color with close texture and interlocking grain. Pores are not visible to unaided eye, but rays are visible on all surfaces. Average weight 34 lbs. to cubic foot.

32-A

Rock elm   American elm

ROCK ELM: Stronger, harder and stiffer than other commercial elms. Difficult to work with both hand and power tools. Heartwood is brown to dark brown, and sometimes contains shades of red. Summerwood pores are arranged in concentric wavy lines that appear lighter than the background wood. Springwood pores are visible only upon magnification. Average weight 44 lbs. to cubic foot.

AMERICAN ELM: Moderately heavy, moderately strong. Has good shock resistance and bending qualities; moderate resistance to nail withdrawal and decay. Heartwood is brown to dark brown, sometimes containing shades of red. Summerwood pores which are not visible as individuals, are arranged in concentric wavy lines with boundaries of growth rings. Wavy lines appear lighter than background wood. Shows a springwood pore zone with a single row of large and easily visible pores. Average weight 35 lbs. to cubic foot.

Black walnut   Black cherry

BLACK WALNUT: A wood that is strong, stiff, and has good shock resistance. Holds its shape well after seasoning, is durable, and easy to work with both hand tools and power machines. Finishes beautifully with handsome grain pattern. Color varies from light to dark chocolate brown and occasionally has darker, sometimes purplish streaks. Pores are barely visible on end grain but are easily seen on longitudinal surfaces as darker streaks or grooves. Average weight 38 lbs. to cubic foot.

BLACK CHERRY: Sometimes called wild cherry or choke cherry. Stiff, strong, moderately hard and heavy. After seasoning, is comparatively free from warping and checking. Difficult to work with hand tools but machines well. Sapwood is narrow in old trees and nearly white. Heartwood varies from light to dark reddish brown and has distinctive luster. Wood rays barely visible on end-grain surfaces, but tend to produce flake pattern on quartersawed surfaces. Average weight 35 lbs. to cubic foot.

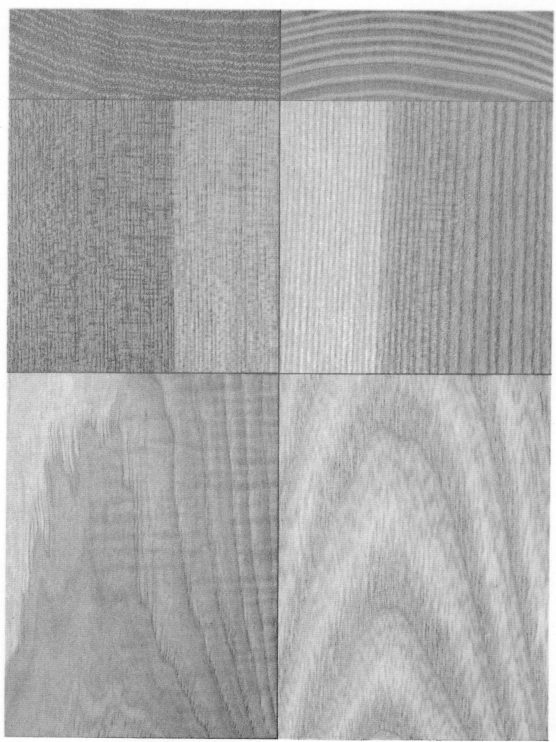

True hickory   White ash

TRUE HICKORIES: Shagbark, shellbark, pignut, mockernut hickories. Very tough, heavy, hard and strong, a combination not found in any other native commercial wood. Sapwood is white, heartwood is reddish. Pores are visible but not sharply outlined as the oak and ash. From standpoint of strength no distinction should be made between sapwood and heartwood. Average weight 42 to 52 lbs. to cubic foot.

WHITE ASH: Strong and stiff. Used extensively in making handles for shovels, forks, hoes, etc. In ease of working, tendency to split and ability to hold nails and screws, it has moderately high rank. Heartwood is brown to dark brown, sometimes with a reddish tint. Sapwood is light colored or nearly white. Zone of large pores is visible and usually sharply defined. Small wood rays are generally visible only on quarter-sawed surfaces. Average weight 42 lbs. to cubic foot.

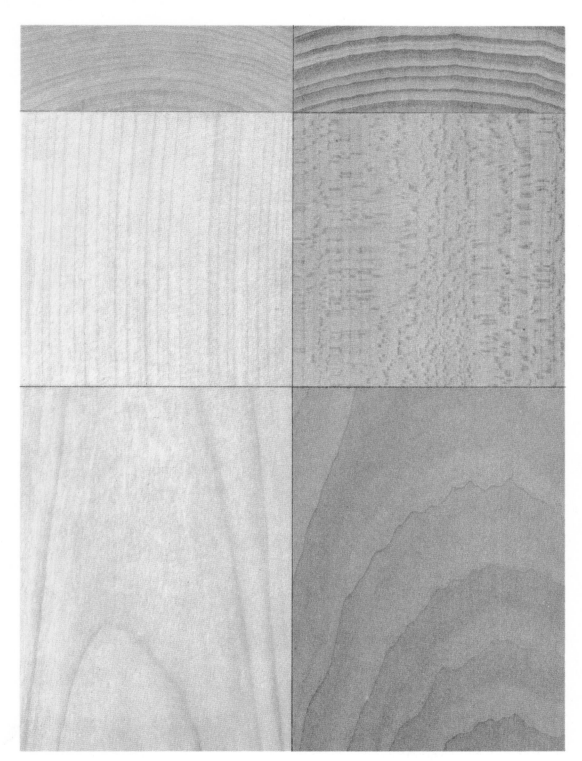

Quaking aspen Basswood

QUAKING ASPEN: Light weight hardwood, classified as soft, weak, and low in decay resistance. Low in nail-withdrawal resistance. Heartwood is white to light brown, with occasional brown streaks associated with defects. Pores are very small and generally not visible to unaided eye. Growth rings usually faint. Average weight 26 lbs. to cubic foot.

BASSWOOD: Soft and light in weight, has fine even texture. Straight grained and easy to work with tools. Highly resistant to warping while in use. Does not split easily while being nailed. Heartwood is pale, yellowish brown with occasional darker streaks. Pores are very small, growth rings generally faint. Average weight 26 lbs. to cubic foot.

Sweetgum   Black tupelo

SWEETGUM: Moderately heavy, and hard, moderately strong. Nail-holding ability and ability to resist splitting by nails, intermediate. Sweetgum lumber is usually divided into two classes—sap gum, the light-colored lumber made from sapwood; and red gum, the reddish-brown heartwood which is illustrated above. Pores are visible only upon magnification. Growth rings are usually inconspicuous. Rays are visible on quartersawed faces. Average weight 36 lbs. to cubic foot.

BLACK TUPELO: Rated as hard, moderately heavy. Heartwood is low to moderate in decay resistance. Moderately weak when used as beams or posts. Ranks below average of other hardwood in machining properties. Has intermediate rank in nail-withdrawal resistance, and to splitting by nails. Heartwood is pale to moderately dark brownish gray, or dirty gray. Pores are very small, as in sweetgum. Average weight 35 lbs. to cubic foot.

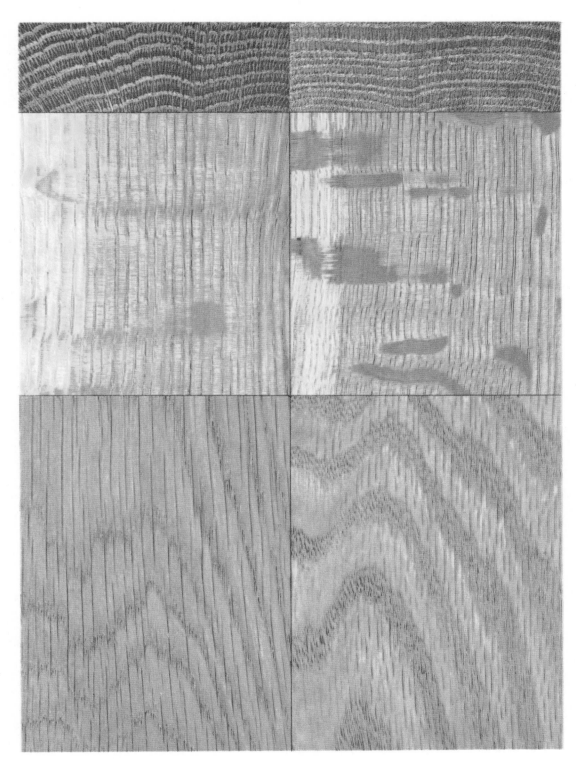

White oak   Red oak

WHITE OAK GROUP: Heavy, very hard, ranks high in strength properties. Pores of heartwood, with exception of chestnut oak, usually plugged with tyloses, a frothlike growth that make wood impervious to liquids. Heartwood is comparatively decay resistant. Above average for machining, except shaping. Heartwood is grayish brown. Outlines of larger pores are indistinct except in chestnut oak, which has open pores with distinct outlines. Wood rays are generally higher than in red oak. Rays appear lighter in color than background wood on end-grain surfaces, and darker than background wood on side-grain surfaces. Average weight 47 lbs. to cubic foot.

RED OAK GROUP: Most properties similar to white oak except pores are extremely porous. Heartwood is grayish brown with reddish tint. Outlines of larger pores are distinct. Wood rays are comonly ¼ to 1 in. high along grain. On end-grain surfaces, rays appear as lines crossing growth rings. Average weight 44 lbs. to cubic foot.

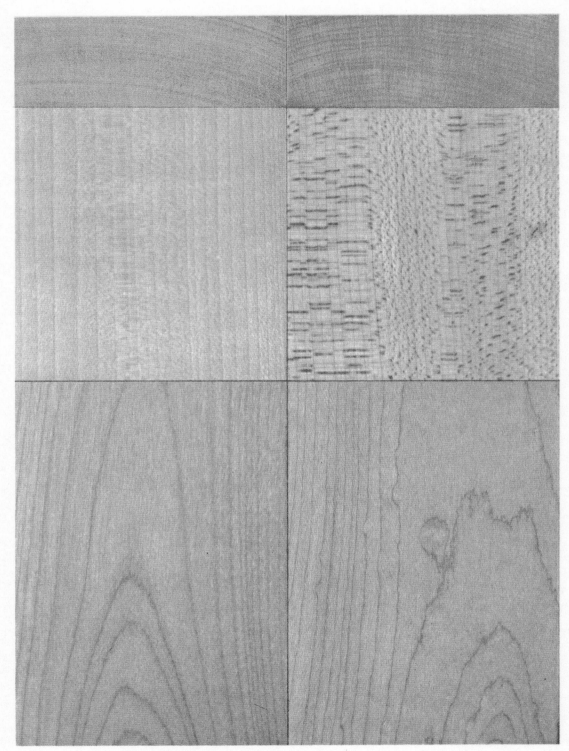

Yellow birch   Sugar maple

YELLOW BIRCH: Fine, close-grained and uniform in texture. Heavy, hard, stiff, takes beautiful natural finish. Difficult to work with hand tools, but easily shaped by machines. Ranks high in nail-withdrawal resistance, low in decay resistance. Light reddish brown in color. Pores are very small. Growth rings moderately distinct on plainsawed surfaces. Wood rays may be seen on quartersawed surfaces. Average weight 43 lbs. to cubic foot.

SUGAR MAPLE: Also known as hard, rock maple, sugar tree, black maple. Strong, stiff, moderately resistant to decay. High in nail-withdrawal resistance. Capable of taking high polish. Occasionally has curly, wavy or bird's eye-grain. Turns well on lathe; is markedly resistant to abrasive wear. Heartwood is light reddish brown. Sometimes shows greenish-black streaks. Pores, extremely small. Wood rays may be seen on end grain, are very prominent on quartersawed faces. Average weight 44 lbs. to cubic foot.

Yellow-poplar   Cottonwood

YELLOW POPLAR: Classed as moderately soft, moderately stiff. Intermediate in machining properties. Low in nail-withdrawal resistance; has little tendency to split when nailed. Holds paint well. Low to moderate resistance to decay. Heartwood is brownish yellow, usually with definite greenish tinge. Average weight 30 lbs. to cubic foot.

COTTONWOOD: Classified as moderately soft to soft, moderate in weight. Low decay resistance. Wood is difficult to work with tools without producing chipped or fuzzy grain. Has low nail-withdrawal resistance, but does not split easily when nailed. It has a good reputation for holding paint. Heartwood is grayish white to light grayish brown. Annual rings are rather wide. Pores are barely visible on smooth cut, end-grain surfaces. Average weight 24 to 28 lbs. to cubic foot.

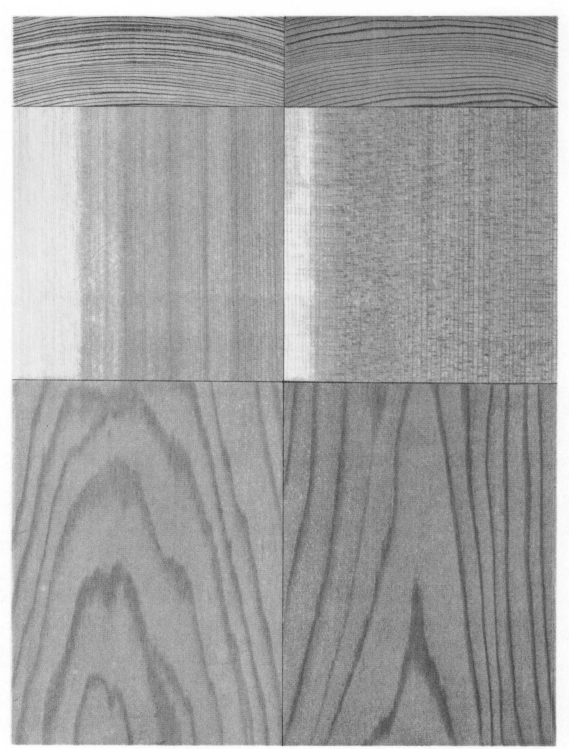

Baldcypress   Redwood

SOFTWOODS (Cone-Bearing Species)

BALDCYPRESS: Technically known as baldcypress but popularly as white, red, yellow or southern cypress, this wood is highly resistant to decay. It has straight, mild grain, is moderately strong, hard and heavy but works easily. Wood of certain cypress trees contains pockets or localized areas that have been attacked by a fungus. Such wood is known as pecky cypress. The decay caused by this fungus is arrested when the wood is cut into lumber and dried. Cypress heartwood varies in color from pale brown to blackish brown and sometimes has a reddish tinge. Average weight 32 lbs. to cubic foot.

REDWOOD: One of the most durable woods for outdoor use. Grain is mild and straight, with smooth, silky sheen and thin, dark lines. Moderately hard, moderately strong and stiff. Has intermediate nail-withdrawal resistance. Is easily worked with hand tools. Takes and holds paint very well. Heartwood is usually uniform deep reddish brown. Average weight 28 lbs. to cubic foot.

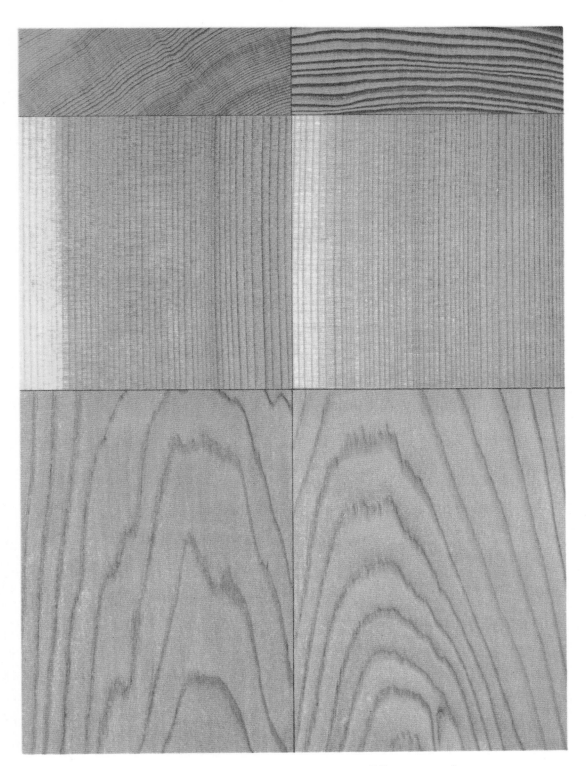

Incense-cedar   Western redcedar

INCENSE CEDAR: Ranks among most decay-resistant woods. Splits easily and is easy to work with tools. Is light in weight, and holds paint exceedingly well. Sapwood is white or cream colored. The heartwood is light brown, often tinged with red, has a fine, uniform texture and a strong, spicy odor. Average weight 26 lbs. to cubic foot.

WESTERN REDCEDAR: Light in weight, moderately soft, weak as a beam or post, and low in ability to resist shock. In decay resistance ranks high. Comparatively low in nail-withdrawal resistance; holds paint well. Heartwood is reddish or pinkish brown to dull brown. Has characteristic cedar odor. Transition from springwood to summerwood is abrupt and makes growth rings prominent on flat-grained surfaces. Average weight 23 lbs. to cubic foot.

Shortleaf pine   Ponderosa pine

SHORTLEAF PINE: Moderately heavy but ranking with lightest of important southern pines. Moderately hard, stiff. Heartwood is moderately decay resistant. In nail-withdrawal resistance ranks above hemlock, spruce and Douglas fir. Like other southern pines, produces resinous substance from which turpentine and rosin can be made. Heartwood ranges from shades of yellow and orange to reddish brown or light brown. Transition from springwood to summerwood is abrupt, with annual rings being prominent on all surfaces. Average weight 36 lbs. to cubic foot.

PONDEROSA PINE: Wood of the outer portions of ponderosa pine of saw-timber size is moderately light in weight, moderately low in strength, moderately soft and stiff. It is generally straight grained and uniform in texture. It is not easily split by nails. Heartwood has low to moderate decay resistance. Heartwood is yellowish to light reddish or orange brown. Transition from springwood to summerwood is abrupt as in southern pines, but summerwood bands are narrow. Average weight is 28 lbs. to cubic foot.

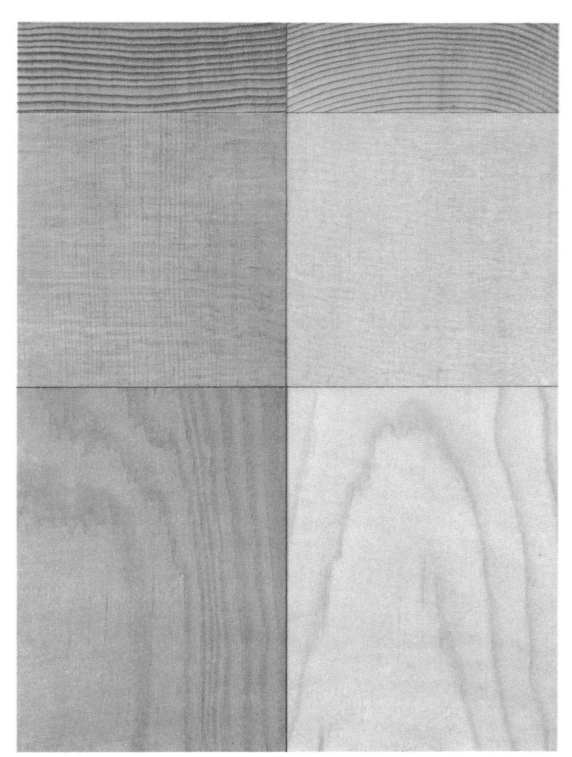

Sitka spruce   Engelmann spruce

SITKA SPRUCE: Also known as yellow spruce, western spruce. Has comparatively fine, uniform texture, generally straight grain, has no distinct odor. On the basis of weight, it rates high in strength properties. Works easily, holds fastenings well, is low in decay resistance. Has tendency to produce wooly or fuzzy grain under action of planer knives. Heartwood is light pinkish yellow to pale brown. Transition from springwood to summerwood is gradual making the annual rings appear rather inconspicuous on flat-grained surfaces. Average weight 28 lbs. to cubic foot.

ENGELMAN SPRUCE: Sometimes known as white spruce, mounted spruce, silver spruce and balsam. Rated as light in weight, soft. Is weak as a beam or post, moderately limber and low in ability to resist shock. Is without characteristic odor. Heartwood is not distinct from sapwood and ranges from nearly white to pale yellowish brown. Transition from springwood to summerwood is somewhat more abrupt than in other spruces. Average weight 24 lbs. to cubic foot.

32-M

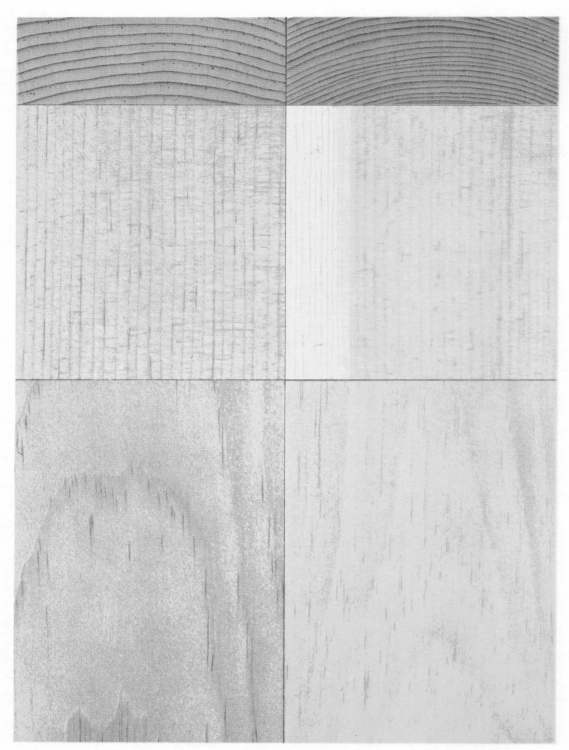

Sugar pine   Western white pine

SUGAR PINE: Straight grained, fairly uniform in texture, easy to work with tools and has good nailing properties. Has very small shrinkage, but is readily seasoned without warping or checking; stays in place well. Light in weight, moderately low in strength, moderately soft, low in stiffness. Moderate in decay resistance. Heartwood is light brown to pale reddish brown. Resin canals are abundant and commonly stain the surface of the wood with resin. Average weight 25 lbs. to cubic foot.

WESTERN WHITE PINE: Also known as Idaho white pine. Wood is straight grained, easy to work, easily kiln-dried and stays in place well after seasoning. Moderately light in weight, and in strength, moderately soft and stiff. In decay resistance it is ranked as low to moderate. Heartwood is cream colored to light brown or reddish brown. Resin canals are abundant. Has practically the same uses as sugar pine, and eastern white pine. Average weight 27 lbs. to cubic foot.

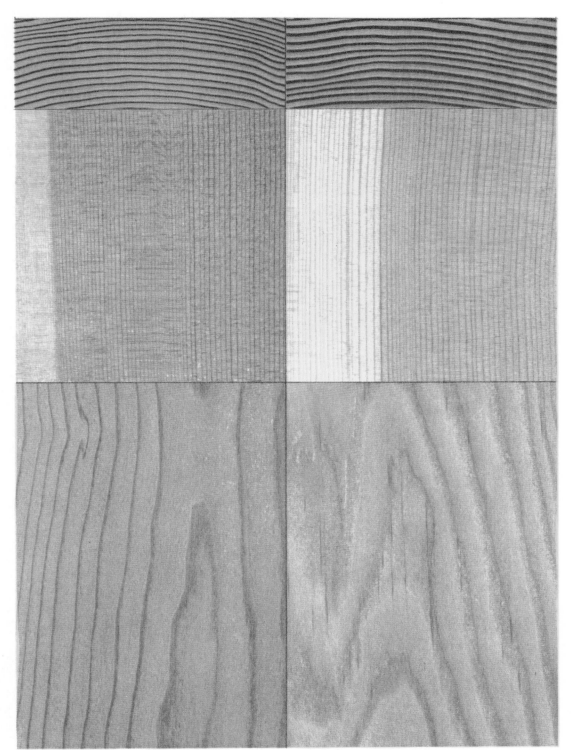

Western larch   Douglas-fir

WESTERN LARCH: Wood is stiff, moderately strong and hard, moderately high in shock resistance and moderately heavy. Usually straight grained, splits easily. High in nail-withdrawal resistance. Moderately decay resistant. Heartwood is yellowish brown and the sapwood yellowish white. Average weight 38 pounds to cubic foot.

DOUGLAS FIR: Varies widely in weight and strength. Most old-growth Douglas fir from Pacific coast, and northern Rocky Mountain States is moderately heavy, very stiff, moderately strong, and moderately shock resistant. Wood is moderately hard. Is more difficult to work with hand tools than soft pines, but holds fastenings well. Has moderate decay resistance. Heartwood is orange red to red or yellowish. Resin canals, which are seen as brownish streaks in summerwood, appear to be more abundant and more readily detectable than in western larch. Heartwood of Douglas fir may be confused with southern yellow pines, but resin canals are larger and more abundant than in pines. Most Douglas fir has a distinctive odor. Average weight 33 lbs. to cubic foot.

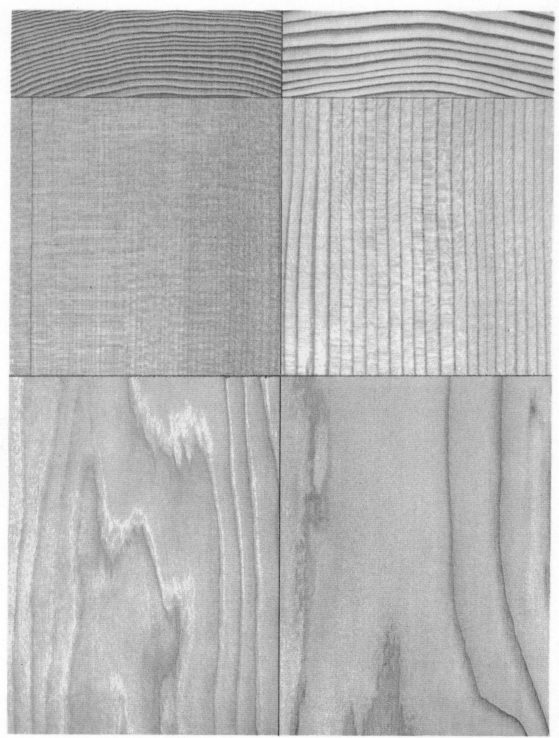

Western hemlock   White fir

WESTERN HEMLOCK: Moderately light in weight, moderately low in strength. Moderate in hardness, stiffness. Heartwood is low in decay resistance but is easy to work with tools. Heartwood is light reddish brown and frequently has purplish cast, especially in the summerwood bands. Wood lacks normal resin canals. Average weight 39 lbs. to cubic foot.

WHITE FIR: Species names—white fir, grand fir, Pacific silver fir, California red fir, Noble fir. Light in weight, moderately soft, moderately weak, low in nail-withdrawal resistance. Decay resistance is low. Heartwood is nearly white to pale reddish brown. Wood lacks normal resin canals. Color of springwood and summerwood on end-grain surfaces is more contrasting than in western hemlock. Average weight 26 to 28 lbs. to cubic foot.

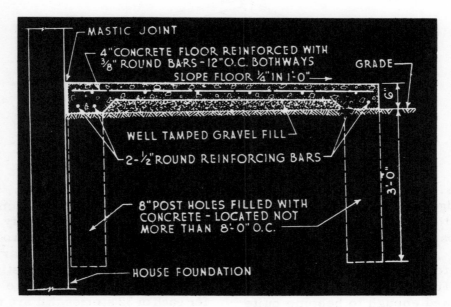

A-20. Suggested construction for concrete porch floor built on shallow fill. Floor slab is supported on concrete piers made by filling 8 in. post holes with concrete.

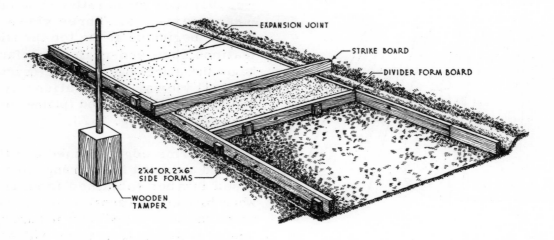

A-21. Constructing one-course (all poured at one time) sidewalk. Walks are usually made 4 in. thick except where heavy vehicles are driven over them. Then, the thickness should be increased to 6 in.

of tarred felt may be placed against the divider form boards, and left in place between the sections of concrete as construction progresses.

Edges of the walk should be rounded by working an edging tool along the

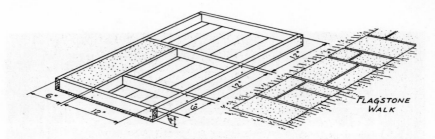

A-22. Method of constructing forms for a flagstone walk.

side forms. The edging tool or a combination edger and groover is also used to finish the joints across the walk where expansion strips are installed.

Concrete walks and floors should never be finished until the concrete has hardened enough to become quite stiff. The wood float is used for final finishing, if a gritty, nonslip surface is desired. For a smooth, dense surface, the steel trowel should be used.

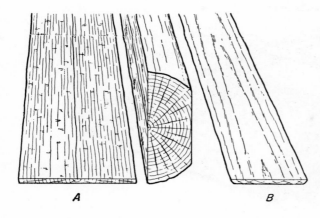

A-23. How quartersawed (A) and plain-sawed (B) boards are cut from a log.

WOOD IDENTIFICATION

A key element in any business transaction involving wood is the proper identification of the species. The color insert page 32-A is presented as an aid to learning to identify the more common native species of wood. Characteristics that are apparent to the naked eye, and that help distinguish the woods from each other are described for each of 32 species that are most commonly found in retail lumber markets.

The full-color illustrations (from U. S. Dept. of Agriculture Handbook No. 101) show grain pattern and other characteristics. Three views are given--beginning at the top the illustrations show end-grained surfaces, below these are edge-grained (quarter-sawed) views. Illustrations at the bottom show flat-grained (plain-sawed) surfaces. See Fig. A-23.

The terms edge-grained and flat-grained are used in reference to softwood lumber (obtained from trees which have broad leaves). while quarter-sawed and plain-sawed refer to hardwood lumber (obtained from trees with scale like leaves such as cedars, or needle like leaves such as pines). The terms hardwood and softwood have no direct application to the hardness or softness of the wood.

Cubic foot weights of species described are averages taken at 12 per cent moisture content.

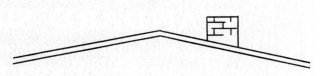

Lumber Measuring, Selecting

LUMBER MEASUREMENT

Lumber is measured by the board foot, which is a piece of lumber 12 in. x 12 in. x 1 in. thick. This is indicated by the abbreviation b. m. (board measure).

The b. m. is determined by multiplying the thickness of the stock in inches times the width in inches, dividing by 12, and multiplying the figure obtained by the length in feet. Stock less than 1 in. thick is figured as 1 in. The number of board feet in stock of various sizes is given in Table B-2.

YARD LUMBER

Yard lumber is less than 5 in. in thickness and is intended for general building purposes. Unlike factory or shop lumber, it is graded upon the use of the entire piece.

Yard lumber is classified by dimension as follows:
1. Strips—less than 2 in. thick and less than 8 in. wide.
2. Boards — less than 2 in. thick and 8 in. or more in width.
3. Dimension — classified as yard lumber, except boards, strips and timbers.

Yard lumber which is between 2 and 5 in. thick and of any width comes under the classification:
Planks—yard lumber of 2 in. and less than 4 in. in thickness and 8 in. or over in width.
Scantlings—yard lumber of 2 in. and under 5 in. in thickness and less than 8 in. wide.
Heavy joists—yard lumber 4 in. and less than 6 in. in thickness and 8 in. or over in width.

ACCEPTED MEASUREMENTS, ABBREVIATIONS

Table B-1 gives the American standard thicknesses and widths for yard lumber, including finish, boards, dimension and heavy joists, siding, flooring, ceiling, partition, shiplap and dressed and matched lumber.

Abbreviations ordinarily used in the description, purchase and sale of lumber and timbers are given in B-3.

STANDARD SIZES OF LUMBER

Conforming with the recommendations of the Lumber Industry as set forth in Simplified Practice Recommendations No. R16 published by the United States Department of Commerce.

Type of Lumber	Nominal Size		Actual Size S4S At Comm. Dry Shp. Wt.	
	Thickness	Width	Thickness	Width
Dimension	2 in.	4 in.	1 ⅝ in.	3 ⅝ in.
	2 in.	6 in.	1 ⅝ in.	5 ⅝ in.
	2 in.	8 in.	1 ⅝ in.	7 ½ in.
	2 in.	10 in.	1 ⅝ in.	9 ½ in.
	2 in.	12 in.	1 ⅝ in.	11 ½ in.
Timbers	4 in.	6 in.	3 ⅝ in.	5 ⅝ in.
	4 in.	8 in.	3 ⅝ in.	7 ½ in.
	4 in.	10 in.	3 ⅝ in.	9 ½ in.
	6 in.	6 in.	5 ½ in.	5 ½ in.
	6 in.	8 in.	5 ½ in.	7 ½ in.
	6 in.	10 in.	5 ½ in.	9 ½ in.
	8 in.	8 in.	7 ½ in.	7 ½ in.
	8 in.	10 in.	7 ½ in.	9 ½ in.
Common Boards	1 in.	4 in.	$^{25}/_{32}$ in.	3 ⅝ in.
	1 in.	6 in.	$^{25}/_{32}$ in.	5 ⅝ in.
	1 in.	8 in.	$^{25}/_{32}$ in.	7 ½ in.
	1 in.	10 in.	$^{25}/_{32}$ in.	9 ½ in.
	1 in.	12 in.	$^{25}/_{32}$ in.	11 ½ in.
Shiplap Boards	1 in.	4 in.	$^{25}/_{32}$ in.	3 ⅛ in. face
	1 in.	6 in.	$^{25}/_{32}$ in.	5 ⅛ in. face
	1 in.	8 in.	$^{25}/_{32}$ in.	7 ⅛ in. face
	1 in.	10 in.	$^{25}/_{32}$ in.	9 ⅛ in. face
	1 in.	12 in.	$^{25}/_{32}$ in.	11 ⅛ in. face
Tongued and Grooved Boards	1 in.	4 in.	$^{25}/_{32}$ in.	3 ¼ in. face
	1 in.	6 in.	$^{25}/_{32}$ in.	5 ¼ in. face
	1 in.	8 in.	$^{25}/_{32}$ in.	7 ¼ in. face
	1 in.	10 in.	$^{25}/_{32}$ in.	9 ¼ in. face
	1 in.	12 in.	$^{25}/_{32}$ in.	11 ¼ in. face

B-1. American standard thicknesses and widths for yard lumber including finish, boards, dimension and heavy joist, siding, flooring, ceiling, partition, shiplap and dressed and matched lumber.

SUITABILITY OF VARIOUS WOODS

The first two essentials in the construction of a house are good workmanship and good materials. But not all housing lumber needs to be select structural lumber any more than all parts of an automobile need to be high grade tempered steel. The prime consideration is the right use. An average house may contain from 1,000 to 2,500 pieces of lumber, each piece having a specific function to perform. It must add stiffness, insulation, strength or pleasing appearance to the home.

Today, lumber is graded for specific uses. Each grade is designed to meet certain requirements. In the well-constructed home there are places where No. 1 lumber belongs and there are many places also where the wise builder with an eye for savings finds that No. 2 and No. 3 amply meet the need. A key to economical construction is the proper use of the lowest grade which is suitable for the purpose.

KEEPING LUMBER IN CONDITION

Wood swells and shrinks with changes in moisture content. Across the grain these changes may be large, along the grain they are usually negligible. It is important, therefore, that the lumber used in a house be thoroughly seasoned. It must be remembered that, while seasoned lumber and well-seasoned and intelligently manufactured millwork may be specified and delivered on the job, the value of these precautions may be sacrificed if the material is not protected from the weather before and during installation.

WHAT IS MODULAR DESIGN?

This term is being added to the vocabulary of those interested in the building industry.

Modular design is a simplified and efficient system of design and construction which results in building economy. It involves the size co-ordination of materials and units of the building being erected, to permit assembly without excessive cutting and fitting. Basis of the co-ordination is a 4 in. unit or module.

In actual construction the economies in the use of a 4 in. module arise from the fact that products designed on the modular basis may be combined into a finished structure with a minimum amount of costly cutting and fitting.

For example, when the exterior wall of a house is modularly designed and when modular brick and modular windows are used, window openings will be exactly right and windows will fit into the wall with little or no trimming and no large gaps to be filled.

LUMBER GRADES

Grading is based on the occurrence of knots and other defects in relation to the appearance and general utility value of the lumber. Rules which are considered standard in grading hardwood (birch, oak, etc.) lumber are those adopted by the National Hardwood Lumber Association. Softwood lumber (sugar pine, redwood, etc.) is graded under a number of different association rules. Other kinds of lumber are graded by still different rules.

Following is a list of the principal lumber manufacturers' associations and the woods graded:

Woods Covered by Grading Rules

Hardwood Dimension Manufacturers' Association _____

Hardwoods (dimension or cut stock).

Hardwood Interior Trim Manufacturers' Association _____

Hardwood (trim).

Maple Flooring Manufacturers' Association _____

Maple (northern hard), beech, birch (flooring).

National Hardwood Lumber Association _____

Hardwoods, cypress, aromatic red cedar.

National Oak Flooring Manufacturers' Association _____

Oak (flooring).

California Redwood Association
Northeastern Lumber Manufacturers' Association _____

Redwood.

Balsam fir, northern white pine, eastern hemlock, and eastern spruce.

Northern Hemlock & Hardwood Manufacturers' Association _____

Eastern hemlock, tamarack, northern white cedar.

Northern Pine Manufacturers' Association _____

Northern white pine, Norway pine, eastern spruce, and jack pine.

Southern Cypress Manufacturers' Association _____

Southern cypress (upland and tidewater types).

Southern Pine Association _____

Longleaf and shortleaf southern yellow pine.

West Coast Lumbermen's Association

Douglas fir (coast region), west coast hemlock, Sitka spruce, western red cedar, Port Orford cedar.

Western Pine Association _____

Ponderosa pine, Idaho white pine, sugar pine, western larch, Douglas fir, ("Inland Empire" and California), white fir, Engelmann spruce, incense cedar, and western red cedar.

Red Cedar Shingle Bureau _____

Western red cedar (shingles).

FRAMING (HOUSE)

Usual requirements:

High stiffness, good bending strength, good nail-holding power, hardness, freedom from pronounced warp. For this use dryness and size are more important factors than inherent properties of the different woods.
Woods combining usual requirements in a high degree:

Douglas fir, western larch, southern yellow pine. (Extensively used.)
Ash, American beech, birch, maple, oak. (Sometimes used, but more difficult to obtain in straight pieces and harder to nail and saw than preceding group.)
Cypress, redwood. (Seldom used.)
Woods combining usual requirements in a good degree:

Eastern hemlock, western hemlock, eastern spruce, Sitka spruce, white fir. (Extensively used.)
Eastern white pine, ponderosa pine, sugar pine, western white pine. (Seldom used because of adaptability to more exacting uses. Low strength may be compensated for by the use of larger members.)
American chestnut, yellowpoplar. (Seldom used.)

Woods combining usual requirements in a fair degree:

Elm, sweetgum, American sycamore, tupelo. (Seldom used.)
Grades used:

No. 1 Dimension is the usual softwood grade for all framing items in both high- and medium-class construction. No. 2 Dimension renders satisfactory service once it is in place, but is not so straight or easily fabricated as No. 1. No. 3 Dimension is serviceable for studs and joists in the more economical and low-cost homes, especially when warped pieces and short lengths resulting from cutting out defects can be used to advantage. When hardwoods are used for framing, sound square edge is used in the better types of construction and for such items as joists, rafters, and sills. Hardwood Common Dimension is used in the more economical type of buildings and for studding in all types.

EXTERIOR TRIM (HOUSE)

Usual Requirements:

Medium decay resistance, good painting and weathering characteristics, easy-working qualities, maximum freedom from warp.
Woods combining usual requirements in a high degree:

Cedars, cypress, redwood. (Heartwood only. Adapted to blinds, rails, and balcony and porch trim, where decay hazard is high.)
Eastern white pine, sugar pine, western white pine, yellowpoplar. (Heartwood only. Adapted to ordinary trim where decay hazard is moderate or low.

Woods for special architectural treatments:

American chestnut, white oak. (Heartwood only. Used with natural finish.)

Size of piece (inches)	Length of piece (feet)								
	8	10	12	14	16	18	20	22	24
2 by 4	5⅓	6⅔	8	9⅓	10⅔	12	13⅓	14⅔	16
2 by 6	8	10	12	14	16	18	20	22	24
2 by 8	10⅔	13⅓	16	18⅔	21⅓	24	26⅔	29⅓	32
2 by 10	13⅓	16⅔	20	23⅓	26⅔	30	33⅓	36⅔	40
2 by 12	16	20	24	28	32	36	40	44	48
2 by 14	18⅔	23⅓	28	32⅔	37⅓	42	46⅔	51⅓	56
2 by 16	21⅓	26⅔	32	37⅓	42⅔	48	53⅓	58⅔	64
3 by 6	12	15	18	21	24	27	30	33	36
3 by 8	16	20	24	28	32	36	40	44	48
3 by 10	20	25	30	35	40	45	50	55	60
3 by 12	24	30	36	42	48	54	60	66	72
3 by 14	28	35	42	49	56	63	70	77	84
3 by 16	32	40	48	56	64	72	80	88	96
4 by 4	10⅔	13⅓	16	18⅔	21⅓	24	26⅔	29⅓	32
4 by 6	16	20	24	28	32	36	40	44	48
4 by 8	21⅓	26⅔	32	37⅓	42⅔	48	53⅓	58⅔	64
4 by 10	26⅔	33⅓	40	46⅔	53⅓	60	66⅔	73⅓	80
4 by 12	32	40	48	56	64	72	80	88	96
4 by 14	37⅓	46⅔	56	65⅓	74⅔	84	93⅓	102⅔	112
4 by 16	42⅔	53⅓	64	74⅔	85⅓	96	106⅔	117⅓	128
6 by 6	24	30	36	42	48	54	60	66	72
6 by 8	32	40	48	56	64	72	80	88	96
6 by 10	40	50	60	70	80	90	100	110	120
6 by 12	48	60	72	84	96	108	120	132	144
6 by 14	56	70	84	98	112	126	140	154	168
6 by 16	64	80	96	112	128	144	160	176	192
8 by 8	42⅔	53⅓	64	74⅔	85⅓	96	106⅔	117⅓	128
8 by 10	53⅓	66⅔	80	93⅓	106⅔	120	133⅓	146⅔	160
8 by 12	64	80	96	112	128	144	160	176	192
8 by 14	74⅔	93⅓	112	130⅔	149⅓	168	186⅔	205⅓	224
8 by 16	85⅓	106⅔	128	149⅓	170⅔	192	213⅓	234⅔	256
10 by 10	66⅔	83⅓	100	116⅔	133⅓	150	166⅔	183½	200
10 by 12	80	100	120	140	160	180	200	220	240
10 by 14	93⅓	116⅔	140	163⅓	186⅔	210	233⅓	256⅔	280
10 by 16	106⅔	133⅓	160	186⅔	213⅓	240	266⅔	296⅓	320
12 by 12	96	120	144	168	192	216	240	264	288
12 by 14	112	140	168	196	224	252	280	308	336
12 by 16	128	160	192	224	256	288	320	352	384
14 by 14	130⅔	163⅓	196	228⅔	261⅓	294	326⅔	359⅓	392
14 by 16	149⅓	186⅔	224	261⅓	298⅔	336	373⅓	410⅔	448
16 by 16	170⅔	213⅓	256	298⅔	341⅓	384	426⅔	469⅓	512

B-2. Table giving number of board feet in stock of various sizes.

Woods combining usual requirements in a good degree:

Hemlocks, ponderosa pine, spruces, white fir. (When drainage is good.) Douglas fir, western larch, southern yellow pine. Special priming treatment advisable to improve paint-holding qualities.)

Grades used:

A, B, or B and Better finish is used in the best construction, C and D finish in more economical construction, and No. 1 or No. 2 boards where appearance is not important.

SUBFLOORS (HOUSE)

Usual requirements:

Requirements are not exacting, but high stiffness, medium shrinkage and warp, and ease of working are desired.

Woods combining usual requirements in a high degree:

Douglas fir, western larch, southern yellow pine. (Commonly used.) Cypress, redwood, a s h, yellow-poplar. (Seldom used because of adaptability to more exacting uses.)

Woods combining usual requirements in a good degree:

Hemlocks, ponderosa pine, spruces, white fir. (Commonly used.) Eastern white pine, sugar pine, western white pine. (Seldom used because adaptable to more exacting uses.) American beech, birch, American chestnut, elm, hackberry, maple, oak, tupelo. (Seldom used. Not readily available and hard to work.)

Grades used:

No. 2 boards are used extensively in higher type homes. In more economical construction both No. 2 and No. 3 are used. No. 3 is serviceable, but not so tight as No. 2. No. 4 and No. 5 are available in some species, but entail waste in cutting. When hardwoods are used, No. 2 Common is adapted to the better class houses and No. 3 Common to the more economical.

WALL SHEATHING (HOUSE)

Usual requirements:

Easy working, easy nailing, moderate shrinkage. All woods can be used for sheathing with satisfactory results although some woods are less time-consuming to work than are others.

Woods combining usual requirements in a high degree:

Cedar, cypress, hemlocks, eastern white pine, ponderosa pine, sugar pine, western white pine, redwood, spruce, white fir, American basswood, American chestnut, yellow-poplar.

Woods combining usual requirements in a good degree:

Douglas fir, western larch, southern yellow pine, cottonwood.

Grades used:

No. 3 grade of softwoods makes a serviceable sheathing when covered with good building paper. No. 1 and No. 2 make a tighter coverage, but do not warrant omitting use of building paper. No. 4 and No. 5 are used in low-cost homes, but are not generally available. They both entail some waste in cutting. When a hardwood is used for sheathing, No. 2 Common is adapted to the better type homes, and No. 3 Common to the more economical.

B-3. ABBREVIATIONS OF LUMBER TERMS

AD.-----------Air dried.
a.l. -----------All lengths.
av.-----------Average.
av.w.---------Average width.
av.l. ---------Average length.
a.w.---------All widths.

B1S. ---------Beaded one side.
B2S. ---------Beaded two sides.
bd.-----------Board.
bd.ft---------Board foot; that is,
               an area of 1 square
               foot by 1 inch thick,
               or the product
               thereof.
bdl.-----------Bundle.
Bev. ---------Beveled.
b.m. ---------Board (foot)
               measure.
Btr.-----------Better.

Clg.-----------Ceiling.
Clr.-----------Clear.
CM.-----------Center matched; that
               is, the tongue and
               groove joints are
               worked along the
               center of the edges
               of the piece.
Com.-----------Common.
Csg. ---------Casing.
cu.ft.---------Cubic foot.
Cust.---------Custom (sawed).

D&CM.-------See S&CM.
D&H.---------Dressed and headed;
               that is, dressed one
               or two sides and
               worked to tongue
               and groove joints on
               both the edge and
               the ends.

D&M.---------Dressed and
               matched; that is,
               dressed one or two
               sides and tongued
               and grooved on the
               edges. The match
               may be center or
               standard.
D&SM.---------See S&SM.
D2S&CM.------See S2S&CM.
D2S&M.--------See S2S&M.
D2S&SM.-------See S2S&SM.
Dim.-----------Dimension.
D.S.-----------Drop siding.

E. -----------Edge.
E&CB1S-------Edge and center
               bead one side; sur-
               faced one or two
               sides and with a
               longitudinal edge
               and center bead on
               a surfaced face.
E&CB2S-------Edge and center
               bead two sides; all
               four sides surfaced
               and with a longitudi-
               nal edge and center
               bead on the two
               faces.
ECM.----------Ends center
               matched.
E&CV1S.------Edge and center V
               on one side; sur-
               faced one or two
               sides and with a
               longitudinal edge
               and center V-shaped
               groove on a surfaced
               face.
E&CV2S-------Edge and center V
               two sides; all four

sides surfaced and with a longitudinal edge and center V-shaped groove on each of the two faces.

E.G.----------Edge grain.

EM.----------End matched-either center or standard.

ESM.---------Ends standard matched.

FAS.----------Firsts and seconds—a combined grade of the two upper grades of hardwoods.

f.bk.----------Flat back.

fcty.----------Factory (lumber).

F.G.----------Flat grain.

Flg.----------Flooring.

Frm.---------Framing.

ft. ----------Foot or feet. Also one accent ('). See Symbols.

ft.b.m.--------Feet board measure.

ft.s.m.--------Feet surface measure.

G.R.----------Grooved roofing.

H.bk.---------Hollow back.

hdwd.---------Hardwood.

Hrt.----------Heart.

Hrtwd.--------Heartwood.

1s&2s.--------Ones and twos—a combined grade of the hardwood grades of firsts and seconds.

in.----------Inch or inches. Also two accent marks ("). See Symbols.

KD.----------Kiln-dried.

k.d.----------Knocked down.

lbr.----------Lumber.

l.c.l.----------Less carload lots.

lgth.----------Length.

lgr.----------Longer.

lin.ft.---------Linear foot; that is, 12 inches.

Lng.----------Lining.

LR.----------Log run.

Lr,MCO-------Log run, mill culls out.

Lth.----------Lath.

M.-----------Thousand.

Mb.m.--------Thousand (feet) board measure.

MCO.---------Mill culls out.

Merch.--------Merchantable.

m.l.----------Mixed lengths.

Mldg.---------Molding.

MR.----------Mill run.

Ms.m. --------Thousand (feet) surface measure.

m.w.----------Mixed widths.

No.----------Number.

Ord.----------Order.

P. ----------Planed.

Pat.----------Pattern.

Pln.----------Plain, as plain sawed.

Pn.----------Partition.

Prod.---------Production.

Qtd.----------Quartered—when referring to hardwoods.

rdm.----------Random.
res.----------Resawed.
Rfg.----------Roofing.
Rfrs.----------Roofers.
rip.----------Ripped.
r.l.----------Random lengths.
rnd.----------Round.
R.Sdg.----------Rustic siding.
r.w.----------Random widths.

S1E.----------Surfaced one edge.
S2E.----------Surfaced two edges.
S1S.----------Surfaced one side.
S2S.----------Surfaced two sides.
S1S1E.----------Surfaced one side and one edge.
S2S1E.----------Surfaced two sides and one edge.
S1S2E.----------Surfaced one side and two edges.
S4S.----------Surfaced four sides.
S4SCS.----------Surfaced four sides with a calking seam on each edge.
S&CM.----------Surfaced one or two sides and center matched.
S&M.----------Surfaced and matched; that is, surfaced one or two sides and tongued and grooved on the edges. The match may be center or standard.
S&SM.----------Surfaced one or two sides and standard matched.
S2S&CM.----------Surfaced two sides and center matched.
S2S&M.----------Surfaced two sides and (center or stand-ard) matched.
S2S&SM.----------Surfaced two sides and standard matched.
Sap.----------Sapwood.
SB.----------Standard bead.
Sd.----------Seasoned.
Sdg.----------Siding.
Sel.----------Select.
s.f.----------Surface foot; that is, an area of one square foot.
Sftwd.----------Softwood.
Sh.D.----------Shipping dry.
Ship.----------Shipment or shipments.
Shlp.----------Shiplap.
s.m.----------Surface measure.
SM.----------Standard matched.
snd.----------Sound.
sq.----------Square.
Sq.E.----------Square edge.
sqrs.----------Squares.
Std.----------Standard.
stnd.----------Stained.
stk.----------Stock.
stp.----------Stopping.
Symbols: "—inch or inches, as 12".
'—foot or feet, as 12'.
x—by, as 6x8 timber. When referring to the thickness of lumber, 4/4, 5/4, 6/4, 8/4, etc.= 1 inch, 1 1/4 inches, 1 1/2 inches, 2 inches, etc.
T&G.----------Tongued and grooved.

TB&S.----------Top, bottom, and sides.

Tbrs --------Timbers.

V1S. ---------V one side; that is, a longitudinal V-shaped groove on one face of a piece of lumber.

V2S. ---------V two sides; that is, a longitudinal V-shaped groove on two faces of a piece of lumber.

V.G. ----------Vertical grain.

w.a.l. ---------Wider, all lengths.

Wth. ----------Width.

wdr. ----------Wider.

wt. -----------Weight.

LUMBER SELECTION (Continued)

ROOF BOARDS (HOUSE)

Usual requirements:
High stiffness, good nail holding, small tendency to warp, ease of working.

Woods combining usual requirements in a high degree:
Douglas fir, western larch, southern yellow pine. (Commonly used.)
Cypress. (Not commonly used because of adaptability to more exacting uses.)
Ash, American beech, birch, American chestnut, elm, hackberry, maple, oak, tupelo. (Seldom used because not readily available and hard to work.)

Woods combining usual requirements in a good degree:
Hemlocks, ponderosa pine, spruces, white fir. (Commonly used.)
Eastern white pine, sugar pine, western white pine, redwood, yellow-poplar. (Seldom used because of adaptability to more exacting uses.)

Grades used:
No. 2 boards are used extensively in higher type homes. In more economical construction both No. 2 and No. 3 are used. No. 3 is serviceable, but not so tight as No. 2. No. 4 and No. 5 are available in some species, but entail waste in cutting. When hardwoods are used No. 2 Common is adapted to the better class houses and No. 3 Common to the more economical.

SIDING (HOUSE)

Usual requirements:
Good painting characteristics, easy working qualities, freedom from warp.

Woods combining usual requirements in a high degree:
Cedars, cypress, eastern white pine, sugar pine, western white pine, redwood.

Woods combining usual requirements in a good degree:

Western hemlock, ponderosa pine, spruce, yellowpoplar.
Woods combining usual requirements in a fair degree:
Douglas fir, western larch, southern yellow pine.
Grades used:
Redwood and cypress are available in special siding grades of Clear Heart, and western red cedar and Port Orford white cedar in a siding grade of Clear. In other softwoods the B and Better siding is used in the highest class of construction. Siding in more economical types of construction is usually of C or D grade, but No. 1 and No. 2 are available in a number of species.

FLOORING (HOUSE)

Living Room and Bedroom Flooring

Usual requirements:
High resistance to wear, attractive figure or color, minimum warp and shrinkage.
Woods combining usual requirements in a high degree:
Hard maple, red and white oak. (Most commonly used hardwoods.) Ash (white), American beech, birch, walnut. (Not commonly used.) Hickory, black locust, pecan. (Not commonly available. Hard to work and nail.)
Woods combining usual requirements in a good degree:
Cypress, Douglas fir, western hemlock, western larch, redwood, southern yellow pine. (Vertical grain.) Cherry, sweetgum, American sycamore (quartered.) (Not commonly available. Highly decorative and

suitable where wear is light and maintenance good.)
Grades used:
In American beech, birch, and maple flooring the grade of First is ordinarily used for the better class of homes and Seconds and sometimes Thirds in low-cost jobs. In oak the grade of Clear (either plain or quartered) is used in better class work and Selects and sometimes No. 1 Common in low-cost work. Other hardwoods are ordinarily used in the same grades as oak. When softwood flooring is used (without covering) in better class homes grade A or B and Better vertical grain is used. Grade D or C (vertical grain) is used in more economical and low-cost homes.

KITCHEN FLOORING (UNCOVERED)

Usual requirements:
Resistance to wear, fine texture, ability to withstand washing and wear without discoloring and slivering, minimum warp and shrinkage.
Woods combining usual requirements in a high degree:
American beech, birch, hard maple. (Fine textured.)
Woods combining usual requirements in a good degree:
Ash, red and white oak. (Open textured.)
Soft maple.
Woods combining usual requirements in a fair degree:
Cypress, Douglas fir, western hemlock, western larch, redwood, southern yellow pine. (Vertical grain preferred.)
Elm, hackberry. American sycamore.

Grades used:

The flooring grades, Seconds in American beech, birch, and hard maple, and Selects in the oaks are used in high-priced houses. In more economical construction Thirds in American beech, birch, and hard maple, and No. 1 Common or No. 2 Common in the oaks are used. D (vertical grain) is the lowest grade of softwood that proves thoroughly satisfactory in high-class construction. A grade and B and Better grade (vertical grain) are used most extensively. No. 1 and No. 2 are serviceable in low-cost construction, but wear unevenly around knots.

PORCH FLOORING

Usual requirements:

Medium to good decay resistance, medium wear resistance, nonsplintering, freedom from warping.

Woods combining usual requirements in a high degree:

Cypress, Douglas fir (vertical grain), Western larch (vertical grain), Southern yellow pine (vertical grain), redwood, white oak. (If full drainage is not obtainable only the heartwood of cypress, redwood, and white oak can be given a high rating.)

Black locust, walnut. (Usually impractical except when cut from homegrown timber.)

Grades used:

Grades C to A are used in the better types of homes. No. 1 and No. 2 are used in lower cost homes and are serviceable, but wear unevenly around knots, and the maintenance of paint on the knots is difficult. The superior paint-holding qualities and uniform wearing surface of vertical grain makes it preferred in all grades. Hardwoods, if used at all, should be of Select or No. 1 Common quality.

SASH USED IN A MOIST LOCATION (HIGH DECAY HAZARD)

Usual requirements:

High decay resistance. Moderate shrinkage, good paint qualities, freedom from warping, ease of working, screw-holding power.

Woods combining usual requirements in a high degree:

Eastern white pine, ponderosa pine, sugar pine, western white pine. (Principal woods used for sash. Require good perservative treatment.)

Cypress, cedars, redwood, American chestnut. (Heartwood only or sapwood when treated.)

Woods combining usual requirements in a good degree:

Douglas fir, western larch, southern yellow pine. (Heartwood only.)

White oak. (Harder to work and higher shrinkage than the softwoods.)

Grades used:

Grades of lumber used for sash are primarily of interest to manufacturers rather than users.

SASH Sash Used in a Dry Location (Low Decay Hazard)

Usual requirements:

Moderate shrinkage, good paint qualities, freedom from warping, ease of working, screw-holding power.

Woods combining usual requirements

in a high degree:
  Eastern white pine, ponderosa pine, sugar pine, western white pine. (Principal woods used for sash.) Cypress, redwood.
Woods combining usual requirements in a good degree:
  Douglas fir, western larch, southern yellow pine. (Vertical grain. Use limited because of milling and finishing characteristics.)

SHELVING (HOUSE)

Shelving with Natural or High-Class Paint Finish

Usual requirements:
  Stiffness, good finishing qualities, freedom from pitch and warp.
Woods combining usual requirements in a high degree:
  Ash, birch, maple, oak, walnut. (Suitable for natural finishes used principally to match interior trim.)
  Cypress, redwood, yellowpoplar. (Suitable for high-class paint finishes, but use limited.)
  Eastern white pine, ponderosa pine, sugar pine, western white pine, (Principal woods used for high-class paint finishes.)

Woods combining usual requirements in a good degree:
  Douglas fir, hemlocks, western larch, southern yellow pine, spruces, white fir, American basswood, American chestnut. (May be used with either natural or paint finishes.)

SHELVING WITH UNFINISHED OR PLAIN PAINT COATING

Usual requirements:
  Stiffness, ease of working, freedom from pitch and warp.

Woods combining usual requirements in a good degree:
  Eastern white pine, ponderosa pine, sugar pine, western white pine. (Principal woods used.)
  Cypress, hemlocks, redwood, white fir, spruces, American basswood, American chestnut, yellowpoplar. Douglas fir, western larch, southern yellow pine. (Softwoods with high stiffness.)
  Birch, maple, oak. (Seldom used; difficult to work.)
Grades used:
  The grade best adapted to use depends on the character of the shelving as well as on type of construction.

USING STANDARD SIZE LUMBER, MILLWORK

  Planning of a home so that stock or standard size materials, including doors, windows, stairs, kitchen, bathroom cabinets, etc. may be used without unnecessary cutting or waste will result in substantial savings in the cost of a home. Be sure that the stock plans you select, or plans you have drawn up by your architect, make the best possible use of standard size materials.

C or a better grade is used for shelves that are to receive a high-class paint or enamel finish. D grade is serviceable, but may entail some waste. No. 1 and No. 2 are used for shelving that is unpainted or receives only a rough-paint finish. No. 3 is serviceable, especially when cut into short lengths, but may entail some waste. When hardwoods are used for shelving in closets or storerooms, No. 1 or No. 2 Common is used. These two grades are suitable for higher class shelving where short-length or narrow, clear cutting can be used to advantage.

SHINGLES (HOUSE)

Usual Requirements:
   High decay resistance, small tendency to curl or check, freedom from splitting in nailing.
Woods combining usual requirements in a high degree:
   Cedars, cypress, redwood. (Principal shingle woods; heartwood only, edge grain.)
   Eastern white pine, ponderosa pine, sugar pine, western white pine. (Hand-made shingles or shakes from locally grown timber; require good preservative treatment.)
   American chestnut, white oak. (Hand-made shingles or shakes from locally grown timber; require care in nailing.)
Grades used:
   In western redcedar, cypress, and redwood No. 1 shingles (all heart, edge-grain clear stock) should be used for the longest life and greatest ultimate economy in dwelling roofs. Other all-heart, but not edge-grain

grades, such as No. 2 in redwood and western redcedar and Bests in cypress, are frequently used to reduce the first cost. Other grades permitting sapwood and flat grain are available and are used where low initial cost is the determining factor.

STEPPING (OUTDOOR USE)

Usual requirements:
   High decay resistance, nonsplintering, good bending strength and wear resistance, freedom from warping.
Woods combining usual requirements in a high degree:
   Cypress, white oak (especially when quartersawn). (Heartwood only.)
   Black locust, walnut. (Usually impractical except when cut from home-grown timber.)
Woods combining usual requirements in a good degree:
   Douglas fir, western larch, redwood, southern yellow pine. (Vertical-grain heartwood only.)
Woods combining usual requirements in a fair degree:
   Cedar, Douglas fir, western larch, southern yellow pine. (Flat grain.)
Grades used:
   C or a higher grade of softwoods and Firsts and Seconds in hardwoods are used in high-class construction. In the less costly construction, No. 1 Common in hardwoods and as low as No. 2 grade in softwoods are used. No. 1 and No. 2 grades in softwoods are serviceable, but wear unevenly around knots. Dense No. 1 southern pine is sometimes used in better type homes.

INTERIOR TRIM (HOUSE)

Interior Trim with Natural Finish

Usual requirements:
  Pleasing figure, hardness, freedom from warp.
Woods combining usual requirements in a high degree:
  Ash, birch, cherry, American chestnut, oak, American sycamore (quartered), walnut.
Woods adaptable to special selection and architectural treatment:
  Pecky cypress, etched or special-grain cypress, Douglas fir, western larch, southern yellow pine, curly or bird's eye maple.
  Knotty cedars, ponderosa pine, spruces, sugar pine, white pine. (Lack hardness of the preceding group.)
Woods combining usual requirements in a good degree:
  Cypress, Douglas fir, western hemlock, western larch, southern yellow pine, redwood, American beech, maple, sweetgum. (With conventional treatment.)
Grades used:
  High-class hardwood interior trim is usually of A grade. The softwood grade A or B and Better is commonly used in a high-class construction. In the more economical types of construction C grade is serviceable. D grade requires special selection or some cutting to obtain clear material. Special grades of knotty pine, pecky cypress, and sound wormy oak and chestnut are available to meet special architectural requirements in some types of high-class construction.

Interior Trim with Paint Finish

Usual requirements:
  Fine and uniform texture, hardness, absence of discoloring pitch, freedom from warp and shrinkage.
Woods combining usual requirements in a high degree:
  Birch, cherry, walnut, yellowpoplar. Eastern white pine, ponderosa pine, sugar pine, western white pine. (Where liability to marring is negligible and special priming is used.)
Woods combining usual requirements in a good degree:
  Hemlocks, redwood, spruce, white fir.
  American basswood, American beech, sweetgum, maple, tupelo. Cypress, Douglas fir, western larch, southern yellow pine, ash, American chestnut, oak. (Used satisfactorily where requirements for smoothness of finish are not exacting.)

LATH (HOUSE)

Usual requirements:
  Low shrinkage, easy nailing, nondiscoloration of plaster.
Woods combining usual requirements in a high degree:
  Jack pine, lodgepole pine, eastern white pine, sugar pine, ponderosa pine, western white pine, spruce, white fir, yellowpoplar.
Woods combining usual requirements in a fair degree:
  Cypress, Douglas fir, hemlocks, western larch, southern yellow pine, American basswood.

House Framing Methods

Framing of a house must be strong enough to carry its own weight plus that of the floors and walls, roof, movable materials stored within the house and the people who occupy it, with an ample factor of safety.

It must resist wind and rain, earthquakes in some parts of the country, and in others, heavy loads of damp snow. The frame should be built to reduce shrinkage and warping to a minimum and last but not least, it should be properly protected against the hazards of fire.

OPINIONS DIFFER

No two men will frame a building exactly the same, nor is there general agreement among carpenters as to which is the best framing for a given condition.

Light frame construction may be classified into three general types:

1. Balloon frame, Fig. C-1.

2. Western or platform frame, Fig. C-2.

3. Braced frame, Fig. C-3.

BALLOON FRAMING

The distinguishing feature of the balloon type of framing is that the 2 x 4 wood members (studs) are continuous from the foundation to the attic floor. Ends of the second floor joists, which are spiked to their sides, rest upon a false girt or "ribbon board" which is notched into the joists on the inside.

Balloon framing offers the advantages of speed and economy and is desirable where a good grade of studding, sufficiently long to permit its use in interior walls, is available.

WESTERN OR PLATFORM FRAMING

In platform framing, Fig. C-2, the first floor is built on top of the foundation walls as though it were a platform. Outer ends of floor joists rest on sills, while the inner ends rest on a beam. A sub-floor, preferably laid diagonally, is nailed onto the joists.

The wall and partition framing is run up another story to support a platform for the second floor. The third or attic floor consists of a third platform built upon the second floor wall and partition framework, making the

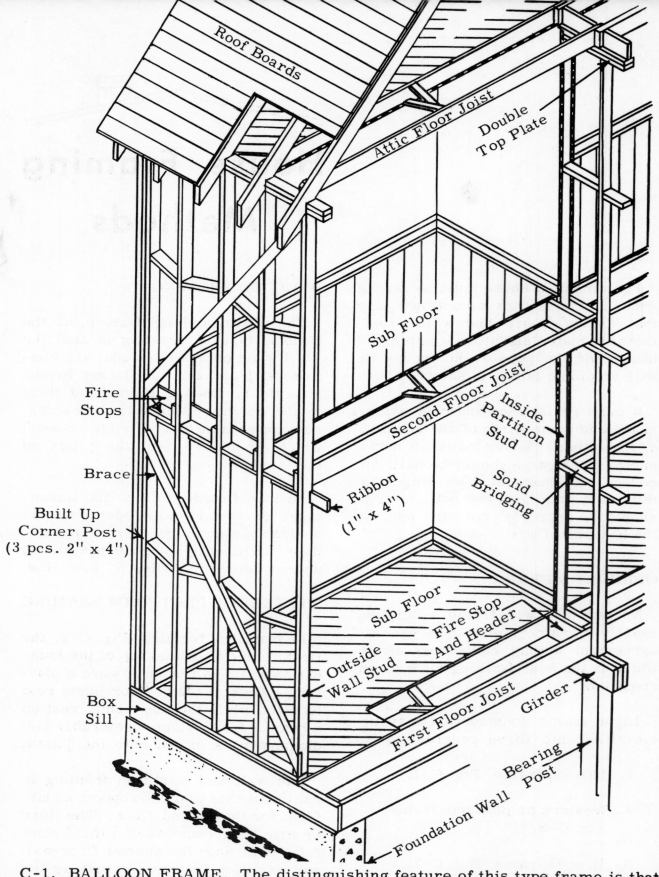

Roof Boards

Attic Floor Joist

Double Top Plate

Sub Floor

Second Floor Joist

Inside Partition Stud

Solid Bridging

Fire Stops

Brace

Ribbon (1" x 4")

Built Up Corner Post (3 pcs. 2" x 4")

Sub Floor

Fire Stop And Header

Outside Wall Stud

Box Sill

First Floor Joist

Girder

Bearing Post

Foundation Wall

C-1. BALLOON FRAME. The distinguishing feature of this type frame is that the wall studs extend up two stories high with the ends of the second floor joists spiked to their sides and resting upon a false girt or "ribbon board" which is notched into them on the inside.

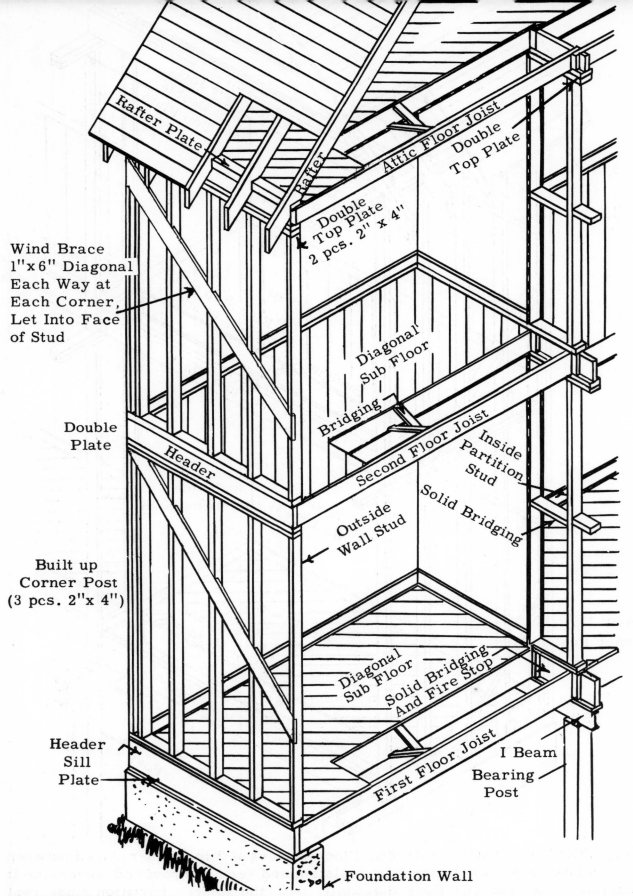

Rafter Plate

Attic Floor Joist

Double Top Plate

Rafter

Double Top Plate 2 pcs. 2" x 4"

Wind Brace 1"x6" Diagonal Each Way at Each Corner, Let Into Face of Stud

Diagonal Sub Floor

Bridging

Second Floor Joist

Inside Partition Stud

Double Plate

Header

Solid Bridging

Built up Corner Post (3 pcs. 2"x 4")

Outside Wall Stud

Diagonal Sub Floor

Solid Bridging And Fire Stop

I Beam

Bearing Post

Header Sill Plate

First Floor Joist

Foundation Wall

C-2. WESTERN OR PLATFORM FRAME. Each floor is framed separately, with the sub-floor in place before the wall and partition studs are raised.

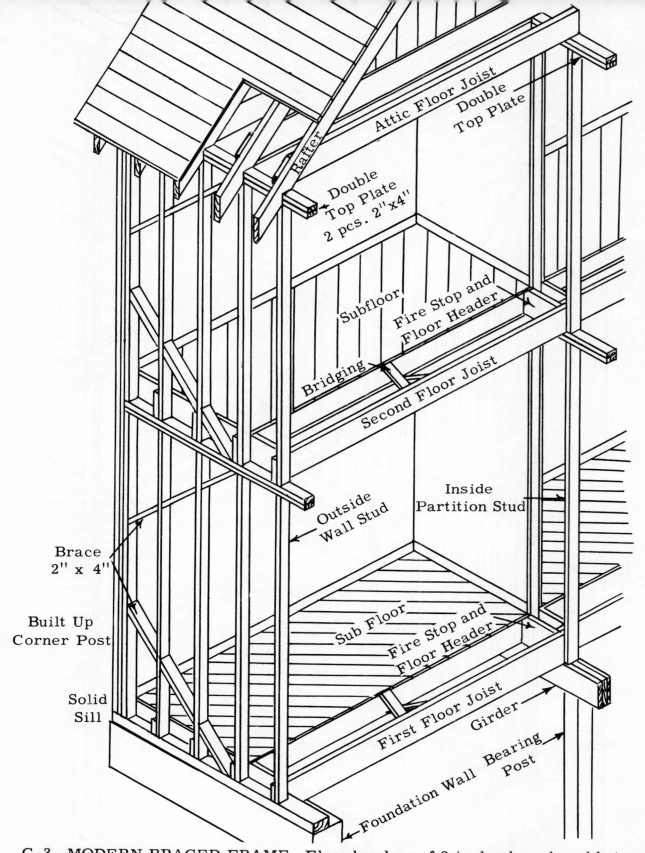

C-3. MODERN BRACED FRAME. Floor headers of 2 in. lumber placed between floor joists make this frame fire-resistant and vermin proof and also make it possible to lay the sub-floor diagonally with the joists. Partition studs rest directly upon the girder.

whole house a series of platforms, each supported by independent partitions.

The platforms thus formed automatically firestop the walls and partitions at each of the floor levels. Diagonal sub-flooring may be laid on each platform before studs are raised, speeding up the sub-flooring operation and assuring workmen of a sound floor on which they may work.

Another advantage of platform framing is that if any settlement, due to shrinkage, occurs, it will be even and uniform throughout and unnoticeable.

This type framing should be avoided with brick veneer or with masonry-walled buildings for either inside or outside construction.

BRACED FRAMING

Originally, this type was characterized by heavy timber posts at the corners, often with intermediate posts between, all of which extended continuously from a heavy foundation sill to a heavy plate at the roof line. At the second floor were introduced heavy timber girts running from post to post, carefully mortised and tenoned with oak pins. With the introduction of wire nails, modern tools and hardware, this type is gradually being modified.

A modern-type braced frame is shown in Fig. C-3.

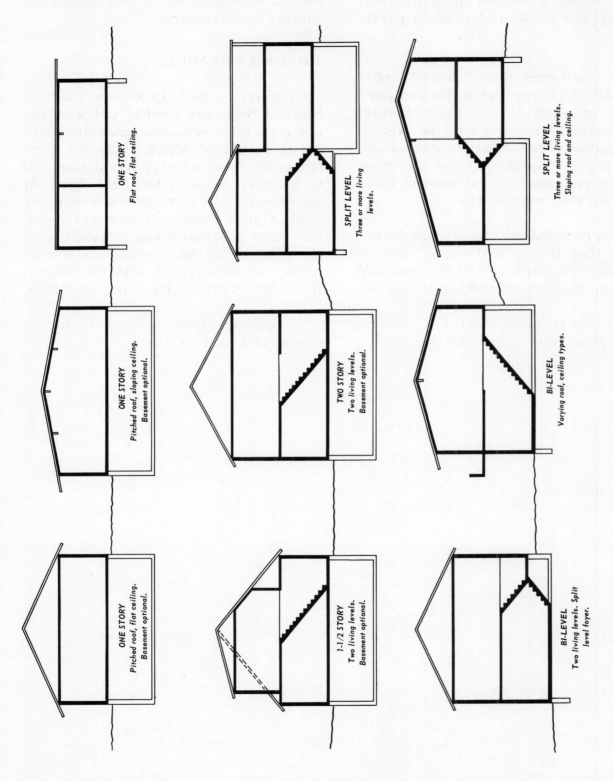

ONE STORY
Flat roof, flat ceiling.

SPLIT LEVEL
Three or more living levels.

SPLIT LEVEL
Three or more living levels.
Sloping roof and ceiling.

ONE STORY
Pitched roof, sloping ceiling.
Basement optional.

TWO STORY
Two living levels.
Basement optional.

BI-LEVEL
Varying roof, ceiling types.

ONE STORY
Pitched roof, flat ceiling.
Basement optional.

1-1/2 STORY
Two living levels.
Basement optional.

BI-LEVEL
Two living levels. Split level foyer.

MODERN BASIC HOUSE TYPES

Floor, Wall Framing

GIRDERS

A girder is a large wood beam, (either solid or built-up from planks on edge) or a steel beam which takes the place of interior foundation walls and supports the inner ends of the first floor joists. Since girders usually support at least one-fourth of the weight of the building it is obvious that this part of the construct must not be slighted.

FIGURING GIRDER SIZES

To determine the size of a girder it is necessary to: (1) Find the distance between girder supports (span). (2) Find the "girder load width." A girder must carry the weight of the floors on each side to the mid-point of the joists which rest upon it. (3) Find the "total floor load" per square foot carried by joists and bearing partitions to girder. This will be the sum of loads per square foot listed in the diagram, Fig. E-1, with the exception of the roof loads, which are carried on the outside walls unless braces or partitions are placed under the rafters, in which case a portion of the roof load is carried to the girder via joists and partitions. (4) Find the total load on the girder. This is the product of: (a) "girder span," (b) "girder load width," (c) "total floor load." (5) Select proper size of girder from the table, Fig. E-2, which indicates safe loads on standard size girders for spans from 6 ft. to 10 ft. Shortening the span is usually the most economical way to increase the load that a girder will carry.

Girders may be either solid lumber or built up as shown in E-3.

In built-up girders, joints should occur only at the posts or supports.

USING STEEL GIRDERS

In many localities steel girders are used instead of wood girders. Sizes required depends upon the load to be carried and may be figured the same as specified for wood girders. After approximate weight has been determined, Fig. E-1, size girder to use can be obtained by reference to Fig. E-4.

As wood beams vary in width for a given depth, so steel beams vary in weight, depth and thickness of web and flanges. While all weights as

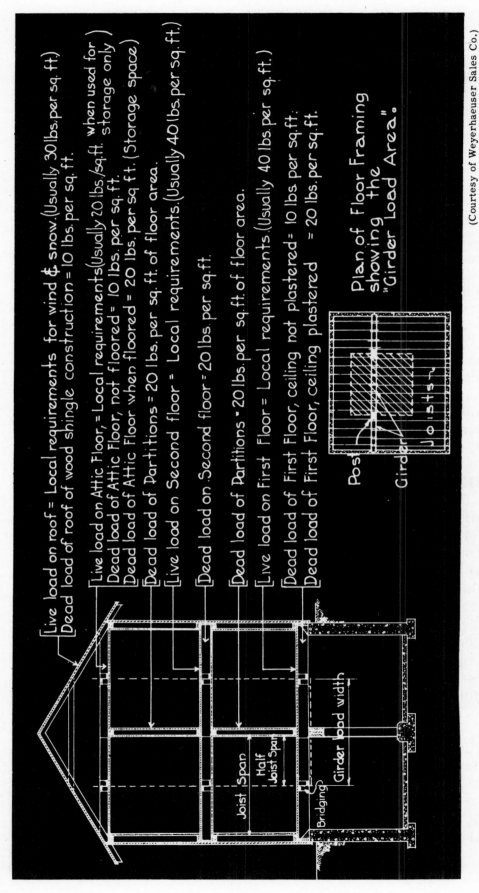

[Live load on roof = Local requirements for wind & snow. (Usually 30 lbs. per sq. ft.)
[Dead load of roof of wood shingle construction = 10 lbs. per sq. ft.

[Live load on Attic Floor, = Local requirements (Usually 20 lbs./sq.ft. when used for storage only)
[Dead load of Attic Floor, not floored = 10 lbs. per sq. ft.
[Dead load of Attic Floor when floored = 20 lbs. per sq. ft. (Storage space)
[Dead load of Partitions = 20 lbs. per sq. ft. of floor area.
[Live load on Second floor = Local requirements. (Usually 40 lbs. per sq. ft.)

[Dead load on Second floor = 20 lbs. per sq. ft.

[Dead load of Partitions = 20 lbs. per sq. ft. of floor area.
[Live load on First Floor = Local requirements. (Usually 40 lbs. per sq. ft.)

[Dead load of First Floor, ceiling not plastered = 10 lbs. per sq. ft.
[Dead load of First Floor, ceiling plastered = 20 lbs. per sq. ft.

Plan of Floor Framing showing the "Girder Load Area."

Post

Girder

Joists

Joist Span

Half Joist Span

Girder load width

Bridging

(Courtesy of Weyerhaeuser Sales Co.)

E-1. Diagram showing method of figuring loads for house framing.

GIRDERS	Safe Load in lbs. for Spans from 6 to 10 feet.				
Size	6 ft.	7 ft.	8 ft.	9 ft.	10 ft.
6×8 solid	8,306	7,118	6,220	5,539	4,583
6×8 built up	7,359	6,306	5,511	4,908	4,062
6×10 solid	11,357	10,804	9,980	8,887	7,997
6×10 built up	10,068	9,576	8,844	7,878	7,086
8×8 solid	11,326	9,706	8,482	7,553	6,250
8×8 built up	9,812	8,408	7,348	6,544	5,416
8×10 solid	15,487	14,732	13,608	12,116	10,902
8×10 built up	13,424	12,768	11,792	10,504	9,448

(Courtesy of Weyerhaeuser Sales Co.)

E-2. Table indicating safe loads on standard size girders for spans 6 ft. to 10 ft.

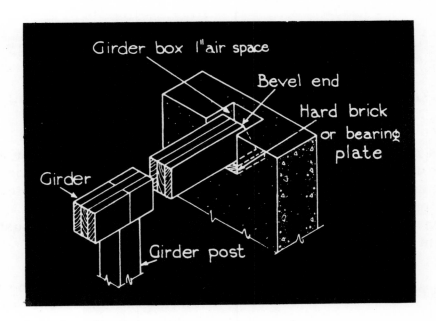

E-3. Three-piece girder. This should be nailed from each side with 20d nails, two near each end of each piece, others staggered with a horizontal distance of not more than 32 in. between nails. Girder joints should occur only at supports. Where a four-piece girder is used, the additional part should be nailed to the three-piece girder with 20d nails, two near each end of each piece, others staggered with a horizontal distance of about 32 in. between nails.

Span in feet	4 inches deep by—				5 inches deep by—			6 inches deep by—			7 inches deep by—		
	7.7	8.5	9.5	10.5	10.0	12.25	14.75	12.5	14.75	17.25	15.3	17.5	20.0
4	9.0	9.5	10.1	10.7	14.5	16.2	18.0	21.8	23.8	26.0	31.0	33.4	36.0
5	7.2	7.6	8.0	8.5	11.6	13.0	14.4	17.4	19.0	20.8	24.8	26.7	28.7
6	6.0	6.3	6.7	7.1	9.7	10.8	12.0	14.5	15.9	17.3	20.7	22.2	24.0
7	5.1	5.4	5.7	6.1	8.3	9.3	10.3	12.5	13.6	14.9	17.7	19.1	20.5
8	4.5	4.7	5.0	5.3	7.3	8.1	9.0	10.9	11.9	13.0	15.5	16.7	18.0
9	4.0	4.2	4.5	4.7	6.5	7.2	8.0	9.7	10.6	11.6	13.8	14.8	16.0
10	3.6	3.8	4.0	4.3	5.8	6.5	7.2	8.7	9.5	10.4	12.4	13.3	14.4
11					5.3	5.9	6.5	7.9	8.7	9.5	11.3	12.1	13.1
12								7.3	7.9	8.7	10.3	11.1	12.0
13								6.7	7.3	8.0	9.5	10.3	11.1
14								6.2	6.8	7.4	8.9	9.5	10.3
15											8.3	8.9	9.6
16											7.7	8.3	9.0
17													
18													
19													
20													

Span in feet	8 inches deep by—				9 inches deep by—				10 inches deep by—			
	18.4	20.5	23.0	25.5	21.8	25.0	30.0	35.0	25.4	30.0	35.0	40.0
4	42.7	45.2	48.2	51.1	56.6	60.9	67.6	74.2	73.3	80.1	87.5	94.8
5	34.1	36.1	38.5	40.9	45.3	48.7	54.1	59.4	58.6	64.1	70.0	75.8
6	28.5	30.1	32.1	34.1	37.7	40.6	45.1	49.5	48.8	53.4	58.3	63.2
7	24.4	25.8	27.5	29.2	32.3	34.8	38.6	42.4	41.9	45.8	50.0	54.2
8	21.3	22.6	24.1	25.5	28.3	30.5	33.8	37.1	36.6	40.1	43.7	47.4
9	19.0	20.1	21.4	22.7	25.2	27.1	30.0	33.0	32.6	35.6	38.9	42.1
10	17.1	18.1	19.3	20.4	22.6	24.4	27.0	29.7	29.3	32.0	35.0	37.9
11	15.5	16.4	17.5	18.6	20.6	22.2	24.6	27.0	26.6	29.1	31.8	34.5
12	14.2	15.1	16.1	17.0	18.9	20.3	22.5	24.7	24.4	26.7	29.2	31.6
13	13.1	13.9	14.8	15.7	17.4	18.7	20.8	22.8	22.5	24.6	26.9	29.2
14	12.2	12.9	13.8	14.6	16.2	17.4	19.3	21.2	20.9	22.9	25.0	27.1
15	11.4	12.0	12.8	13.6	15.1	16.2	18.0	19.8	19.5	21.4	23.3	25.3
16	10.7	11.3	12.0	12.8	14.2	15.2	16.9	18.6	18.3	20.0	21.9	23.7
17	10.0	10.6	11.3	12.0	13.3	14.3	15.9	17.3	17.2	18.8	20.6	22.3
18	9.5	10.0	10.7	11.4	12.6	13.3	15.0	16.5	16.3	17.8	19.4	21.1
19	9.0	9.5	10.1	10.8	11.9	12.8	14.2	15.6	15.4	16.9	18.4	20.0
20	8.5	9.0	9.6	10.2	11.3	12.2	13.5	14.8	14.7	16.0	17.5	19.0

NOTE.—If the reading in the table above is 12.4, the safe load is 12,400 pounds.
Example: If the total load on the girder is 13,500 pounds uniformly distributed and the span or distance between basement piers is 9 feet, then a 7 inch by 15.3 pound I-beam is the proper size to use, for by the table it will carry 13,800 pounds (13.8 in the table). This figure will be found on the line of 9-foot span and in the 15.3-pound column of the 7-inch beam.
These figures are taken from A. I. S. C. Manual.

E-4. STEEL GIRDERS. Safe loads in thousands of pounds uniformly distributed.

shown in E-4 are manufactured, frequently only the lightest weight of each depth is carried in stock at local sources of supply. The lightest weight for any given depth is the strongest for the amount of material used.

GIRDER POSTS

For ordinary girder posts (not longer than 9 ft. or smaller than 6 in. x 6 in.) it will be safe to assume that a post whose greatest dimension is equal to the width of the girder it supports will carry the girder load. For example, a 6 x 6 in. post would be suitable for a girder 6 in. wide; for a girder 8 in. wide, a 6 in. x 8 in. or 8 in. x 8 in. post should be used, etc.

Adequate footings must be provided for girder posts.

Wood posts should be supported on footings which extend above the floor level, as shown in E-5.

To make sure the posts won't slide off their footing pieces of 3/4 in. diameter reinforcing rod or iron bolts of that size should be inserted in the footing before the concrete sets and be allowed to project about 3 in. into holes bored in the bottom of the posts.

Be sure that cuts, both top and bottom, are square in order to provide even bearing for the girder and a level seat on the foundation.

If a wood column supports a steel girder a metal cap carefully fitted for even bearing on both the girder and the post is desirable, Fig. E-6. If wood supports wood, a carefully fitted metal cap should be provided to give an even bearing surface to prevent end grain of the post from crushing the horizontal grain of the wood girder.

Often it is practical to use a built-up wood post; for example one made by spiking together three 2 x 6's. The pieces used should be free from defects and securely nailed together, as excessive loading may cause the members to buckle away from each other and fail individually instead of acting together.

POST SPACING

Girder support posts should be spaced according to some suitable division of total length of the girder between walls, keeping in mind that excessive spans should be avoided and that joints in built-up girders should occur only at the supports.

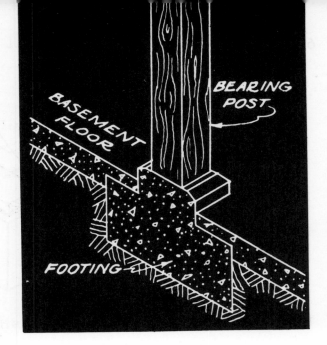

E-5. Broad and flat footings for basement columns are more effective in preventing settlement than are undersized footings with rounded or wedge-shaped surfaces. All column footings should extend above the floor level to protect the columns from dampness.

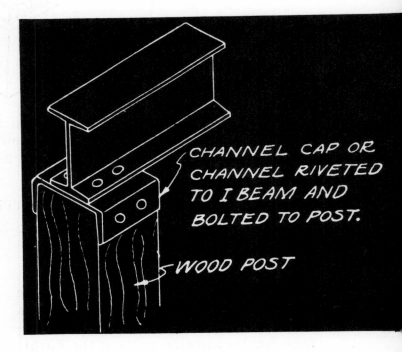

E-6. Making connections between girder and wood column.

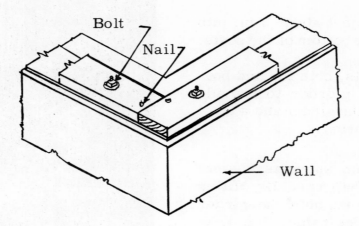

E-7. Adjoining pieces of a foundation sill should be toenailed with two 10d nails.

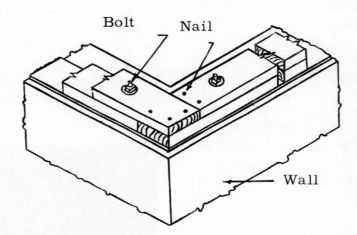

E-8. Built-up sills should be lapped at the corners and upper part nailed to lower with 10d nails; two nails near each end of each piece, others staggered with a distance of about 24 in. between nails.

FOUNDATION SILLS

ANCHORING SILLS
TO FOUNDATION

Foundation sills (sometimes known as mudsills or plates) are planks which form a support or bearing surface for the outside walls of the building. Usually the first floor rests on sills; but occasionally sills are omitted and floor joists rest directly on the foundation. Omission of sills, however, is not recommended because of the difficulty of obtaining a level surface upon which joists may rest, and the problem of anchoring the joists.

SILL - JOIST FRAMING

E-9. Joists are planks set on edge, usually 16 in. apart on centers. They must be strong enough to carry load and resist bending and vibration. Type of framing specified by plans should be used.

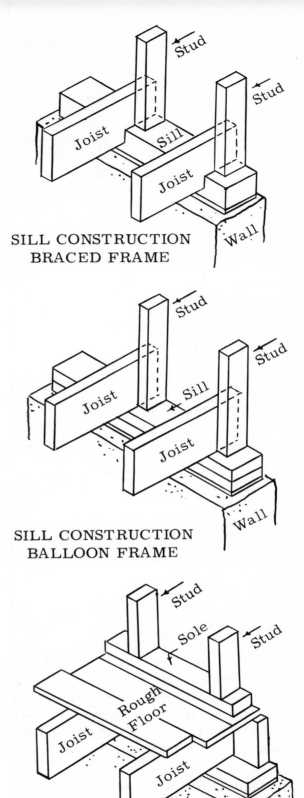

SILL CONSTRUCTION
BRACED FRAME

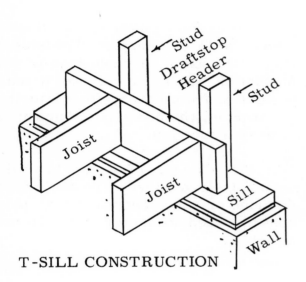

T-SILL CONSTRUCTION

SILL CONSTRUCTION
BALLOON FRAME

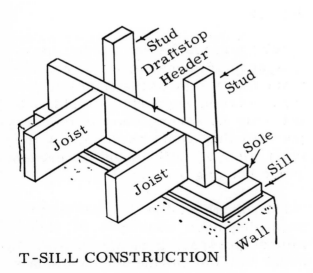

T-SILL CONSTRUCTION

BOX-SILL CONSTRUCTION
WESTERN FRAME

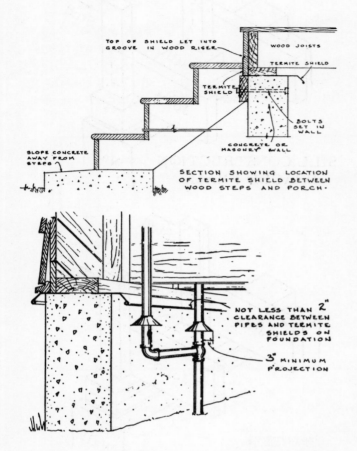

TOP OF SHIELD LET INTO GROOVE IN WOOD RISER

WOOD JOISTS

TERMITE SHIELD

TERMITE SHIELD

BOLTS SET IN WALL

SLOPE CONCRETE AWAY FROM STEPS

CONCRETE OR MASONRY WALL

SECTION SHOWING LOCATION OF TERMITE SHIELD BETWEEN WOOD STEPS AND PORCH.

NOT LESS THAN 2" CLEARANCE BETWEEN PIPES AND TERMITE SHIELDS ON FOUNDATION

3" MINIMUM PROJECTION

E-10.   Using sheet copper to protect. steps, porch and sills from termites.

SILL SIZES

For average size homes of frame construction, a 2 x 6 in. sill is large enough under most conditions. For large two-story structures, and particularly in localities subject to high winds, a sill 4 in. deep is desirable.

Material for sills may be almost any wood available locally. Great strength is ordinarily not necessary. Resistance to crushing across the grain and ability to withstand decay and insect attack are the principal

requirements. Information on sill and joist framing is given in Fig. E-9.

PROTECTING FROM TERMITES

If wood devouring termites are prevalent in your locality, sills should be protected against attack by using a course of slate embedded in strong cement mortar, or by using termite shields, as shown in Fig. E-10.

A satisfactory metal for a termite shield is 16 oz. copper. The shield should be used on each face of all foundation walls, except that it may be omitted from a face, either interior or exterior, which is exposed and open to easy inspection.

In the absence of a shield, sills should be treated with creosote, zinc chloride or other chemical that poisons the wood so the termites will not attack it.

JOISTS

Joists are planks set on edge, usually spaced 16 inches apart on centers, that carry weight of the floors or ceilings between supports. Joists must not only be strong enough to carry the load that rests on them, but they must also be stiff enough to prevent undue bending or vibration.

The length of the lath or width of sheathing used, usually 4 ft., determines the spacing of the joists. In order to avoid cutting such materials, joists would have to be spaced 12, 16 or 24 in. apart. As 24 in. is too great for proper stiffness, especially on ceilings, 16 in. has become the standard spacing for joists and studs except where special considerations require something different. Ordinarily it is

Sills should be set back about 3/4 in. from the face of the foundation to allow for sheathing. In placing them, mortar is first spread on the foundation and the sill placed over

SPAN OF JOISTS		Span Calculations provide for carrying the live loads shown and the additional weight of the joists and double flooring.								
Size	Spacing	20# L.L.	30# Live Load		40# Live Load		50# Live Load		60# Live Load	
		Plaster Clg.	Plaster Clg.	No Plaster	Plaster Clg.	No Plaster	Plaster Clg.	No Plaster	Plaster Clg.	No Plaster
2×4	12"	8'-8"								
	16"	7'-11"								
	24"	6'-11"								
2×6	12"	13'-3"	11'-6"	14'-10"	10'-8"	13'-2"	10'-0"	12'-0"	9'-6"	11'-1"
	16"	12'-1"	10'-6"	12'-11"	9'-8"	11'-6"	9'-1"	10'-5"	8'-7"	9'-8"
	24"	10'-8"	9'-3"	10'-8"	8'-6"	9'-6"	8'-0"	8'-7"	7'-7"	7'-10"
2×8	12"	17'-6"	15'-3"	19'-7"	14'-1"	17'-5"	13'-3"	15'-10"	12'-7"	14'-8"
	16"	16'-0"	13'-11"	17'-1"	12'-11"	15'-3"	12'-1"	13'-10"	11'-5"	12'-9"
	24"	14'-2"	12'-3"	14'-2"	11'-4"	12'-6"	10'-7"	11'-4"	10'-1"	10'-6"
2×10	12"	21'-11"	19'-2"	24'-6"	17'-9"	21'-10"	16'-8"	19'-11"	15'-10"	18'-5"
	16"	20'-2"	17'-6"	21'-6"	16'-3"	19'-2"	15'-3"	17'-5"	14'-6"	16'-1"
	24"	17'-10"	15'-6"	17'-10"	14'-3"	15'-10"	13'-5"	14'-4"	12'-8"	13'-3"
2×12	12"	26'-3"	23'-0"	29'-4"	21'-4"	26'-3"	20'-1"	24'-0"	19'-1"	22'-2"
	16"	24'-3"	21'-1"	25'-10"	19'-7"	23'-0"	18'-5"	21'-0"	17'-5"	19'-5"
	24"	21'-6"	18'-8"	21'-5"	17'-3"	19'-1"	16'-2"	17'-4"	15'-4"	16'-0"
3×8	12"	20'-0"	17'-7"	24'-3"	16'-4"	21'-8"	15'-4"	19'-10"	14'-7"	18'-4"
	16"	18'-6"	16'-1"	21'-4"	14'-11"	19'-1"	14'-1"	17'-4"	13'-4"	16'-0"
	24"	16'-5"	14'-3"	17'-9"	13'-2"	15'-9"	12'-4"	14'-4"	11'-9"	13'-3"
3×10	12"	25'-0"	22'-0"	30'-2"	20'-6"	27'-1"	19'-3"	24'-10"	18'-4"	23'-0"
	16"	23'-2"	20'-3"	26'-8"	18'-10"	23'-10"	17'-8"	21'-9"	16'-10"	20'-2"
	24"	20'-7"	17'-11"	22'-3"	16'-7"	19'-10"	15'-7"	18'-1"	14'-10"	16'-8"

(Courtesy of Weyerhaeuser Sales Co.)

E-11. Table showing maximum safe spans for joists under various live loads with both plastered and nonplastered ceilings below.

best to start at one end and space joists 16 in. o. c. regardless of special requirements for partitions, etc. and to insert extra joists as required.

FIGURING JOIST SPANS

The table, E-11, shows the maximum safe span for joists under various live loads with plastered and nonplastered ceilings below. It is only necessary to know the span, the live load (local codes or practice, usually 40 pounds per square foot) and whether or not the ceiling below is plastered, in order to select the proper sizes of joists for ordinary loading conditions. Attention is again called to Fig. E-1.

anchor bolts inserted while the foundation was being constructed. Gentle tapping is necessary to secure an even, level bearing throughout its length. Nuts of the anchor bolts should be tightened only with the fingers and, after the mortar has set, they can be tightened with a wrench.

Adjoining pieces of solid sills should be toenailed, Fig. E-7, and built-up or double sills lapped and nailed as in E-8.
Joist framing is shown in E-9 and E-13 to E-19 inclusive.

Fig. E-12 shows a typical house construction job with the girders, girder

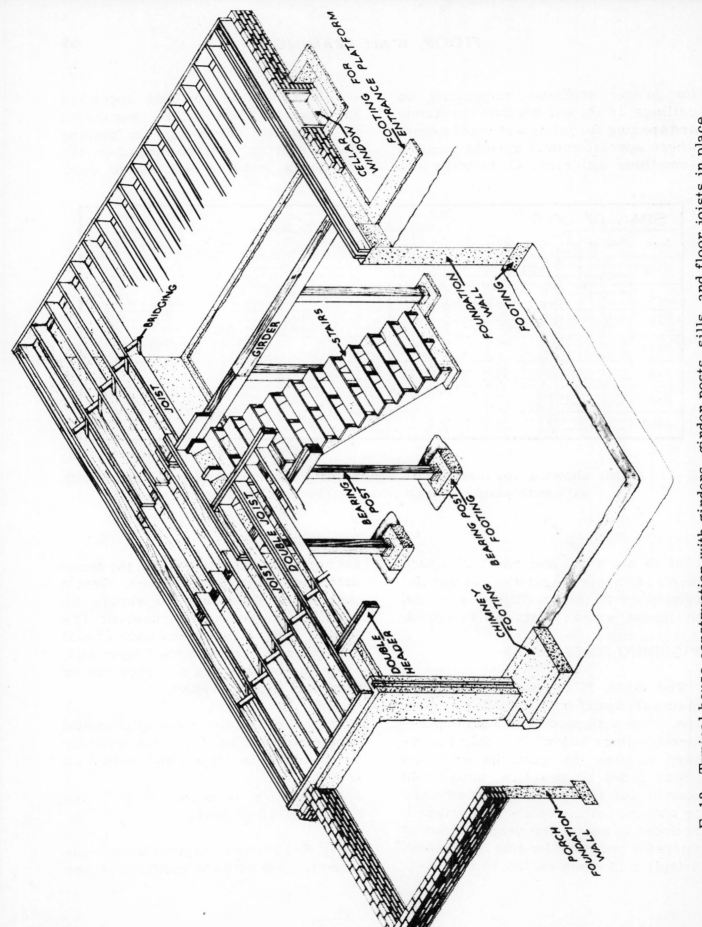

E-12. Typical house construction with girders, girder posts, sills, and floor joists in place.

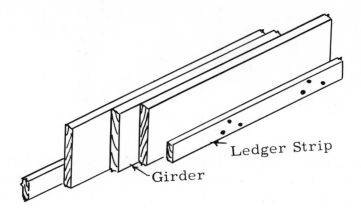

E-13. Ledger strip which helps support joist is nailed to girder with three 20d nails under each joist position. This nailing will safely support a concentrated load of 300 lbs. at any point on the floor, or a uniformly distributed load of 50 lbs. per square foot over any joist span and spacing ordinarily used in small house construction.

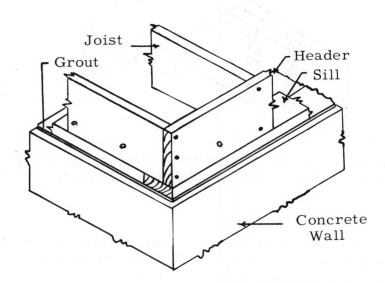

E-14. Header joist is nailed to other joists with 20d nails, three to end joist and two to others. End and header joist is toenailed to sill with 10d nails 16 inches on centers. If diagonal sheathing or plywood sheathing is used and is properly nailed toenailing to sill is not necessary except to hold joist in position during construction.

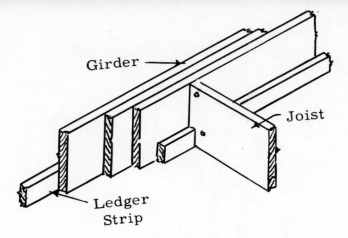

Girder

Joist

Ledger
Strip

E-15. Joist notched over ledger strip. The joist is toenailed to both the girder and to ledger strip with one 10d nail as shown or from opposite sides of joist. Notching of joists over the member on which they bear should be avoided whenever possible.

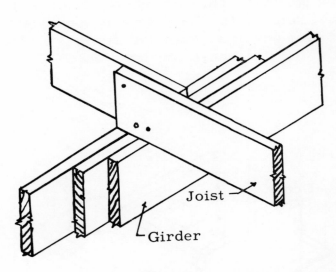

Joist

Girder

E-16. Joist bearing on girder or partition. Joists nailed together with two 10d nails and toenailed to girder with one 10d nail on each side of the pair of joists.

posts, box sills, floor joists (including double joists around openings for cellar stairs and chimney) in place. Double joists are also used under all partitions set parallel to the joists. Beam filling (with incombustible material which serves as a fire stop) as shown, is held in place with 1 in. boards.

Bridging has been fitted in between the joists in the middle of the spans

and nailed to the joists and rough stair horses for cellar stairs fitted into place.

The length of each joist should be sufficient for at least a 4 in. bearing at each end. This means that the total length of the joist must be either 6 or 8 in. longer than the distance between the faces of the walls or plates on

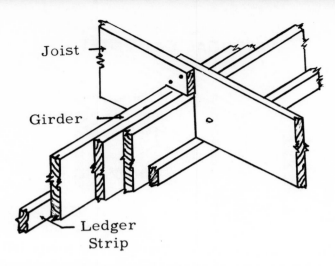

Joist

Girder

Ledger
Strip

E-17. Overlapping joists notched over girder and bearing on ledger strip. Each joist is toenailed to girder with one 10d nail and joists are nailed together with two 10d nails. Clearance is provided in the notch over the girder so the joists bear only on the ledger strip.

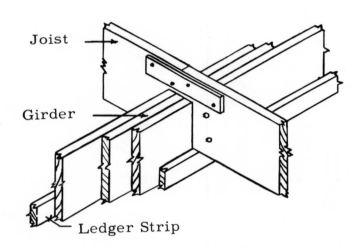

Joist

Girder

Ledger Strip

E-18. Joists notched over girder and bearing on ledger strip. Each joist is toenailed to girder with two 10d nails, one near bottom of joist, other on same or opposite side near top of girder. Wood strip nailed with two 8d nails in each joist furnishes additional tie. Clearance is provided in notch over girder so joists bear only on ledger strip.

which it rests. It is also desirable to cut joists about 1/4 in. shy of the inside face of sheathing to insure that they will not project beyond the stud faces and cause bulging

In framing for masonry, the cut should be made at an angle as indicated in Fig. E-20, for self-releasing in case fire should burn through a joist and cause it to fall.

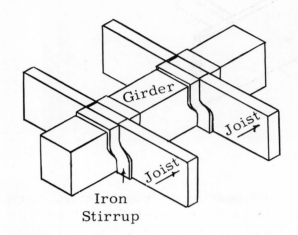

E-19. Joists hung on girder with
iron stirrups.

Joists that are not of uniform depth
should be trimmed slightly on the
underside at the point of bearing to
make the top edges level.

JOIST NAILING

Nailing differs slightly with the type
of framing used.

In balloon framing joists should be
placed next to and spiked securely
to the stud with two 20d nails at or
near the bottom and with only enough
spikes at the top to hold the joist in
place during construction.

The same applies for braced framing.

In platform framing, joists should
be securely toenailed to the plate with
not less that 8d or 10d nails. If there
is a box header across the ends, it
should be spiked securely with 20d
nails driven into the ends of the joists.

Some additional information on proper nailing may be obtained from Figs.
E-13 to E-18.

BRIDGING

Bridging, Fig. E-21, is composed
of diagonal pieces of lumber, usually
1 x 3 or 1 x 4 in. stock, nailed to form
an X pattern and arranged in rows
running at right angles to the joists.
Bridging provides a means of stiffen-
ing floors and distributing the load.

Fig. E-22 shows how to use a steel
square in cutting bridging to the proper angle.

If joists have a span of 8 ft. one row
of bridging should be used; if the span
is 14 to 16 ft., two rows of bridging
should be used. Considerable time
can be saved by starting nails in both
ends of the bridging before fastening
the pieces in place.

JOIST HEADERS

Whenever regular joists must be
cut to provide openings; a stair well
for example, it is necessary to provide auxiliary joists, called headers,
at right angles to the regular joists
to carry the ends of those that are cut.

Fig. E-23 shows how framing around
such an opening should be framed
and nailed.

BATHROOM JOISTS

Bathroom joists must support unusually heavy loads — heavy fixtures and
often additional weight of a tile floor.

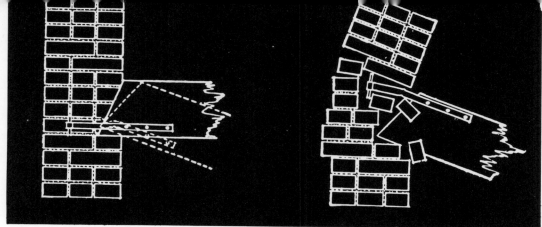

E-20. In framing for masonry, joists should be sawed at an angle and anchored at the bottom for releasing in case of fire, as shown at the left. Incorrect anchoring is shown at the right.

The fixed dead load imposed by a tile floor will average around 30 lbs. per square foot and the load from bathroom fixtures from 10 to 20 lbs. per square foot, making a total of between 40 and 50 lbs. dead load. To make matters even worse, it is frequently necessary to cut joists to provide for water pipes and waste, some of which measure almost 5 in. in outside diameter.

Some precautions must therefore be taken in framing bathroom floors to provide adequate support.

HOW CUTTING AFFECTS JOIST STRENGTH

If a joist is supported on edge at the ends between two sawhorses and it is desired to cut the joist in two at the center, it is a well known fact that after a short time the saw will bind. The sides of the cut will close in and bind the saw, compressing the top of the joist.

Now let's suppose the cut was started from underneath. With this type cut the saw would not bind; in fact as the sawing progressed the opening made by the saw would open up. The lower part would be pulled or stretched.

When the top of a joist is in compression and the bottom in tension there is a point at which the stresses change from one to the other. At this point, called the neutral axis, there is neither tension nor compression.

In the usual rectangular joist the neutral axis is assumed to be halfway between the top and bottom. While variations in the quality of lumber and other conditions may shift the axis slightly this assumption is near enough for all practical considerations.

If there is neither compression nor tension at the neutral axis or center of the piece, it is obvious that a hole, provided it is not too large, (not over one-fourth the total depth of the joist) would have but little effect on the

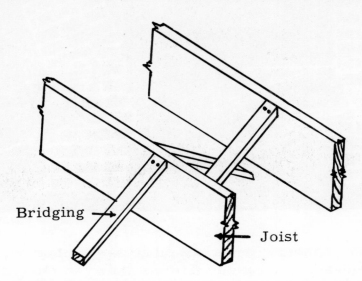

Bridging →

← Joist

E-21. Each piece of bridging nailed at each end with two 8d nails. Nailing of bottom ends should be deferred until after placement of subfloor and, if possible, until after placement of finished floor, since at that time the tops of joists will have been drawn into better alignment.

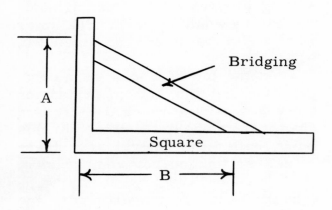

A

Bridging

Square

B

E-22. Using steel square to lay out bridging patterns. Let dimension A (tongue of square) represent width of joist and the blade B space between joists. Put square on material and mark cut on outside of blade B; also mark point on stock on outside of tongue A; reverse square and mark the second cut.

strength of the beam, because it does not cut or interfere with the important fibers near the upper and lower edges.

As a weight is most effective in producing bending if it is at the center of the span, so a weakness is more likely to reduce the strength of a beam if it is near the center of the span.

With this principle in mind we can, therefore, suggest the following precautions that should be observed:

1. Whenever possible, holes cut into the joist should be made at or near the neutral axis and if limited to one-fourth of the total depth no material reduction in a strength will result.

2. In cases where it is necessary to cut joists, the cuts should be made from

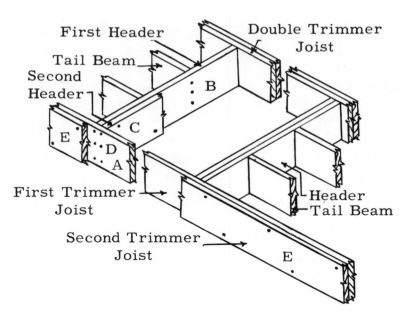

First Header

Tail Beam

Second Header

Double Trimmer Joist

First Trimmer Joist

Second Trimmer Joist

Header

Tail Beam

E-23. Framing for floor opening. (a) Nail through first trimmer joists into ends of first headers with three 20d nails. (b) Nail through first headers into ends of tail beams with three 20d nails. (c) Nail second headers to first with 16d nails spaced 6 in. longitudinally and placed near top and near bottom alternately. (d) Nail through first trimmer into ends of second header with three 20d nails. (e) Nail second trimmer joist to first with 16d nails spaced 6 in. longitudinally and placed near top and near bottom alternately. Note: This nailing will support a concentrated load of 300 lbs. at any point on the floor, or uniformly distributed load of 50 lbs. per square foot with any spacing and span of tail beams ordinarily used in small house construction, provided the length of floor opening is parallel to the length of the joist. If length of opening is at right angles to joists, excessive loading may be brought to junction of headers with trimmers. Anticipated loads should be checked and increased nailing or additional supports provided at these junctions if needed for the expected loads.

E-24. In cases where it is necessary to cut bathroom joists, cuts should be made at the top. Drawing shows one practical method of taking care of such situations.

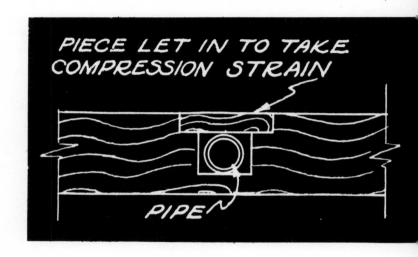

PIECE LET IN TO TAKE COMPRESSION STRAIN

PIPE

the top. For example, a 2 x 8 joist is cut to a depth of 4 in.; its strength will be reduced to that of a 2 x 4. If the cut from the top were 2 in., it would be equivalent to a 2 x 6. Whenever a joist is cut, the loss in strength must be compensated for by providing headers and trimmers (joists which support the ends of headers) or by adding extra joists. One way of taking care of situations requiring extensive cutting of bathroom joists is shown in drawing E-24.

3. If the cut were made elsewhere than at center of span, the weakening effect would not be as great, but it is well to provide fully as much compensating strength as lost by the cut.

Bathroom joists should be computed for a total load of 60 to 70 lbs. per square foot compared with 40 to 50 for other rooms. This usually necessitates 12 in. joist spacing instead of 16 in. spacing.

SECOND FLOOR BATHROOMS

Bathrooms on the second floor over halls or where the joist span is short may not require additional strength. If the bathroom is over the living room, the joists should be figured independently and their size and spacing proportioned to carry the heavier loads.

CEILING JOISTS

Ceiling joists are joists which carry no floor load, or at least only that of an attic floor used for light storage.

As in the case of floor joists, the spacing of ceiling joists is fixed in most instances at 16 in. because of the length of lath. The size of ceiling joists is determined by the span and by the load as follows:

1. Where the weight of the ceiling with plaster alone has to be carried, or if the attic is floored and used for light storage only, figure on using joists that will carry a load of 20 lbs. (see joist table, Fig. E-11.)
2. If the attic is used for living space, the floor joists should be figured with the regular residential minimum of 40 lbs. per square foot.

SUBFLOORS

A subfloor is a wood floor, usually made of 1 in. lumber, or plywood, laid over the floor joists, over which the finish floor is laid. It increases the strength of the floor and makes possible the laying of a thin finish floor. A subfloor stiffens the building, especially if laid diagonally, and it serves as a working surface during construction.

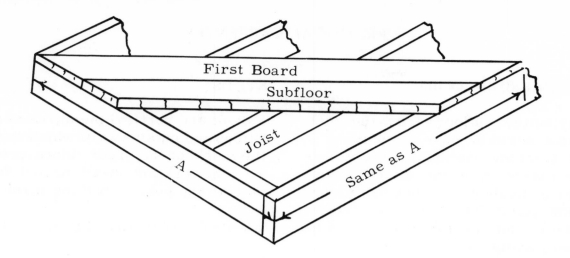

E-25. Subfloors laid diagonally should be started with the long boards. The procedure illustrated shows an easy way to get proper angle for first board.

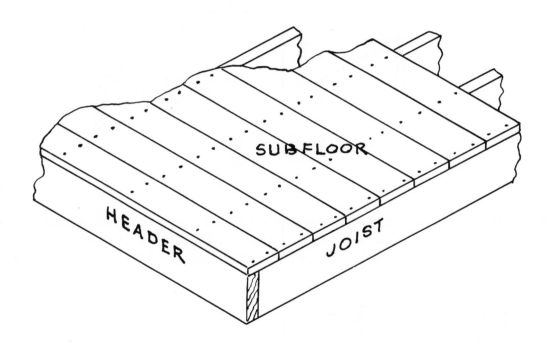

E-26. Subfloor or attic floor with boards laid straight. Boards 6 in. or less in width nailed with two 8d nails and wider boards with three 8d nails at each crossing of framing member. If subfloor is tongued and grooved on ends and edges, end joints need not be made over joints. Subfloor is preferably laid without cracks between boards. When, however, accumulation of water on the subfloor during construction is likely, it may be desirable to leave sufficient cracks to permit drainage and avoid swelling of the subfloor with resultant cupping and warping.

PLACING SUBFLOORS

Laying the subfloor across the joists at right angle is more economical in time, labor and material with the possible exception of end-matched subflooring lumber. Laying subfloors across joists has the disadvantage, however, that the finish floor can be laid only at right angles to the subfloor and parallel with the joists.

STUDS

Studs are vertical members of partitions and outside walls which support the weight of the upper floors, provide a framework for sheathing and finish on both the outside and the inside.

2 x 4's GENERALLY USED

So standardized is the practice of

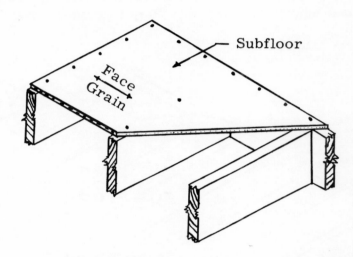

E-27. Plywood subfloor is nailed with 8d nails, spaced 5 in. along all edges and 10 in. along intermediate members. Plywood subfloor is preferably placed with grain of face plies at right angles to the joists.

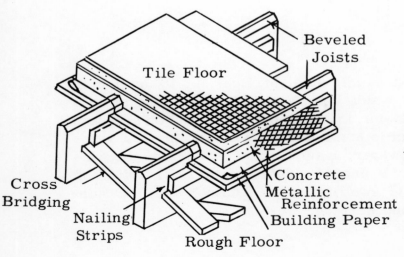

E-28. Joists are beveled and nailing strips provided to support subfloor so tile floor will be flush with main floor.

using 2 x 4's for studs that little thought
is given to using other lumber, or to
strength requirements. Each stud in
a weight-bearing partition acts as a
post, which is braced along its weakest
dimension by sheathing and siding on
the outside and by lath and plaster on
the inside. With this bracing it is
possible to use 2 x 4's as long as 15
ft. with reasonable safety. For buildings of three or four stories studs in
the lower stories should be 2 x 6 or
3 x 4 in. lumber.

Subflooring laid diagonally should
be placed at a 45 degree angle. An
easy way to get started is shown in
drawing E-25.

Information on subfloor nailing is
given in Figs. E-26 and E-27. Figs.
E-28 and E-29 show subflooring for
bathrooms.

Adding an extra rough floor for supporting insulation beneath the floor
is shown in Fig. E-30.

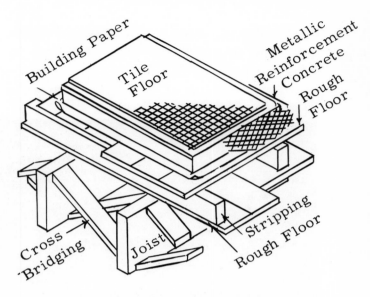

E-29. Stepped up tile floor.

E-30. Adding rough floor beneath subfloor to support insulation.

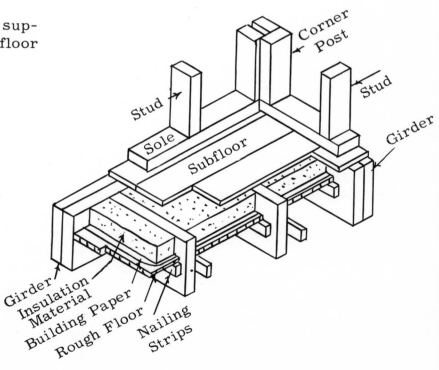

LUMBER SPECIES AND GRADES

Species of lumber and grades which are considered suitable for studs are as follows:

The method shown in E-33 is probably the most satisfactory type to use. It provides the necessary strength, is easy to assemble and furnishes a place to nail lath.

Species	Grade recommended for standard permanent construction	Species	Grade recommended for standard permanent construction
Red cypress	No. 2 common.	Douglas fir (coast type)	No. 2 common.
Redwood	Do.	West coast hemlock	Do.
Eastern hemlock	No. 1 common. / No. 2 common.	Longleaf southern pine	Do.
Eastern spruce	Do.	Shortleaf southern pine	Do.
Tamarack	Do.	North Carolina pine	Do.
Douglas fir—inland empire	Do.	Arkansas soft pine	Do.
White fir	No. 1 common. / No. 2 common.	California white pine	Do.
Western larch	Do.	White pines (northern, Idaho, and sugar).	Do.
		Norway pine	Do.

E-31. Lumber species suitable for studs.

Length to cut the studs is determined by the type of framing and required information may be obtained from the plans. Straight lumber should be selected in order to avoid bulges and hollows in the walls and partitions.

It is usually best to assemble studs for sections of the sides of the building on the ground, then raise them into place. They should be spaced accurately, set plumb and truly vertical, Fig. E-32.

CORNER STUDS

Corner studs are those which occur at intersections of two walls at right angles with each other. Ways of framing corners with studs built-up from 2 x 4's are shown in drawings E-33, E-34 and E-35.

Studding assembled as in E-34 provides equal thickness in both directions, but it is somewhat more difficult to assemble and there is likelihood of splitting the single stud in nailing it together.

Fig. E-35 shows a desirable type of corner stud, one assembled from three 2 x 4's and 1 in. filler blocks. This provides equal thickness in both directions.

Fastening of studs to sills and nailing of sole plate at base of studs is shown in Figs. E-36, E-37 and E-38.

RIBBANDS FOR JOIST SUPPORT

The ribband or ribbon as it is commonly called, is a horizontal strip of wood notched into the studs in balloon frame construction, which forms a support for joists above the first floor, Fig. E-39.

Because the joists which rest upon the ribband are spiked to the studs into which the ribband is notched, 1 x 4 in. stock is sufficient. Any wood suitable for framing, sheathing or bridging may be used but the material used should be free from defects that will affect its strength. Splices should be made only at the center of studs.

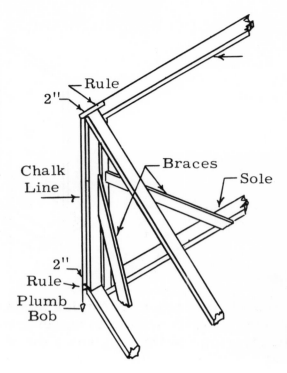

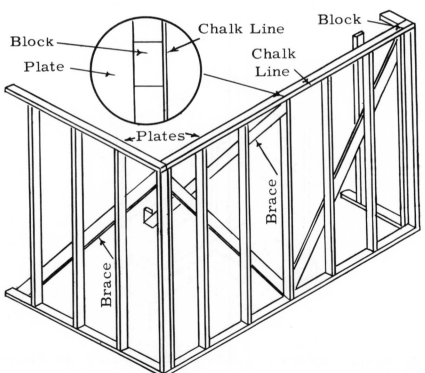

E-32. Method of plumbing studs and straightening walls. If no plumb bob or level is available a small piece of metal or brick may be tied to the chalk line.

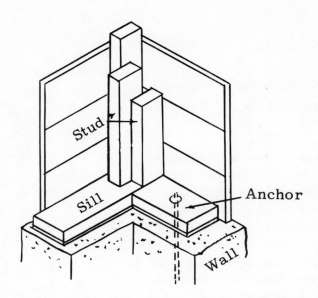

E-33. This method of framing studs at corners of a building provides necessary strength and is simple to put in place. It furnishes good nailing for lath. The disadvantage is that it gives a distance from the sheathing of 3 1/4 in. one way and 3 5/8 in. the other so plaster must be built up an extra 3/8 in. on one side if a square corner is to be obtained.

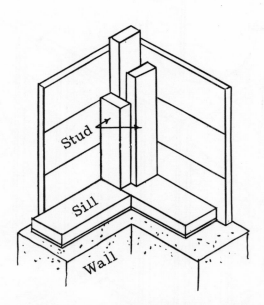

E-34. Framing studs at corners by this method makes the distance from the sheathing to lath the same on both sides of the corners. Laths in both directions form a straight line with other studs. An objection to this framing is that there is a possibility of splitting the single stud in nailing the three 2 x 4's together.

E-35. Corner posts assembled from three 2 x 4's and filler blocks provide equal thickness in both directions and are more substantial than the type shown in E-33. In assembling, stud A should be nailed to studs B and C with 10d nails staggered 12 in. apart, and to each filler block D with three 10d nails. Corner post is toenailed to sole plate with two 8d nails on each face.

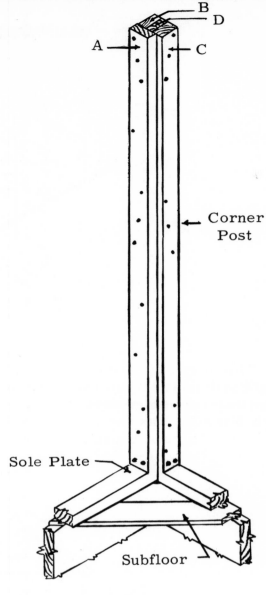

E-36. Studs are toenailed to sole plate with two 8d nails on each wide face. One nail on each wide face is sufficient if diagonal boards or plywood is used as sheathing.

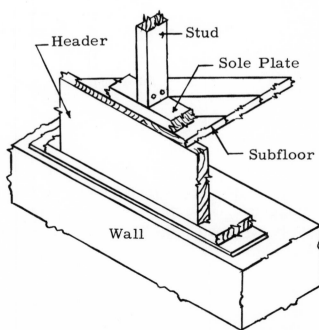

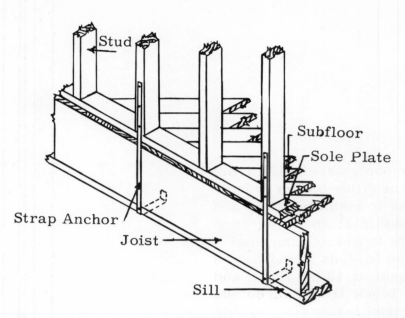

E-37. Using metal straps to anchor studs to sill. Straps not less than 22 gauge by 1 in. wide are nailed to inner and outer edges of sill with one nail and to outer face of alternate studs with three 8d nails. Such an anchorage is not needed if diagonal boards or plywood is used as wall sheathing.

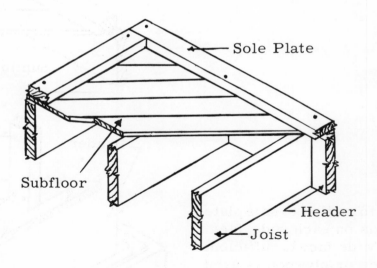

E-38. Sole plate is anchored by nailing through subfloor to joists using 16d nails staggered. Sole plate over end joist is nailed through subfloor to joist with 16d nails spaced 16 in. on centers. Nailing of plates on which rafters bear will be covered elsewhere.

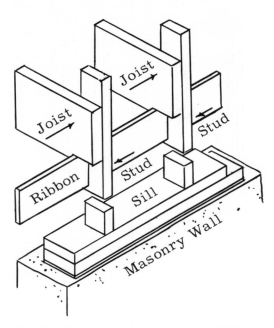

E-39. Ribbon or ledger board which supports second floor joints should be nailed with two 8d nails through the ribbon into each stud.

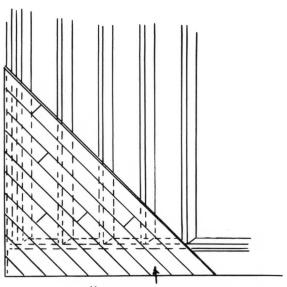

1 x 6" Endless Lumber

E-40. Bracing of the frame is accomplished by placing the sheathing at 45 degree angle. Tests prove this type of bracing increases rigidity of the house from two to seven times, depending on the number of openings which must be cut for doors and windows. End-matched sheathing, which may be used without making joints on studs is desirable. Joints should be made only at studs with ordinary sheathing.

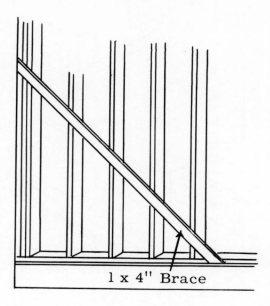

1 x 4" Brace

E-41. Some good builders prefer to brace a house frame with let-in bracing. This is accomplished by notching the studs to receive a continuous piece of 1 x 4 which is securely nailed to each stud. This bracing must be installed prior to sheathing the building.

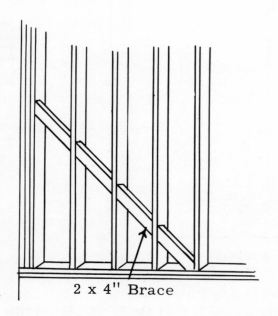

2 x 4" Brace

E-42. Another popular method of bracing a frame house—the cut-in type. This consists of 2 x 4's carefully cut and fitted between the studs after the sheathing has been nailed in place.

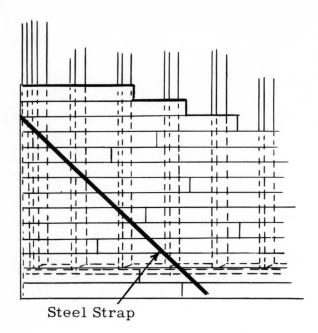

Steel Strap

E-43. A recent bracing development —using 1 in. metal stripping which may be applied quickly. This should be 1 x .022 in. nailed 3 in. o. c. with roofing nails and to each stud with 8d nails. It should be placed as close to a 45 degree angle as possible.

STUD BRACING

Bracing is any means used to stiffen a building against a tendency to lean or to collapse as the result of high winds. It is also helpful in preventing plaster cracks.

Several practical types of bracing are shown in Figs. E-40, E-41, E-42 and E-43.

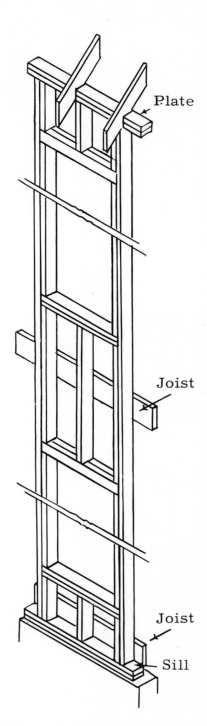

Plate

Joist

Joist

Sill

E-44. Framing openings in walls or partitions parallel to the joists.

HEADERS AT OPENINGS

Where doors or windows occur in outside walls or partitions, part of the studs must be cut away. In such cases, some form of framing must be provided to support the ends of the studs that have been cut.

Headers are of two types: Non-bearing which occur in walls which are parallel with the joists of the floor above and carry only the weight of the framing immediately above; and Load-bearing which occur in walls which carry the ends of floor joists either on plates or on ribbands immediately above the openings.

Illustrations E-44 and E-45 show how to frame around openings in out-side walls. Note the double headers above and below and at the sides of the openings. Information on nailing is given in drawings E-46 and E-47.

TRUSSING OVER OPENINGS

A truss over an opening in light frame house construction is in general a triangular arrangement of 2 x 4's forming a rigid framework as required to support the weight above. Figs. E-48 and E-49 show trussing for both large and small openings. It should be kept in mind that a good fit in all trusses is necessary if maximum strength is to be obtained.

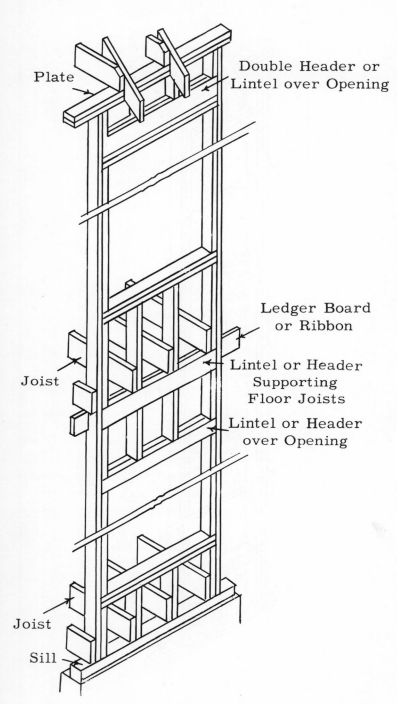

Plate

Double Header or Lintel over Opening

Ledger Board or Ribbon

Lintel or Header Supporting Floor Joists

Lintel or Header over Opening

Joist

Joist

Sill

E-45. Framing average openings in weight bearing wall or partition.

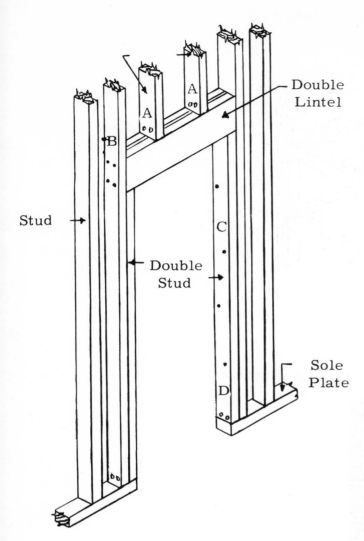

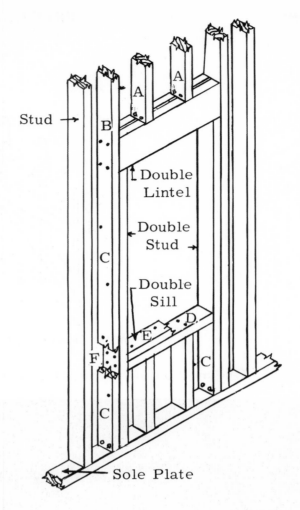

E-46. Studs above door openings in wall or partition should be toenailed to each part of lintel or header with one 10d nail as shown at A. B. Long studs nailed to ends of each part of lintel with two 10d nails and toenailed to sole plate with two 10d nails. C. Double studs nailed together with 10d nails spaced 16 in. apart and staggered. D. Studs alongside opening nailed into end of sole plate with two 10d nails.

E-47. Nailing framework around window opening. A. Studs above openings are toenailed to each part of lintel with one 10d nail. B. Long studs are nailed to ends of each part of lintel with two 10d nails. C. Double studs nailed together with 10d nails spaced 16 in. and staggered, and toenailed to sole plate with four 10d nails, two from each side. D. Lower part of sill member nailed to end of each stud below it with two 10d nails. E. Upper part of sill member nailed to lower with 10d nails spaced 8 in. and staggered as indicated. F. Studs alongside opening nailed to ends of each part of sill member with two 10d nails

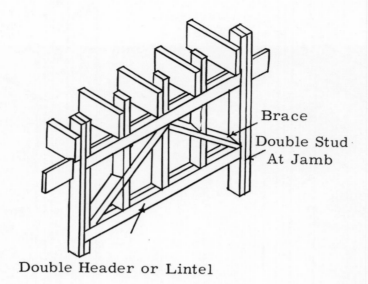

Brace

Double Stud
At Jamb

Double Header or Lintel

E-48. One method of framing for wide opening in load bearing wall or partition.

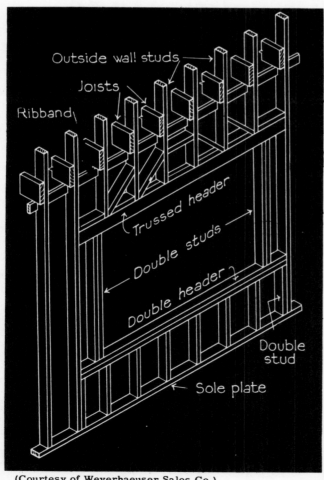

Outside wall studs

Joists

Ribband

Trussed header

Double studs

Double header

Double stud

Sole plate

E-49. Where wide openings occur in framing, extreme care must be taken in header construction since much of the load above is carried on these members. Note carefully the accurately fitted diagonal members.

(Courtesy of Weyerhaeuser Sales Co.)

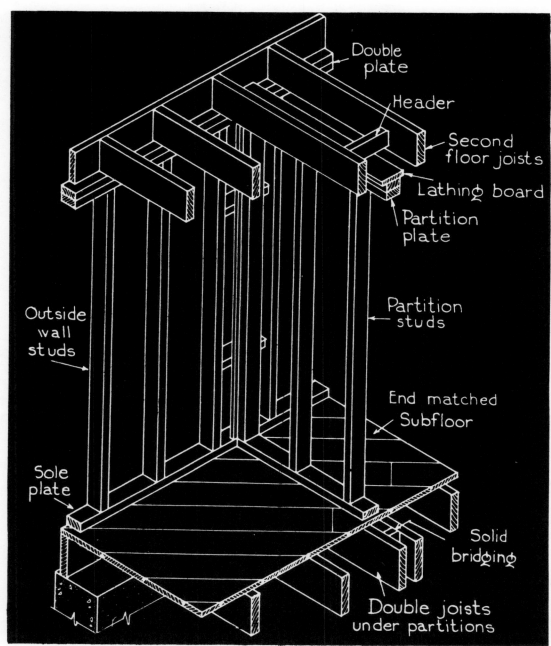

Double plate

Header

Second floor joists

Lathing board

Partition plate

Outside wall studs

Partition studs

End matched Subfloor

Sole plate

Solid bridging

Double joists under partitions

(Courtesy of Weyerhaeuser Sales Co.)

E-50. Framing for non-bearing partition. Double joists with solid bridging 18 in. o. c. should be under non-bearing partitions because of the extra weight of the partition itself. If the spans are more than 10 ft. triple joists should be used.

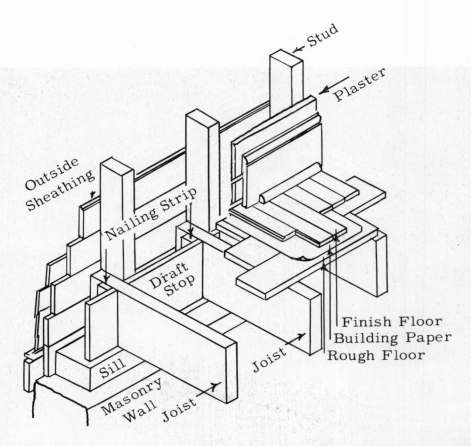

E-51. Fire stopping in balloon-frame construction. This could be modified by omitting the ribbon and letting the 2 x 4 stop be continuous in the form of a plate.

FIRE STOPPING

Fire stops are obstructions provided in air passages, which will interfere with the passage of flames up or across a building.

Fireproofing cannot prevent the occurrence of fire, but it will do these things to help save lives and money:

1. Help to confine fires occurring within the home to the rooms in which they start.

2. Protect the structural (load carrying) frame from destruction or weakening by fire and help prevent collapse of the building.

A high degree of fire protection may be built into a home by following a few simple construction rules and by using fireproof materials at points where fire is most likely to start and spread. The small additional expense of fireproofing should go into the budget as a "must" item.

METHODS OF FIRE STOPPING

Some practical methods of fire stopping are:

1. Boxing in vital points with 1 in. boards and filling the boxes with incombustible material such as loose mortar, mineral wool, concrete, etc., Fig. E-51.
2. Fitting 2 in. lumber between the wall studs, Fig. E-52.
3. Using brick as a fire stopping material at a partition which is not directly over another partition or support, Fig. E-53.
4. Using metal lath bent and nailed into place between studs and joists, plastering lath and filling box thus formed with incombustible material.

5. Fire stopping at cornice using 1 in. board and insulation material, E-54.

Fire stopping when properly placed also makes worthwhile extra bracing for a home.

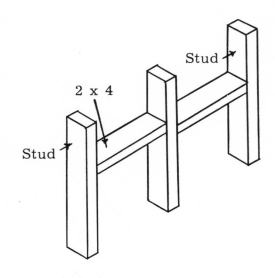

E-52. Solid bridging between studs serves as a fire stop.

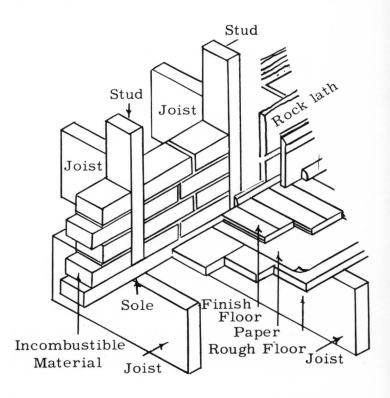

E-53. Using brick as a fire stopping material at partition which is not directly over another partition.

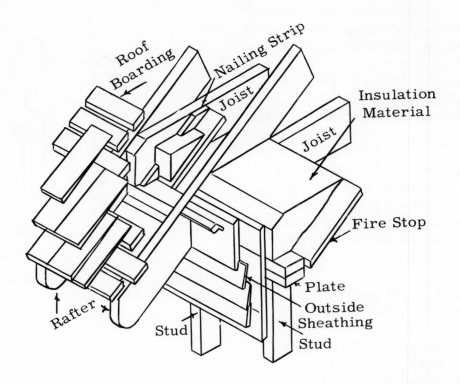

E-54. Fire stopping at cornice using 1 in. board
and incombustible insulation material.

INTERIOR PARTITIONS

There are two types of partitions, bearing and non-bearing. A bearing partition or wall is one which runs at right angles to and supports ends of the joists. A bearing partition, in other words, is one which bears or supports a load from above. A non-bearing wall or partition serves only as an enclosure and supports no joists.

Plates on bearing partitions should be doubled. Single plates are okay for non-bearing partitions.

Interior partitions may run at right angles to or parallel to the joists upon which they rest.

PARTITIONS PARALLEL TO JOISTS

In this case most of the weight of the partition will be concentrated upon a single joist so additional strength must be provided. Such partitions should be supported by double joists. These are sometimes placed together and sometimes spaced and bridged as shown in Fig. E-55.

PARTITIONS AT RIGHT ANGLES TO JOISTS

For non-bearing partitions it is not ordinarily necessary to increase the size or number of joists because of the large margin of safety in the live loads for which joists are designed.

When a bearing partition crosses joists at right angles near their center of span supporting joists should be doubled.

Economy in construction can be obtained by planning a house so bearing partitions are directly over one another as well as above the supporting girders.

PARTITION FRAMING

Details on framing studs at partition corners is shown in drawing E-56.

Another way to attach a partition to a wall, along with information on proper nailing is given in drawing E-57. Framing partitions at right angles to joists and with joists is illustrated in Fig. E-58.

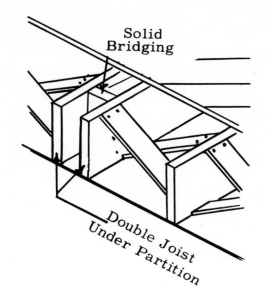

E-55. Double joists with solid bridging support partition.

E-56. Framing studs at partition corners.

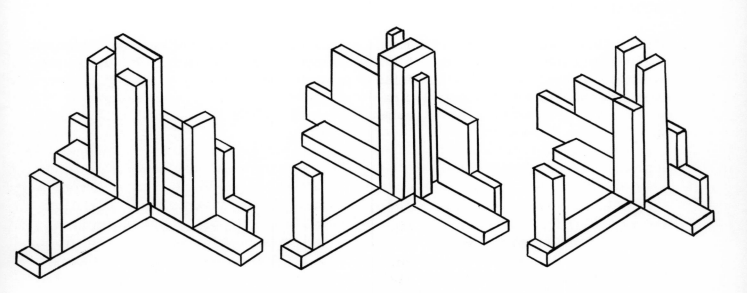

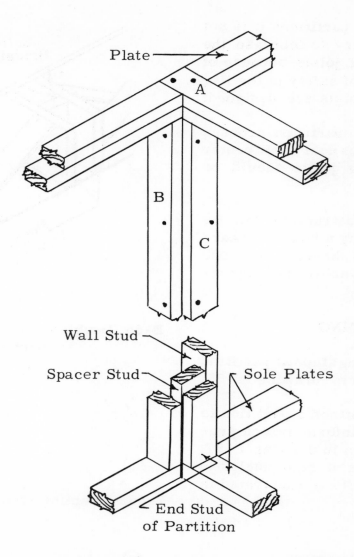

Plate

A

B

C

Wall Stud

Spacer Stud

Sole Plates

End Stud
of Partition

E-57. Attaching partition to wall. A. Upper member of partition plate is nailed to lower continuous member of wall plate with two 16d nails. B. Wall studs nailed to spacer stud with 16d nails 12 in. on centers. C. End stud of partition is nailed to spacer stud with 10d nails staggered with a vertical distance of 12 in. between nails.

Fig. E-59 shows a way to build a strong partition for carrying pipes from first to second floors, one which is not weakened by cutting and notching. In this partition 2 x 6 studs are used, which allows ample room for all pipes. The joist notched out for the pipe should be cut in the manner shown and the piece replaced to provide nailing surface for the floor.

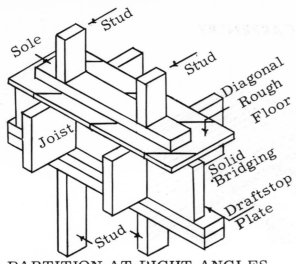

PARTITION AT RIGHT ANGLES
TO JOISTS—WESTERN FRAME

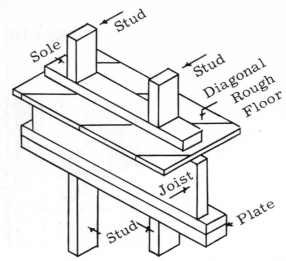

PARTITION PARALLEL WITH JOISTS
WESTERN FRAME

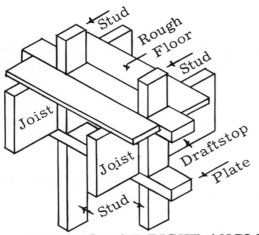

PARTITION AT RIGHT ANGLES
TO JOISTS—BALLOON AND
BRACED FRAME

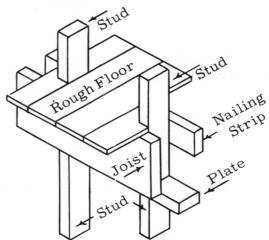

PARTITION PARALLEL WITH
JOISTS—BALLOON AND
BRACED FRAME

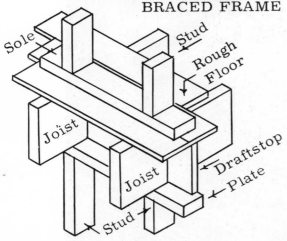

PARTITION AT RIGHT ANGLES
TO JOISTS—BALLOON FRAME

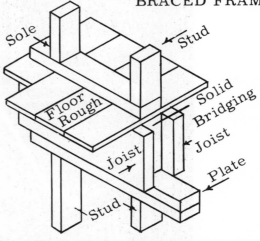

PARTITION PARALLEL WITH JOISTS
AND JOISTS SPREAD FOR PIPES, ETC.

E-58. Balloon and Western frame construction. Framing partitions at right
angles to joists and parallel to joists.

Joist Nailed on
Each Side of
Partition

Note "Bridge"
To Support
Floor Boards

E-59. Using 2 x 6 studs in partition to form passage for bathroom pipes. Piece cut from joist to admit soil pipe is replaced to strengthen joist and to provide nailing surface for the floor.

E-60. Framing second story overhang with cantilever joists, when overhang is parallel to joists.

(Courtesy of Weyerhaeuser Sales Co.)

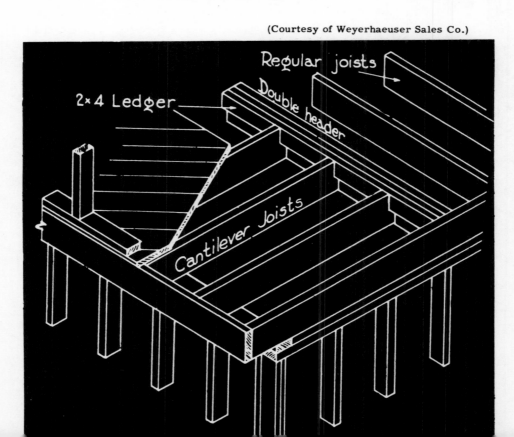

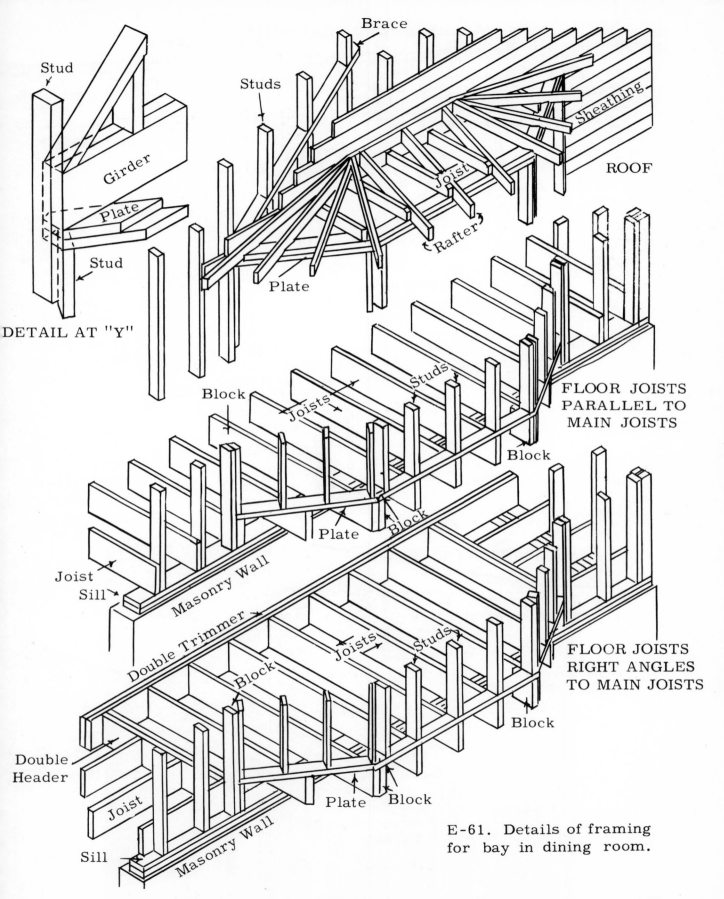

Stud

Studs

Brace

Sheathing

ROOF

Girder

Plate

Stud

DETAIL AT "Y"

Joist

Rafter

Plate

FLOOR JOISTS
PARALLEL TO
MAIN JOISTS

Block

Joists

Studs

Block

Plate

Block

Joist

Sill

Masonry Wall

Double Trimmer

Block

Joists

Studs

FLOOR JOISTS
RIGHT ANGLES
TO MAIN JOISTS

Block

Double
Header

Joist

Plate

Block

Sill

Masonry Wall

E-61. Details of framing
for bay in dining room.

97

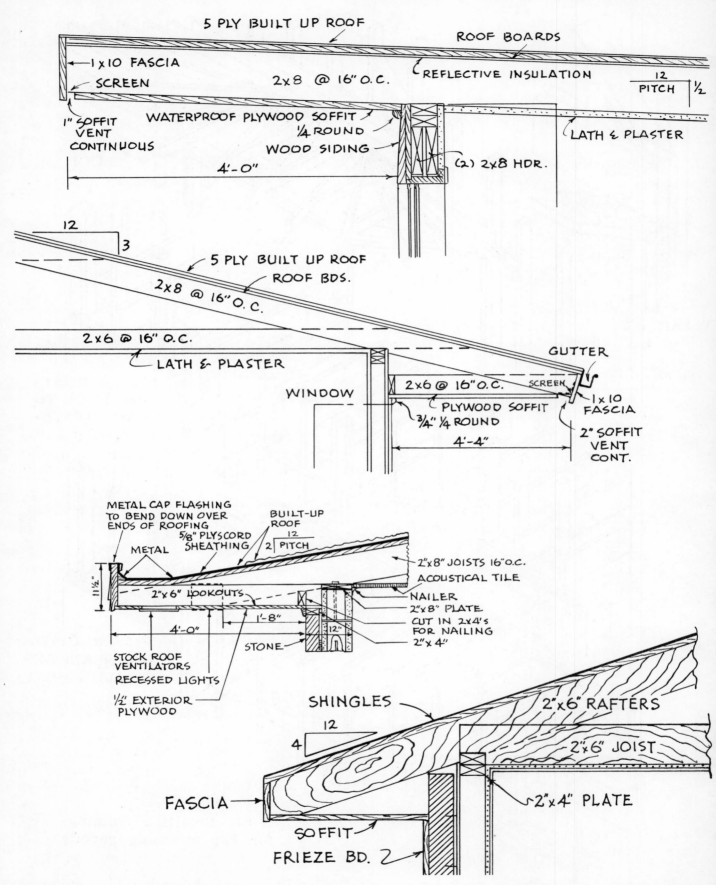

5 PLY BUILT UP ROOF

ROOF BOARDS

1 x 10 FASCIA

SCREEN

REFLECTIVE INSULATION

2x8 @ 16" O.C.

12
PITCH 1/2

1" SOFFIT VENT CONTINUOUS

WATERPROOF PLYWOOD SOFFIT

1/4 ROUND

WOOD SIDING

LATH & PLASTER

(2) 2x8 HDR.

4'-0"

12
3

5 PLY BUILT UP ROOF

ROOF BDS.

2x8 @ 16" O.C.

2x6 @ 16" O.C.

LATH & PLASTER

WINDOW

2x6 @ 16" O.C.

GUTTER

SCREEN

PLYWOOD SOFFIT

1 x 10 FASCIA

3/4" 1/4 ROUND

4'-4"

2" SOFFIT VENT CONT.

METAL CAP FLASHING TO BEND DOWN OVER ENDS OF ROOFING

BUILT-UP ROOF

12
2 PITCH

5/8" PLYSCORD SHEATHING

METAL

11 1/2"

2"x6" LOOKOUTS

2"x8" JOISTS 16"O.C.

ACOUSTICAL TILE

NAILER

2"x8" PLATE

CUT IN 2x4's FOR NAILING

2"x 4"

1'-8"

4'-0"

12"

STONE

STOCK ROOF VENTILATORS RECESSED LIGHTS

1/2" EXTERIOR PLYWOOD

SHINGLES

2"x6" RAFTERS

12
4

2"x6" JOIST

FASCIA

2"x4" PLATE

SOFFIT

FRIEZE BD.

98   E-62. Sections from ranch house plans, showing overhang construction.

Roof Types Framing

Four types of roofs — hip, gable, gambrel and shed, are shown in drawing F-1.

ROOF PITCH is the slope or angle of the roof, from the plate to the ridge which may vary from flat to a steep slope.

SPAN of a roof is the horizontal distance between the two supports — not the length along the rafter. Or, the measurement between the outside plates measured at right angles to the direction of the ridge of the building. See F-2.

TOTAL RISE is the distance up and down from the plate to the top of the ridge.

TOTAL RUN refers to the level distance over which any rafter passes which ordinarily is one-half the span distance. Again refer to F-2.

UNIT OF RUN or measurement, 1 ft. is the same as used elsewhere in building construction. By using this common unit the frame square may be used in roof layout.

CUT OF ROOF is the rise in inches and the unit of run (12 inches) and the

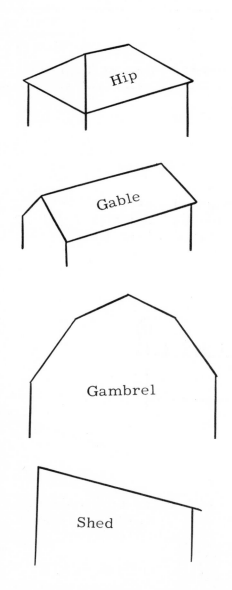

F-1. Four main types of roofs — hip, gable, gambrel and shed.

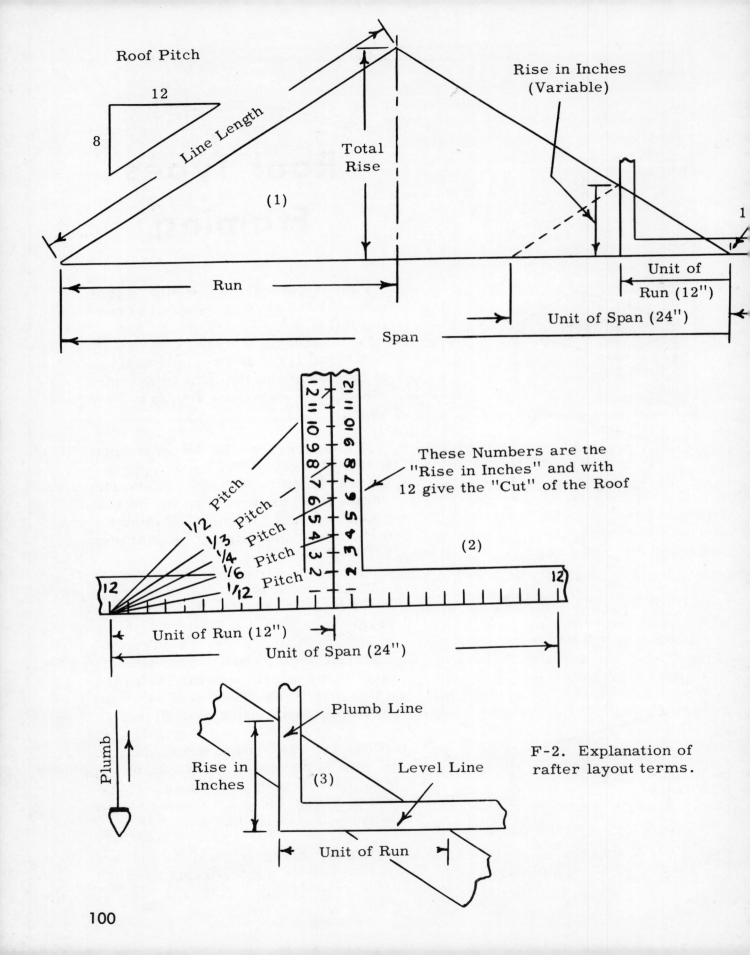

Roof Pitch

12

8

Line Length

Total Rise

Rise in Inches (Variable)

(1)

1

Run

Unit of Run (12")

Unit of Span (24")

Span

Pitch

1/2 Pitch

1/3 Pitch

1/4 Pitch

1/6 Pitch

1/12 Pitch

These Numbers are the "Rise in Inches" and with 12 give the "Cut" of the Roof

(2)

12

12

Unit of Run (12")

Unit of Span (24")

Plumb

Plumb Line

Rise in Inches

(3)

Level Line

Unit of Run

F-2. Explanation of rafter layout terms.

SPAN OF RAFTERS

Span Calculations provide for carrying the live loads shown and the additional weight of the rafters, sheathing and wood shingles.

Size	Spacing	15# L.L.		20# L.L.		30# L.L.		40# L.L.	
		No Plaster	Plaster	No Plaster	Plaster	No Plaster	Plaster	No Plaster	Plaster
2×4	12"	11'-6"	8'-11"	10'-4	8'-4"	8'-10	7'-6"	7'-10"	6'-11"
	16"	10'-0"	8'-2"	9'-0"	7'-7"	7'-8"	6'-10"	6'-10"	6'-3"
	24"	8'-3"	7'-2"	7'-5"	6'-8"	6'-4"	6'-0"	5'-7"	5'-6"
2×6	12"	17'-6"	13'-8"	15'-9"	12'-9"	13'-6"	11'-6"	12'-0"	10'-8"
	16"	15'-4"	12'-6"	13'-10"	11'-8"	11'-10"	10'-6"	10'-6"	9'-8"
	24"	12'-8"	11'-0"	11'-5"	10'-3"	9'-9"	9'-3"	8'-7"	8'-6"
2×8	12"	22'-10"	17'-11"	20'-9"	16'-10"	17'-10"	15'-3"	15'-10"	14'-1"
	16"	20'-1'	16'-6"	18'-3"	15'-5"	15'-7"	13'-11"	13'-10"	12'-11"
	24"	16'-9	14'-7"	15'-1"	13'-8"	12'-11"	12'-3"	11'-5"	11'-4"

(Courtesy of Weyerhaeuser Sales Co.)

F-3. Table listing maximum spans for 2 x 4, 2 x 6 and 2 x 8 rafters.

Line Length is the hypotenuse of a triangle whose base is the total run and whose altitude is the total rise. See (2) in drawing F-2.

PLUMB AND LEVEL LINES have reference to the direction of a line on a rafter and not to any particular cut, (3) in F-2. Any line that is vertical after the rafter has been nailed in position on the roof is called a plumb line and any line that is level when the rafter is in place is called a level line.

RAFTERS

Rafters serve the same purpose in a roof as do joists in a floor—they provide a support for sheathing and roofing materials.

The size of roof rafter depends on three factors:

1. Span
2. Weight of roofing material
3. Snow and wind loads

The table, Fig. F-3, lists maximum safe spans for 2 x 4's, 2 x 6's and 2 x 8's under various live loads for open attics (not plastered) and also for attics where plaster is applied to the rafters. The LL (Live Load) varies according to local building codes but the figure ordinarily used is 30 lbs. per sq. ft.

TYPES OF RAFTERS

Rafter types are shown in drawing F-4. AAA are common rafters running from the plate to the ridge in the cen-

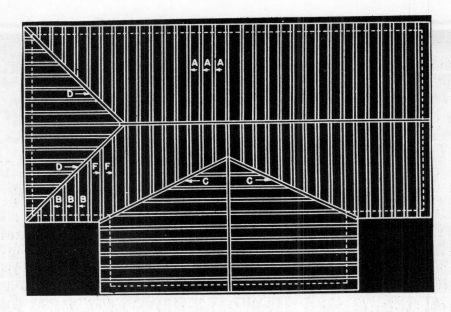

F-4. Rafter types. AAA are common rafters; BBB jack rafters; CC valley rafters; DD hip rafters; FF cripple rafters.

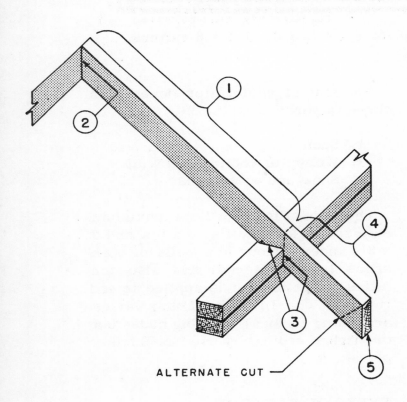

ALTERNATE CUT

F-5. Rafter terms. (1) Line length; (2) Plumb cut; (3) Seat cut; (4) Overhang; (5) Tail cut.

ter of the building and are not connected to other rafters. BBB are jack rafters and are shorter than common rafters. They connect at one end to hip rafters. CC are valley rafters and are needed at every corner between the main building and a projection. DD are hip rafters. FF are cripple rafters. They are so called because they have no feet or bearing on wall plates.

RAFTER TERMS

Terms used in cutting rafters are indicated in drawing F-5.

RIDGE CUT is the cut of the rafter that fits against the opposite rafter at the ridge (1).

SEAT CUT is made horizontal to plate. The notch sawed in the rafter to fit on the plate (3) is called the bird's mouth.

TAIL CUT is the cut on the lower end (5).

102

OVERHANG is the part of the rafter that projects past side of building.

LAYING OUT RAFTERS

Rafters must be properly laid out and cut with the slope, length and overhang exactly right.

The first step is to determine the length of the rafter and to make sure that the lumber obtained for rafters is of the proper length.

Rafter length can usually be obtained from the plans. If no plans are being used, the first step is to measure the exact width of the building with a tape.

ROOF PITCH EXPLAINED

Gable roofs are built in a variety of pitches. Two of the most common are 1/4 and 1/3 pitch.

In a 1/3 pitch roof, for example, the vertical height from the plate or timber, on which the bottoms of the rafters rest, to the ridge, equals 1/3 the span or width of the building. This is the pitch shown in part 1 of Fig. F-2. One-third of the span shown, 24 ft., would give us 8 ft., the total rise for this particular roof.

In a 1/4 pitch the rise would be 1/4 the span, 1/6 pitch, 1/6 of the span, etc.

F-6. Small triangles indicate roof pitches. In the 1/3 pitch roof, for example, the roof rises 8 ft. for every 24 ft. in length.

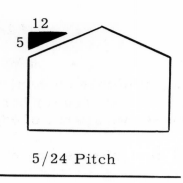

5/24 Pitch

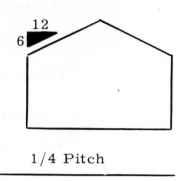

1/4 Pitch

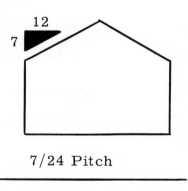

7/24 Pitch

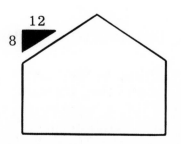

1/3 Pitch

The amount of rise or vertical distance for each foot of run or horizontal distance is shown in part 2 of Fig. F-2.

Several roof pitches are shown in Fig. F-6.

To determine the approximate overall length of a rafter for a 1/3 pitch roof, for example, measure on the steel square the distance between 8 on the tongue and 12 on the blade, as 8 is the rise and 12 is the unit of run.

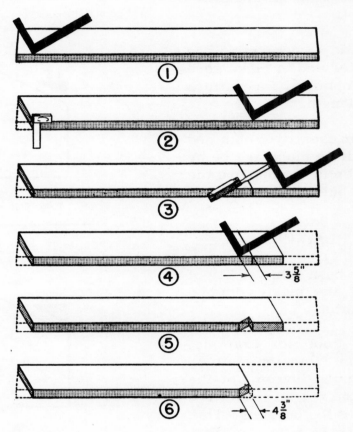

F-7. Laying out a rafter with framing square. A full explanation will be found in the text.

HOW TO USE FRAMING SQUARE

Before going further let's get acquainted with the framing square. The "face" of a square is the side bearing the manufacturer's name. The reverse is the "back." The longer arm is the "body," or blade, the shorter is called the "tongue."

This distance is 14 5/12 in. and represents the line length of a rafter with a run of 1 ft. and an 8 in. rise (1/3 pitch). If we had a building with a run of 10 ft., we would multiply the 14 5/12 by 10. This gives 144 2/12, or 12 ft. and 2/12. To this we must add the amount the rafter extends beyond the building, or overhang. If the overhang is 1 ft. we would have a rafter length of 13 2/12 ft. This is an odd length for lumber so 14 ft. timber would be used.

After the length has been determined the timber to be used, preferably a good straight one, is laid on sawhorses. The crown, or high point, if any, should be on the top side of the rafter.

Hold the square with the tongue in the right hand, the blade in the left, the heel away from the body and place the square as near the upper end of the rafter as possible. Figures 8 on the tongue and 12 on the blade should be placed along the edge of timber which is to be the top edge as shown in (1) Fig. F-7. Mark along the tongue edge of the square. This will give you the plumb cut at the ridge. Since the length of the rafter is known to be 12 ft., measure that distance from the top of the plumb cut and mark it on the timber. Now, hold the square in the same manner with the 8 mark of the tongue directly over the 12 ft. mark. Mark along the tongue of the square to get the plumb cut for the seat, F-7, (2).

Next mark off, perpendicular to this mark, the length of overhang along the timber and make a plumb-cut mark in the same manner, keeping the square on the same edge of the timber as shown in (3). This will be the tail cut. Sometimes the tail cut is made square across the timber.

The level cut or width of the seat is the width of the plate, measured perpendicular to the plumb cut as indicated in (4). This finishes laying

out the rafter and it is now ready to be cut.

When two rafters have been cut, it is best to put them in place to see if they fit. Minor adjustment, if any, should be made and these rafters used as patterns.

"STEPPING OFF" RAFTERS

Fig. F-8 shows a practical way to "step off" a rafter, using a framing square, one step being required for each foot of run. The tongue, or short side is held at 8 and the blade or long side at 12. The blade is always held at 12 regardless of the pitch.

For a 1/4 pitch roof you would hold the tongue of the square at 6; 7/24 at 7; 1/3 pitch at 8. You can multiply the pitch by the building width to get the roof rise. For example, if the building is 18 ft. wide and the roof pitch is 7/24 the rise is 7/24 x 18 or 5 1/4. Fig. F-8 also shows how to mark plumb, tail and seat cuts.

USING RAFTER FRAMING TABLES

Framing squares may have rafter tables as shown in Figs. F-9 and F-10.

The square shown in F-9 gives both the line length of any pitch of rafter per foot of run, F-9 length of hip or valley rafter and side cut of jack, hip and valley rafters.

Each set of figures under each inch division mark indicates the length of rafter per foot of run with a rise corresponding to the number of inches shown over the number.

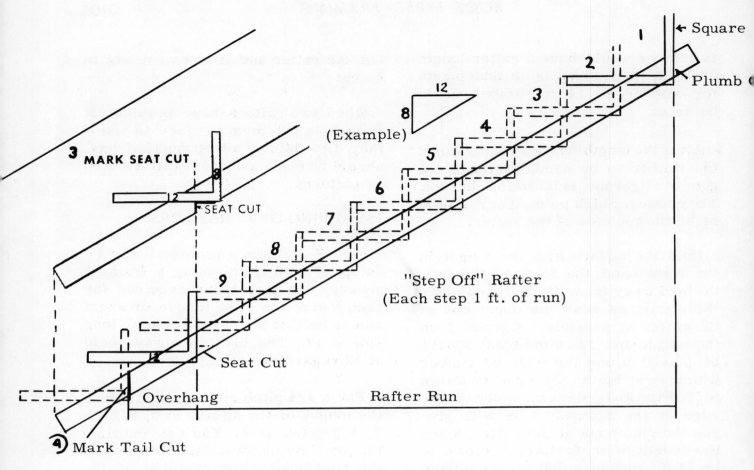

F-8. Using framing square to "step off" a rafter. One step is required for each foot of run. The short side is held at 8 and the blade or long side at 12. The blade is always held at 12 regardless of the pitch. For 1/4 pitch you would hold the tongue at 6, 7/24 pitch at 7, etc.

Under the 16 in. mark, for example, appears the number 20.00 inches. This number equals the length of a rafter with a run of 12 inches and a rise of 16 inches.

To use the table, the width of the building must be known. Let's suppose the building is 20 ft. 8 in. wide and the rise of the rafters is 8 in. per foot of run. The total run of the rafter will be 10 ft. 4 in. In the first line of figures, under the 8 in. mark appears the number 14.42, which is the length

in inches of a rafter with a run of one foot and a rise of eight inches. To find the line length of a rafter with a run of 10 ft. 4 in., multiply 14.42 by 10 1/3 then divide by 12 to get the answer in feet. 14.42 x 10 1/2 equals 149.007 inches. Divide this by 12 and we get 12 5/12, or 12 ft. 5 in. which is the line length of the rafter.

ANOTHER TYPE OF SQUARE

A different type of roofing square is shown in F-10. This one gives the run rise and the pitch of rafters of

106

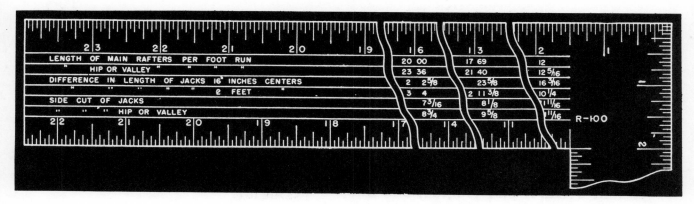

F-9. Framing square which gives line length of pitch or rafter per foot of run, line length of hip or valley rafter and side cut of jack, hip and valley rafters.

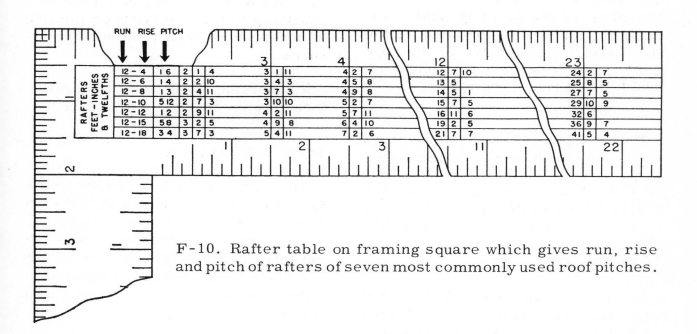

F-10. Rafter table on framing square which gives run, rise and pitch of rafters of seven most commonly used roof pitches.

seven most commonly used pitches of roofs.

The figures are based on the length of the horizontal measurement of the building from the center to the outside. The rafter table and the outside edge of the back of the square, both the body and tongue are in twelfths. The inch marks may represent either inches or feet, and the twelfth marks may represent twelfths of an inch or twelfths of a foot.

The rafter table is used in connection with the marks and figures on the outside edge of the square. At the left end of the table are figures representing the run, the rise and the pitch. In the first column, the figures are all 12. These may be used as 12 inches or 12 feet as they represent the run of 12. The second column of figures represents the various rises. The third column in fractions shows the various pitches.

These three columns of figures show that a rafter with a run of 12 and a rise of 4, for example, has one-sixth pitch, 12 and 6 has a one-fourth pitch and 12 and 12 has one-half pitch.

To use the scale for a roof with one-sixth pitch, or rise of one-sixth the width of the building, and a run of 12 ft., find 1/6 in the table, follow the same line of figures to the right until directly beneath the figure 12, which is the run of the rafter.

Under figure 12 are the numbers 12, 7, 10 which is the rafter length required—12 ft., 7 in. and 10/12 of an inch. For a pitch of one-half (or a rise of one-half the width of the building) and a run of 12 ft., the rafter length would be 16, 11, 6 or 16 ft., 11 6/12 inches.

In figuring runs over 23 ft., some extra figuring is required. Let's take 27 ft. for example. We find the length for a run of 23 ft., then find the length of 4 ft. and add the two.

RAFTER SPACING

Since plaster is not generally applied to the undersides of rafters, it is not necessary to adhere to the 16 in. spacing standard ordinarily used on joists and studs. Spacing is determined more by stiffness of sheathing, by weight of the roof and by rafter span.

Spacings of 16 to 24 inches are common, but for ordinary roof sheathing 20 in. is probably used most. Greater spacing should not be used except where sheathing is tongued-and-grooved flooring not over four inches wide or where extreme economy is essential.

Spacing of rafters closer than 20 inches is seldom necessary, except in cases where roofing materials are unusually heavy or there is possibility of heavy snows or extreme wind pressures.

If underside of rafters is to be plastered, 16 in. spacing is desirable.

ROOF ANCHORAGE

Those who have helped on roof framing jobs are familiar with the outward thrust of rafters that are supported only at the walls. On steep roofs the outward thrust is largely eliminated, but some support at midlength of the rafters is desirable to resist wind pressure.

Rafters solidly supported at the wall and leaning against each other at the ridge provide mutual support. To offset the outward thrust at the base of the rafter several methods can be used.

1. When attic floor joists are adjacent to rafters and rest on floor plates, they should be solidly

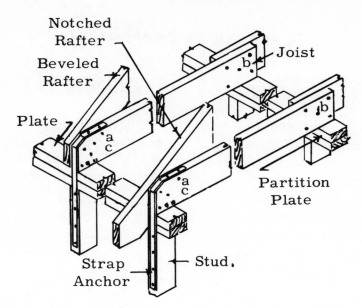

Notched Rafter
Beveled Rafter
Plate
Joist
a
c
b
b
a
c
Partition Plate
Strap Anchor
Stud.

F-11. Rafters both beveled and notched and ceiling joists resting on wall plates. A, five 10d nails through joist into rafter or through rafter into joist. B, overlap of joists at bearing partition nailed with five 10d nails. C, joist and rafter toe-nailed to plate by using four 10d nails, two on each side. For still extra security metal straps may be used as shown.

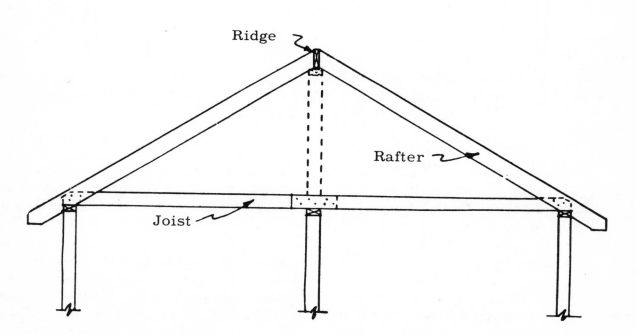

Ridge
Rafter
Joist

F-12. Framing a building so ceiling joists tie rafters together. Where span is too long for one-piece joists, the joists should be lapped at least a foot and spiked. They should also be securely nailed at the eaves. On jobs where the slope of rafters is small, causing considerable outward thrust, the ridge should be supported as indicated by the dotted lines.

nailed to the rafters, Fig. F-11.

2. If spacing of rafters is different from that of attic floor joists, every third or fourth rafter will be adjacent to a ceiling joist and should be solidly nail-

COLLAR BEAMS OR TIES

Collar beams are ties between rafters on opposite sides of a roof, Figs. F-13 and F-14. When the attic is used for rooms, the collar beams may serve as ceiling supports, provided they are properly spaced.

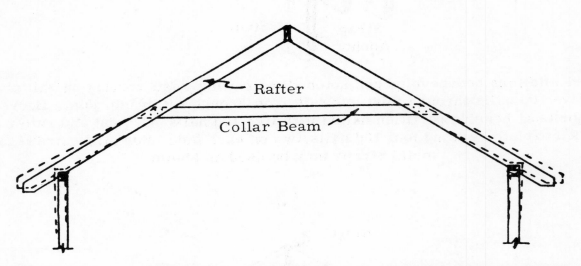

F-13. Collar beams, unless placed near the plate, should not be depended upon for ties, as there is a tendency for rafters to bend and building to spread as indicated by dotted lines.

ed to it. Besides, all attic floor joists should be nailed solidly to the plate to take the thrust between those rafters which are securely tied.

If slope of rafters is small, the outward thrust at eaves will be more than ties can be depended on to resist. Under such conditions, there should be a vertical support under the rafters at the ridge and perhaps midway of the rafter span also, which will prevent the outward thrust at the base. See Fig. F-12.

Collar beams should not be depended upon to serve as ties unless the rafters are quite steep; their function is to stiffen a roof, not support it.

Sometimes when the roof slope shows a little in upper rooms, joists occurring not exactly at the heel but a little above, Fig. F-14, will be permitted. No floor should be placed on such beams.

Collar beams, where required, are usually placed at every second or third rafter. The most effective position is at the midpoint of the rafter.

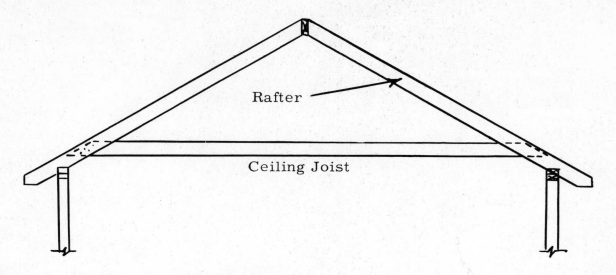

F-14. Ceiling joists slightly above the plate may frequently be used as ties.

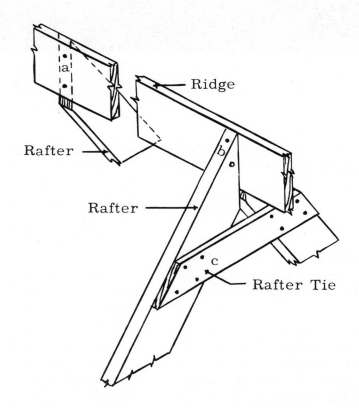

F-15. Roof peak. A, ridge is nailed to first rafter of pair with two nails—10d for 1 in. ridge or 16d for 2 in. ridge. B, second rafter of pair is nailed through its top edge to ridge with one 10d nail and toenailed to ridge with one 10d nail. C, rafter tie or collar beam placed near peak and nailed to each rafter with four 10d nails. Such a rafter tie is desirable to resist spreading tendency which might result from wind action, or heavy snow load.

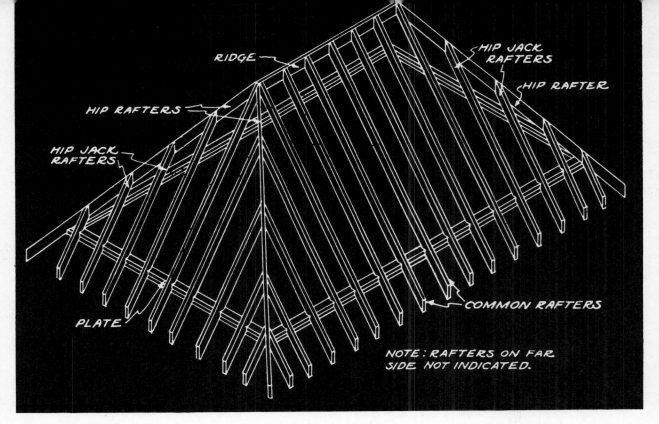

RIDGE

HIP JACK RAFTERS

HIP RAFTER

HIP RAFTERS

HIP JACK RAFTERS

PLATE

COMMON RAFTERS

NOTE: RAFTERS ON FAR SIDE NOT INDICATED.

F-16. Typical hip roof. The hip rafter is the one which runs from the corner of the building upward forming a hip.

For light roofs 2 x 3's or 2 x 4's should be used. For heavy roofs 2 x 4's or 3 x 4's are recommended.

RIDGE BOARD

The ridge board is a horizontal member against which rafters rest at their upper ends, drawing F-15.

A 1 in. board with a width equal to the depth of the rafters is usually satisfactory. The length of the board will be the length of the building, measured from the inside face of the sheathing. Splices as required should be made between two rafters.

HIP RAFTERS

A typical hip roof is shown in drawing F-16. The hip rafter is the one which runs from the corner of the building upward along the hip. This acts as a ridge board and to a slight degree, when the roof pitch is low, as a girder supporting the ends of jack rafters.

Where hip rafters are not over 8 ft. and upper ends come together at the center of the roof, the hip rafter may safely be of the same size as a regular rafter of equal length. For longer spans, and in particular where the upper end of the hip is supported vertically from below, an increase in rafter size is necessary.

For spans up to 12 ft., the hip rafter should be 2 in. deeper or 1 in. wider than a regular rafter of the same span. For spans over 12 ft., the hip rafter should be doubled in width.

112

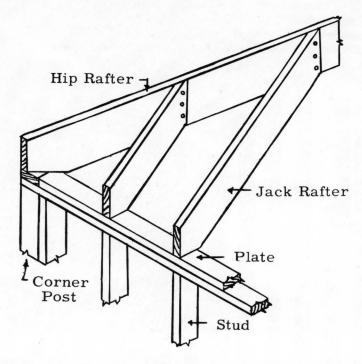

Hip Rafter

Jack Rafter

Plate

Corner Post

Stud

F-17. Jack rafter is toenailed to hip rafter with three 10d nails.

JACK RAFTERS

Jack rafters are rafters which extend from wall plates to hips or valley rafters, Fig. F-17. They are obviously shorter than the regular rafters.

Cripple rafters are the same except they do not bear on wall plates. Both ends bear on other rafters.

In constructing jack and cripple rafters the size and spacing should be the same as the regular rafters.

VALLEY RAFTERS

Where two roof surfaces meet at an interior corner or valley a rafter is required to carry such jack rafters as may rest upon it. This is called a valley rafter.

Material requirements are the same as described for hip rafters.

ADDITIONAL RAFTER FRAMING INFORMATION

Other rafter framing and nailing information which will be found helpful in solving problems that confront carpenters from time to time is given in Figs. F-18 to F-29 inclusive.

The sizes of nails indicated are the minimum sizes considered suitable for the particular purpose. In some cases it may be desirable to increase the size in order to have fewer sizes to be supplied to the job and to be carried by those doing the construction work. Ordinarily, nails one size larger than specified are acceptable, provided they do not cause splitting.

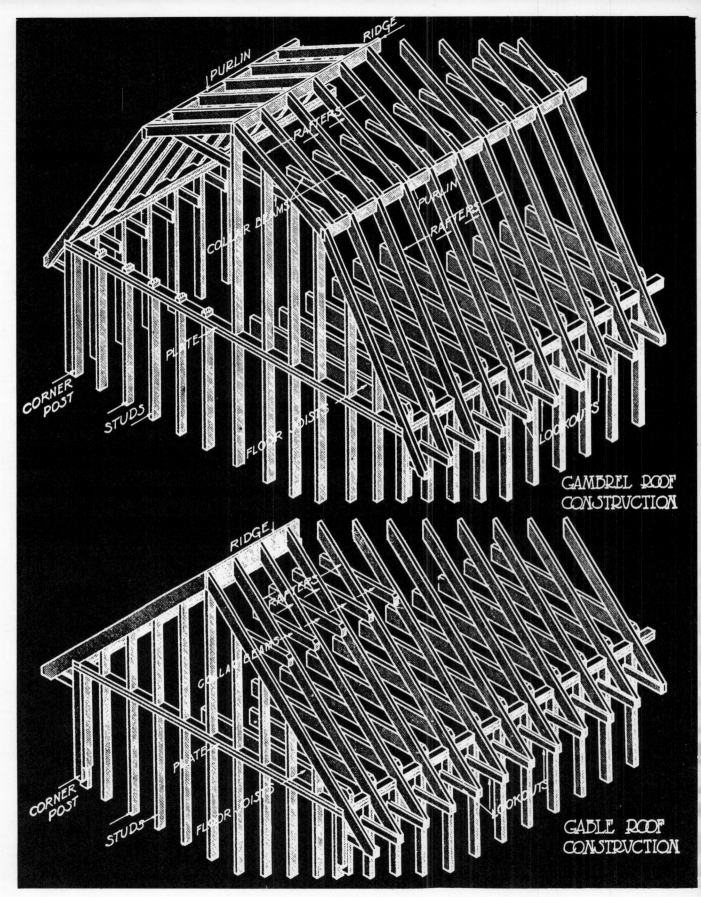

F-18. Gambrel and gable roof construction.

114

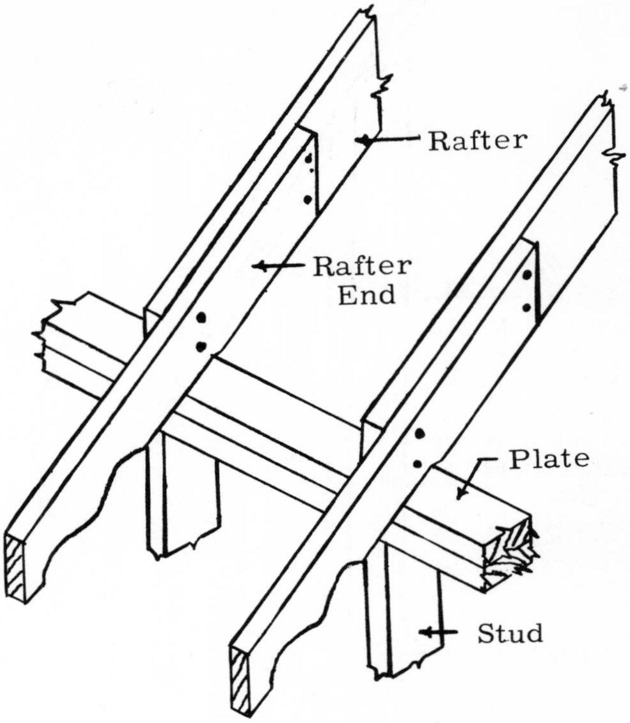

F-19. Rafter ends are nailed to rafters with four 10d nails.

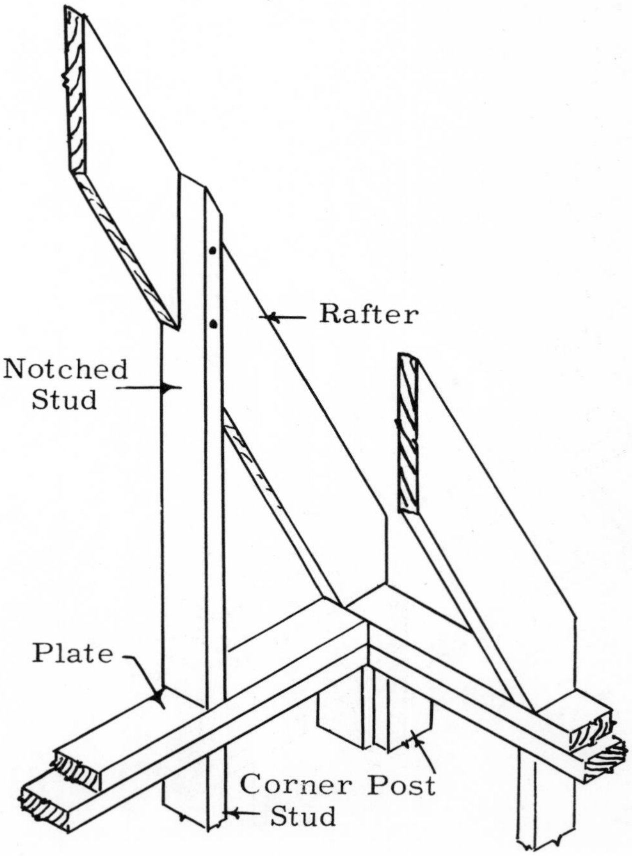

Rafter

Rafter End

Plate

Stud

F-20. Notched gable stud is nailed to rafter with two 10d nails.

Rafter

Notched Stud

Plate

Corner Post Stud

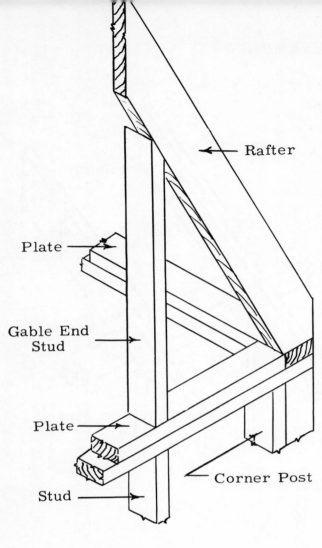

Rafter

Plate

Gable End
Stud

Plate

Stud

Corner Post

F-21. Fastening beveled gable stud. The rafter is toenailed to the stud and stud nailed to rafter with 10d nails.

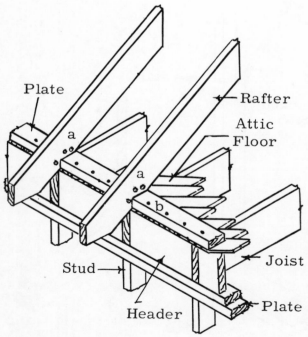

Plate

Rafter

Attic
Floor

a

a

b

Stud

Header

Joist

Plate

F-22. Notched rafters resting on plate. A, rafters are toenailed to upper face of plate with two 10d nails on each side of rafter and to outer edge of plate with one 10d nail on each side. B, plate is nailed through attic floor to each joist with one 16d nail and to headers or header joist with 16d nails spaced about 4 in. on centers. In localities where high winds are encountered still additional security may be obtained by the use of metal straps as shown in drawing F-27.

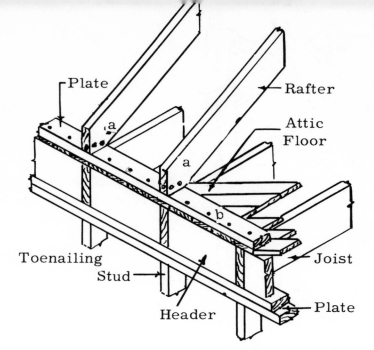

F-23. Beveled rafters resting on plate. A, rafter is toenailed to plate with five 10d nails, two on each side and one through vertical cut of rafter. B, plate is nailed through attic floor to each joist with one 16d nail and to headers or header joist with 16d nails spaced 4 in. apart.

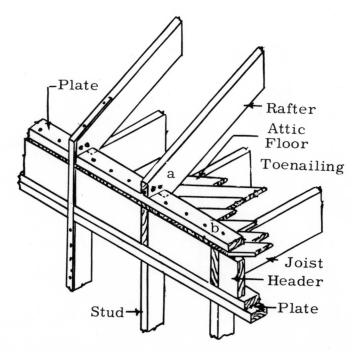

F-24. Beveled rafters backnotched over plate. A, rafter is toenailed to upper face of plate with two 10d nails on each side and with one 10d nail through vertical cut of rafter. B, plate is nailed through the attic floor into each joist with one 16d nail and into headers or header joist with 16d nails spaced 4 in. apart. Extra security may be obtained by the use of straps as shown at the left and in the drawing, F-27.

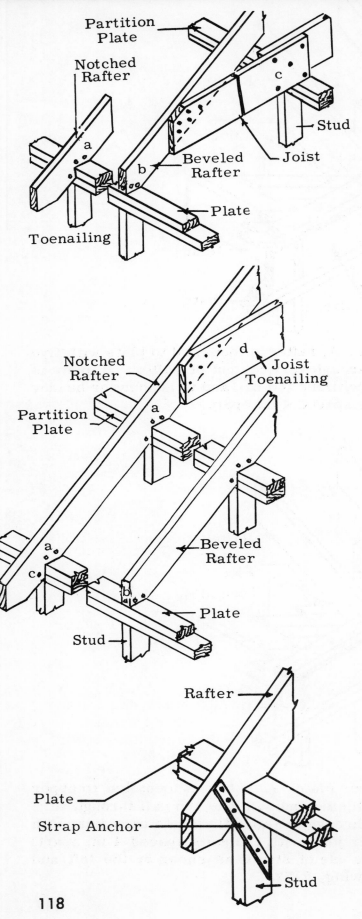

Partition Plate

Notched Rafter

a

Toenailing

c

Stud

Beveled Rafter

Joist

Plate

F-25. Rafter notched or beveled at wall plate with the ceiling joist at a higher level.

Notched Rafter

Partition Plate

d

Joist Toenailing

a

a

Beveled Rafter

c

b

Plate

Stud

F-26. Rafters notched or beveled at wall plate and notched over partition plate with ceiling joist above the partition plate.

Rafter

Plate

Strap Anchor

Stud

F-27. Straps for notched rafters. Straps are placed on opposite sides and as nearly vertical as possible. Straps supplement nailing in localities where high winds are encountered.

118

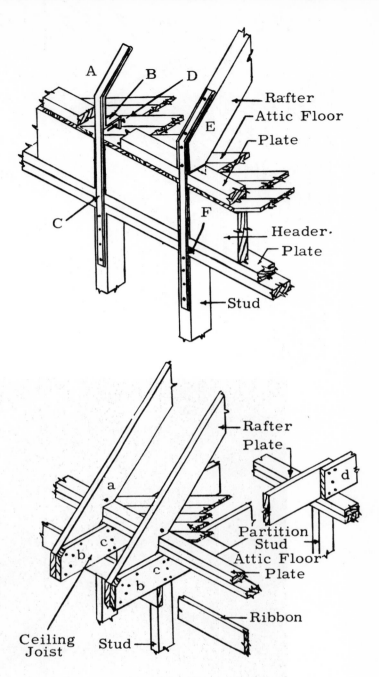

F-28. Using straps on beveled rafter to resist horizontal thrust and uplift. A, strap is double along upper edge and vertical cut of rafter with B, single thickness extending across upper and inner faces of plate and C, single thickness extending down along the outer edge of the stud.

F-29. Suggested method of framing that provides superior resistance to the forces to which rafters are subjected.

FRAMING FOR DORMERS

Any type of window protruding from a roof may be called a dormer. Dormer windows may be used to provide additional usable space on the top floor, light, or for architectural effect.

When framing the roof for a dormer window, an opening is ordinarily left and the dormer built into this opening. Two examples of how dormers may be properly framed are shown in Figs. F-30 and F-31.

Note particularly that the rafters on both sides of the dormers are strengthened by trimmers extending from the plate to the ridge and that the plates are doubled.

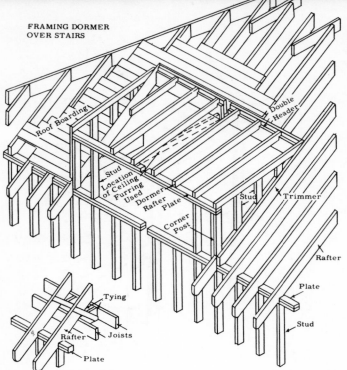

FRAMING DORMER
OVER STAIRS

Roof Boarding

Double
Header

Stud
Location
of Ceiling
Furring
Used
Dormer
Rafter
Plate

Stud

Trimmer

Corner
Post

Rafter

Plate

Stud

Tying

Rafter

Joists

Plate

F-30. Dormer framing. Dormer may be framed on roof boards or on the top of the rafters.

F-31. Below. Framing small dormer. Note particularly that the rafters or trimmers on both sides of the opening have been doubled.

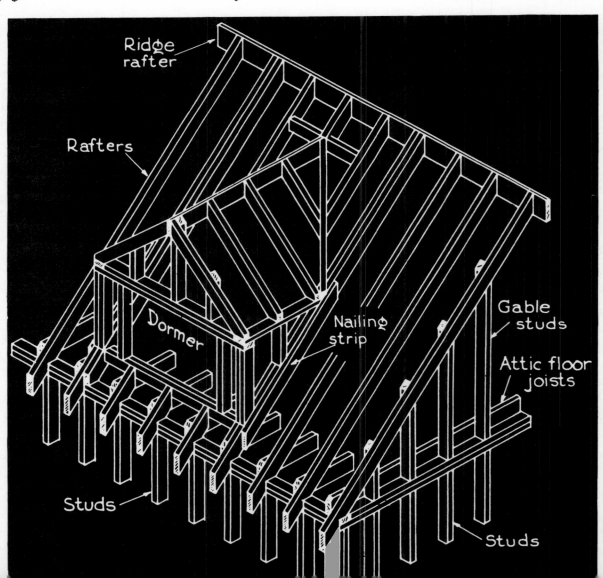

Ridge rafter

Rafters

Dormer

Nailing strip

Gable studs

Attic floor joists

Studs

Studs

RAFTER SPAN, CONVERSION DIAGRAM

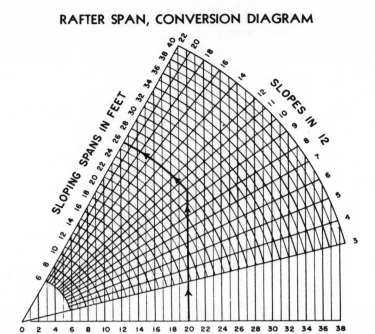

F-32. To find the rafter span when its horizontal span and slope are known, follow the vertical line from the horizontal span to its intersection with the radial line of the slope. From the intersection follow the curve line to the sloping span. The diagram also may be used to determine the horizontal span when the sloping span and slope are known, or to determine the slope when the sloping and horizontal spans are known. EXAMPLE: For a horizontal span of 20 ft. and a slope of 10 in 12, the sloping span of the rafter is read directly from diagram as 26 ft.

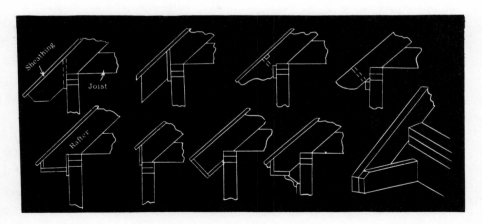

F-33. Above, typical open cornices. Below, five styles of closed or boxed cornices. A design should be used that is in harmony with style of house being built.

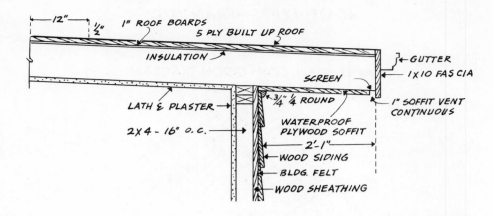

Labels in figure: 12", 1/2", 1" ROOF BOARDS, 5 PLY BUILT UP ROOF, INSULATION, GUTTER, 1 X 10 FASCIA, SCREEN, LATH & PLASTER, 3/4" 1/4 ROUND, 1" SOFFIT VENT CONTINUOUS, 2X4 - 16" O.C., WATERPROOF PLYWOOD SOFFIT, 2'-1", WOOD SIDING, BLDG. FELT, WOOD SHEATHING

F-34. Typical flat roof construction. Note pitch is 1/2 in. in 12.

FLAT ROOFS

The so-called flat roof usually has some slope for drainage. The slope is expressed as the number of inches of vertical rise in 12 in. of horizontal run, the rise being given first, as 4 in 12. For purposes of definition, flat roofs may be classed as roofs having less than a 3 in 12 slope. This slope is the greatest for which a built-up

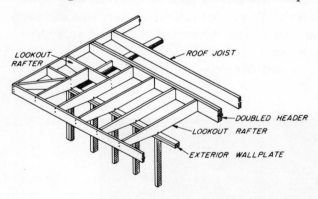

Labels in figure: LOOKOUT RAFTER, ROOF JOIST, DOUBLED HEADER, LOOKOUT RAFTER, EXTERIOR WALLPLATE

F-35. Flat roof with overhang, typical construction.

covering is ordinarily allowed. The slope may be provided by tapering the joists, or by adding cant strips to the top.

Most species of softwood framing lumber are acceptable for framing of flat roofs, subject to maximum allowable spans for the particular species, grade and specific use. Size of material to use must be established on the basis of both roof and ceiling loads.

Construction of a typical flat roof is shown in Fig. F-34. Note that insulation, sheathing and built-up roof are above the joist and that the underside is utilized to support the plastered ceiling.

Where overhang is involved on all sides of the house, lookout rafters are ordinarily used, Fig. F-35. A double header rafter is used, and lookout rafters are nailed to the header and toenailed to the wallplate. The distance from the double header to the wall line is usually twice the overhang.

In modern construction, flat roofs or roofs with a low pitch are frequently built with 2-in. matched plank for roof sheathing supported on large beams spaced 4 to 8 feet apart, with the planking and the beams exposed on the underside, to show as decorative part of living areas.

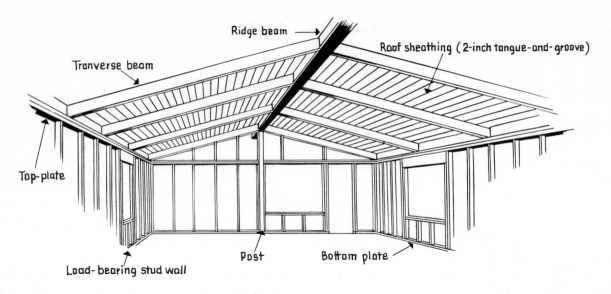

F-36. Transverse beam system of roof framing.

TRANSVERSE BEAMS

The transverse-beam system of roof framing, Fig. F-36, may be used for low-pitched gable, shed, flat, or butterfly roofs. Beams which are spaced 4 to 8 feet apart, extend from exterior walls to the center of the house, and are supported by a ridge beam which runs the length of the house. In some cases, a load-bearing wall is used instead of a ridge beam. In this type of roof 2-inch tongue and groove stock is generally used for sheathing. The transverse beams must be heavy enough to adequately support the load.

LONGITUDINAL BEAMS

The longitudinal-beam roof framing as shown in Fig. F-37, is suitable for flat, gable, shed and butterfly roofs. The beams are supported by end walls of the building, or by posts or partitions.

Space between the heavy, wide spaced beams is usually spanned by 2 in. tongue-and-groove stock. Or,

F-37. Longitudinal beam framing.

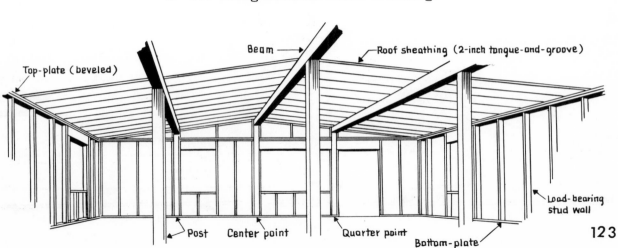

123

standard rafters and sheathings may be used in place of 2 in. sheathing.

ROOF TRUSS CONSTRUCTION

In the truss type of roof framing, rafters and joists support one another.

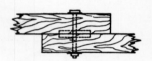

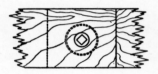

f-40. Using split ring (S.R.) metal timber connector between timber faces to increase joint strength. The ring fits into grooves in timber faces, which are cut with special tool.

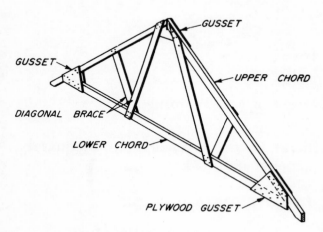

F-38. Light-weight roof truss.

the entire width of the building. The trusses relieve interior partitions of the weight of the roof, thus permitting considerable freedom in planning and division of space within the building.

Trusses are well suited to ground-level fabrication; each being lifted into place as a unit. Spacing of roof trusses is usually 24 in. compared to 16 in. for conventional joists and rafters.

See Fig. F-38, F-39 and F-40. Such framing consists essentially of top and bottom chords connected by suitable diagonal members. Trusses rest on exterior walls and usually span

In building roof trusses, particularly trusses for long spans, specifications prepared by competent engineers, should be carefully followed.

F-39. Roof truss for a 24 ft. span with a 5 in 12 slope, based on Timber Engineering Co. design. Load limit 45 lbs. per sq. ft. when trusses are spaced 2 ft. o. c.

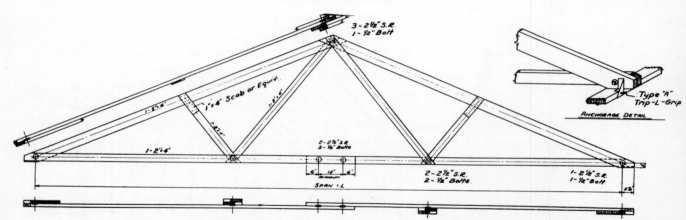

Exterior Wall Construction

WALL SHEATHING

Outside sheathing, or sub-siding, as it is sometimes called, is nailed directly on the framework and forms a base for the finish siding, shingles or other covering.

As with subflooring, there seldom is need for greater thickness than 25/32 in. Diagonal sheathing, Fig. G-1, is of considerable importance in localities subject to wind storms

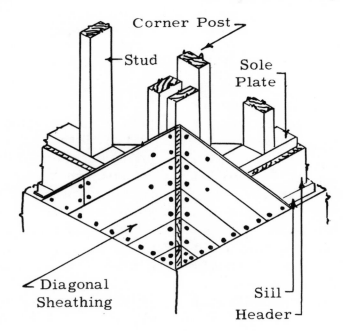

G-1. Diagonal wall sheathing should be fastened with 8d nails. For boards 8 in. and less in width, use two nails at each end of each board, two nails through each board into the studs and three nails through each board into the corner post assembly. For wider boards use an additional nail at each of these points. Joints in adjacent runs of sheathing should be separated by at least two stud spaces. Besides affording high resistance to windstorms, diagonal sheathing effectively ties together sills, joists, plates and studs. End joints need not be made over studs if boards used for diagonal sheathing are tongued and grooved.

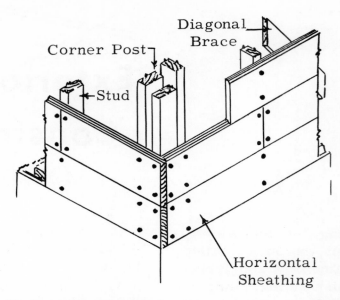

Corner Post

Diagonal Brace

Stud

Horizontal Sheathing

G-2. Horizontal wall sheathing—boards 8 in. or less in width should be nailed to the framing members with one 8d nail near each edge of the board. Wider boards should be nailed with three 8d nails, one near each edge and one near the middle of the piece.

and tornados. In fact, it is considered good practice in all sections unless the building is otherwise braced.

Placing and nailing of horizontal sheathing is covered in the drawing, G-2. Boards 8 in. or less in width should be nailed to the framing members with two 8d nails, one near each edge of the board. Wider boards should be nailed with three 8d nails, one near each edge and one near the middle of the piece.

PLYWOOD SHEATHING

Plywood also makes good sheathing. See Fig. G-3. Plywood less than one-half inch in thickness should be nailed with 6d nails spaced 5 in. on centers along edges and 10 in. on intermediate

framing members. Plywood one-half inch or thicker should be nailed with 8d nails with the same spacings. Vertical joints between plywood sheets should not be on the same stud or joist in succeeding rows of sheathing. For horizontal joints nailing strips are provided, as indicated in the drawing.

FIBERBOARD SHEATHING

Fiberboard, or gypsum board sheathing, Fig. G-4, should be nailed with 8d rust-resisting nails spaced 6 in. around edges and 10 in. on intermediate framing members. When using fiberboard wall sheathing the framework should be braced diagonally.

Vertical joints between sheets should not be on the same stud or joist in succeeding rows of sheathing. Nailing strips should be provided as required between the studs or joists.

STRIPS FOR SHINGLES

In the south and in certain construction where economy is important, wood strips may be substituted for solid sheathing. The strips, usually 1 x 3 or 1 x 4 in. stock, rough or dressed, are spaced to provide nailing for shingles. Strip sheathing should be used only over framework that is adequately braced. Such construction has low resistance to heat transmission and is to be discouraged in cold climates.

BUILDING PAPER

Tar paper should be used between wood sheathing and the outside finish, to prevent the passage of air through the walls.

Paper used should be tough enough to withstand rough handling while it is being put on and should retain its strength to a considerable degree after becoming wet. It should be sufficiently waterproof to prevent passage of moisture, if any should find its way through the outside wall covering.

Tar paper should be applied so it lies smoothly and special care should be taken to close all openings and cracks around doors and windows.

On jobs where sheathing is omitted, building paper should be placed in vertical strips with the edges lapped over studs and held in place by lath cleats until the siding is applied.

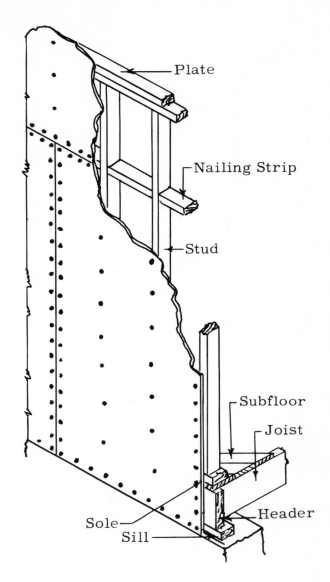

G-3. Using plywood for wall sheathing. Plywood less than 1/2 in. in thickness should be nailed with 6d nails spaced 5 in. on centers along edges and 10 in. on intermediate framing members. Plywood 1/2 in. or thicker should be nailed with 8d nails at same spacings.

Vertical joints between sheets of plywood should not be on the same stud or joist in succeeding rows of sheathing. For horizontal joints nailing strips as indicated should be provided.

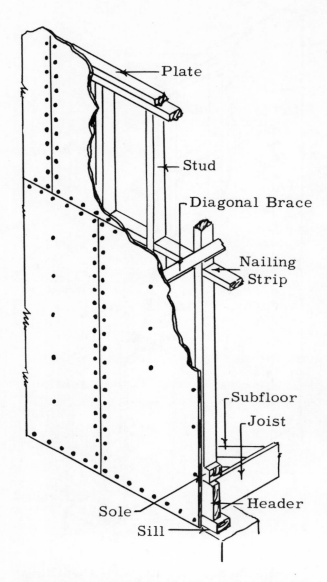

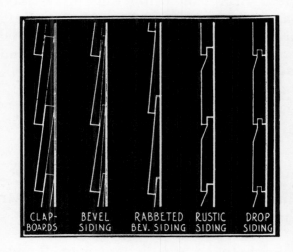

WOOD SIDING

Fig. G-5 shows an end view of five popular types of siding.

Usually finish siding is applied over sheathing paper and sheathing on wood studs. In mild climates or on such buildings as summer cottages, finish siding is sometimes applied directly to the studs without sheathing. Where

G-5. End view of five popular types of wood siding. This shows the slight difference between drop siding and rustic siding and makes possible quick comparison of the five types.

G-4. Using fiberboard for wall sheathing. Nail with 8d rust-resisting nails spaced six inches apart around edges and ten inches on intermediate framing members. Vertical joints between fiberboard sheets should not be on the same stud or joist in succeeding rows of sheathing. To receive nails at the horizontal joints, nailing strips should be provided as illustrated. Note, too, the diagonal brace.

sheathing is omitted or the type of sheathing used does not add sufficient strength to the wall to resist a racking load, wall framing should be braced at corners and at door frames with let-in or blocked-in diagonal bracing. Bracing should extend from plate to sill and be strongly nailed at each end and at intervening studs.

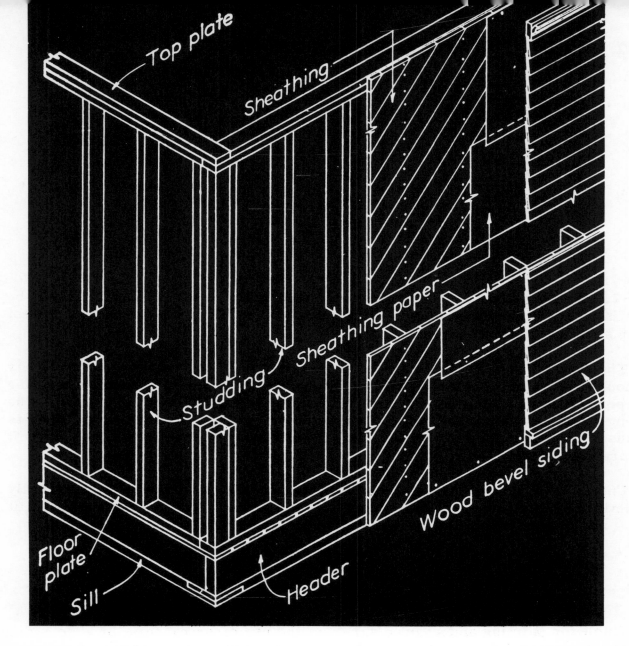

Top plate

Sheathing

Studding

Sheathing paper

Wood bevel siding

Floor plate

Sill

Header

G-6. Wall section showing installation of bevel siding. Note diagonal sheathing and overlapping of building paper. Bevel siding is made by sawing boards diagonally to produce the wedge-shaped pieces.

Fig. G-6 shows a typical wall section with beveled siding. Bevel or lap siding is customarily made in 4, 5, 6, 8, 10 and 12 in. widths. The 8 in. and wider bevel siding is often called wide Colonial or bungalow siding. It is made by sawing square edged surface

boards diagonally to produce two wedge shaped pieces. The pieces of siding are usually 3/16 in. thick on the thin edge and 1/2 to 3/4 in. thick on the other edge, depending on the width of the piece. This method of manufacture gives one planed face

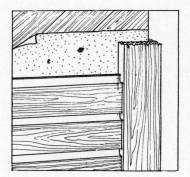 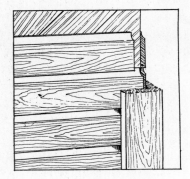 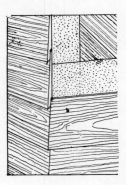

G-7. The use of corner boards or a mitered corner is optional. Either will be satisfactory if carefully made. Corner boards are older but they are still best for some architectural types.

The drawing at the left shows the proper way to install corner boards. They should always rest on the sheathing and be separated from it only by building paper. Ends of siding butting against corner boards should be painted. The center drawing shows the WRONG way to install corner boards. Little pockets caused by the moulded top of the siding running under corner boards will permit storage of water.

Unless well jointed, mitered corners, as shown at the right, will eventually admit water and cause trouble. Tight, careful miters, well cut for a perfect fit and jointed with paint are essential requirements of a good siding job.

suitable for painting and a sawed surface which may be stained for rustic effects.

PATTERNS AND SIZES OF WOOD SIDING

Wide bevel siding often has shiplapped or rabbeted joints so that the siding lies flat against the studding instead of touching it only near the joints as ordinary bevel siding does. This reduces the apparent thickness of the siding by 1/4 in. but permits the use of extra nails in wide siding and reduces the chance of warping. It is also economical, as the rabbeted joint requires less lumber than does the lap joint used with plain bevel siding. The rabbet should be deep enough so that where the siding is applied the width of the boards can be varied to meet window sill, head casing and eave lines as desired. Rabbeted joints are not so necessary in the 4 and 6 in. widths of bevel siding. These narrow widths of siding are usually but 1/2 in. thick, so rabbeting would make them too thin.

Rustic and drop siding are usually 3/4 in. thick and 6 in. wide, and are machined in a wide variety of patterns. Drop siding has tongued-and-grooved joints while rustic has shiplapped joints.

Drop siding is heavier, has more structural strength and because of its

The increasing popularity of the cottage types of architecture is bringing about the more common use of vertical siding, particularly in combination with other types of wood siding. Vertical siding consists of matched boards 10 or 12 inches wide or of random widths, the joints of which may be V-cut or covered with battens.

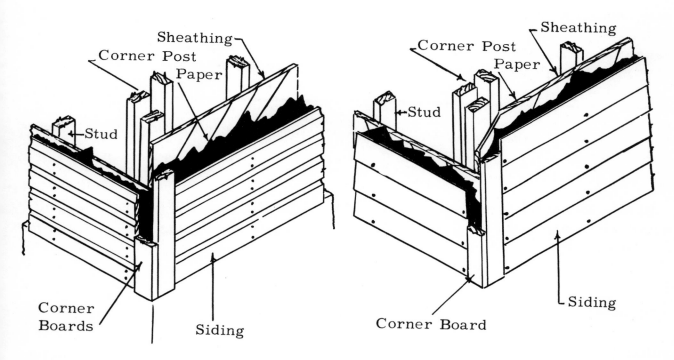

G-8. Bevel siding (right hand drawing) should be face-nailed to each stud with two 8d rust-resisting casing nails driven through overlap of siding and through sheathing into each stud. Siding nails should be set and puttied. If necessary to prevent splitting, holes should be bored for nails near ends of pieces of siding.

Drop siding (left hand drawing) should be face-nailed to each stud with two 9d casing nails, one near lower edge and one above midheight of piece of siding.

design has tighter joints than bevel siding, so is often used on garages and barns where there is no sheathing, as well as on homes.

Battens may be placed over every other joint alternating with moulded or flush joints according to the effect desired. Often the vertical siding is run up to the eave line, and shingles or bevel siding are used in the gables.

Various types of unusual sidings are made to secure special rustic effects. One of the commonest of these is a thick siding made to give the appearance of logs. There are several patterns of it to resemble logs of different sizes, and the chinking which goes between the logs. Such special sidings are used principally on summer homes. Log cabin siding, used alone or in combination with other material, and painted rather than stained, may be very satisfactory in the expression of an ultra-modern effect. Its use in this connection is not limited to exteriors.

Wood shingles and shakes are often used for siding as well as roofing materials. Shingles are usually 16, 18 or 24 inches long, 2/5 or 1/2 in. thick at one end, and 1/16 in. at the other. In addition to the types of shingles regularly stocked it is possible to secure shingles of special thicknesses, lengths, and shapes.

(The thicknesses apply to all widths and the widths to all thicknesses except as modified.*)

Siding	Size, Board Measure		Dressed Dimensions	
	Thickness	Width	Standard thickness	Standard face width
	Inches	Inches	Inches	Inches
Bevel	. . . .	4	** 7/16 by 3/16	3 1/2
	. . . .	5	10/16 by 3/16	4 1/2
	. . . .	6	. . . .	5 1/2
Wide beveled	. . . .	8	** 7/16 by 3/16	7 1/4
	. . . .	10	9/16 by 3/16	9 1/4
	. . . .	12	11/16 by 3/16	11 1/4
Rustic and drop	. . . .	4	9/16	3 1/8
(shiplapped)	. . . .	5	3/4	4 1/8
	. . . .	6	. . . .	5 1/16
	. . . .	8	. . . .	6 7/8
Rustic and drop	. . . .	4	9/16	3 1/4
(dressed and matched)	. . . .	5	3/4	4 1/4
	. . . .	6	. . . .	5 3/16
	. . . .	8	. . . .	7

*In patterned siding, 11/16, 3/4, 1, 1 1/4 and 1 1/2 inches thick, board measure, the tongue shall be 1/4 in. wide in tongued-and-grooved lumber, and the lap 3/8 in. wide in shiplapped lumber, with the over-all widths 1/4 in. and 3/8 in. wider, respectively, than the face widths shown above.

**Minimum thicknesses.

Shakes, either split or taper sawed, usually 24 in. or more in length, with thick butts make possible widely spaced, heavy horizontal shadow lines with interesting texture between.

SIDING SIZES AND ESTIMATING QUANTITIES

The nominal sizes which are used in computing the footage of lumber are based upon the rough green sizes of boards which are cut from the logs. These rough green boards shrink somewhat in width and thickness as they dry, and their size is further reduced by machining to pattern. The board measure table given on the preceding page is an extract from the American Lumber Standards giving the nominal and finished sizes for siding to which, with minor variations, most siding is produced. It will serve as a sufficiently accurate guide for the design of exterior wall surfaces.

In figuring the quantity of siding required for a home it is necessary to increase the square foot area of the walls, omitting openings, by enough to compensate for the machining of joints shiplapped or dressed and matched and the overlap of bevel siding. The following allowances are approximately those usually made:

Bevel siding	1x4 with	3/4 lap	Add 45%
	*1x5	7/8 lap	38
	1x6	1" lap	33
	1x8	1 1/4" lap	33
	1x10	1 1/2" lap	29
	1x12	1 1/2" lap	23
Rustic & drop siding (shiplapped)	1x4	Add 28%	
	*1x5	21	
	1x6	19	
	1x8	16	
Rustic & drop siding (dressed & matched)	1x4	23	
	*1x5	18	
	1x6	16	
	1x8	14	

*Unusual sizes.

An additional 3 to 5 percent should be allowed for cutting and fitting around openings and under the eaves.

SPECIES AND GRADES

Siding is graded under rules adopted by the regional associations of lumber manufacturers. The lumber dealer can readily advise the interested siding user concerning the grades and species available locally. A wide selection of siding suitable for any purpose can be readily purchased from the lumber dealer.

APPLICATION OF THE SIDING

Siding is kiln or air dried to the necessary low moisture content by the manufacturer and delivered in that condition by the retail lumber dealer. It should be carefully protected from moisture after it is delivered to the job until the carpenters are ready to lay it. The lumber sheathed frame which is to receive it should also be dry. Then the siding will stay put just as it is laid and will not shrink, warp or split.

Siding Width	Minimum Lap For Beveled Siding
4"	3/4"
5"	7/8"
6"	1"
8"	1 1/4"
10"	1 1/2"
and wider	

This spacing may be varied so that siding joints coincide with the bottoms of window sills and the tops of drip caps at window and door heads. One method is to begin at the bottom with a wider lap than indicated in the table and decrease the lap slightly as each succeeding board is applied. The result is a graduated spacing.

The joints in adjacent courses of siding should be staggered as widely as possible. Sometimes on high grade work splice joints are made with a miter saw but usually square cut butt joints are used. The corners should be mitered unless there is a vertical piece of trim at the corner against which the ends of the siding are butted.

Plain mitered corners, if they are to look well, must fit closely and stay in place. Open miters are nearly always the result of using siding lumber which has not been properly seasoned or which has been exposed to rain after delivery to the job, so their prevention is easy. An added advantage is to paint the ends of the siding as the siding is laid, to prevent the absorption of moisture. This is recommended for corners and also for points where siding meets window and door frames.

Corner boards, which are commonly used with drop siding, should lie flat against the tar paper with the siding butting up to them. The practice of nailing corner boards on over the siding is a very poor one, as it allows water to run in behind the corner boards and into the ends of the siding, and should not be followed.

NAILING

Nails cost little compared with the cost of siding or shingles and labor but the use of good nails is important. It is poor economy to buy siding which will last for many generations and then fasten it to the sheathing with nails which will rust badly within a few years. Rusty nails, even though they do not rust in two, stain the paint.

Copper nails or zinc coated nails will hold the siding permanently and will not streak light colored paint surfaces. Their slight added cost is a good investment. Information on nail sizes is given in Fig. G-8.

PAINTING AND MAINTENANCE

Long exposure to the elements will cause the deterioration of any building material but some materials will, if properly used, last for many generations. Properly applied and protected wood siding is one of the longest lived materials with which walls can be covered.

When wood siding deteriorates it is from but two causes, decay or rot and weathering, neither of which need occur if simple precautions are taken. Decay is the disintegration of wood caused by the growth of fungi. These fungi grow in wood only when the moisture content is higher than that of properly seasoned lumber. If the home is built upon a foundation which has been carried well above the ground and the construction is such that water runs off instead of into the walls, decay will never give trouble. It is when the flashings or drip caps above windows are omitted and the window sills do not drain properly that water seeps in behind the siding and may cause decay even though the home may be well painted.

Weathering is the separation of wood fibers on the surface of a board caused by alternate shrinking and swelling of the surface when it is dry or wet. Painting keeps the moisture content of this surface layer from changing rapidly and so prevents weathering. It is for this purpose, and to improve the appearance of a building, that paint is used.

All of the woods commonly used for siding are painted successfully where paint materials of good quality are properly applied.

The priming coat should be put on as soon as possible after the siding has been applied to prevent rapid changes in the moisture content of the surface of the siding. If an unexpected rain should wet the unprimed wood, the first coat of paint should not be applied until all the water has re-evaporated from the siding.

Paint usually fails most rapidly over knots, so if the common grades of siding are used the knots should be given some special treatment before the priming coat is put on. A good treatment is a thin coat of aluminum primer which is allowed to dry firmly before the priming coat is applied. To secure the most durable and satisfactory paint job use pure white lead in oil or the highest grade of mixed paint, selecting a brand sold by a reliable dealer.

There are certain fundamentals of common sense good construction that should be observed for permanence of both building decorations and painting.

There are a number of faults against which simple precautions should be taken in order to realize the maximum benefits from good lumber and paint.

1. Improper protection of lumber after delivery to the building site and before it is used; allowing siding to lie directly on the ground and to be rained or snowed on will naturally cause it to absorb moisture. Siding should always be protected from weather and kept dry.

2. Painting too soon after a rain.

3. Closing up a newly plastered house and heating it to dry the plaster. The moisture from the plaster is vaporized and, in cold weather, condenses on the inside of the siding since it cannot escape. More ventilation and slower drying of plaster will correct this condition.

4. Faulty construction, particularly inadequate flashings and drip caps, which allows water to run in behind the siding.

5. Damp basements, siding carried too close to the ground, and poor ventilation under porches or other parts of homes under which basements do not extend.

All of the above sources of excessive moisture can easily be avoided. The observance of suitable precautions should be considered a part of good construction practice, regardless of the siding material used. Neglect means trouble with other materials just as often as it does with wood siding, so good construction practices are always worthwhile.

USING SHINGLES ON SIDE WALLS

Shingles are usually separated into three grades. Generally speaking, the first grade is composed of clear shingles. The second grade consists of shingles with clear butts and admits defects in that portion of the shingle which will normally be covered in use. Third grade shingles are those which have defects other than permitted in the second grade.

Most shingles are made in random widths, varying in the No. 1 grade from 3" to 14" with only a small proportion of the narrow width permitted. Shingles of a uniform width known as dimension shingles are also obtainable. The latter are cut uniformly to widths of 4," 5" or 6," as may be specified. For side wall maximum exposure to the weather recommended for 16" shingles is 7 1/2," for 18" shingles 8 1/2" and for 24" shingles 11 1/2." Shingles on side walls are frequently laid in what is called "double-coursing." This is done by using a lower grade shingle under the shingle exposed to the weather. The exposed shingle butt extends about 1/2" below the butt of the under course. When butt nailing is used a greater weather exposure is possible, frequently as much as 12" for 16" shingles, 14" for 18" shingles and 16" for 24" shingles.

In mild climates, sheathing spaced apart on centers equal to the shingle exposure and shingled with high grade shingles provides a satisfactory wall.

Tar paper should always be used with such construction, either between the shingles and sheathing or between the sheathing and the studding.

Spaced sheathing is also satisfactory on implement sheds, garages and other structures where protection from the elements is the principal factor.

Tight sheathing is preferably applied diagonally, but this is not necessary from the standpoint of the application of the shingles. It is desirable in localities subject to high winds. Horizontal sheathing can be used, with let-in braces used to provide the necessary strength.

Plywood sheathing also makes a satisfactory base for shingles.

When gypsum board or other sheet material of adequate strength is used as sheathing a special type of fastener, known as the ES nail can be used to excellent advantage. The use of this nail is shown in Fig. G-9. This nail automatically clinches when the head is driven flush with the surface of the shingle. In applying the ES nails to 1/2 in. gypsum sheathing, the manufacturer specifies the use of nails 1 3/4 in. long.

In double-coursing, ES nails are used in applying the under course, while the outer course is butt-nailed to the under course using 5d No. 14

gauge double-coursing nails. Heads of ES nails should never be exposed to the weather and such nails should not be used in applying shingles on wood sheathing.

PROPER EXPOSURE

In choosing the exposure to be used on side walls, to obtain the best effect and to avoid unnecessary cutting of shingles, butt-lines should be even with the upper lines of window openings, and also, wherever possible, with the lower lines of such openings. It is better to tack a temporary strip to the wall to use as a guide for placing the butts of the shingles squarely, rather than to attempt to shingle to a chalk line.

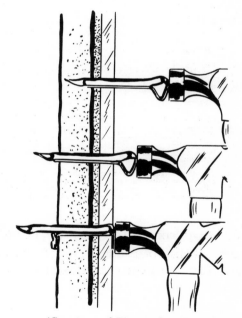

(Courtesy of Elastic Stop Nut Corp.)

G-9. Special type of fastener which may be used for anchoring exterior wall covering to gypsum board sheathing. It clinches when the head is driven flush with the surface.

MAKING NEAT CORNERS

Making neat corners may be accomplished by following this procedure: Place corner shingles in each course first, lining up edges of corner shingles at each course with the faces of the two walls alternately, so that a single line will not be formed. The inside corners can be made by nailing a 1 1/2 in. or 2 in. square strip, S4S, (surfaced four sides) in the corner and jointing shingles in each course against this strip. For wide exposures mitered inside corners over a narrow metal flashing strip are preferable.

tion of shingles on side walls, with various exposures:

SINGLE-COURSING OF SIDE WALLS

The single-coursing method of shingle side wall application is similar to shingle roof application, the major difference being in the exposures employed. In roof construction, maximum permissible exposures are slightly less than one-third the shingle length to produce a three-ply covering. Vertical surfaces of side walls present less weather-resistance problems than do roofs and according-

16-Inch CERTIGRADE	5½-Inch Exposure			6-Inch Exposure			6½-Inch Exposure			7-Inch Exposure			7½-Inch Exposure		
	Number	Weight		Number	Weight		Number	Weight		Number	Weight		Number	Weight	
		Lbs.	Oz.		Lbs.	Oz.		Lbs.	Oz.		Lbs.	Oz.		Lbs.	Oz.
No. 1 Blue Label Grade	933	2	7	852	2	4	784	2	1	735	1	15	680	1	13
Red Label Grade	1190	3	2	1060	2	13	974	2	10	914	2	7	851	2	4
No. 3 Black Label Grade	1348	3	9	1245	3	4	1150	3	0	1044	2	12	945	2	8

18-Inch CERTIGRADE	6-Inch Exposure			6½-Inch Exposure			7-Inch Exposure			7½-Inch Exposure			8-Inch Exposure		
No. 1 Blue Label Grade	852	2	4	784	2	1	735	1	15	680	1	13	628	1	11
Red Label Grade	1060	2	13	974	2	10	914	2	7	851	2	4	785	2	10
No. 3 Black Label Grade	1245	3	4	1150	3	0	1044	2	12	945	2	8	845	2	6

24-Inch CERTIGRADE	8-Inch Exposure			9-Inch Exposure			10-Inch Exposure			11-Inch Exposure			12-Inch Exposure		
No. 1 Blue Label Grade	619	1	10	558	1	8	502	1	5	456	1	3	405	1	1
Red Label Grade	745	2	0	692	1	13	620	1	10	565	1	8	515	1	6
No. 3 Black Label Grade	798	2	2	745	2	0	672	1	12	610	1	10	558	1	8

Note: The above figures are for butt-nailing of new double-coursed side walls, using small-headed 5d nails. For the weight of 3d nails to hold the under course in double coursing, one nail per shingle, use one-third of the above weights. For single coursing with 3d nails, subtract one-third from the above weights. For over-walling with 24-inch shingles, add one-half to above weights. Remember that a 12-inch exposure will require half as many nails as a 6-inch exposure, a 14-inch half as many as a 7-inch, and so on.

G-10. Approximate number required and weight of rust-resistant or zinc coated nails per square of random width shingles when applied to side walls, for weather exposure given. Read note above before using table.

FINDING QUANTITY OF NAILS

The above table, G-10, shows the number of pounds of rust-resisting or zinc clad nails required for application

ly a two-ply covering of shingles on an exterior wall is usually adequate.

In single-coursing side walls, weather exposure of shingles should never be greater than half the length of the shingle, minus 1/2 in. so two layers of wood will be found at every point in the wall. For example, when 16 in. shingles are used, the maximum exposure should be 1/2 in. less than 8 in. or 7 1/2 in. The maximum exposure for a single coursed wall of 18 in. shingles is 8 1/2 in., for 24 in. shingles 11 1/2 in., etc.

G-11. Single-course method of applying shingles to side walls. Solid backing and nailing base is provided by the use of wood sheathing and nailing strips over non-wood sheathing.

Single-course side walls should have concealed nailing. This means that the nails must be driven approximately one inch above the butt line of the succeeding course, so the shingles of this course will adequately cover them. Two nails should be driven in each shingle up to 8 in. in width, each nail placed about 3/4 in. from the edge of the shingle. On shingles wider than 8 in. a third nail should be driven in the center of the shingle, at the same distance above the butt line as the other nails. Rust-resistant nails should be used, 3d size, 1 1/2 in. in length.

DOUBLED STARTING COURSE

The bottom or starting course at the base of the wall should be doubled to introduce the proper tension to following courses. Joints between shingles in adjacent courses of a single-coursed wall should be kept out of vertical alignment at least 1 1/2 in. Joints themselves may be either closed or

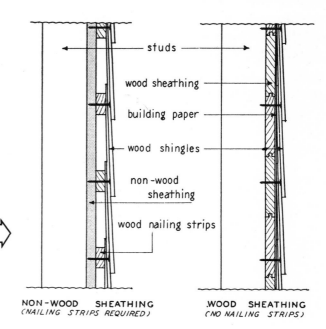

studs
wood sheathing
building paper
wood shingles
non-wood sheathing
wood nailing strips

NON-WOOD SHEATHING
(NAILING STRIPS REQUIRED)

WOOD SHEATHING
(NO NAILING STRIPS)

spaced, at the option of the owner. If there is space left between the shingles an effect of individual shingles is obtained, while with shingles laid closely against each other, an unbroken siding effect is achieved. In applying shingles with closed joints slight irregularities can be shaved off with a sharp knife.

FIGURING QUANTITIES FOR SINGLE COURSING

The covering capacity, in square feet, of one bundle of shingles applied single-coursed on a side wall is shown in Fig. G-12.

In estimating the quantity of shingles required for one side wall, the actual areas to be shingled should be determined in terms of square feet. Window and door areas should be deducted. By consulting the table G-12, the coverage of one bundle at the exposure to be used (for example, 39 in the case of 16 in. shingles at 7 1/2 in. exposure) should be divided into the wall area

shadow lines in the sun, has caused the double-coursing method of applying shingles to side walls to have considerable popularity.

In double coursing a low-cost shingle is used for the inner layer and this is covered with a No. 1 grade shingle on the outside. A variety of types of shingles are available for the outer course. Pre-stained shingles, which are available in a wide variety of attractive colors are particularly suitable.

One Bundle	No. of Inches Exposed to the Weather						
	5½	6	6½	7	7½	8	8½
Sixteen-inch shingles	28	31	33	36	39	....	....
Eighteen-inch shingles	....	28	30	32	34	37	39
Twenty-four-inch shingles	....	....	....	....	....	28	29

	No. of Inches Exposed to the Weather					
	9	9½	10	10½	11	11½
Twenty-four-inch shingles	31	33	35	36	38	40

G-12. Covering capacity, in square feet, of one bundle of shingles applied single coursed on a side wall.

to be covered. The figure obtained will be the number of bundles needed. To this figure, add about 5 per cent to allow for waste in cutting, fitting around openings, starter course, etc. If the shingles are applied with tight joints instead of open joints, an extra 3 per cent should be added to the total number of shingles required.

DOUBLE COURSING OF SIDE WALLS

The attractive appearance of side walls when shingles are given an extra wide exposure, combined with deep

Cedar shakes, processed and pre-stained are a popular type used for double-coursing. The shakes are produced from shingles by a machine which produces a rived or fluted effect on one face, the butt and both edges being re-trimmed.

WIDE EXPOSURES RECOMMENDED

Although wide exposures imply the use of very long shingles, this effect is obtained in double-coursing by the application of doubled layers of regular 16 in. or 18 in. shingles. The maximum exposure to the weather of

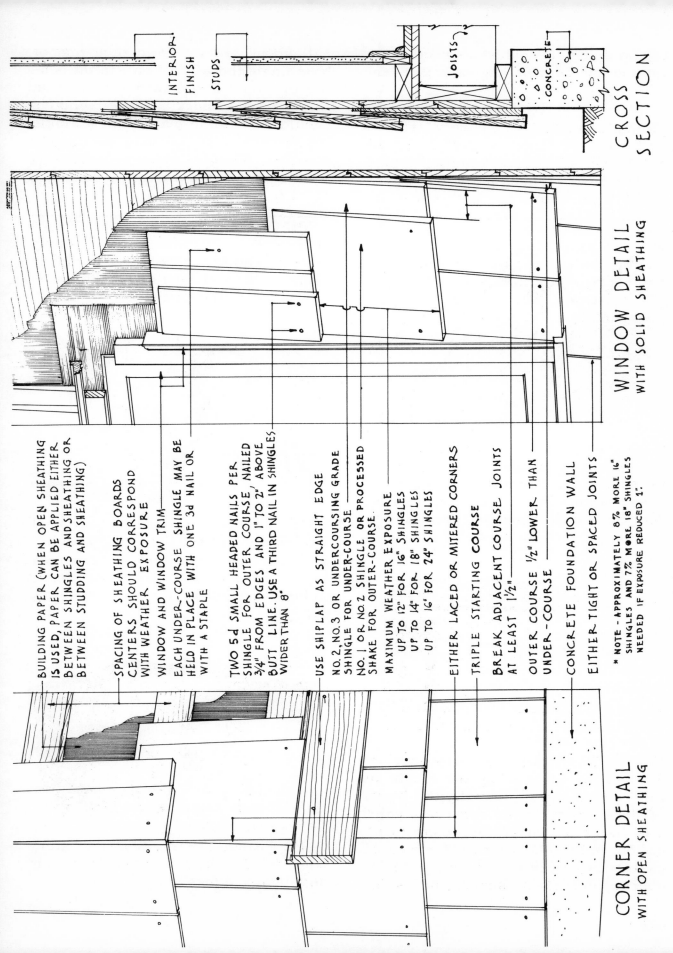

CROSS SECTION

INTERIOR FINISH

STUDS

JOISTS

CONCRETE

WINDOW DETAIL
WITH SOLID SHEATHING

BUILDING PAPER (WHEN OPEN SHEATHING IS USED, PAPER CAN BE APPLIED EITHER BETWEEN SHINGLES AND SHEATHING OR BETWEEN STUDDING AND SHEATHING)

SPACING OF SHEATHING BOARDS CENTERS SHOULD CORRESPOND WITH WEATHER EXPOSURE

WINDOW AND WINDOW TRIM

EACH UNDER-COURSE SHINGLE MAY BE HELD IN PLACE WITH ONE 3d NAIL OR WITH A STAPLE

TWO 5d SMALL HEADED NAILS PER SHINGLE FOR OUTER COURSE, NAILED 3/4" FROM EDGES AND 1" TO 2" ABOVE BUTT LINE. USE A THIRD NAIL IN SHINGLES WIDER THAN 8"

USE SHIPLAP AS STRAIGHT EDGE

NO.2, NO.3 OR UNDERCOURSING GRADE SHINGLE FOR UNDER-COURSE
NO.1 OR NO.2 SHINGLE OR PROCESSED SHAKE FOR OUTER-COURSE.

MAXIMUM WEATHER EXPOSURE
UP TO 12" FOR 16" SHINGLES
UP TO 14" FOR 18" SHINGLES
UP TO 16" FOR 24" SHINGLES

EITHER LACED OR MITERED CORNERS

TRIPLE STARTING COURSE

BREAK ADJACENT COURSE JOINTS AT LEAST 1½"

OUTER COURSE ½" LOWER THAN UNDER-COURSE

CONCRETE FOUNDATION WALL

EITHER TIGHT OR SPACED JOINTS

* NOTE – APPROXIMATELY 8% MORE 16" SHINGLES AND 7% MORE 18" SHINGLES NEEDED IF EXPOSURE REDUCED 1".

CORNER DETAIL
WITH OPEN SHEATHING

G-13. Using red cedar shingles on double-coursed sidewall.

16 in. shingles double-coursed is 12 in. and for 18 in. shingles it is 14 in.

Shingles should be securely fastened by so-called "butt nailing" using 5d small headed rust-resistant or zinc coated nails. These nails are driven about 2 in. above the butt line—one nail about 3/4 in. from each edge of the shingle and a third nail in the center of each shingle wider than 8 in. Each of the under course shingles should be held in place with a single 3d nail, or a staple may be used if desired. Shingle-laying procedure is illustrated in the series of drawings G-14 to G-28 inclusive.

G-14. When solid sheathing is used, lay a good grade of building paper over the sheathing. Use a stapling hammer to save time. Paper requires no nails. See Fig. G-18 if spaced sheathing is to be used.

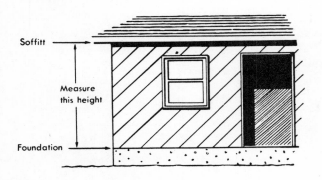

G-15. Determine the exposure of courses by measuring the height of the dominant wall (usually the front) of the home from the soffit to a point 2 in. below the top of the cement foundation, and divide that height into equal parts—as nearly as possible to 12 in. courses for 16 in. shakes, or 14 in. courses for 18 in. shakes. You may wish to modify the exposures slightly so as to have them line up with windows and door frames.

G-16. Lay out courses on a long stick commonly called the "story pole." Courses can vary slightly in exposure so as to line up with bottom and top of principal windows and under eaves.

G-17. Transfer marks from the "story pole" to all corners of the house and on window casings.

G-18. When open sheathing is used, apply paper over studs, then transfer "story pole" marks to the paper and apply 1 x 4 in. nailing strips so that the course lines fall 2 in. below strip centers. Double-courses are applied over the strips.

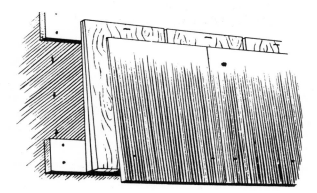

G-19. Bottom course is laid with two under-coursings and one outer-course.

G-20. Select a good straightedge, shiplap or 1 x 4, and lightly tack along a chalked line snapped between bottom "story pole" marks. Lay under-course shingles on upper lip of straightedge, and fasten with a single staple anywhere near top. Space under-coursing shingles approximately 1/8 in. apart.

G-21. Outer course of pre-stained shakes is then applied, laid tight, without spacing. As each double-course is laid, stretch a chalked string from opposite corner marks to indicate the level for the next course of shakes and to locate the new position of the straightedge.

G-22. Each shake must be nailed with a minimum of two nails. Use only small-headed 5d (1 3/4 in.) nails and apply them 2 in. above the butt line, 3/4 in. from each edge of each shake. On wider shakes, additional nails must be applied not more than 3 in. apart.

G-23. Outside corners are alternately lapped, commonly called "lacing." Allow one outer-course to protrude slightly past the corner, butting the shake on the other side to it. Trim protruded corner with knife and plane.
Touch up corners with stain.

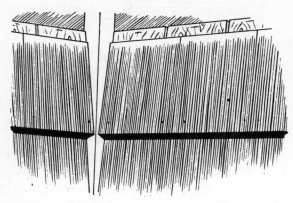

G-24. Inside corners are fitted with a lumber strip approximately 1 1/2 in. square to receive the under-course and shakes with a minimum of fitting. Stain strip after application.

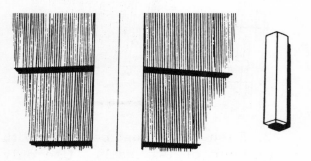

G-25. An inexpensive way to make neat outside corners is to get a standard fir "corner moulding" from your lumber dealer and run your coursing up flush to this moulding, eliminating uneven edges. Stain moulding in color to match shakes. Prefabricated metal corners are available also.

G-26. On old wood walls, regardless of their type, shakes can be applied directly as on new sheathing; building paper is applied over old siding and

other steps are the same. On over-walling around windows and doors, moulding strips should be nailed on the face of old casings, flush with the outer edges, to which the shakes should be jointed—and before the application of courses.

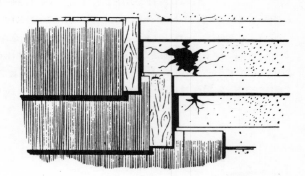

G-27. In overwalling over stucco, nailing strips should first be nailed over the wall to provide a good base for nailing double-coursing. Space these horizontal strips with centers 2 in. above butt lines of each course to receive the nails.

G-28. Measure up the total square footage of wall area to be double-coursed. Subtract the window and door areas. Divide by 100 to arrive at the number of double-coursed squares you require for the job. Order 5 per cent extra to provide for trimming, corners, etc. To save time, distribute cartons of shakes around the house before starting the application so that workmen save steps.

OVERWALLING WITH SHINGLES

Shingles may be used to good advantage in over-walling and re-styling old houses, regardless of the nature of the existing outer walls.

In beginning an over-wall job, it is best to run a spirit-level line around the building, starting at the highest point of the foundation. This will insure the proper running and spacing of all courses above and below the starting line.

Brick walls, which are troublesome because of water absorption may be covered by furring the walls and applying spaced nailing strips to the vertical furring strips. Furring should be fastened to the window frames and to wall by using anchors or special nails which are driven between the bricks.

Application of shingles to old, unsightly stucco is an easy matter. Here nailing strips are attached with nails long enough to reach through the stucco into the underlying sheathing. New building paper can be applied and shingling may then proceed as in new construction.

ASBESTOS CEMENT SIDING

Asbestos cement siding is a long-lasting exterior sidewall covering for either new or old houses. It is made from asbestos fibers and Portland cement in shapes, colors and surface treatments to meet a variety of needs.

Once put on, asbestos cement siding seldom needs replacing as it becomes harder and stronger with the years.

Two most commonly used types of asbestos cement siding are one with the exposed surface textured in wood grain or tapered lines and one with a smooth surface. Both textured and smooth surfaced siding may be obtained with either straight or wavy exposed butt lines. And, the textured type comes with a staggered butt line (straight except that the butt of some shingles extend below the others) which reproduces the effect of shingles applied in the "thatch" method.

HOW ASBESTOS SIDING IS SOLD

Asbestos siding usually comes in shingles 24 in. wide and 12 in. deep. When applied the shingles are lapped 1 1/2 in. at the head, leaving an exposed area of 10 1/2 by 24 in.

This siding is sold in squares, a square being sufficient to cover 100 square feet of wall surface. Ordinarily there are three bundles per square, each containing 57 pieces of the 12 by 24 in. material. Approximate shipping weight per square is 187 pounds.

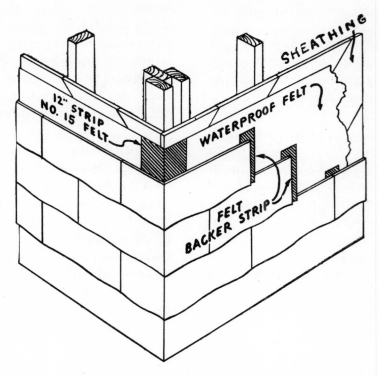

G-29. Applying asbestos shingles to sidewalls, over sheathing and weatherproof
felt. Felt backer strips, furnished with the shingles, protect the joints.

Backer strips for use behind the vertical joints and corrosion resistant face nails are usually furnished by the manufacturer. Head nails, or nails that are covered must be furnished by the user.

Asbestos siding is easily applied over existing shingles or clapboards to bring structural soundness and rejuvenated appearance to worn, drab houses. And, in recent years such siding is being used on many new homes, especially in rural areas.

It is easily applied over wood sheathing and it can be applied over gypsum or fiber-board sheathing by using special fasteners. Clapboard asbestos siding in length multiples of 16 in. can be nailed through old siding and sheathing directly into the wood studding.

APPLICATION AND HANDLING

Asbestos siding should be stored on edge, in a dry place or on planks at least 4 in. off the ground and covered with a tarpaulin to protect it from moisture and dampness.

Siding should be laid in dry weather and a given wall area, from the base to the top, completed as quickly as possible. Wood trim should be given at least a prime coat of paint promptly; gutters and metal work should be in place before starting with the siding.

Nails, brackets, etc. which are liable to rust, should be painted to avoid staining from this source. All metal, particularly copper, used for flashings, downspouts, screens, etc. should be initially and periodically coated with spar varnish or given some other protective treatment to prevent staining of the siding.

Asbestos siding shingles are intended for vertical side walls only. They are not suitable for roof surfaces.

FELT SHOULD BE USED

A layer of waterproof felt or waterproof backing board should be applied to the area to be sided before the siding is put on, Fig. G-29. It is recommended that asphalt saturated felt be used as an underlayment instead of tar saturated felt. Tarred felt, in some cases, may stain the siding.

Joints should be protected by using felt backer strips, furnished with the shingles. When re-siding 1 lb. of 2 in. galvanized needle-point nails per square are required for head or covered-up nailing; on new work 3/4 lb. of 1 1/4 in. nails. Face nails to be used are furnished by manufacturer.

JOINTS SHOULD BE CAULKED

Asbestos caulking putty should be applied before siding is put on, at all mitered corners and wherever siding butts against wooden trim, masonry or other materials. Care should be

taken in applying the putty to avoid smearing the face of siding.

CUTTING ASBESTOS SIDING

It is desirable to use a regular asbestos siding cutter which in many cases may be borrowed from the dealer where the siding was purchased. In using a cutter, waste is avoided and a more efficient job is possible. However, a little experimenting will be required to get best results. Try cutting a siding piece in two and examine both parts for cracks. If there are cracks, a little more opening between the knives is required. When cutting requires too much pressure, knife edges should be slightly closer.

Asbestos siding may be sawed with a 5 or 6 tooth per inch crosscut saw. A sharp saw will become dull rapidly at first but will do a good job for a considerable length of time. Siding may also be scored and broken off. Lay the siding on a smooth bench or floor, use a straightedge and a jackknife, ice pick or other sharp pointed tool to scratch a deep score. After this is done the siding may be placed over the edge of a board and broken without much trouble. For angular or circular cuts, use a sharpened nail set, punch holes as close together as possible and tap out center portion with a hammer.

On re-siding work, existing wall surfaces should be as true and even as possible to get them. Beveled wood strips, called "horse-feathers" are obtainable, which may be applied to level up wall surfaces. See Fig. G-30.

When old siding has thick butts, it may be necessary to apply two layers of beveled strips at some course lines to provide a solid bearing. Lap the ends of the beveled strips at building corners.

ASBESTOS SIDING OVER STUCCO

When stucco walls are in good shape, asbestos cement siding can be put on by first applying wood nailing strips. Nailing strips used should be either 1 in. by 2 in. or 1 in. by 3 in. Nailing strips may also be used when applying

START WITH A CANT STRIP

A common procedure is to start an asbestos siding job by nailing a strip 1/4 in. by 1 in., called a cant strip, to the bottom of the area to be sided, Fig. G-30. This gives the siding a slight cant and adds to its appearance. Getting the courses properly aligned is made easy by snapping a chalkline for the top of each course. Each chalkline should be continued all around the house. This is especially necessary for the first course, because it is the only way to assure a correct and accurate meeting and mitering of each course at corners of the house.

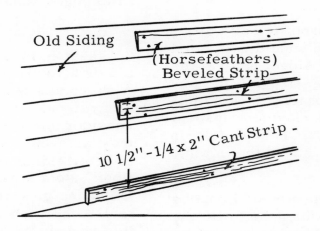

G-30. On residing jobs, old wall surfaces should be made as even and true as possible. Beveled wood strips called "horsefeathers" are used to level up the surface. Corner boards or pre-finished metal corner beads may be used at the corners or the siding used by alternating shingles in log cabin style.

this siding over gypsum or insulating board sheathing. It is usually desirable to put on nailing strips as the job progresses, so that any inequalities in spacing which are located may be adjusted.

Before siding is started the height of each corner from eave to sill should be determined. If inequalities are found, they should be taken up, if possible by adjusting the courses slightly out of level. If this is not done, a

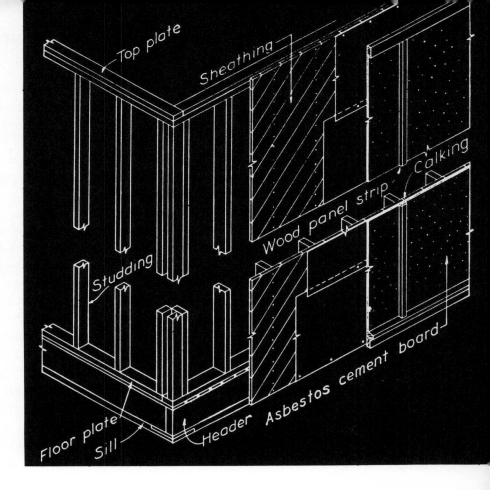

G-31. Using asbestos cement board for exterior wall covering. Standard size sheets of this material are 4 ft. x 8 ft. and it comes in thicknesses of 1/8 in., 3/16 in., 1/4 in. and 3/8 in.

wedge shaped course may occur at the eave line.

In extreme cases, the starting course may be applied level and following courses just slightly off level to take up the variation in height at corners.

Start the first course with a whole siding unit. A galvanized needle-point head nail is first driven through the punched hole at the end nearest the corner. Then, a backer strip is placed behind the other end edge of the siding, centered under the edge and located so it extends 3/8 in. above the unit. The other head nail is then driven in to hold the shingle snugly. Special-coated face nails next are driven in each of the two small holes near the shingle butt. Other units in the first course

are applied in the same way. Place backer strips behind all vertical joints, being sure at least one nail penetrates each of the strips.

Face nails lay on top of under course, providing the gauge for overlaps.

The second course is started with a half piece of siding applied at the corner the same way as the first piece of the starting course. A full piece is used to start the third course and this alternating of full pieces and half pieces at the corners is continued in succeeding courses.

Whether or not an asphalt felt saturated underlayment is used over the entire surface, a vertical strip of this material should extend back over the sheathing 6 in. back from the corners.

FIGURING QUANTITIES

Use a tape measure to measure all areas to be sided. Multiply length by height to get number of square feet in area. From this deduct combined window and door square foot area.

To allow for waste, add 8 per cent and figure to the nearest larger half or full square of shingles.

USING ASBESTOS CEMENT BOARD

Asbestos cement board, a fire-safe material made of asbestos fibers and Portland cement, is stone gray in color and has a smooth, hard surface.

Standard size sheets are 4 ft. wide and 8 ft. long; thicknesses are 1/8 in., 3/16 in., 1/4 in., and 3/8 in. It may be curved to a considerable degree without breaking. No special equipment or special tools are needed in fastening asbestos cement board in place. Nailing is the usual means of fastening. Drilling is required only on the 3/8 in. stock.

A typical wall section showing the use of asbestos-cement wallboard is shown in Fig. G-31.

NAILING ASBESTOS BOARD

For exterior service, be sure to use a non-corrodible metal, or rustproof, hot dipped galvanized nail. On exterior applications open to the weather ex-posed nail heads may leak water. It is therefore desirable to either use a galvanized lead-headed nail or to cover the exposed nail head with a generous amount of gray asbestos putty or high grade caulking compound.

Nails should be long enough to penetrate well into good sound wood. Barbed or ring shanked nails usually hold better than others. Nails with medium-size heads are okay when asbestos is applied to a side wall but large headed nails should be used when the board is used on ceilings. In general select nails having sharp needle points, no larger than 12 gauge, made of hard material or hardened, like nails you would use for oak or birch.

Quarter inch or thinner board can be nailed without pre-punching. A starting tool for use where required may be made by grinding down a nail set so it is straight and not tapered. Drive nail heads snug against boards but do not sink them into the surface, unless you are using a countersunk head nail. Thick nails should be kept 3/4 in. away from edges of the sheet.

Where nails must be driven close to the edges of the material, holes should be drilled for them.

OTHER USES

Asbestos cement board may be applied as an exterior siding to give distinction to certain areas, such as gable ends or "half-timber" panels. On the inside of the home this board may often be used to advantage as a wall and ceiling finish for basement,

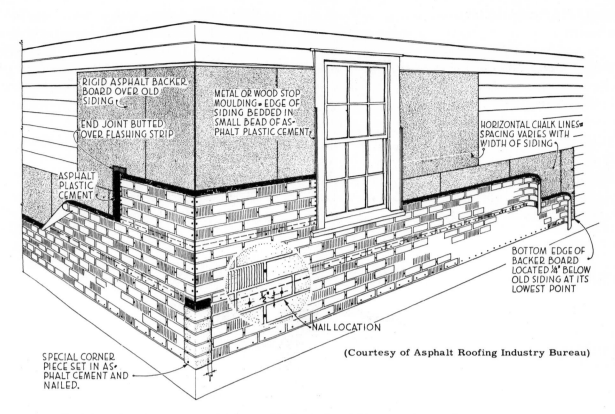

G-32. Applying asphalt roll brick siding. Note the corner, trim, end joint and nailing details.

kitchens, bathrooms and laundries, where damp and humid conditions are common. Its incombustibility recommends it too for lining closets and garages, for making laundry chutes, heating ducts, stove shields and firewall partitions.

ASPHALT SIDING

Asphalt siding materials as used for sidings are available in two forms, as roll products and as shingles. Roll materials are mineral surfaced, and are embossed to simulate both brick and stone. Shingles may be either strip type or individual type.

These products may be applied on either new wall surfaces or over old materials when remodeling.

PREPARATION OF NEW WALL SURFACE

Any surface intended to be covered with asphalt siding should have the following general characteristics:

It should be reasonably smooth.
It should have suitable
  nail holding power.
It should be dry when
  siding is applied.

WOOD SHEATHING

All sheathing should be not less than 1 in. (nominal) thick and not more than 8 in. wide. Six inch width is preferable.

Siding should be well seasoned, containing not more than 17 per cent moisture. Boards containing an excessive number of solid or loose knots or pitchy and resinous areas are un-

The sheathing must be dry at the same time the siding is applied. As soon as it is applied, the sheathing should be covered with asphalt saturated felt or building paper laid horizontally. The upper felt course should overlap the lower course 2 in. and where ends meet the lap should be 4 in.

Wall surfaces most commonly involved in residence work are:

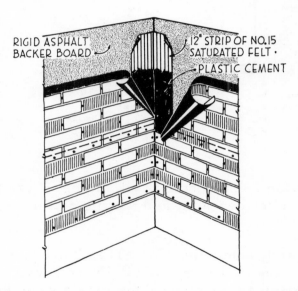

G-33. At inside corners a 12 in. wide flashing strip of No. 15 asphalt saturated felt, long enough to overlap the selvage edge of the underlying course is bent into the angle. Siding strips are cut to fit snugly in the corner and the ends embedded in asphalt cement applied to the flashing strip before nailing.

desirable, and badly warped boards should be rejected. Lumber should be protected from excessive wetting by rain, snow, condensation, or by contact with damp earth.

The maximum center spacing between studs should be 24 in.

a. Old wood shingles or siding.
b. Old asphalt shingles or siding.
c. Old stucco applied over wood sheathing.

In each case recommendations for preparing the surface of the wall to be covered are as follows:

Old Wood Shingles or Siding

Renail all loose siding or shingles securely. Pull loose nails and drive new nails in new locations. Replace badly damaged, knotted or missing portions of siding material with sound material of same style and size.

Fill to the general plane of the wall surface with beveled wood strips or lath and cover it with No. 15 asphalt saturated felt, lapping the upper over the lower courses 2 in. and the ends of adjacent strips 4 in. Nail the felt sufficiently to hold it in place until new siding material is applied over it.

To provide a smooth surface to receive the siding a rigid asphalt backerboard may be applied in place of the beveled wood "feathering strips," if desired. They should be secured with a row of nails 1 in. in from the edges of the units on 12 in. centers except at the ends and along the top and bottom edges of the walls, where the nails should be 6 in. apart.

Old Asphalt Shingles or Siding

Pull all loose and protruding nails, and nail down tightly or cut away all loose, curled or lifted material.

Fill in with asphalt material areas where old material is missing.

Inspect the wall as work progresses, and replace with sound materials those areas where rotted sheathing is found or where nail holding power is deficient.

Applied Over Old Stucco

In most cases, it is best to remove the stucco, stucco lath, building paper and of course all protruding nails.

Replace rotted or defective sheathing with sound material and firmly renail all loose and warped sheathing.

Apply horizontally No. 15 asphalt saturated felt lapping and nailing as specified for wood shingles and siding.

APPLICATION OF ROLL BRICK SIDING

Material should be dry when applied and should be applied to a dry surface.

Nails

Use non-corrodible nails with checkered or smooth heads (0.250 in. diameter) long enough to penetrate 3/4 in. into the wall surface to which the material is applied. Nail heads should be colored to match the siding material through which they are driven. This usually calls for black-headed nails at the mortar joints and other appropriate color for face nailing. See Fig. G-32.

Chalk Lines

Snap a horizontal chalk line around the building at a distance above the lower edge of the prepared wall surface equal to 1/4 in. less than the width of one course of siding. As the work progresses, space additional chalk lines up the wall at intervals equal to the amount each course is exposed, for checking purposes.

Vertical chalk lines should be used on each side of windows and other openings to insure proper alignment of vertical mortar joints.

First Course

Square off a strip of siding through a vertical mortar joint. Set the end even with a corner, and the top edge even with the first horizontal chalk line. Secure it with enough roofing nails along the selvage edge to hold it in place, and face nail with appropriate color-coated nails at the points indicated in Fig. G-32.

Second and Succeeding Courses

Second and succeeding courses are placed so that the top of each strip is on a horizontal chalk line. When properly spaced, this strip will lap the course next below by the amount of the selvage less the width of one mortar joint. Broken "brick" joints are maintained by aligning the centers of the bricks in the lower row of the overlying course with the vertical mortar joints between bricks in the top row of the underlying course, the alignment being further checked with the vertical chalk lines.

End Joints

Adjoining edges of meeting strips are cut and butted along a line passing through vertical mortar joints in the upper, middle and lower brick courses and through the center of the scored bricks in second and fourth courses.

A flashing strip of No. 15 asphalt saturaged felt 6 in. wide and as long as the height of the course, set to overlap the selvage edge of the course below, is centered behind each butted joint. Before nailing, the siding strip is secured to the flashing strip with asphalt cement recommended by the manufacturer.

Nailing Roll Brick Siding

Nails along the horizontal lapped edges are located in a line 1/2 in. above the lower edge of the overlying course, and are spaced approximately 4 in. apart.

Along the top of the walls the nails are located 1/2 in. below the top edge of the final course and spaced the same distance apart, 4 in.

At the vertical joints, at inside corners, and at windows, doors, and other openings, nails are located in a line 1/2 in. from the cut edge of the strip and spaced 2 in. apart.

A nail is placed in each vertical mortar joint throughout the siding.

Avoid driving nails too tightly. Tight nailing has a tendency to create an uneven (quilted) effect.

Outside Corners

Outside corner pieces, manufactured to match the siding, are used at the corners, as shown at the corner detail in Fig. G-32. The corner piece is bedded in cement of a type recommended by the manufacturer. Care must be exercised to avoid using so much cement that the excess will ooze out along the edge of the strip when it is nailed. Nails are placed in each mortar line 1 in. in from the edge of the strip on both sides of the corner.

Inside Corners

At inside corners a 12 in. wide flashing strip of No. 15 asphalt saturated felt, long enough to overlap the selvage edge of the underlying course is bent into the angle at each course, as shown in Fig. G-33. The siding strips are cut to fit snugly in the corner, and ends are bedded in asphalt cement applied to flashing strip before nailing.

Windows, Doors and Other Openings

Where the wood trim around the opening protrudes beyond the face of the wall surface on which the siding is being applied, the siding is cut to fit against the edge of the trim and under the window sills, and is embedded in a narrow bead of asphalt cement before being nailed.

Where the wood trim around the opening is flush with the old siding material or underlying backer board, either a narrow wood moulding or a special metal stop, manufactured for the purpose, is applied to the trim 1 in. in from its edge, and the siding is butted snugly against it. Before nailing, the siding is embedded in a narrow bead of asphalt cement.

Finish at Top of Wall

The siding is carried to the top of the wall and embedded along its top edge in asphalt cement in a manner appropriate to the construction of the eaves and rake. It is important that the top edge of the uppermost course be protected from direct exposure to the weather.

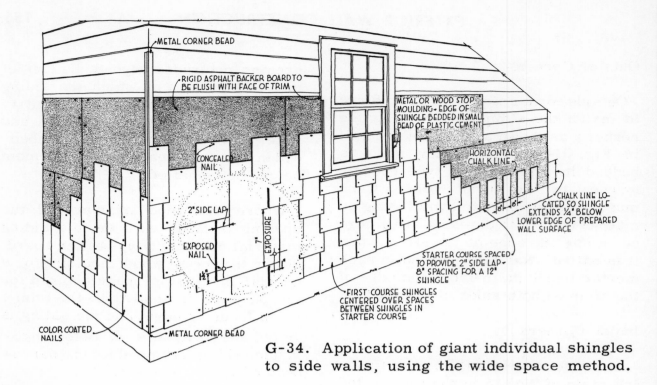

- METAL CORNER BEAD
- RIGID ASPHALT BACKER BOARD TO BE FLUSH WITH FACE OF TRIM
- METAL OR WOOD STOP MOULDING - EDGE OF SHINGLE BEDDED IN SMALL BEAD OF PLASTIC CEMENT
- CONCEALED NAIL
- HORIZONTAL CHALK LINE
- 2" SIDE LAP
- EXPOSURE
- 7"
- EXPOSED NAIL
- 1½"
- CHALK LINE LOCATED SO SHINGLE EXTENDS ¼" BELOW LOWER EDGE OF PREPARED WALL SURFACE
- 8"
- STARTER COURSE SPACED TO PROVIDE 2" SIDE LAP - 8" SPACING FOR A 12" SHINGLE
- FIRST COURSE SHINGLES CENTERED OVER SPACES BETWEEN SHINGLES IN STARTER COURSE
- COLOR COATED NAILS
- METAL CORNER BEAD

G-34. Application of giant individual shingles to side walls, using the wide space method.

APPLICATION OF GIANT INDIVIDUAL SIDING SHINGLES

Before starting to apply siding shingles it is important that the wall surface be properly prepared, as shown in Fig. G-34.

NAILS TO USE

Either non-corrodible nails with checkered heads, or common galvanized roofing nails long enough to penetrate at least 3/4 in. into the wall surface, are recommended for concealed locations. Exposed nails should preferably have heads colored to match the shingles.

Number and Location of Nails

There are two methods of nailing commonly used. The method described and illustrated herein indicates that, except for the shingles in the starter course, which require two exposed nails, each shingle is secured with three nails, one concealed and two exposed. The concealed nail is centered on the shingle 1/2 in. down from its top edge, and the exposed nails are placed, one in each corner, 1 in. in from the side and 1 1/2 in. above the lower edge.

The other method calls for four nails, two concealed and two exposed. The concealed nails are placed one on each side of the shingle, 1 in. in from the side and approximately 8 in. above the bottom edge. The exposed nails are placed as described for the three-nail method. This second method of

placing concealed nails is required
when plastic cement is used in place
of exposed nails as is sometimes done.

Outside Corners

At each outside corner a metal corner bead manufactured for the purpose
is applied.

At each succeeding corner after the
first, a better appearance will result
if the width of the finishing shingle
portion in each course is equal to the
width of the starting shingle portion
in the same course on the adjacent
intersecting wall.

Starter Course

The starter course consists of shingles spaced at intervals which will
provide for a side lap by the overlying
(first course) shingles of not less than
2 in. For a 12 in. wide shingle, the
space between shingles will be 8 in.
At the first outside corner, the course
begins with a half shingle, the cut edge
of which is set into the moulded recess
of the corner bead. The first and all
succeeding shingles in the course are
lined even with the first horizontal
chalk line and each is secured with
two nails, one located 1 in. in from
each side high enough to insure solid
nailing.

APPLICATION OF SIDING SHINGLES

A horizontal chalk line is snapped
around the building at a height above
the lowest point of the old siding or
backing equal to the length of a shingle
less 1/4 in. This will insure that when

the shingles are set to this line they
will extend at least 1/4 in. below the
bottom edge of the prepared wall surface. Other horizontal chalk lines
are placed at intervals up the wall
equal to the pre-determined exposure
of the shingles for checking the alignment of subsequent courses.

Vertical chalk lines are snapped
along each side of wall openings, perpendicular to the lower horizontal
chalk lines at intervals which will
maintain correct spacing of shingles.

First Course

The first course consists of full size
shingles centered over the spaces
between shingles in the starter course
and at the same level. Each shingle
is secured with one concealed and two
exposed nails, as shown in Fig. G-34.

Second Course

The second course begins with a half
shingle, adjusted to and laid against
the corner bead at a height above the
first course equal to the pre-determined exposure. Full shingles are
thereafter applied along the wall,
spacing them so they come above the
starter course shingles, and securing
them with nails as specified.

Third Course

Starting a half space away from the
corner, full shingles are centered over
the spaces between the shingles in
the course below and secured with
nails in the manner specified.

Succeeding Courses

The second and third course specifications are repeated in regular sequence up the wall, both horizontal and vertical chalk lines being used to maintain proper alignment.

Inside Corners

A 12 in. wide flashing strip of No. 30 asphalt saturated felt is centered in each inside corner, and shingles are cut to fit snugly in the corner over it.

Doors, Windows and Other Openings

If the trim around wall openings is flush with the old siding or backerboard, either a narrow wood moulding or a special metal stop moulding is applied 1 in. in from the outside trim edge and the shingles are butted tightly against it, the edges being bedded in a narrow bead of plastic cement or calking compound.

If the trim projects beyond the face of the prepared wall surface, the end shingles are cut to fit against the edge of the trim and under window sills. Asphalt plastic cement is used under the joint between shingles and trim.

USING STUCCO FOR EXTERIOR WALLS

Portland cement stucco finishes for exterior walls, Fig. G-35, when properly applied are durable, fire-resistant and require but little maintenance. The usual ingredients are Portland cement, aggregate (gravel and sand) water and sometimes mineral pigments for color and materials to provide increased workability.

The aggregate should be clean fine sand, crushed stone or crushed slag and should be free from harmful amounts of vegetable matter, silt, loam, etc. It is important that the aggregate be well graded and have a sufficient amount of coarse particles to produce the densest possible mixture. One of the main causes of cracking is an excessive amount of fine material in the aggregate.

REFINISHING OLD STUCCO

The color or texture of an old stucco wall may be changed by resurfacing. If the old stucco is sound and will provide a good bond, one coat of new stucco may be applied directly over the existing surface. The old stucco should be washed with clear water and cleaned with an acid solution of 1 part muriatic acid and 6 parts water, applied with a stiff bristle brush. Put the acid in the water—never put water in acid. After this treatment, the old stucco should be thoroughly rinsed with clear water to remove all traces of acid; allowed to dry and moistened again before applying the new coat.

REPAIRING CRACKS IN STUCCO

Hair or very small cracks may develop if a stucco mixture is too rich or if the stucco material is inferior. Cracks may also be caused by too rapid drying of the stucco. Large cracks are usually the result of settle-

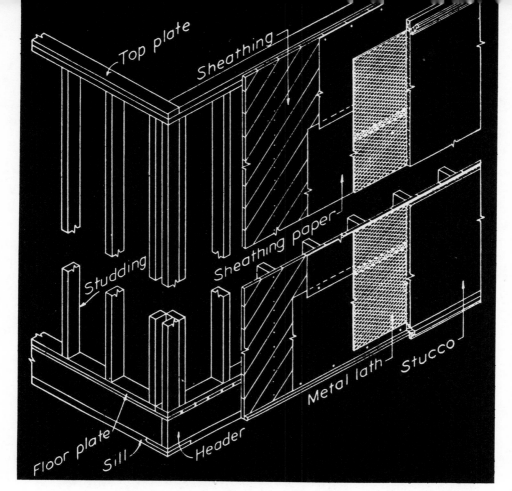

G-35. Portland cement stucco finish for exterior wall. Stucco is made from Portland cement, aggregate, water and sometimes mineral pigment for color and materials to provide increased workability.

ment of the walls of a house or movement within the walls caused by improperly constructed foundations or poorly designed framing.

Cracks which are large enough to admit moisture should be repaired. If the cracks are unnoticeable and seem to be doing no damage, repairs may be postponed, since plastered cracks often look worse than the open cracks.

BRICK VENEER EXTERIOR WALLS

A brick veneer wall is usually but 4 in. in thickness, or the width of a single brick. Cut stone, pre-cast concrete and the like, usually 8 in. thick, may be used in similar manner.

The veneer is not designed to carry any of the weight of the building and is partially supported by or held in place by ties fastened to the wood framework of the building.

ALLOWING FOR
DIFFERENT CHARACTERISTICS

Whenever two materials of differing characteristics are combined in the same building care must be taken to allow for their different characteristics.

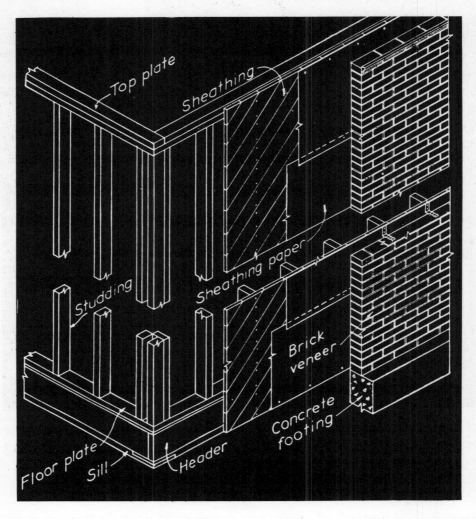

G-36. A brick veneer wall is usually but 4 in. in thickness or the width of a single brick. It carries no weight and is partially supported by ties fastened to the wood framework of the building. The drawing shows an auxiliary foundation as would be used on a remodeling job. On a new house the brick would be supported by the regular foundation.

The fact that steel and concrete expand and contract substantially the same makes it possible to use steel reinforcing in concrete. If one of the materials expanded or contracted more than the other, one would have to slip through the other, thus destroying the bond between the two.

The problem of using a wood framework in conjunction with masonry veneer is similar, except that changes in length or size are not so much affected by changes as they are by atmospheric changes. For this reason, it is essential in this type of construction that the wood be so arranged as to minimize effect of relative changes in the two materials which may be caused from atmospheric changes.

For this reason, the use of the platform frame with veneer construction should be avoided. The balloon type of framing is preferable because of the small amount of horizontal grain wood in the wall construction.

BRICK VENEER FOUNDATION

On new construction, both the brick veneer and the wood framework should rest on the same foundation, to preclude possibility of settlement. In remodeling, where the original foundation is insufficient to support the veneer, a second foundation may be used as shown in drawing G-36.

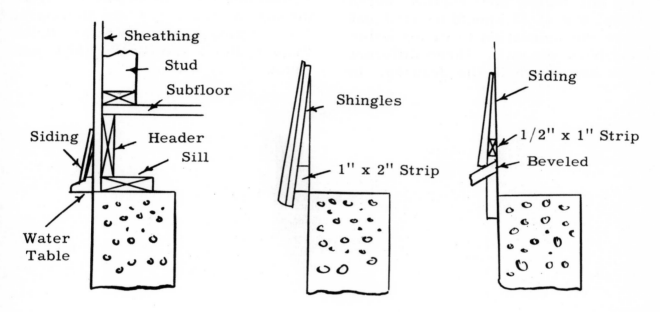

G-37. Three types of water tables. Water tables protect foundations by diverting water away from the wall. In fitting the type shown at the left, splices and outside corners should be mitered.

In constructing a brick or stone veneer wall, it is necessary to insert metal ties at the joints of the brickwork at vertical intervals of about five courses or 15 in. and about 24 in. apart. Brick veneer should be limited to two or at most three stories. Ties should be rustproof, should afford means of firmly securing the wall and provide a good bond in the brickwork mortar.

Wood sheathing under brick veneer should preferably be applied diagonally. Waterproof, coated building paper should be used, as brickwork is porous and readily admits moisture.

An air space of 1/2 to 1 in. should be left between the brick veneer and the framework of the building.

EXTERIOR PLYWOOD FOR WALL COVERING

Information on using plywood for exterior walls will be found in the chapter on Building With Plywood.

WATER TABLES PROTECT FOUNDATIONS

On all frame construction, water tables, Fig. G-37, should be used just above the foundation to divert water away from the wall. Three different types are shown in the drawing. In fitting the type shown at the left, all splices and outside corners should be mitered.

WALL SECTION DRAWINGS FROM STOCK PLANS

So that readers of this book can see how various types of construction are shown on typical stock plans we are reproducing on the next five pages, through the courtesy of the HomOgraf Co., section views of Frame, Brick Veneer, Brick and Block, Block, and Brick Cavity Walls.

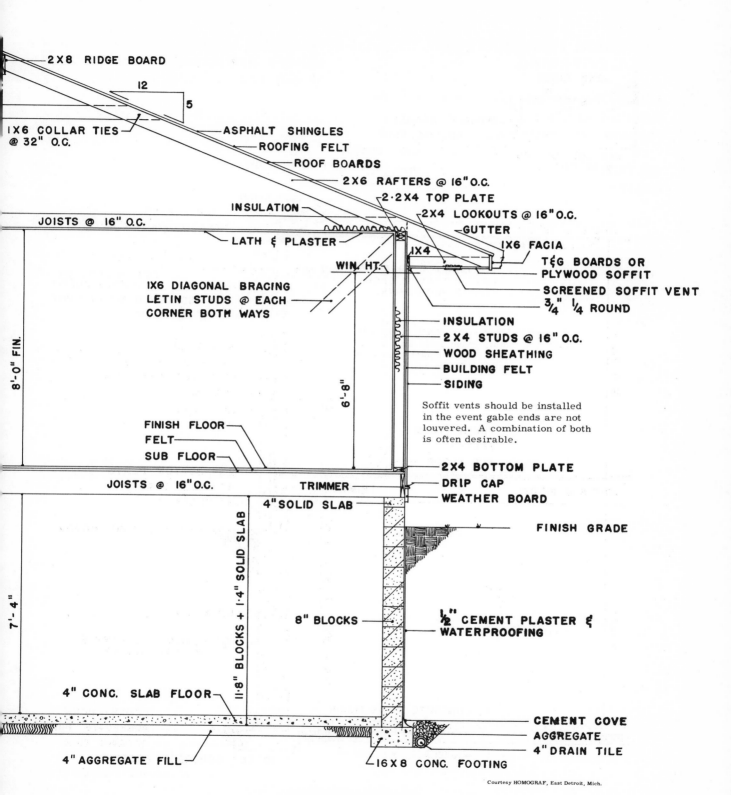

2X8 RIDGE BOARD

12
5

IX6 COLLAR TIES
@ 32" O.C.

ASPHALT SHINGLES
ROOFING FELT
ROOF BOARDS
2X6 RAFTERS @ 16" O.C.
2·2X4 TOP PLATE
2X4 LOOKOUTS @ 16" O.C.
GUTTER
IX4
IX6 FACIA
T&G BOARDS OR
PLYWOOD SOFFIT
SCREENED SOFFIT VENT
3/4" 1/4 ROUND

JOISTS @ 16" O.C.

INSULATION

LATH & PLASTER

WIN. HT.

IX6 DIAGONAL BRACING
LETIN STUDS @ EACH
CORNER BOTH WAYS

INSULATION
2X4 STUDS @ 16" O.C.
WOOD SHEATHING
BUILDING FELT
SIDING

8'-0" FIN.

6'-8"

FINISH FLOOR
FELT
SUB FLOOR

Soffit vents should be installed
in the event gable ends are not
louvered. A combination of both
is often desirable.

2X4 BOTTOM PLATE
DRIP CAP
WEATHER BOARD

JOISTS @ 16" O.C.

TRIMMER

4" SOLID SLAB

FINISH GRADE

7'-4"

I'8" BLOCKS + 1'·4" SOLID SLAB

8" BLOCKS

1/2" CEMENT PLASTER &
WATERPROOFING

4" CONC. SLAB FLOOR

CEMENT COVE
AGGREGATE
4" DRAIN TILE

4" AGGREGATE FILL

16X8 CONC. FOOTING

Courtesy HOMOGRAF, East Detroit, Mich.

FRAME WALL SECTION
This type of wall section will accommodate wood
siding, stucco, asphalt veneer, asbestos, etc.

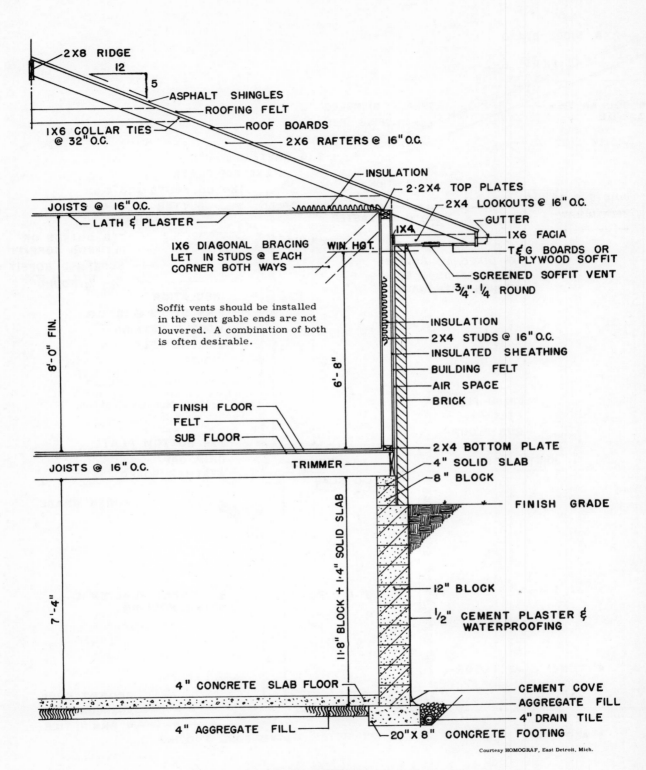

2X8 RIDGE

12
5

ASPHALT SHINGLES
ROOFING FELT
ROOF BOARDS
1X6 COLLAR TIES @ 32" O.C.
2X6 RAFTERS @ 16" O.C.

INSULATION
2·2X4 TOP PLATES
2X4 LOOKOUTS @ 16" O.C.
GUTTER
1X4
1X6 FACIA
T&G BOARDS OR PLYWOOD SOFFIT
SCREENED SOFFIT VENT
¾". ¼ ROUND

JOISTS @ 16" O.C.
LATH & PLASTER

1X6 DIAGONAL BRACING
LET IN STUDS @ EACH
CORNER BOTH WAYS

WIN. HGT.

Soffit vents should be installed
in the event gable ends are not
louvered. A combination of both
is often desirable.

INSULATION
2X4 STUDS @ 16" O.C.
INSULATED SHEATHING
BUILDING FELT
AIR SPACE
BRICK

8'-0" FIN.

6'-8"

FINISH FLOOR
FELT
SUB FLOOR

JOISTS @ 16" O.C.

TRIMMER

2X4 BOTTOM PLATE
4" SOLID SLAB
8" BLOCK

FINISH GRADE

7'-4"

1'-8" BLOCK + 1'-4" SOLID SLAB

12" BLOCK

½" CEMENT PLASTER &
WATERPROOFING

4" CONCRETE SLAB FLOOR

CEMENT COVE
AGGREGATE FILL
4" DRAIN TILE

4" AGGREGATE FILL

20"X 8" CONCRETE FOOTING

Courtesy HOMOGRAF, East Detroit, Mich.

BRICK VENEER WALL SECTION
This type of wall section is suitable for any 4 in. masonry veneer such as brick, cut stone, block slab, split field stone, etc.

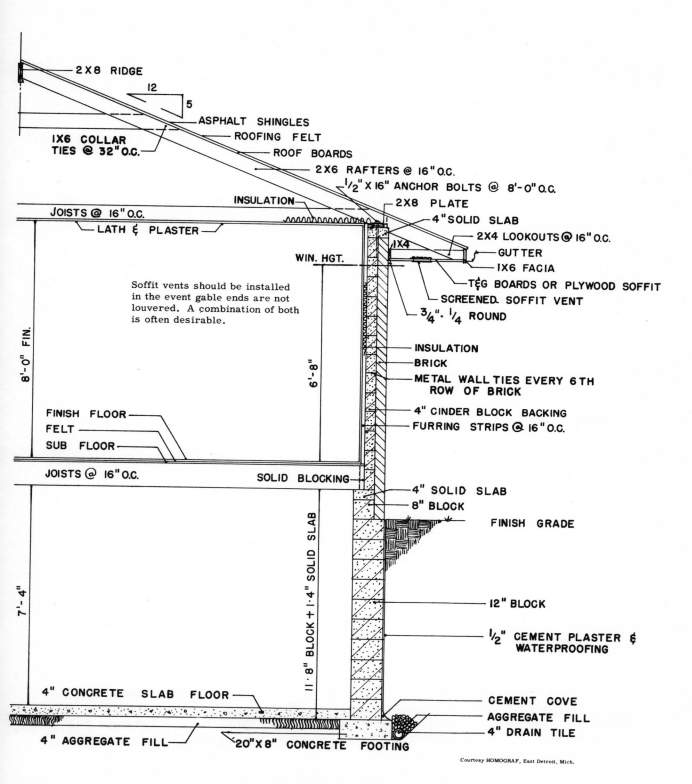

2X8 RIDGE

12

5

ASPHALT SHINGLES

ROOFING FELT

IX6 COLLAR
TIES @ 32" O.C.

ROOF BOARDS

2X6 RAFTERS @ 16" O.C.

½" X 16" ANCHOR BOLTS @ 8'-0" O.C.

INSULATION

2X8 PLATE

JOISTS @ 16" O.C.

4" SOLID SLAB

LATH & PLASTER

2X4 LOOKOUTS @ 16" O.C.

1X4

GUTTER

WIN. HGT.

1X6 FACIA

T&G BOARDS OR PLYWOOD SOFFIT

Soffit vents should be installed
in the event gable ends are not
louvered. A combination of both
is often desirable.

SCREENED SOFFIT VENT

¾". ¼ ROUND

8'-0" FIN.

6'-8"

INSULATION

BRICK

METAL WALL TIES EVERY 6TH
ROW OF BRICK

FINISH FLOOR

FELT

4" CINDER BLOCK BACKING

SUB FLOOR

FURRING STRIPS @ 16" O.C.

JOISTS @ 16" O.C.

SOLID BLOCKING

4" SOLID SLAB

8" BLOCK

FINISH GRADE

7'-4"

11 · 8" BLOCK + 1·4" SOLID SLAB

12" BLOCK

½" CEMENT PLASTER &
WATERPROOFING

4" CONCRETE SLAB FLOOR

CEMENT COVE

AGGREGATE FILL

4" AGGREGATE FILL

20"X8" CONCRETE FOOTING

4" DRAIN TILE

Courtesy HOMOGRAF, East Detroit, Mich.

BRICK AND BLOCK WALL SECTION

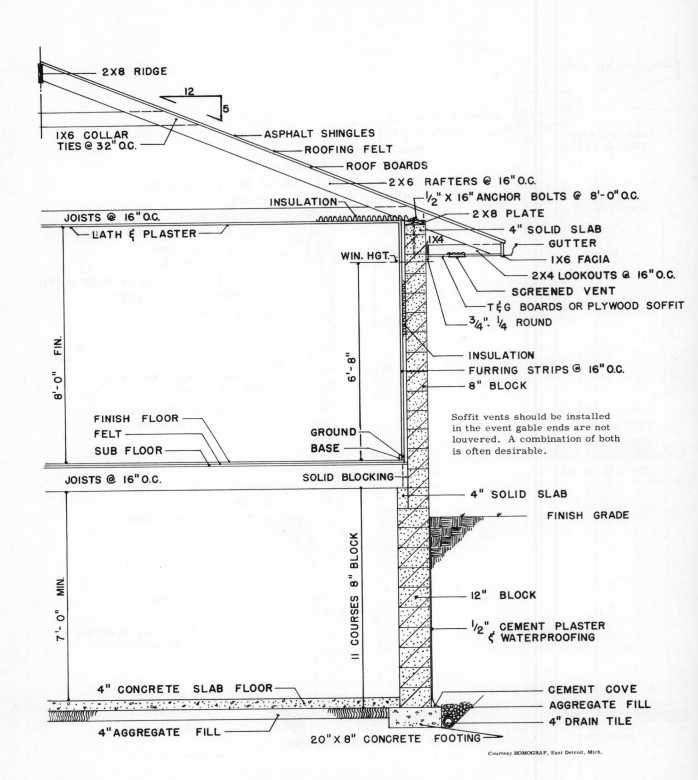

2X8 RIDGE

12
5

1X6 COLLAR TIES @ 32" O.C.

ASPHALT SHINGLES
ROOFING FELT
ROOF BOARDS
2X6 RAFTERS @ 16" O.C.
1/2" X 16" ANCHOR BOLTS @ 8'-0" O.C.
INSULATION
2X8 PLATE
JOISTS @ 16" O.C.
LATH & PLASTER
4" SOLID SLAB
GUTTER
1X4
1X6 FACIA
WIN. HGT.
2X4 LOOKOUTS @ 16" O.C.
SCREENED VENT
T&G BOARDS OR PLYWOOD SOFFIT
3/4". 1/4 ROUND

INSULATION
FURRING STRIPS @ 16" O.C.
8" BLOCK

8'-0" FIN.

6'-8"

Soffit vents should be installed in the event gable ends are not louvered. A combination of both is often desirable.

FINISH FLOOR
FELT
SUB FLOOR

GROUND
BASE

JOISTS @ 16" O.C.

SOLID BLOCKING

4" SOLID SLAB
FINISH GRADE

7'-0" MIN.

11 COURSES 8" BLOCK

12" BLOCK

1/2" CEMENT PLASTER & WATERPROOFING

4" CONCRETE SLAB FLOOR

CEMENT COVE
AGGREGATE FILL
4" DRAIN TILE

4" AGGREGATE FILL

20" X 8" CONCRETE FOOTING

Courtesy HOMOGRAF, East Detroit, Mich.

BLOCK WALL SECTION

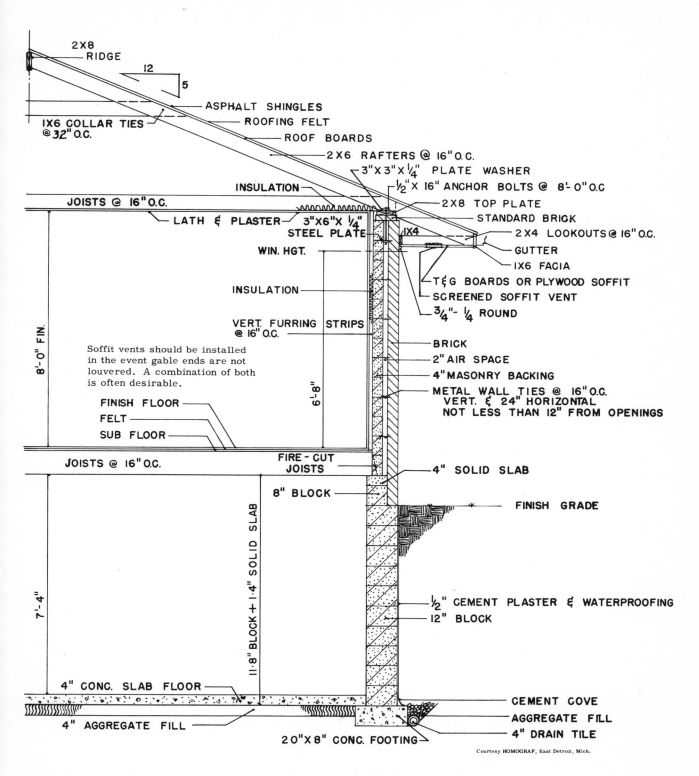

2X8 RIDGE

12
5

ASPHALT SHINGLES
ROOFING FELT
ROOF BOARDS

1X6 COLLAR TIES @ 32" O.C.

2X6 RAFTERS @ 16" O.C.
3"X3"X 1/4" PLATE WASHER
1/2" X 16" ANCHOR BOLTS @ 8'-0" O.C.

INSULATION

JOISTS @ 16" O.C.

LATH & PLASTER
3"X6"X 1/4" STEEL PLATE

2X8 TOP PLATE
STANDARD BRICK
1X4
2X4 LOOKOUTS @ 16" O.C.
GUTTER
1X6 FACIA

WIN. HGT.

INSULATION

VERT. FURRING STRIPS @ 16" O.C.

T&G BOARDS OR PLYWOOD SOFFIT
SCREENED SOFFIT VENT
3/4"- 1/4 ROUND

Soffit vents should be installed
in the event gable ends are not
louvered. A combination of both
is often desirable.

8'-0" FIN.

6'-8"

BRICK
2" AIR SPACE
4" MASONRY BACKING
METAL WALL TIES @ 16" O.C.
VERT. & 24" HORIZONTAL
NOT LESS THAN 12" FROM OPENINGS

FINISH FLOOR
FELT
SUB FLOOR

JOISTS @ 16" O.C.

FIRE - CUT JOISTS

8" BLOCK

4" SOLID SLAB

FINISH GRADE

11-8" BLOCK + 1-4" SOLID SLAB

7'-4"

1/2" CEMENT PLASTER & WATERPROOFING
12" BLOCK

4" CONC. SLAB FLOOR

4" AGGREGATE FILL

20"X8" CONC. FOOTING

CEMENT COVE
AGGREGATE FILL
4" DRAIN TILE

Courtesy HOMOGRAF, East Detroit, Mich.

BRICK CAVITY WALL SECTION

Roofing Materials Installation

In this section we will discuss both roofing of new buildings and re-roofing job requirements.

There are many kinds and forms of roofing materials and nearly all are intended to be laid over a layer of boards or sheathing supported by roof rafters, light trusses, or joists. Sheathing usually consists of 1 in. boards laid tight together, Figs. H-1 and H-2, but if wood shingles are to be used, the boards may be laid solid, H-3, or spaced apart as will be discussed later in this section.

Other types of sheathing are precast metal-bound gypsum boards, precast reinforced concrete planks, sheet-metal panels and plywood, Fig. H-4. Sometimes fiberboards are laid over sheathing to provide insulation. The principal roofing materials are wood shingles, prepared asphalt, built-up rigid and metal roofings.

ASPHALT ROOFING PRODUCTS

Asphalt roofing made on a felt base may be classified broadly into three groups: saturated felts, roll roofing and roofing shingles.

Saturated felts, used under shingles, for sheathing paper and for laminations in constructing a built-up roof, consist of dry felt impregnated with asphalt or coal tar. Saturated felt is made in different weights, the most common being 15 lb. which weighs approximately 15 lbs. per square (sufficient to cover 100 sq. ft. of roof surface) and 30 lb.

Roll roofing is made by adding a coating of weather-resistant asphalt to a felt which has been impregnated with a saturant asphalt. Some types of roll roofing are surfaced with mineral granules to produce desired colors. The granules also help make the roofing fireproof and protect it from the rays of the sun.

The table, Fig. H-5, shows important characteristics of typical asphalt roofing products. Column 1 names and illustrates the product; Column 2 indicates the weight per square; Column 3 states the number of packages required to cover 100 sq. ft. of roof surface; Columns 4 and 5 state the over-all dimensions of one unit of the product according to length and width; Column 6 states the number of shingles required to cover one square; Column 7 indicates the side lap or distance

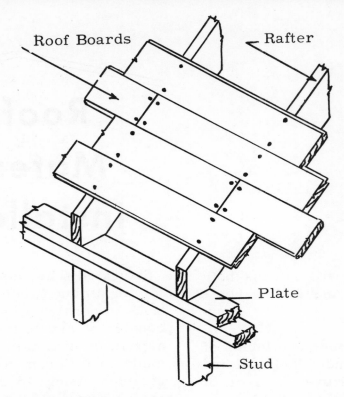

Roof Boards

Rafter

Plate

Stud

H-1. Horizontal roof sheathing. Boards which are 6 in. or less in width should be nailed to rafters with two 8d nails. Wider boards should be nailed with three 8d nails. Joints in succeeding runs of sheathing boards should never occur on the same rafter.

in inches which horizontally adjacent elements of the roofing overlap each other; Column 8 shows the head lap or shortest distance between an exposed edge of a shingle and the roof deck, measured at right angles to the eaves or parallel to the rake. See Fig. H-6.

ASPHALT SHINGLES

Asphalt shingles are surfaced with mineral granules. They are available in many patterns; some are individual shingles and some come in strips 36 in. long.

NAILS FOR ASPHALT ROOFING

Nails used in applying asphalt roofing should be large-headed, sharp-point-ed, hot galvanized wire nails, with barbed shanks. The table, H-7, gives the estimated quantity of nails requir-ed for various jobs.

WEIGHTS OF ASPHALT ROOFING

Asphalt roofings are made in weights varying from 45 lbs. to 325 lbs. per square on the roof. Heavier roofings such as strips or individual shingles are best suited for permanent struc-tures having sloping roofs. Roll roof-ing is well adapted for farm buildings, garages, summer cottages, etc.

PITCH LIMITATIONS

Of considerable importance in the selection of roofing are the limita-

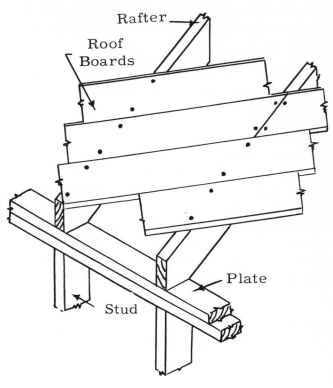

H-2. Diagonal sheathing. Boards 6 in. or less in width should be nailed to rafters with two 8d nails; wider boards with three 8d nails. Diagonal sheathing, although seldom used, adds rigidity to any roof, and is desirable in cases where extra rigidity is required.

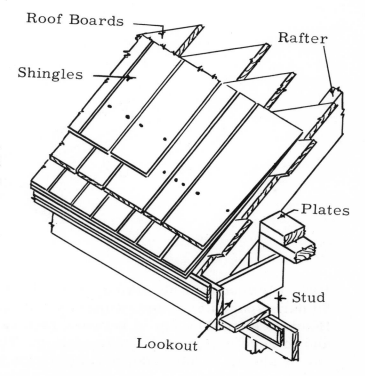

H-3. Roofing with wood shingles. Wood shingles are ordinarily nailed 1 in. above the exposure line and 3/4 in. from edge of shingle, with rust-resisting nails long enough to penetrate through sheathing. Nails should be driven flush with face of shingles. Shingles wider than 8 in. should be split and nailed as two shingles.

tions imposed by the "pitch," or slope of the roof and "exposure" or the portion of the roofing unit which is exposed to the weather.

Pitch limitations are shown in the chart, Fig. H-8.

Any asphalt shingle can be used on a roof with a slope of 4 in. rise or more per horizontal foot. Wherever possible, exposure should be minimized on all lower pitches as this increases the head lap and provides better protection against water reaching the sheathing by being forced up

under the shingle by a driving rain or by an accumulation of ice or snow.

The lowest pitch recommended for roll roofing when exposed nail method is used is 3 in. per foot. The concealed nail method of application, when providing a 3 in. head lap, can be used when the pitch is as low as 2 in. If a 4 in. lap is used, the pitch may safely run as low as 1 1/2 in. The only roll product that is recommended as being suitable for a 1 in. pitch is 19 in. double coverage roof. Only a properly built-up (laminated) roof should be used when the pitch is less than 1 in. per foot.

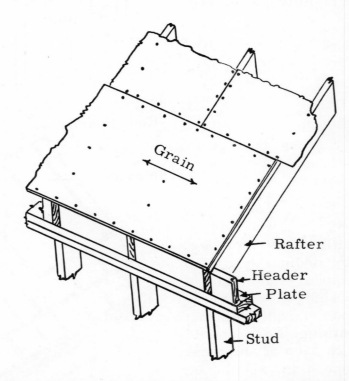

H-4. Plywood roof sheathing. Such sheathing should be nailed around edges with 8d nails spaced 5 in. and to intermediate rafters with 8d nails spaced about 10 in. Headers should be cut in between rafters as shown to support edges of plywood and to receive specified edge nailing. To receive nails at horizontal joints between sheets of plywood, nailing strips should be placed between rafters and securely nailed to them.

ASPHALT ROOFING APPLICATION

First of all the sheathing or deck must be rigid. Sheathing used should not be over 6 in. wide, Fig. H-1. It is also important that the attic space be properly ventilated to minimize condensation of moisture after the building is completed and ready for use. Sometimes moisture vapor from the lower stories, rising to the attic will be chilled below its dew point and will condense out on the under side of the roof deck, causing sheathing boards to warp and buckle. To avoid this, louvered openings should be constructed high up under the eaves in the gable ends or at such locations as will insure adequate venting. Such louvers should have a total effective area equivalent to 1/2 square inch per square foot of attic floor space.

After the deck or sheathing has been completed, it should be protected from dampness by an underlayment of asphalt saturated felt not heavier than 15 lb. Don't use a coated product as this might form a vapor barrier and cause an accumulation of moisture or frost between the deck and the shingle underlayment.

DECK TREATMENT FOR REROOFING

In most localities when a reroofing job is being considered, a choice must be made between removing the old roofing and leaving it in place. It is usually not necessary to remove old wood shingles, old asphalt shingles, or old roll roofing before putting on a new asphalt roof provided that:

1. The strength of the existing deck and framing is adequate to support the weight of workers and additional new roofing, as well as snow and wind loads.
2. The existing deck is sound and will provide good anchorage for the nails used in applying new roofing.

OLD ROOFING TO REMAIN

If it is decided to put on new roofing over old wood shingles all loose or protruding nails should be removed and the shingles nailed in new locations; loose shingles nailed down, warped shingles split and segments renailed, missing shingles replaced, shingles at eaves and rakes cut back far enough to allow the application of 4 in. to 6 in. nominal 1 in. thick strips. These strips should be nailed in place allowing their outside edges to project beyond edges of deck, same distance as did wood shingles.

To provide a smooth deck for asphalt roofing it is often advisable that a "backer board" be applied over the wood shingles or that beveled wood "feathering strips" be used along the butts of each course of old shingles.

COVERING OLD ASPHALT SHINGLES

When old asphalt shingles are to remain in place, nail down or cut away

1	2	3	4	5	6	7	8	9
PRODUCT	Wt. Per Square Applied	Packages Per Square	Length	Width	Shingles Per Square	Side or End Lap	Headlap	Exposure
Roll Brick Siding	105 lb.	1	43'	31"			1-5/8"	13-7/8"
3 Tab Square Butt Strip Shingle	210 lb. 262 lb.	2 or 3	36" 36"	12" 12"	80 100		2" 4"	5" 4"
Two and Three Tab Hex Strip Shingle	167 lb.	2	36"	11-1/3"	86		2"	4-2/3"
Individual Lock-Down	135 to 138 lb.	2	16"	16"	82	$2\frac{1}{2}$"		
Giant Ind. American	325 lb.	4	16"	12"	226		6"	5"
Dutch Lap	162 lb.	2	16"	12"	113	3"	2"	10"

H-5. Typical asphalt roofing products —weight per

1	2	3	4	5	6	7	8	9
PRODUCT	Wt. Per Square Applied	Packages Per Square	Length	Width		Side or End Lap	Headlap	Exposure
Asphalt Saturated Felt	15 lb. 30 lb.	1/4 1/2	144' 72'	36" 36"		4" 4"	2" 2"	34" 34"
Mineral Surfaced Roll	90 lb. 93 lb. 95 lb.	1.0 1.075 1.15	36' 36' 36'	36" 36" 36"	Exp. Conc. Conc.	4" 6" 6"	2" 3" 4"	34" 33" 32"
Smooth Roll	65 lb. 55 lb. 45 lb.	1 1 1	36' 36' 36'	36" 36" 36"		4" 4" 4"	2" 2" 2"	34" 34" 34"
Pattern Edge Roll	105 lb. 105 lb.	1 1	42' 48'	36" 32"			2" 2"	16" 14"
19" Selvage Double Coverage	144 lb. 140 lb.	2 2	36' 36'	36" 36"	Cold Hot		19" 19"	17" 17"

square, dimensions, quantities required, etc.

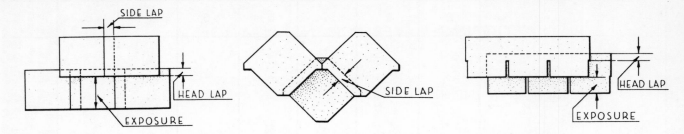

H-6. Head lap as shown at the left, may be defined as the shortest distance between an exposed edge of shingle and the roof deck, measured at right angles to the eaves or parallel to the rake.

Side lap, shown in the center, is the distance in inches which horizontally adjacent elements of roofing overlap each other.

Exposure, illustrated at the right, is the distance between exposed edges of adjacent courses measured at right angles to the eaves.

	Shingles per Square	Nails per Shingle	Nails per Square	Length of (*) Nail	Pounds per Square (approx.)	
					12 ga. by 7/16" head	11 ga. by 7/16 head
Roll Roofing on new deck			252 **	1"	.73	1.12
Roll Roofing over old roofing			252 **	1-3/4"	1.13	1.78
19" Selvage over old shingles			181	1-3/4"	.83	1.07
3 Tab Square Butt New	80	6	504	1-1/4"	1.83	2.32
3 Tab Square Butt Reroofing	80	6	504	1-3/4"	2.38	3.01
Hex Strip New	86	4	361	1-1/4"	1.28	1.68
Hex Strip Reroofing	86	4	361	1-3/4"	1.65	2.03
Giant American	226	2	479	1-1/4"	1.79	2.27
Giant Dutch Lap	113	2	236	1-3/4"	1.07	1.39
Individual Hex	82	2	172	1-3/4"	.79	1.03

(*) Length of nail should always be sufficient to penetrate at least 3/4" into sound wood deck lumber. Nails should show little, if any, below underside of deck lumber.

(**) This is the number of nails required when spaced 2" apart. During the war nails were used on 3" centers and only 168 per roll supplied by the manufacturers. Many are still supplying the smaller number.

H-7. Typical nails for asphalt roofing products.

RISE IN INCHES

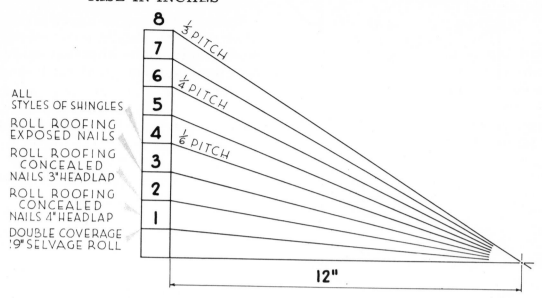

ALL
STYLES OF SHINGLES

ROLL ROOFING
EXPOSED NAILS

ROLL ROOFING
CONCEALED
NAILS 3" HEADLAP

ROLL ROOFING
CONCEALED
NAILS 4" HEADLAP

DOUBLE COVERAGE
19" SELVAGE ROLL

H-8. Of considerable importance in the selection of roofing are the limitations imposed by the pitch or slope of the roof and exposure or portion of the roofing unit which is exposed to the weather. Minimum pitch requirements for different asphalt roofing products are shown above.

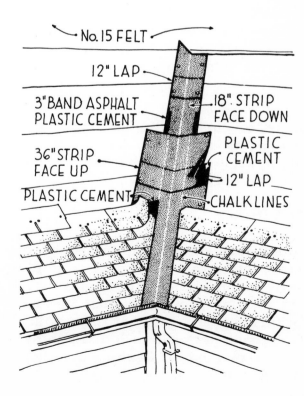

H-9. Using roll roofing for valley flashing. The flashing should be applied after the roofing felt is laid down but before the roofing is applied.

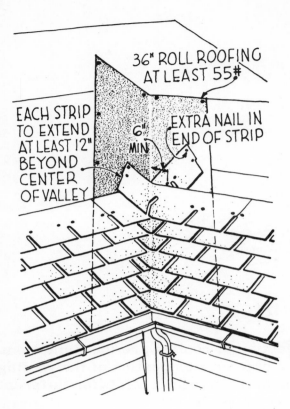

36" ROLL ROOFING AT LEAST 55#

EACH STRIP TO EXTEND AT LEAST 12" BEYOND CENTER OF VALLEY

6" MIN

EXTRA NAIL IN END OF STRIP

H-10. Closed or woven valley. This is limited to strip type shingles. Individual shingles cannot be used because nails might be required at or near the center of the valley lining.

loose, or curled shingles, remove all protruding nails; replace badly worn edging strips, slit all buckled portions and nail segments down smoothly.

FLASHINGS

Roofs are often complicated by the intersection of other roofs, adjoining walls or projections through the deck and special provision must be made for turning the weather at these points. Such construction is called "flashing." Typical methods of flashing are shown in Figs. H-9 to H-14 inclusive.

APPLYING STRIP SHINGLES

Before starting to apply strip shingles, the deck should be properly prepared; in the case of new construction an underlayment applied and in reroofing, the old surface repaired. Figs. H-15 and H-16 show three tab square butt strips applied over an underlayment of No. 15 asphalt saturated felt and Figs. H-17 and H-18 show a similar application of two and three tab hexagonal strips.

In all cases procedure is the same:

Along the eaves and rake and over the felt lay a strip of corrosion-resistant 26-gauge sheet metal. Galvanized steel, painted on both sides is commonly used, but other equivalent metals are satisfactory. Fasten the strips with suitable roofing nails, spaced 8 in. to 10 in. apart along the inner edge. The metal is bent downward even with the rake and eave lines, Fig. H-19, to form a drip and extends from 2 in. to 4 in. back from the edges of the roof deck.

EAVES FLASHING STRIP

Overhanging the lower edge of the drip edge from 1/4 to 3/8 in. an eaves flashing strip of 90 lb. mineral surfaced or 65 lb. smooth roll roofing should be applied. This extends up the roof far enough to cover a point at least 12 in. inside the inside wall line of the building and is intended to prevent damage to the roof deck and interior wall and ceiling finish, should the roof drainage system clog up due to formation of ice in eaves troughs, Fig. H-20.

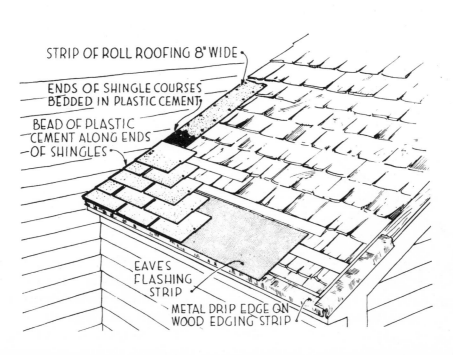

NO 15 ASPHALT SATURATED FELT TURNED UP ON VERTICAL WALL 3" TO 4"

FLASHING TO HAVE 2" SIDE LAP

NAIL

4"   2"

FLASHING TO BE PLACED JUST BACK OF EXPOSED EDGE OF SHINGLE

—FINISH SIDING TO SERVE AS CAP FLASHING

H-11. Using metal flashing shingles to protect joint between sloping roof and vertical wall.

STRIP OF ROLL ROOFING 8" WIDE

ENDS OF SHINGLE COURSES BEDDED IN PLASTIC CEMENT

BEAD OF PLASTIC CEMENT ALONG ENDS OF SHINGLES

EAVES FLASHING STRIP

METAL DRIP EDGE ON WOOD EDGING STRIP

H-12. Flashing against a vertical wall on job of reroofing over old material.

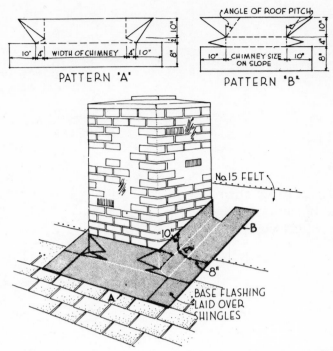

PATTERN "A" PATTERN "B"

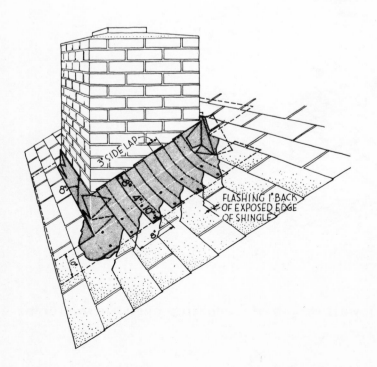

H-13. Base flashing patterns cut and applied. The base flashing for the front, pattern A is first applied. The lower section is laid over the shingles in a bed of asphalt plastic cement, and the upper vertical section is secured against the masonry with cement and with nails driven into the mortar joints. Triangular ends of upper section are bent around corners of chimney and cemented in place.

H-14. Alternate method of applying base flashing, known as "step flashing."

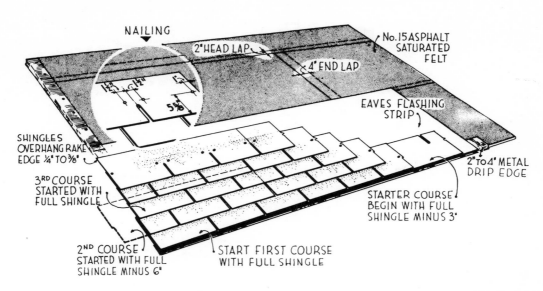

H-15. Three tab square butt strips. Cutouts are centered over the tabs in the course below.

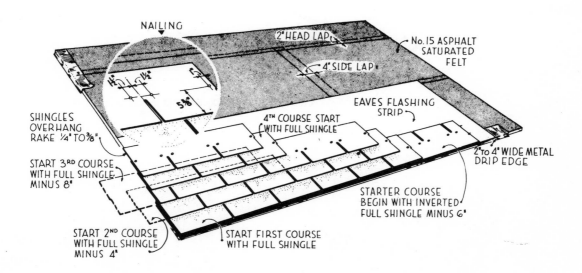

H-16. Three tab square butt strips. Cutouts break joints in thirds.

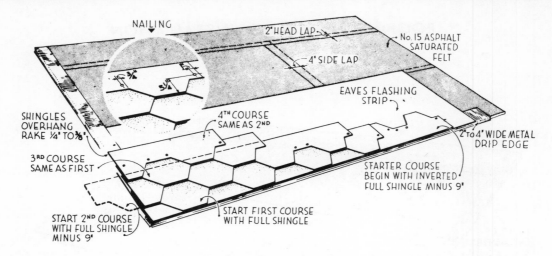

NAILING

2" HEAD LAP

4" SIDE LAP

No. 15 ASPHALT SATURATED FELT

SHINGLES OVERHANG RAKE ¼" TO ⅜"

4ᵀᴴ COURSE SAME AS 2ᴺᴰ

EAVES FLASHING STRIP

3ᴿᴰ COURSE SAME AS FIRST

2" TO 4" WIDE METAL DRIP EDGE

START 2ᴺᴰ COURSE WITH FULL SHINGLE MINUS 9"

START FIRST COURSE WITH FULL SHINGLE

STARTER COURSE BEGIN WITH INVERTED FULL SHINGLE MINUS 9"

H-17. Two tab hex strip asphalt roofing.

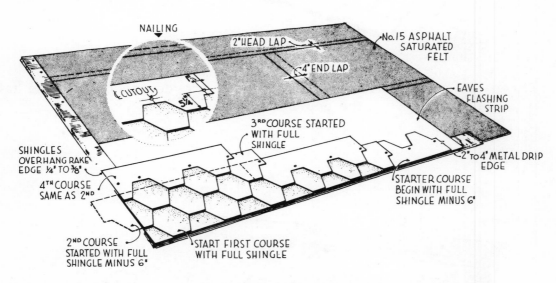

NAILING

2" HEAD LAP

4" END LAP

No. 15 ASPHALT SATURATED FELT

CUTOUT

SHINGLES OVERHANG RAKE EDGE ¼" TO ⅜"

3ᴿᴰ COURSE STARTED WITH FULL SHINGLE

EAVES FLASHING STRIP

4ᵀᴴ COURSE SAME AS 2ᴺᴰ

2" TO 4" METAL DRIP EDGE

2ᴺᴰ COURSE STARTED WITH FULL SHINGLE MINUS 6"

START FIRST COURSE WITH FULL SHINGLE

STARTER COURSE BEGIN WITH FULL SHINGLE MINUS 6"

H-18. Application of three tab hex strip shingles.

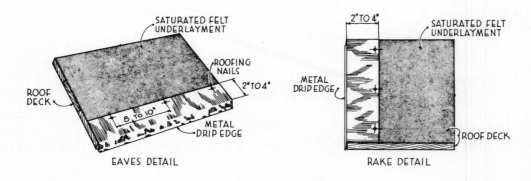

SATURATED FELT UNDERLAYMENT

ROOFING NAILS

2" TO 4"

ROOF DECK

8" TO 10"

METAL DRIP EDGE

EAVES DETAIL

2" TO 4"

SATURATED FELT UNDERLAYMENT

METAL DRIP EDGE

ROOF DECK

RAKE DETAIL

H-19. Details of metal drip edge.

Figs. H-20 to H-24 inclusive show the application of various types of roofing materials over old roofs and on new roofing jobs.

APPLICATION OF ROLL ROOFING

Roll roofing should not be applied when the temperature is below 35 degrees F. When it is necessary to handle roofing at lower temperatures it should be warmed before unrolling to avoid cracking.

Roll roofing should be cut into 12 to 18 ft. lengths and spread on a smooth surface until they flatten out.

Instructions for flashings as described earlier in this chapter, should be followed when applying roll roofing.

CEMENT TO USE

Use lap cement for exposed nail application and a quick setting type of special cement as recommended by

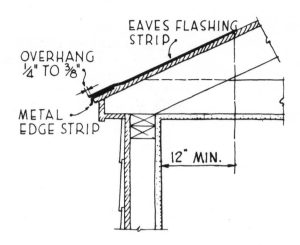

H-20. Eaves flashing strip. Overhanging the lower edge of the drop edge from 1/4 to 3/8 in. an eaves flashing strip of 90 lb. mineral surfaced or 65 lb. smooth roll roofing should be applied. This should extend up the roof far enough to cover a point 12 in. inside the inside wall line of the building. It is intended to prevent damage to the roof deck and interior wall and ceiling, should the roof drainage system clog up.

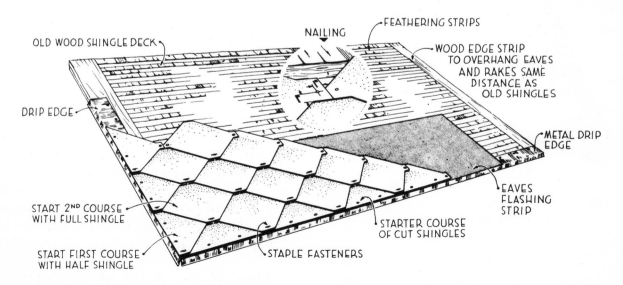

H-21. Individual hex shingles, step down type, applied over old wood shingles.

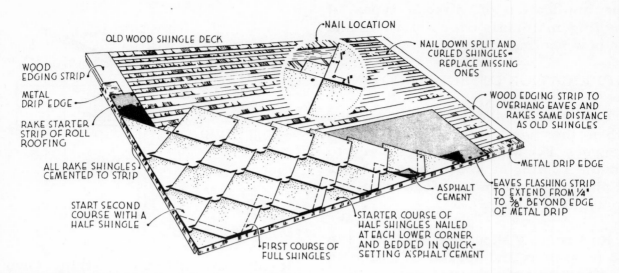

H-22. Application details for windy locations. Lower end of each shingle is set in asphalt cement spread over lapped areas of underlaying starter course shingles. Nails are used only at the side corners.

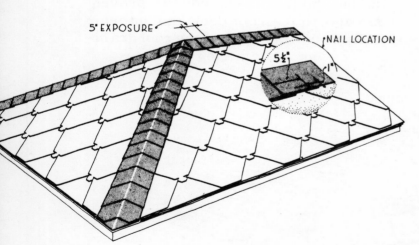

H-23. Hip and ridge finish with individual hex shingles.

the manufacturer for blind nail application. Cement should be kept in a warm place before using. If necessary to warm, place unopened contained in hot water. Never heat any kind of asphalt cement directly over a fire.

USE LARGE HEAD NAILS

For application directly to a wood deck use 7/8 in. or 1 in. galvanized roofing nails having heads at least 3/8 in. diameter. Over old roofing use nails long enough to penetrate the old material and into the roof sheathing at least 3/4 in. Be sure to drive nails straight to prevent cutting the roofing with the edge of the nail head and don't sink heads into surface of roofing.

Figs. H-25, H-26, H-27 and H-28 show how roll roofing is applied by

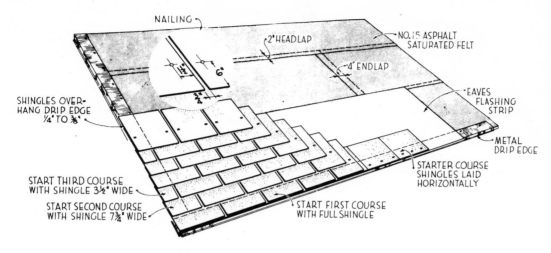

H-24. Application of giant individual shingles. Joints break in thirds.

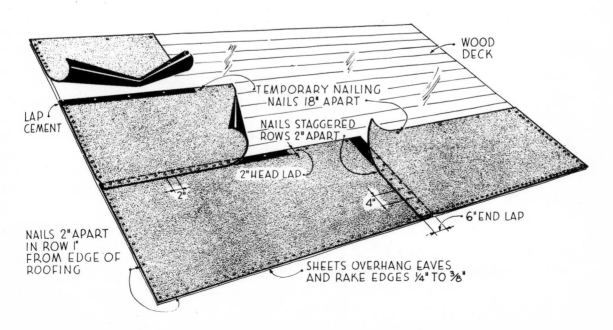

H-25. Exposed nail application of roll roofing parallel to the eaves.

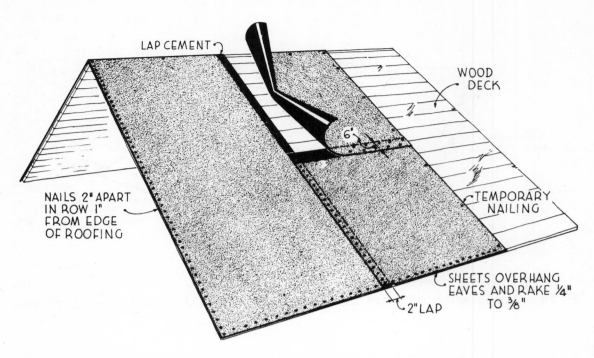

LAP CEMENT

WOOD DECK

6'

NAILS 2" APART
IN ROW 1"
FROM EDGE
OF ROOFING

TEMPORARY
NAILING

SHEETS OVERHANG
EAVES AND RAKE ¼"
TO ⅜"

2" LAP

H-26. Exposed nail application of roll roofing parallel to the rake.

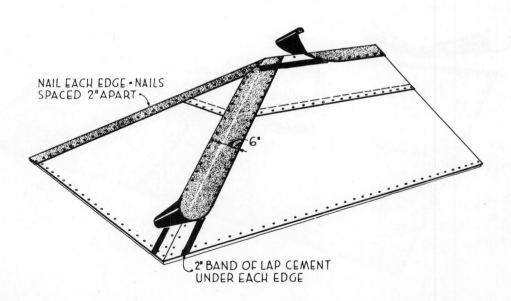

NAIL EACH EDGE - NAILS
SPACED 2" APART

6'

2" BAND OF LAP CEMENT
UNDER EACH EDGE

H-27. Finish for hips and ridges when laying roll roofing by exposed nail method.

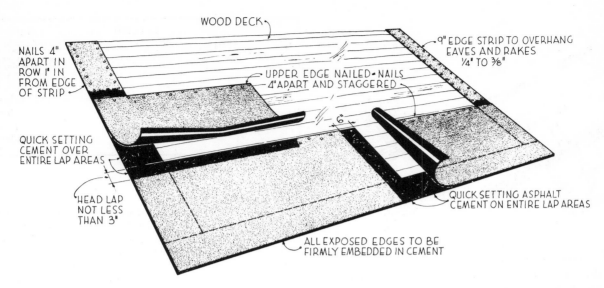

WOOD DECK

NAILS 4" APART IN ROW 1" IN FROM EDGE OF STRIP

UPPER EDGE NAILED - NAILS 4" APART AND STAGGERED

9" EDGE STRIP TO OVERHANG EAVES AND RAKES ¼" TO ⅜"

QUICK SETTING CEMENT OVER ENTIRE LAP AREAS

6"

HEAD LAP NOT LESS THAN 3"

QUICK SETTING ASPHALT CEMENT ON ENTIRE LAP AREAS

ALL EXPOSED EDGES TO BE FIRMLY EMBEDDED IN CEMENT

H-28. Application of roll roofing by concealed nail method parallel to the eaves.

using both the exposed nail and concealed nail methods.

BUILT UP ROOFINGS

Built-up roofing, Fig. H-29, is used for roofs with a rise of 1/2 to 3/4 in. per foot and consists of 3 to 5 layers of asphalt impregnated felt (made of rags, wood and other cellulose fibers), lapped and cemented together with hot asphalt or coal tar pitch. Fine gravel or slag is then spread over the top layer to provide a weathering surface. When properly applied, built-up roofings do not require major repairs or renewals for a long time.

When a leak occurs in a built-up roof, flashings at parapet walls, skylights and vents should be inspected carefully, because the first roof failures usually occur at these locations. Bituminous flashings are made of saturated felt and flashing cement. Flash-

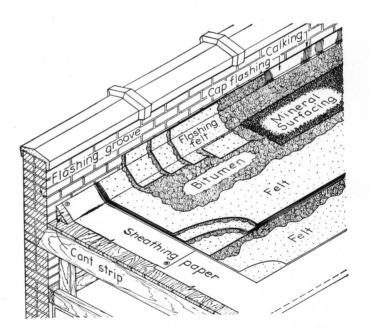

Calking

Cap flashing

Mineral Surfacing

Flashing groove

Flashing felt

Bitumen

Felt

Sheathing paper

Cant strip

Felt

H-29. Built-up roof consists of three to five layers of asphalt impregnated felt lapped and cemented together and covered with fine gravel or slag.

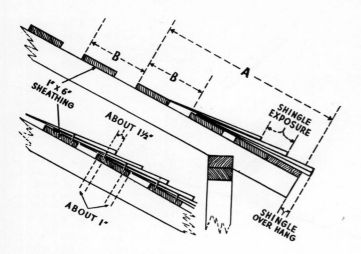

H-30. Spacing of 1 x 6 in. sheathing boards with shingle exposures of 3 3/4, 4 1/4, 4 1/2 and 5 in.

SHEATH-ING SIZE	SHINGLE EXPO-SURE	COLUMN 1 (A) Distance between upper edge of arbitrarily placed key sheathing board and lower edge of starting sheathing board at the eave	COLUMN 2 (B) Proper spacing of sheathing boards (upper edge to upper edge) below and above the key sheathing board indicated in Column 1.
1 x 6″..	3¾″	27½″	7½″ Edge to Edge
	4¼″	30½″	8½″ Edge to Edge
	4½″	32 ″	9 ″ Edge to Edge
	5 ″	30½″	10 ″ Edge to Edge

EXAMPLE—4½″ shingle exposure, 1 x 6 sheathing, and 1½″ shingle overhang. Apply first sheathing board where desired at lower edge of roof; then attach upper edge of 1 x 6 sheathing board a distance of 32″ (Column 1) from lower edge of first sheathing board at eave-line. Next, nail sheathing boards 9″ apart (upper edge to upper edge as shown in Column 2) below this board until tight sheathing is encountered and above this board until peak or ridge of roof is reached. Starting course of shingles should be given an overhang of 1½″; shingles should be nailed 1½″ above butt line of next course to be applied and nails should strike sheathing about 1″ from each edge.

ing cement should be forced behind the felt if it has separated from the wall at the upper edge, and the edge sealed with a strip of bituminous-saturated cotton fabric 4 in. wide, embedded and coated with flashing cement.

Bare spots on a built-up roof where the mineral surfacing is not properly embedded should be reroofed clean, a heavy coating of hot asphalt applied and more gravel or slag spread over the area. Felts which have disintegrated should be cut away and replaced with new felt of the same kind. New felt should be mopped in place, allowing at least one additional layer of felt to extend not less than 6 in. beyond the other layers.

ROOFING WITH WOOD SHINGLES

Factors that affect the service life of wood-shingle roofs are pitch and exposure of the roof, durability of the wood in the shingles, preservative treatment of the shingles and type of nails used in fastening.

Wood shingles are usually manufactured in random widths, the maximum being 14 in., and in lengths of 16 in., 18 in. and 24 in. They come packed in bundles, four bundles containing enough shingles to cover an area of 100 sq. ft. when properly applied to the roof.

Wood shingles may be used on all roofs that have enough slope or pitch to insure good drainage. Common roof pitches are 1/4, 1/3 and 1/2. An explanation of roof pitches will be found in the section on roof framing.

Standard exposures for 16 in., 18 in. and 25 in. shingles are 5 in., 5 1/2 in. and 7 1/2 in. On roof with less pitch than 5/24, the shingle exposure should be reduced to 3 3/4 in., 4 1/4 in. and 5 3/4 in. With this exposure reduction,

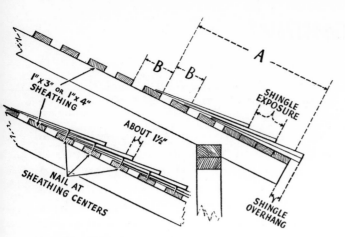

H-31. How to space 1 x 3 in. and 1 x 4 in. sheathing boards.

SHEATH-ING SIZE	SHINGLE EXPO-SURE	COLUMN 1 (A) Distance between lower edge of arbitrarily placed key sheathing board and lower edge of starting sheathing board at the eave	COLUMN 2 (B) Proper spacing of sheathing boards (lower edge to lower edge) below and above the key sheathing board indicated in Column 1.
1 x 3'' or... 1 x 4''	3¾''	24½''	3¾'' Edge to Edge
	4¼''	24 ''	4¼'' Edge to Edge
	4½''	21 ''	4½'' Edge to Edge
	5 ''	23½''	5 '' Edge to Edge
	5¼''	19½''	5¼'' Edge to Edge
	5½''	20½''	5½'' Edge to Edge
	5¾''	21½''	5¾'' Edge to Edge
1 x 4'' or.... 1 x 6''	7 ''	19 ''	7 '' Edge to Edge
	7½''	20½''	7½'' Edge to Edge

EXAMPLE—5½'' shingle exposure, 1 x 3 sheathing, and 1½'' shingle overhang. Apply first sheathing board where desired at lower edge of roof; then attach lower edge of 1 x 3 sheathing board a distance of 20½'' (Column 1) from lower edge of first sheathing board at eaveline. Next, nail sheathing boards 5½'' apart (lower edge to lower edge as shown in Column 2) below this board until tight sheathing is encountered and above this board until peak or ridge of roof is reached. Starting course of shingles should be given an overhang of 1½''; shingles should be nailed about 1½'' above butt line of next course to be applied and nails should strike approximate centers of sheathing boards.

four layers of shingles are assured over the entire roof area. In all roof construction there should be a minimum of three layers of shingles at every point, to insure complete protection in heavy wind-driven rainstorms. Four layers are better.

SHEATHING FOR SHINGLES

Sheathing for wood shingles may be either solid using matched or unmatched 1 in. boards; shiplap; or 5/16 in. Douglas fir plywood (on rafters spaced 16 in. center to center). Open sheathing not only costs less but permits the shingles to dry out quickly. One reason for using solid sheathing is to gain the added insulation that such a deck offers, and in cold climates this is often justifiable.

SPACING OF ROOF SHEATHING

There are two widely accepted methods of applying spaced roof sheathing. One is to space 1 by 3 in., 1 by 4 in. or 1 by 6 in. boards the same distance apart as the anticipated shingle exposure and to nail each course of shingles to a separate board. The other uses 1 by 6 in. lumber as sheathing boards, and two courses of shingles are nailed to each board. The drawings and tables, Figs. H-30 and H-31, show the recommended sheathing placement and spacing for various shingle exposures.

H-32. Flashing around a chimney. Note that the small sheets of flashing extend out under roof material and that they are bent up along the chimney. The counter flashing is embedded in the masonry joints and is bent down over the flashing.

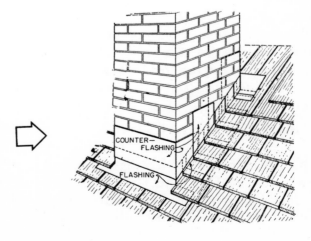

189

USE RIGHT BUILDING PAPER

If it is desirable to use roofing paper to prevent air infiltration the roof may be covered with rosin-sized building paper, "dry" or unsaturated "deadening" felt or light-weight "blue" wallboard. Saturated building paper should not be used because of the condensation trouble it may cause.

lead-clad iron, galvanized iron, lead, copper and aluminum sheets.

If galvanized iron (mild steel coated with a layer of zinc) is selected, 24 or 26 gauge metal should be used. Tin, or galvanized sheets with less than 2 oz. of zinc per square foot, should be painted on both sides with white lead and oil paint and allowed to

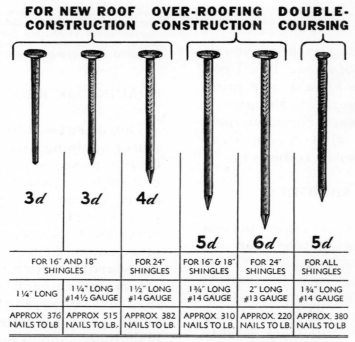

FOR NEW ROOF CONSTRUCTION		OVER-ROOFING CONSTRUCTION			DOUBLE-COURSING
3d	3d	4d	5d	6d	5d
FOR 16" AND 18" SHINGLES		FOR 24" SHINGLES	FOR 16" & 18" SHINGLES	FOR 24" SHINGLES	FOR ALL SHINGLES
1¼" LONG	1¼" LONG #14½ GAUGE	1½" LONG #14 GAUGE	1¾" LONG #14 GAUGE	2" LONG #13 GAUGE	1¾" LONG #14 GAUGE
APPROX 376 NAILS TO LB	APPROX 515 NAILS TO LB.	APPROX. 382 NAILS TO LB.	APPROX. 310 NAILS TO LB.	APPROX. 220 NAILS TO LB.	APPROX. 380 NAILS TO LB

SQUARE CUT NAILS OF SAME LENGTH WILL ALSO GIVE SATISFACTORY SERVICE.
STANDARD "BOX" NAILS OF THE SIZES GIVEN WILL PROVE SATISFACTORY IF PROPERLY ZINC COATED OR MADE RUST-RESISTANT.

H-33. In shingling only rust-resistant nails should be used. Hot dipped, zinc-coated nails have the strength of steel and the corrosion resistance of zinc and are recommended. Sizes to use on various jobs is indicated above.

FLASHINGS AND VALLEYS

The importance of using good materials for valleys and flashings cannot be overemphasized. Materials used for this purpose include tin plate,

dry before being used. In making bends care should be taken not to crack the zinc coating. On roofs of 1/2 pitch or steeper, the valley sheets should extend up on both sides of the center of the valley for a distance of at least

7 in. On roofs of less pitch, wider valley sheets should be used; they should extend at least 10 in. on both sides.

Tight flashing around chimneys is also essential to a good roofing job. A method of flashing and counter flashing around a chimney is shown in Fig. H-32. If the roofing and building of the chimney are done at the same time, the counter flashing may be laid in the joints as construction progresses. If the chimney is already built, the mortar joints must be chiseled out and the flashing forced in. It may be held in place by nails driven into the mortar. Finally, the joints must be filled or pointed with good mortar.

NAILS—A FACTOR OF IMPORTANCE

In applying shingles only rust-resistant nails should be used. Hot-dipped, zinc-coated nails have the strength of steel and the corrosion resistance of zinc and are recommended. Fig. H-33 gives information on sizes of nails for various jobs.

APPLYING SHINGLES ON ROOFS

The first course of shingles at the eaves should be at least doubled. All shingles when laid on the roof should be spaced 1/4 in. apart and only two nails used for each shingle. Of considerable importance in nailing is the proper placing of these two nails. They should be near the butt line of the shingles in the next course that is to be applied over the course being nailed, but should never be driven be-

low this line so they will be exposed to the weather. Driving the nails 1 to 1 1/2 in. above the butt line is good practice, with 2 in. as an allowable maximum. Each nail should be placed not more than 3/4 in. from the edge of the shingle at each side. When nailed in this manner, the shingles will lie flat and give good service. And, don't drive nails into the wood crushing it. Hold that last blow of the hatchet.

PROPER SIDE LAP AND BROKEN JOINTS ARE IMPERATIVE

The second layer of shingles in the first course should be nailed over the first layer so the joints in each course are not less than 1 1/2 in. apart. See Fig. H-34.

A good shingler will use care in breaking the joints in successive courses carefully, so they do not match up in three successive courses. Joints in adjacent courses should be at least 1 1/2 in. apart.

SHINGLE AWAY FROM VALLEY

On a roof section that terminates at one edge in a valley, shingles for the valley should be carefully cut to the proper miter at the butts and nailed in place first, so that shingling is directed away from the valley.

Drip from gables may be prevented by using a piece of 6 in. bevel siding along the edge and parallel to the end rafter, as shown in Fig. H-35.

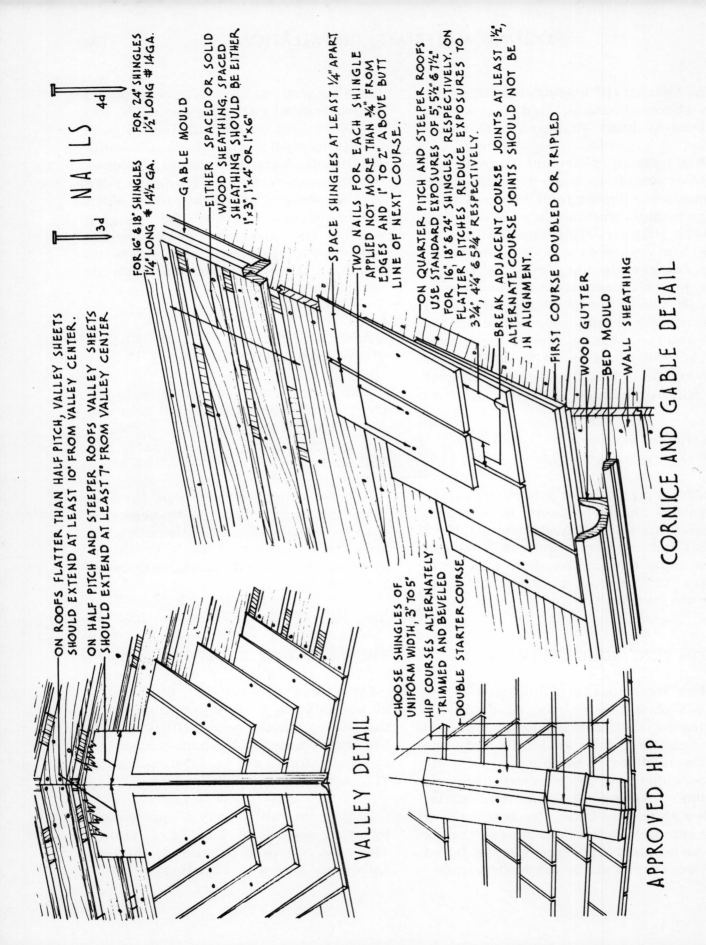

NAILS
3d   4d

FOR 16" & 18" SHINGLES
1¼" LONG #14½ GA.

FOR 24" SHINGLES
1½" LONG #14 GA.

GABLE MOULD

EITHER SPACED OR SOLID WOOD SHEATHING. SPACED SHEATHING SHOULD BE EITHER 1"×3", 1"×4" OR 1"×6"

SPACE SHINGLES AT LEAST ¼" APART

TWO NAILS FOR EACH SHINGLE APPLIED NOT MORE THAN ¾" FROM EDGES AND 1" TO 2" ABOVE BUTT LINE OF NEXT COURSE.

ON QUARTER PITCH AND STEEPER ROOFS USE STANDARD EXPOSURES OF 5", 5½" & 7½" FOR 16", 18" & 24" SHINGLES RESPECTIVELY. ON FLATTER PITCHES REDUCE EXPOSURES TO 3¾", 4¼" & 5¾" RESPECTIVELY.

BREAK ADJACENT COURSE JOINTS AT LEAST 1½", ALTERNATE COURSE JOINTS SHOULD NOT BE IN ALIGNMENT.

FIRST COURSE DOUBLED OR TRIPLED

WOOD GUTTER

BED MOULD

WALL SHEATHING

CORNICE AND GABLE DETAIL

ON ROOFS FLATTER THAN HALF PITCH, VALLEY SHEETS SHOULD EXTEND AT LEAST 10" FROM VALLEY CENTER.

ON HALF PITCH AND STEEPER ROOFS VALLEY SHEETS SHOULD EXTEND AT LEAST 7" FROM VALLEY CENTER

VALLEY DETAIL

CHOOSE SHINGLES OF UNIFORM WIDTH, 3" TO 5"

HIP COURSES ALTERNATELY TRIMMED AND BEVELED

DOUBLE STARTER COURSE

APPROVED HIP

H-34. Applying red cedar shingle standard roof. Wm. J. Bain architect A. I. A.

SHINGLED HIPS AND RIDGES

Good tight ridges and hips are required to avoid roof leakage. In the best type of hip construction, Fig. H-34, nails are not exposed to the weather. Shingles of approximately the same width are sorted out—for a 5 in. exposure roof, these should be 6 in. or wider. Two lines are marked on the shingles on the roof 5 in. back from the center line of the ridge on each side. On small houses, hips may be made narrower, the two lines being spaced 3 in. back from the center line.

RE-ROOFING WITH WOOD SHINGLES

Wood shingles may be applied to old as well as new roofs, Fig. H-36. If the old roofing is in reasonably good shape, it need not be removed. Before applying new shingles, all warped, split and decayed shingles should be nailed tightly or replaced. To finish the edges of the roof, the exposed portion of the first two rows of old shingles along the eaves should be cut off with a sharp hatchet and a 1 in. wood strip nailed in this space with the outer edge flush with the eave line. Edges along the gable ends should be treated in a similar manner.

Level of the valleys should be raised by applying wood strips, over which new flashings should be installed. Hips and ridges should be removed to provide a solid base for new shingles. New shingles should be spaced 1/4 in. apart to allow for expansion in wet weather and allowed to project 1/2 to 3/4 in. beyond the edge of the eaves.

FOLLOW NEW ROOFING PROCEDURE

Usual good practice as described for new roofs should be followed, except that longer nails are required. For 16 in. and 18 in. shingles, rust-resistant or zinc clad 5d "box" nails or special over-roofing nails 1 3/4 in. long, 14 gauge, should be used. The use of 6d rust-resistant nails 13 gauge is desirable for the application of 24 in. shingles.

H-35. Preventing drip from gables. A length of bevel siding is nailed along the edge and parallel with the end rafter, with the thinner edge of the siding inward, giving the shingles a slight tilt away from the edge.

No particular attention need be given the manner in which the nails penetrate the old roof beneath—whether they strike the sheathing strips or not because, with the larger nails that are used, complete penetration is obtained through the old shingles and a sufficient number of nails to anchor all the shingles of the new roof securely will strike sheathing or nailing strips.

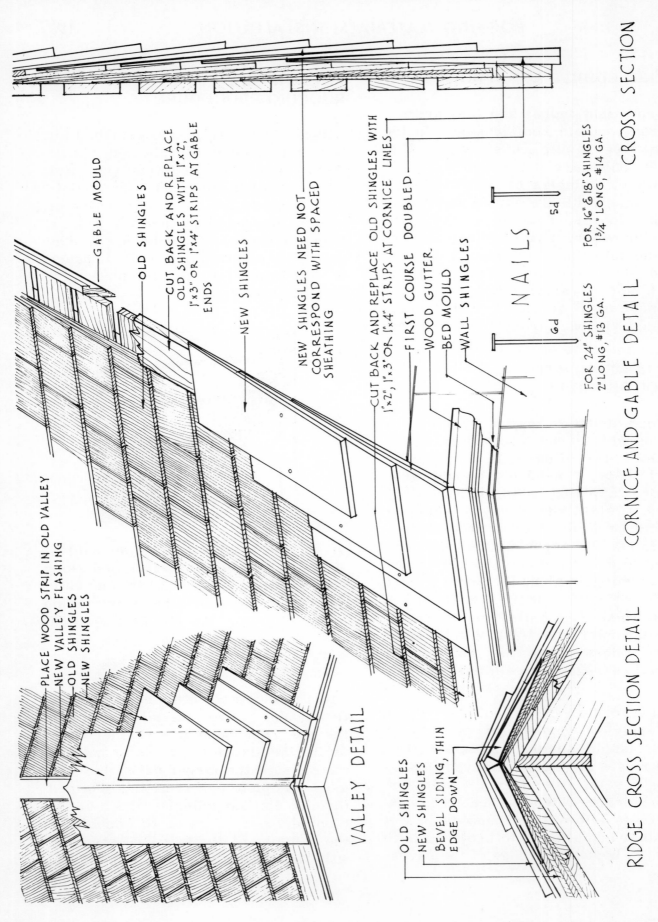

RIDGE CROSS SECTION DETAIL   CORNICE AND GABLE DETAIL   CROSS SECTION

H-36. Red cedar shingle over-roofing.

GABLE MOULD

OLD SHINGLES

CUT BACK AND REPLACE OLD SHINGLES WITH 1"×2", 1"×3" OR 1"×4" STRIPS AT GABLE ENDS

NEW SHINGLES

NEW SHINGLES NEED NOT CORRESPOND WITH SPACED SHEATHING

CUT BACK AND REPLACE OLD SHINGLES WITH 1"×2", 1"×3" OR 1"×4" STRIPS AT CORNICE LINES

FIRST COURSE DOUBLED

WOOD GUTTER

BED MOULD

WALL SHINGLES

NAILS

5d

6d

FOR 24" SHINGLES 2" LONG, #13 GA.

FOR 16" & 18" SHINGLES 1¾" LONG, #14 GA.

PLACE WOOD STRIP IN OLD VALLEY
NEW VALLEY FLASHING
OLD SHINGLES
NEW SHINGLES

VALLEY DETAIL

OLD SHINGLES
NEW SHINGLES
BEVEL SIDING, THIN EDGE DOWN

New flashings should be placed around chimneys without removing the old, liberal use being made of a high grade non-drying mastic to obtain water-tight seal between the brick and the metal.

ROOFING OVER COMPOSITION COVERED ROOFS

In re-roofing houses covered with composition material, whether in the form of roll roofing or imitation shingles, it is usually best to strip off the old material. Otherwise, moisture may condense on the roof deck below and result in rapid decay of sheathing.

ADVANTAGES OF STAINED SHINGLES

Stained shingles offer a choice of color, reduction in rate of expansion and contraction of the shingles and a reduction in the rate of mechanical wear, if the stain is renewed at proper intervals.

Shingle stain should be quite thin so it can be applied evenly and quickly without leaving sages, and it should always be applied when the shingles are thoroughly dry. Red and brown colors have the best lasting qualities. Shingle stains are comparatively inexpensive and can be renewed at small cost when they become dull or dirty.

ASBESTOS CEMENT SHINGLES

Like other asbestos cement products, asbestos cement shingles are manufactured from Portland cement and asbestos fiber and are formed in molds under high pressure. The finished product is immune to rot and decay, unharmed by exposure to salt air, unaffected by ice or snow and completely fireproof because it contains nothing that will burn.

Asbestos shingles are available in a variety of colors and textures and may be obtained in rectangular, square

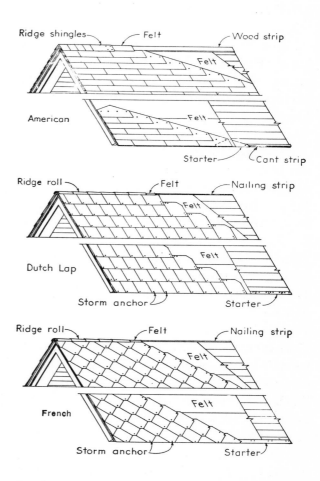

H-37. Asbestos-cement shingles. Top —Rectangular, American; Center— Square, side lap or Dutch lap; Below— Hexagonal, French.

and hexagonal shape, in single or multiple units, Fig. H-37. They are sold by the square, which means sufficient shingles to cover 100 square feet of surface and are equally well adapted for use on new buildings or over old roofs. On old roofs the new shingles can usually be applied right over the old roof, saving the cost of removing the old shingles and giving the roof the added insulation of the old roofing.

ASBESTOS ROOFING ACCESSORIES

Eave Starters, Hip and Ridge Shingles, Ridge Rolls—These items are made especially to simplify the application of asbestos cement shingles. They are purchased separately.

Roofing Felts—No. 15 asphalt saturated felt is used to cover new roof decks before asbestos shingles are laid. The asphalt-saturated felt comes in a three-square roll.

Nails—Galvanized needle-point nails are recommended. For new roofs use 1 1/4 in. nails. When re-roofing over old shingles, use 2 in. nails.

Asbestos Shingle Cutter—Dealers handling asbestos cement shingles should have several shingle cutters on hand for the use of customers. They cut the shingles quickly, accurately and neatly. They also have a punch for punching nail holes wherever necessary. These cutters can be used right on the roof.

Ripper—A ripper is a standard roofer's tool made to be slipped between two courses of shingles. It is used to cut off the nails holding the upper shingle so that it may be removed for replacement.

STORING ASBESTOS SHINGLES

While still packed in bundles, whether in the yard or on the job, asbestos shingles should be kept absolutely dry. Moisture trapped between bundled shingles may cause discoloration due to efflorescence, or what ordinarily is known as blooming. Keep the bundles in a dry place, or if necessary to pile them outdoors, stack them on planks to keep them off the ground and cover them with roofing felt, waterproof paper or a tarpaulin.

APPLY ON DRY ROOF

Asbestos shingles should not be applied on a wet or damp roof deck. When a job is left partially completed, felt should be laid over the upper applied course of shingles to prevent rain from running down underneath the shingles.

Lay shingles in dry weather. Ventilate new buildings while plaster is drying by opening windows in basement or first floor and attic. This removes damp air which might cause roof deck lumber to swell or warp.

In localities subject to extreme winter weather, eave flashing is recommended. This flashing should extend back at least 12 in. up-roof beyond the inside surface of the wall and extend downward to the eave edge of the deck. In this manner occasional roof leaks caused by ice and snow "backing up" from the gutters will be prevented.

MINIMUM PITCH

The roof should have a minimum pitch of 4 in. rise to the foot of horizontal run for American Method shingles. Dutch lap, hexagonal and multiple unit shingles require at least 5 in. to the foot.

NEW WORK

It is important that the roof deck be in proper condition to receive the shingles. The lumber should be well seasoned, dry and of uniform thickness. 1 x 6 tongue-and-groove roofers are specified. No lumber used in roof deck construction should be over 8 in. wide. It must be laid tight together. Square edge lumber is not generally acceptable for roof deck construction.

Nail heads must be driven down and any high spots or edges drawn down. All rubbish, nails, chips, etc., should be removed before application is started. A wood cant strip should be applied along the eaves, flush with the lower edge, to give proper pitch for the shingles. Wood lath or a bevel cant strip the same thickness as butt edge of shingles is recommended.

For treatment at hips and ridges, hip and ridge shingles are recommended. They are cut to a flair or taper and make a waterproof, more attractive and less expensive job.

Nail a furring strip along each side of hips and ridges, butting the strips at the apex of the ridge, in order to provide a nailing base for the hip and ridge covering. The roof shingles are butted against these furring strips;

therefore, they must be as thick as the shingles at that point and need not be over two inches wide, so they will be covered by the ridge covering.

On new jobs or on re-roofing jobs where the old roofing has been removed and sheathing made solid, the roof boards should be covered with one course of waterproof sheathing paper. Horizontal laps need not be over 2 in. End laps should be 6 in., and at hips, ridges and valleys felt shall be lapped 12 in. so double thickness will be assured at these points.

CUTTING SHINGLES

When cutting asbestos shingles, it is recommended an asbestos shingle cutter be used. These cutters can be taken up on the roof and have attachments for punching additional holes and notching. If a cutter is not available, asbestos shingles are easily cut by hand. Use an old chisel, a drift punch, or the blade of the hatchet. Score the shingle with the tool along a straight edge along the line to be cut. After scoring, place the shingle over a solid piece of wood and break off along scored line.

Asbestos shingles can be sawed with a carpenter's cross cut, 6-8 points to the inch, or with a coarse hack saw.

Irregular cuts or round holes are made by punching holes along the line of the cut and breaking out the piece which is to be discarded. There is a punch on the shingle cutter for punching additional holes, or they may be drilled or punched with a drift punch or other suitable pointed tool. A drift punch is recommended because it will punch a clean hole without splitting the material.

Care should be exercised in applying valley flashings. First, a corrosion resistant metal, like copper or stainless steel, should be used for valleys when an everlasting asbestos roof is being put on. Do not use aluminum. Secondly, to insure a leakproof roof, the metal valley should extend out on the roof deck well beyond the edge of the overlapping shingles and well up under the shingles on both sides. Then asbestos cement shingles should be bedded down in a layer of asphalt plastic cement for a distance of 6 in. back from the edge where the shingles end at the valley.

Open type valleys are most generally used. The edges of the metal should be turned back 1/2 in., forming a hem or water seal. The valley metal should be attached to the deck with cleats at the hem. Shingle nails should not be driven through metal valley linings. Edges of metal flashings and flanges also should be hemmed.

RE-ROOFING OVER OLD SHINGLES

2 in. long galvanized needle-point nails should be used when re-roofing over old shingles. Nail down all old shingles which are badly curled or warped. The use of underlayment material generally is not required under asbestos shingles when they are laid over old wood or asphalt shingles unless the old roof is in bad condition. Missing or badly decayed wood shingles should be renewed and the surface brought to an even plane. If the top edges or corners of the asbestos shingles do not rest on the butts of the old shingles, tilting will result. Wood strips, beveled and equal in their greatest thickness to the butts of the old wood shingles, are very satisfactory to use for leveling an old roof deck. If beveled strips are not available, nail wood lath of proper thickness against the butts of old wood shingles to correct the condition.

Remove old boards used for finishing the hips and ridges. In their place nail new 2 in. wide wood strips of the proper thickness, beveled as required to meet the condition, and nail to them the hip and ridge shingles.

Sometimes at the edge of the roof the old wood shingles are found to be in bad condition and the sheathing is not in very good shape. A substantial and more attractive job can be had by cutting away the old shingles and laying a new board 4 to 6 in. wide by 7/8 in. thick along the edges. This gives a solid base to which the new shingles will be nailed.

Build up old valleys with wood strips of a width and thickness adequate to bring them flush with the butts of the old wood shingles. Lay waterproof felt over hips, ridges and at valleys.

TILE ROOFINGS

The most commonly used roofing tile are manufactured products consisting of molded, hard-burned shale or mixtures of shale and clay. Metal tile is also available.

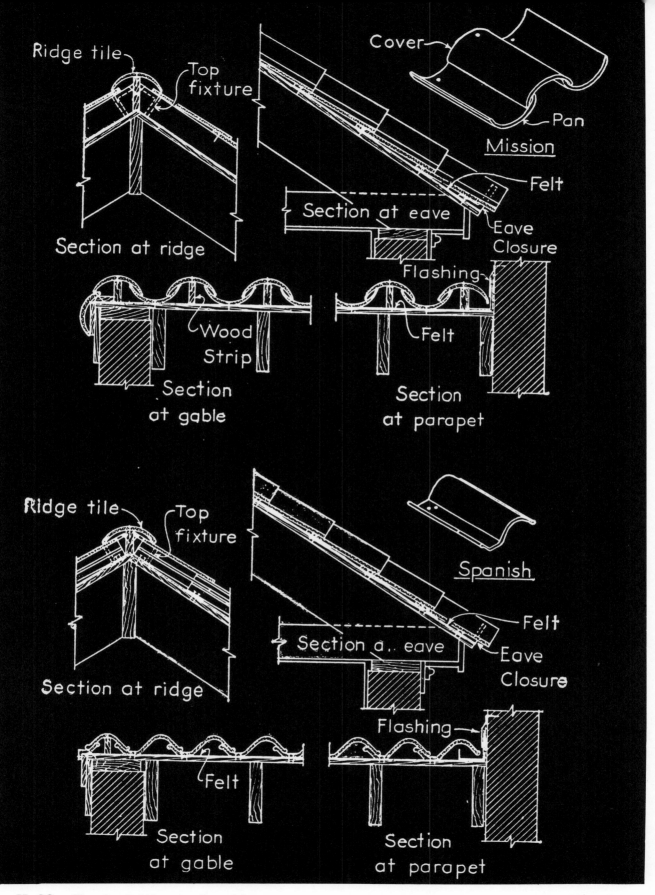

Ridge tile

Top fixture

Cover

Pan

Mission

Section at ridge

Felt

Section at eave

Eave Closure

Flashing

Wood Strip

Felt

Section at gable

Section at parapet

Ridge tile

Top fixture

Spanish

Section at ridge

Felt

Section at eave

Eave Closure

Felt

Flashing

Section at gable

Section at parapet

H-38. Typical tile roofs: Above, two piece pan and cover, known as Mission style. Below, Spanish tile.

When well made, clay tile is hard, fairly dense and durable, and may be obtained in a variety of shapes and textures. Most roofing tile of clay is unglazed, although glazed tile is sometimes used.

Typical tile roofs are shown in Fig. H-38.

TILE MAY BE USED
OVER OLD ROOF

Clay tile may be used over an old roof provided the old covering is in reasonably good condition, and the roof framing is heavy enough to stand the additional weight. Additional roof framing or bracing, if required, should be added before starting with the application of the tile.

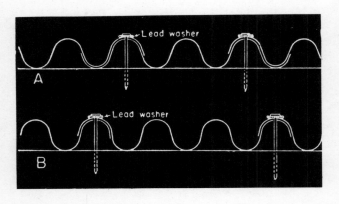

H-39. Applying corrugated sheet metal roofing. A. Sheets properly laid. B. Corrugated sheets improperly laid. Corrugated sheets properly applied make a tight roof. One corrugation laps (B) are likely to leak during driving storms.

GALVANIZED SHEET METAL
ROOFING

Only galvanized sheets that are heavily coated with zinc (2.0 oz. per sq. ft.) are recommended for permanent-type construction. Sheets with lighter coatings of zinc are less durable and are likely to require painting every few years.

On temporary buildings and in cases where strict economy is essential the use of cheaper metal is sometimes justifiable, and will give good results if kept protected by paint. Metallic zinc paint and Venetian red and oil are generally recommended for the purpose.

ROOF PITCH REQUIREMENTS

Galvanized sheets may be laid on slopes as low as a 3 in. rise to the foot (1/8 pitch). If more than one sheet is required to reach the top of the roof, the ends should lap not less than 8 in. On 1/4 and 1/3 pitch roofs, from 4 to 3 in. end laps are usually satisfactory.

MAKING TIGHT ROOFS

To make a tight roof, sheets should be lapped 1 1/2 corrugations at either side, Fig. H-39. The wind is likely to drive rain water over single-corrugation lap joints.

When using roofing 27 1/2 in. wide with 2 1/2 in. corrugations and 1 1/2 corrugation lap, each sheet covers a net width of 24 in. on the roof.

If 27 1/2 in. roofing is not available, sheets of 26 in. in width may be used. In laying the narrower sheets every other one should be turned upside down. So laid, each alternate sheet laps over the two intermediate sheets. The 26 in. roofing with 2 1/2 in. corrugations cover a net width of 22 1/4 in. of roof.

Several types of ridge-drain types of galvanized sheets are on the market. Of these, the ones in which the bends are well rounded promise to be more durable than those bent at sharp angles because heavy zinc coating on sharp bends tends to crack.

SHEATHING FOR CORRUGATED ROOFING

If 26-gauge sheets are used, supports may be 24 in. apart. If 28-gauge sheets are used, supports should be not more than 12 in. apart. The heavier sheets have no particular advantage except their added strength, because the zinc coating is what gives this type roofing its durability.

USE LEAD-HEAD NAILS

For best results, galvanized sheets should be fastened with lead-headed nails or galvanized nails and lead washers. Nails properly located are driven only into tops of the crimps or corrugations. Nails specified by the manufacturer should be used to avoid unnecessary corrosion.

PATCHING HOLES

Small holes in metal roofs may be filled with drops of solder. A large hole may be covered with a piece of the same metal as the roof and the piece soldered in place.

RE-ROOFING WITH CORRUGATED METAL ROOFING

In most cases, a sheet metal roof may be placed over old roofing if the old roof is first repaired so the new roofing will have a smooth surface. Some manufacturers recommend that asbestos felt be laid over the deck before roofing is applied to either old or new roofs. Resin felt and asphalt-saturated felts are also suitable for the purpose. Tar papers or papers which contain any trace of acid should never be used as they may cause the under side of the metal to corrode.

ALUMINUM ROOFING

Corrugated aluminum roofing, if properly applied, usually makes a long-lasting roof.

Seacoast exposure tests reported by the Bureau of Standards indicate this material is capable of resisting corrosion in such localities unless subjected to direct spraying by the salt-laden spray from the ocean. Where this is likely to happen, aluminum roofing cannot be recommended.

Aluminum alloy sheets available for roofing usually have 1 1/4 or 2 1/2 in. corrugations. Precautions given in connection with the application of sheet metal regarding side lap and end lap are also applicable to the laying of aluminum sheets.

As aluminum is soft and the sheets used for roofing are relatively thin, they should be laid on tight sheathing or on decks with openings no more than 6 in. wide. Aluminum roofing should be nailed with not less than 90 nails to a square or about one nail for each square foot.

It is recommended that aluminum alloy nails be used and that non-metallic washers be used between nail heads and the roofing.

If desired, the sheathing may be covered with water-resistant building paper or asphalt impregnated felt.

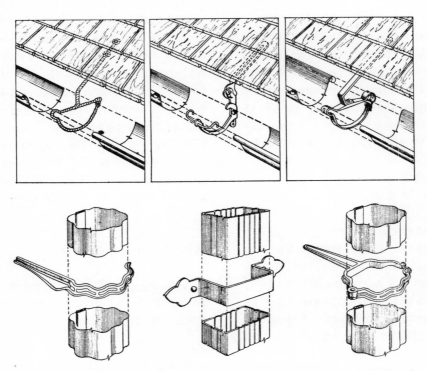

H-40. Hanging metal eaves troughs with typical hangers; also typical downspout fasteners.

The Bureau of Standards suggests that an important precaution to observe in laying aluminum roofing is to make sure that contact with other kinds of metal is avoided. Where this is not possible both metals should be given a heavy coating of asphalt paint at the contact surfaces.

Paper that absorbs and holds water should never be used.

STORING ALUMINUM ROOFING

To avoid corrosion, aluminum sheets should be stored so that air will have free access to all sides; otherwise a white deposit will form and they will deteriorate.

GUTTERS AND DOWNSPOUTS

Gutters or eaves troughs not only prevent dripping of rainwater all around a building but also have a direct relation to durability of foundation.

Eaves troughs on dwellings are sometimes built into the roof and their construction combined with that of the cornice. This arrangement, however, almost invariably gives trouble because of leakage and the formation of ice, and is not recommended.

WOOD GUTTERS

Wood gutters of Douglas fir or red cedar are used in many parts of the country. Such gutters do not corrode or rust and, barring accidents, usually last as long as the house.

When the White House was remodeled in 1927, wood gutter was removed which had been in use 110 years and was still sound and serviceable.

INSTALLING WOOD GUTTER

Wood gutter is most easily erected while the scaffolding is still in place

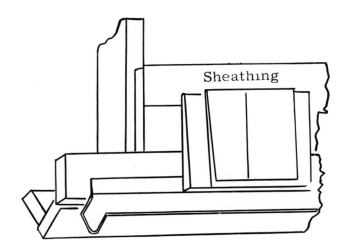

H-41. Metal gutter with flange which overlaps sheathing.

Simple hanging metal eaves trough, Fig. H-40, is less expensive and in general more desirable. Gutters with flanges overlapping the sheathing, Fig. H-41, are also practical. Wood gutters have certain advantages as will be explained in the following paragraphs.

and before the roof is shingled. See Fig. H-42. Cutting, fitting and drilling for nailing is best done on the ground. 16d galvanized nails should be used. For a tight job, white lead should be spread onto ends before the ends are attached, and a permanently flexible

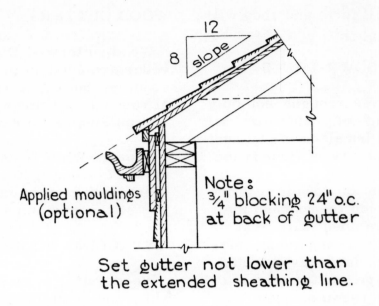

12

8 / slope

Applied mouldings
(optional)

Note:
¾" blocking 24" o.c.
at back of gutter

Set gutter not lower than
the extended sheathing line.

H-42. Installing wood gutter. This drawing shows how to determine the proper height of gutter under normal conditions. For very steep roof slopes, it should be set higher in order to catch all the water rushing off the roof.

calking compound applied to grooves at each joint.

Gutter ends may be sealed with blocks, re-turned and mitered, or butted against the extended rake frieze. Any one of these methods will create a trim appearance. In general, the gutter may be treated exactly as the cornice moulding it replaces. See Fig. H-43.

The gutter may be placed directly against the fascia, Fig. H-44, if flashing is carried from the inside of the gutter up over the edge of the roof sheathing several inches under the shingles. By setting the gutter out away from the face of the building, the need for expensive apron flashing is eliminated. In cold climates where ice will form on the roof it is best to block the gutter out away from the

fascia by nailing 3/8 in. or thicker strips on the back before erection, about 24 in. apart.

Shingles should project an inch or more beyond the eaves. The lip or front top edge of the trough should be at approximately the height of the roof sheathing line extended.

For correct cornice appearance, gutters must be set level. Level gutters will drain perfectly if adequate downspouts are provided and the trough kept clean.

Joints and splices should be cut accurately, fitted tightly and the segments held together with long brass screws having countersunk heads.

Downspout connections are made by cutting a hole through the gutter and inserting a sleeve of sheet metal, or pipe nipple which fits into the downspout. Care should be taken to locate the downspouts for best appearance. These should be sufficient in number and large enough to carry away the water capacity of the gutter. Wooden downspouts are preferable.

Gutters should be primed on the outside with white lead and linseed oil before erection. The inside of the trough should be primed with oil only and not painted. Saturate all cuts and raw ends with pure linseed oil and seal joints with white lead, roofing cement or calking compound.

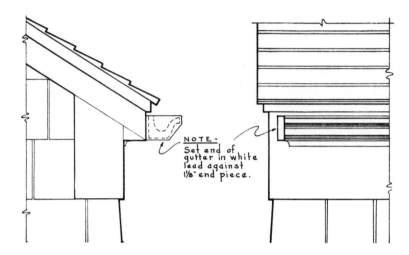

NOTE-
Set end of gutter in white lead against 1⅛" end piece.

H-43. Wood gutter applied to box cornice.

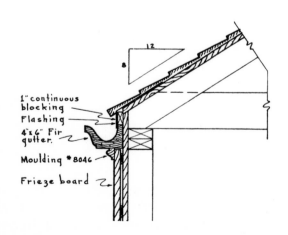

1" continuous blocking
Flashing
4"x6" Fir gutter.
Moulding #8046
Frieze board

H-44. Wood gutter placed directly against fascia, or without blocking at the back. To offset the projection lost by elimination of blocking, it is raised up closer under the shingles. This produces a tight, attractive cornice; but in cold climates where ice will form, it is not recommended. Note how flashing is run from inside of gutter and up under shingles.

SIZE SHOULD CORRESPOND
TO ROOF AREA

For best results, the size of eave troughs must correspond to the roof areas from which they receive water. For roof areas up to 750 sq. ft. a 4 in. wide trough is suitable. For areas between 750 and 1400 sq. ft., 5 in. troughs should be used. For larger areas a 6 in. trough is recommended. Quality of eaves troughs, like that of flashing, should correspond to the durability of the roof covering. If galvanized steel is used, it should have a heavy zinc coating.

Metal eaves troughs or gutters should be sloped 1 in. in 12 to 16 ft. of gutter length.

The size of downspouts or conductor pipes also depends upon the roof area. For roofs up to 1,000 sq. ft., downspouts of 3 in. diameter are okay. For larger roofs, 4 in. downspouts should be used.

Provision should be made to drain the water well away from foundation.

Thermal, Sound Insulation

Insulation used in building construction is of two principal types, thermal or heat insulation, and sound insulation.

HOW HEAT IS TRANSFERRED

Heat seeks a balance with surrounding areas, just as water flows from a high to a low level. When occupied buildings are heated to maintain inside temperature in the comfort range, there is a difference in temperature between the inside and outside.

Heat is transferred through walls, floors, ceilings, windows and doors at a rate that bears some relation to the temperature difference, and to the resistance to heat flow of intervening materials. Transfer of heat takes place by one or more of three methods--conduction, convection, and radiation.

CONDUCTION: Transmission of heat through solid materials, like through an aluminum cooking utensil when the bottom is heated.

CONVECTION: Term applied to transfer of heat by air currents from a warm zone to a cooler zone, like air moving across a hot radiator carrying heat to other parts of a room.

RADIATION: Heat may be transmitted from a warm body to a cold body by wave motion through space. This process is called radiation because it represents radiant energy. Heat obtained from the sun is radiant heat. The waves do not heat the space through which they move, but when they come in contact with a colder object a part of the radiant energy is absorbed and converted into sensible heat and part is reflected.

THERMAL INSULATION

All materials used to enclose walls, roofs and floors of dwellings and air spaces offer some resistance to the transfer of heat from the warm side to the cold side. Some materials used serve as sheathing, or as wall coverings and at the same time have low resistance to heat transfer. The addition of material high in resistance to heat transfer, namely insulation, reduces heat movement through the enclosing surfaces and thereby improves comfort conditions. In cold climates insulation, properly used, materially reduces fuel consumption.

J-1. Blanket or quilt insulation.

J-2. Loose-fill insulation.

TYPES OF INSULATION

Insulation is made in a variety of forms and types, and may be grouped into four broad classes: (1) Flexible, (2) Loose fill, (3) Rigid and (4) Reflective.

FLEXIBLE INSULATION

Flexible insulation is manufactured in two types: Blanket or quilt, and batt. See Fig. J-1. Blanket insulation is generally furnished in rolls or strips of convenient length and in various widths suited to standard stud and joist spacing. It comes in thicknesses of 1 to 3 inches.

The body of the blanket is made of loosely felted mats of mineral or vegetable fibers, such as rock, slag, glass wool, wood fiber, cotton, eel grass, cattle hair, etc. Organic fiber mats are usually treated chemically to make them resistant to fire, decay, insects and vermin. Blanket insulation is usually enclosed in paper covers with tabs on the side for attachment. The covering sheet on one side may be treated to serve as a vapor

barrier. In some cases the covering sheet is surfaced with aluminum foil or other reflective insulation.

Batt insulation is made of a similar fibrous material preformed to a definite thickness, 2 to 3 5/8 in., in widths to suit 16 in. stud spacing, and in 24, and 48 in. lengths. It is furnished both with and without a paper facing.

LOOSE FILL INSULATION

Loose fill insulation is usually composed of materials used in bulk form, supplied in bags or bales, and may be poured or blown into place, or placed by hand, Fig. J-2. It is used to fill spaces and between studs and to build up any desired thickness on horizontal surfaces.

Loose fill insulation is made from such materials as rock, glass, slag wool, wood fibers, shredded redwood bark, granulated cork, ground or macerated wood pulp products, vermiculite, perlite, powdered gypsum, sawdust and wood shavings.

In insulating an old house only a

few boards need be taken out in order to blow loose-fill insulation into the walls.

J-3. Rigid board insulation.

RIGID INSULATION

Rigid insulation, Fig. J-3, as ordinarily used in residence construction, is made by reducing wood, cane, or other fiber to a pulp and then assembling the pulp into lightweight or low-density boards that combine strength with heat and acoustical insulating properties.

Rigid insulation is available in a wide range of sizes, from tile 8 in. square, to sheets 4 ft. wide and 10 ft. or more long. Insulating boards are usually 1/2 in. to 1 in. in thickness. Boards of greater thickness are made by laminating together boards of standard thickness.

Insulating boards are used for many purposes including roof and wall sheathing; as a subfloor; interior surface of walls and ceilings; base for plaster, linoleum or wallpaper.

Insulating boards should not be confused with ordinary wallboard, which is more tightly compressed and has less insulating value. Sheathing board ordinarily comes in two thicknesses, 1/2 and 25/32 in. and in 2 x 8 ft. sheets for horizontal application, and 4 x 8 sheets or longer for vertical application.

Lath are made in 1/2 and 1 in. thicknesses, in sheets 16 x 48 in. Some lath are supplied with an asphalt coating intended to serve as a vapor barrier. For inside walls and ceiling finish you can get insulating board finished on one side with a wide variety of finishes.

REFLECTIVE INSULATION

Reflective insulation, which is usually a metal foil, or foil-surfaced material, differs from other insulating materials in that the number of reflecting surfaces, not the thickness of the material, determines its insulating value. In order to be effective,

COMPLETE END TO END INSULATION

J-4. Aluminum foil "accordion" insulation.

the metal foil must be exposed to an air space, preferably 3/4 in. or more in width.

Aluminum foil is available in sheets

mounted on paper, in corrugated form supported on paper, mounted on the back of gypsum lath, paper-backed wire lath, multiple spaced sheets (accordion insulation) Fig. J-4, and in various other forms.

MISCELLANEOUS INSULATION

There are available on the market today many insulations which do not fit in the classifications covered previously in this section, such as confettilike material mixed with adhesive and sprayed on the surface to be insulated; multiple layers of corrugated paper; light weight aggregates like vermiculite and perlite used in plaster to reduce heat transmission. Light weight aggregates made from blast-furnace slag, burned-clay products and cinders are used in concrete and concrete blocks.

Also available is plastic foam insulation, Fig. J-5. This bonds to masonry walls with Portland cement mortar. Plaster keys directly to the surface.

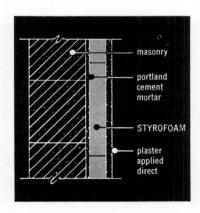

J-5. Plastic foam insulation.

WHERE TO INSULATE

To reduce heat loss from the house during cold weather, all walls, ceilings, roofs, and floors that separate heated from unheated spaces should be insulated. See Fig. J-6.

Insulation should be placed on all outside walls and in the ceiling. In houses involving unheated crawl spaces, insulation should be placed

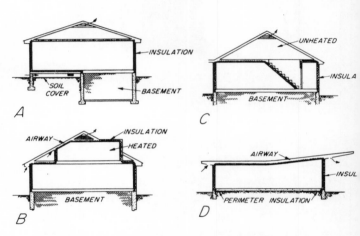

J-6. Placement of insulation. A, In walls, floor and ceiling. B, In 1 1/2 story house. C, At attic door. D, In flat roof.

between the floor joists. If a bulk type of insulation is used, it should be well supported by slats and a galvanized mesh wire or by a rigid board. Reflective insulation is often used for insulation of crawl spaces. Crawl spaces, as well as attic spaces, should be ventilated. A ground cover of roll roofing may also be placed on the soil of crawl spaces to decrease the moisture content of the space.

In 1 1/2-story houses insulation

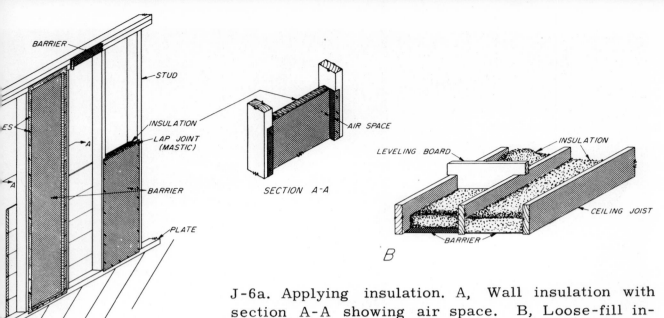

J-6a. Applying insulation. A, Wall insulation with section A-A showing air space. B, Loose-fill insulation

should be placed along all areas that are adjacent to unheated areas.

In flat or low-pitched houses insulation should be used in the ceiling area with sufficient space allowed above for a clear ventilating area between the joists. Insulation should be used along the perimeter of houses built on slabs. A vapor barrier should be included under the slab.

Insulation can be used effectively to improve comfort conditions within the house during hot weather.

Where any system of cooling hot-weather air is used, insulation should be used in all exposed ceilings and walls in the same manner as for preventing heat loss in cold weather.

Ventilation of attic and roof spaces is an important adjunct to insulation. Without ventilation, an attic space may become very hot and hold the heat for many hours.

INSTALLATION OF INSULATION

Blanket insulation should be placed between framing members so that the tabs lap all edges, including both bottom and top plates, Fig. J-6a.

Batt insulation is also placed between framing members (studs or joists) and is fastened with staples. Because of the shorter lengths of the batts, they should be placed so that the barriers lap each other and the lap should be sealed. When batts do not include a vapor barrier, the barrier should be stapled to framing members from bottom to top plate.

Reflective insulation, when used in a single-sheet form should be placed so as to divide the space formed by the framing members into two approximately equal spaces. Some reflective insulations include air spaces and are furnished with nailing tabs.

Fill insulation is poured or blown

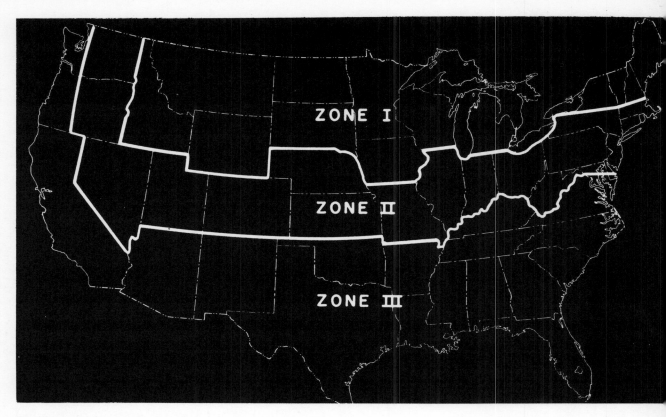

J-7. Condensation zones—Zone I roughly includes the areas with design temperatures -20 degrees F. and colder; zone II 0 degrees to -10 degrees F; and zone III areas warmer than 0 degrees F.

into place. A vapor barrier should be used on the warm side (the bottom, in case of ceiling joists) before insulation is placed. A leveling board may be used, as shown, to give a constant insulation thickness. Thick batts are also used between ceiling joists.

Rigid fiberboard insulation sheets should be nailed at all studs with galvanized roofing nails, or other non-corrosive nails.

KEEPING INSULATION DRY

If you live in the northern part of the country—any section where the average temperature in January is 35 degrees F. or less—you may need to install a vapor barrier to protect the insulation from dampness.

Warm air in the kitchen, bathroom and laundry will carry more moisture than the cold air outside.

Dew does not usually form on walls and ceiling of a well-insulated house, but it may condense in the insulation in the walls or on the sheathing or siding. Insulation and wood then become damp. In time the dampness may cause the wood to rot and the paint to peel off.

Correct use of a vapor barrier (membrane through which water vapor does not readily pass) and proper ventilation make it possible to have tightly-constructed, well insulated houses without wall condensation.

BASEMENTLESS HOUSE TROUBLE

In basementless houses without crawl space, ventilation or soil cover, outside walls, plate, sills and adjoining joists exposed in the crawl space are often cooled to temperatures below the dew point in the enclosed space. When this happens water often condenses on the surfaces in sufficient quantity to produce conditions favorable to decay.

MATERIALS TO USE

A number of satisfactory materials or combination of materials are available which restrict the movement of water vapor. These include asphalt impregnated and coated papers having a glossy or bright finish. Duplex papers composed of two sheets of 30-pound kraft paper with a 60-pound per 3,000 square feet asphalt layer between them; aluminum foil mounted on one or two sides of a paper support, or attached to a plaster base; aluminum paint, oil paint or rubber base in sufficient coats to result in a smooth glossy finish are materials that may be expected to give good results.

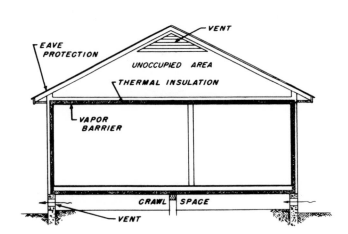

J-8. Basementless house, one-story. Condensation control is effected by the use of a vapor barrier near the warm surface of outside walls and ceilings and floors and by ventilation of the attic and crawl spaces. The vapor barrier in the floor below the thermal insulation protects the finish floor from dampness that might exist in the crawl space and in this case the barrier should be placed below the finish floor. Vapor barriers should be provided in condensation zone I for ceilings, walls, and floors; in zone II for walls and floors; and in zone III for floors. Ventilation should be provided in the side walls of the crawl space for all three zones. Thermal insulation should be included in all walls, ceilings and floors of condensation zones I and II. Eave protection in the form of one course of roll roofing is recommended for zones I and II where wood or composition shingles are used. In zones I and II ice dams may form over the eaves causing water to back between the shingles and into the building.

SHEATHING REQUIREMENTS

In contrast to the vapor-tight properties of the warm side of a wall, those of the cold side are opposite in that a construction capable of losing moisture that might enter the wall is highly desirable.

The exterior surface must of course provide protection from the weather . . . resistance to rain and strong winds, but in order that as little restriction as possible to the release of moisture be built into a wall, the sheathing paper and the sheathing used should be of types that will readily transmit water vapor.

VENTILATION HELPS CONTROL CONDENSATION

Ventilation in proper amounts is a recognized means of controlling con-

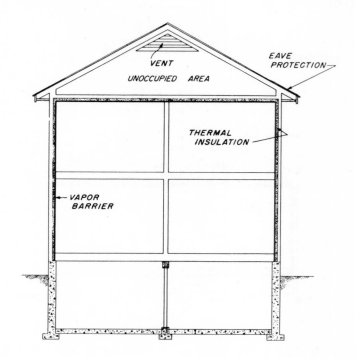

J-9. Two-story house with basement. Condensation control is obtained by means of a vapor barrier and ventilation. The vapor barrier should follow the inside line of the insulation and should effectively close the space between first- and second-floor joists. Vapor barriers should be provided in condensation zone I for ceilings and walls, and in zone II for walls. Ventilation for the attic space should be provided in all three zones. Thermal insulation should be applied to form an envelope around the heated living quarters above the basement in zones I and II. Eave protection in the form of roll roofing is recommended below shingles and over eaves in zones I and II. In zones I and II ice dams sometimes form over eaves causing water from melting snow or rain to back into the house.

densation in buildings. It is especially effective in preventing condensation in unheated attics, spaces below flat roofs and crawl spaces in basement-less houses.

Attic spaces are sometimes a cause of trouble because of condensation on roof boards, shingles or on long nails extending through the attic roof. Where attic floor is well insulated, providing

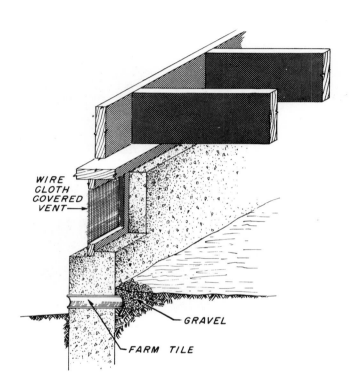

WIRE CLOTH COVERED VENT

GRAVEL

FARM TILE

J-10. Basementless house, crawl space ventilation. The shallow space between the soil and floor joists in basementless houses in some cases may become very damp because of evaporation from the soil surface. Under such conditions a high moisture content will occur in adjacent woodwork and water will condense on sills, joists, and other parts near the outside wall when outside temperatures drop rapidly. Condensation control in this detail depends on ventilation. At least four vents should be used and they should preferably be placed near the corners of the building. The openings should be placed as high as possible since there is likely to be less obstruction to interfere with air movement. In northern climates the floor of the living quarters should be adequately insulated so that the ventilators can be left open all the year. If the building is located on a sloping site, drain tiles on the low side are suggested to permit water to drain from the crawl space. Stones piled over the tile opening will prevent the entrance of small animals but will permit water to escape. Plumbing pipes should be insulated.

adequate ventilation is a safeguard against condensation difficulties.

CONDENSATION CONTROL DETAILS

In Fig. J-7 is shown condensation zones. Figs. J-8 to J-23 inclusive give one construction detail with a description to indicate the proper arrangement of vapor barriers, ventilation openings and other collateral materials. Items not pertinent to points being discussed have been omitted.

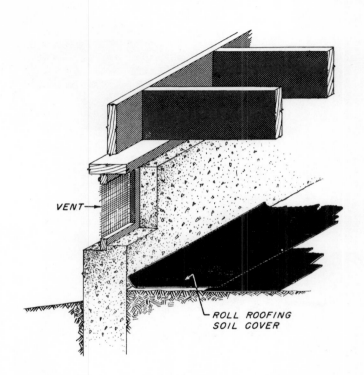

VENT →

ROLL ROOFING
SOIL COVER

J-11. Basementless house, crawl space with soil cover. Condensation control is obtained by means of roll roofing weighing at least 55 pounds per 108 square feet laid over the surface of the soil with edges lapping at least 2 in. and supplemented by ventilation. The soil need not be perfectly smooth for the roofing material will become soft and will conform to the contour of the soil within a short time. Covers of this kind greatly restrict the evaporation of water and somewhat less ventilation is needed than when no covers are used. The soil surface below the building should be above the outside grade if there is a chance that water might get inside the foundation wall. The soil cover is especially valuable where the water table is continually near the surface, or the soil has high capillarity.

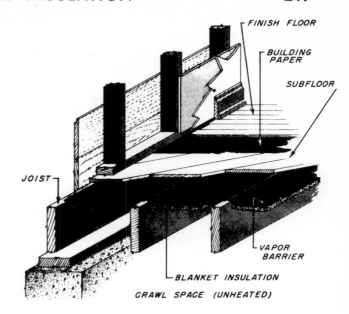

J-12. Basementless house, floor detail. Condensation control in this detail requires the blanket insulation to be provided with a vapor barrier of good quality to prevent excessive water vapor in a damp crawl space from reaching the finish floor.

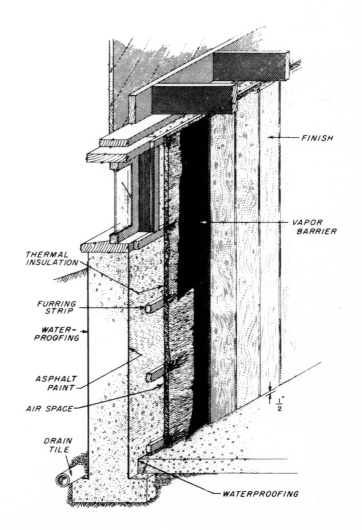

J-13. Outside basement wall, decorative finish. In some houses it is desired to make use of a room in the basement for recreational purposes and in the northern part of the United States this involves a summer condensation problem. Condensation control is obtained by a vapor barrier placed behind the wood surface, running parallel to the furring strips and lapped only over solid supports. Its purpose is to prevent accumulation of free water behind the ornamental panel.

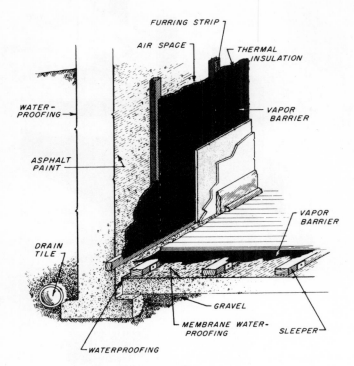

FURRING STRIP

AIR SPACE

THERMAL INSULATION

VAPOR BARRIER

WATER-PROOFING

ASPHALT PAINT

DRAIN TILE

VAPOR BARRIER

GRAVEL

MEMBRANE WATER-PROOFING

SLEEPER

WATERPROOFING

J-14. Outside basement wall, plaster finish, floor treatment. Special attention in this detail is given to the construction of the floor.

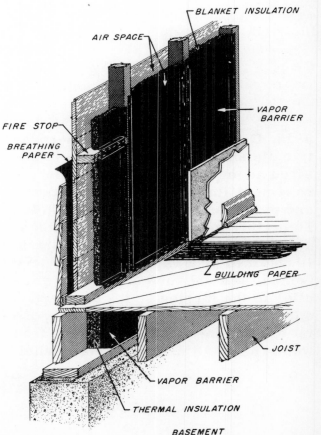

BLANKET INSULATION

AIR SPACE

FIRE STOP

BREATHING PAPER

VAPOR BARRIER

BUILDING PAPER

JOIST

VAPOR BARRIER

THERMAL INSULATION

BASEMENT

J-15. Side wall, first-floor level, fire stop. Condensation control is obtained in this detail by the continuous vapor barrier attached to the blanket-type insulation and by thoroughly closing the openings at the top and bottom of the stud spaces or other horizontal obstruction, such as fire stops.

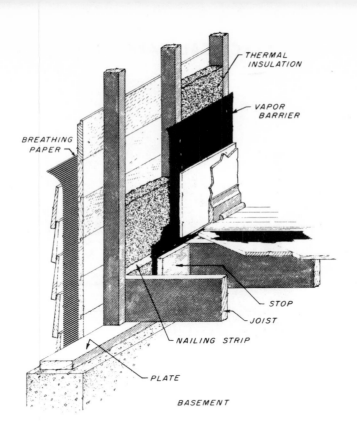

J-16. Side wall, first-floor level. Condensation control in this detail is obtained by the use of a vapor barrier placed over the studs and extending down between the joists and stapled to a wood strip just at the line of the joist tops. A stop is necessary between the joists to support the insulation and the barrier. Since the paper covers supplied with batts are not long enough to be continuous over the height of the studs, they cannot be considered effective vapor barriers. The thermal insulation shown may be fill- or batt-type material extending below the floor line to the plate.

J-17. Junction of second floor and wall, balloon construction. The floor and ceiling areas enclosing the space between joists provide large surfaces through which water vapor can penetrate. Well-installed vapor barriers for condensation control are needed to restrict the flow of water vapor into the outside walls.

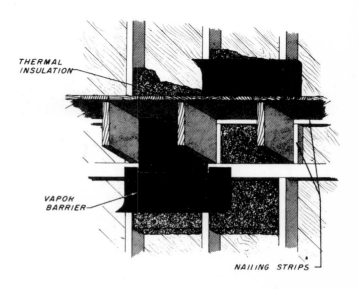

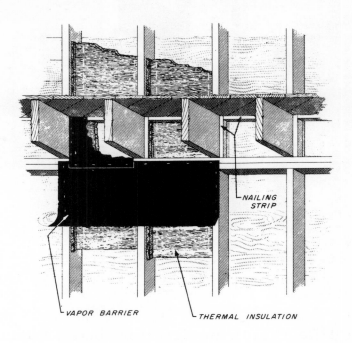

NAILING STRIP

VAPOR BARRIER   THERMAL INSULATION

J-18. Side wall, second-floor level, platform construction. Condensation control is obtained in this detail by the use of a vapor barrier over the studs. As in J-17 the protection of the space between the joists is important because of the large ceiling area feeding vapor to this section of the wall. The thermal insulation consists of a blanket type without a vapor barrier and the two air spaces.

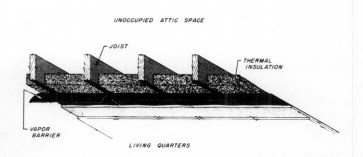

UNOCCUPIED ATTIC SPACE

JOIST   THERMAL INSULATION

VAPOR BARRIER

LIVING QUARTERS

J-19. Ceiling construction adjacent to an attic space. Condensation control is obtained through the use of a vapor barrier applied below the joists and running parallel to them prior to the attachment of the ceiling. The thermal insulation may be fill or batt type placed after the ceiling finish has been applied.

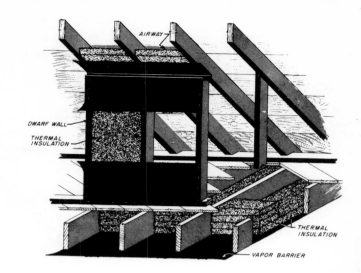

J-20. Junction of a dwarf wall with the attic, floor and roof. The vapor barrier on the floor joists provides condensation control in this detail. It covers the entire ceiling; otherwise a barrier should be installed between the joists below the dwarf wall and extending back to the outside wall.

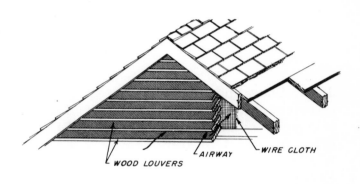

J-21. Louver-type ventilator for gable or modified hip roof. Ventilation in attic spaces is an effective means of gaining condensation control in attics. Ventilators placed near the apex of the roof are more effective than those which are placed at lower levels since warm air tends to move upward and out of the building.

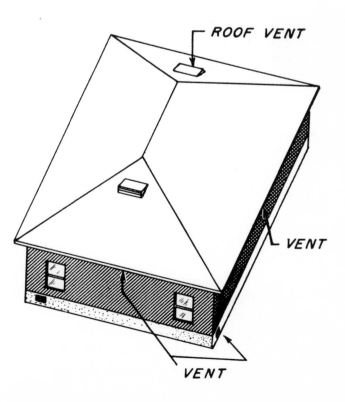

J-22. Special roof vent for hip roof. This type of construction is designed to provide condensation control in the form of roof ventilation. The detail shows a small vent that should be located near the peak of the roof and with supplementary vents below eaves.

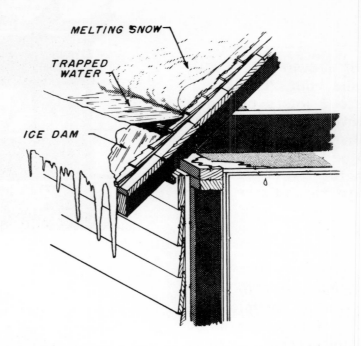

MELTING SNOW

TRAPPED WATER

ICE DAM

J-23. Snow and ice dams. Leakage of water into buildings in the Northern States (condensation zones I and II) is sometimes caused by ice dams and is often mistaken for condensation. Snow and ice dams are usually found after heavy snowfalls followed by temperatures a little below freezing when there is sufficient heat from the living quarters to cause melting along the roof surface. The water creeps down over the roof surface and, on reaching the overhang of the roof, freezes causing a ledge of ice to build up. Water reaching this ice ledge may back under and between the shingles and into the building. Corrective measures consist of a course of heavy roll roofing below the shingles reaching up beyond the wall line.

STORM SASH HELP REDUCE HEAT LOSS

Storm windows and doors, when properly installed, provide a dead air space, reducing heat conduction to the outside and preventing infiltration of cold air.

Draft felt in a room is often due to cooling of air in passing the windows. The cool air is heavier than the warm air in the rest of the room and falls to the floor and moves across the room.

WEATHERSTRIPPING CUTS HEAT LOSSES

Heat losses may be reduced considerably by weatherstripping loose-fitting windows and doors.

Metal weatherstripping of either the flat "contact" type or the interlocking type, gives much longer service than the felt type. Grooving sash for interlocking type can best be handled on a power-driven circular saw. See Fig. J-24.

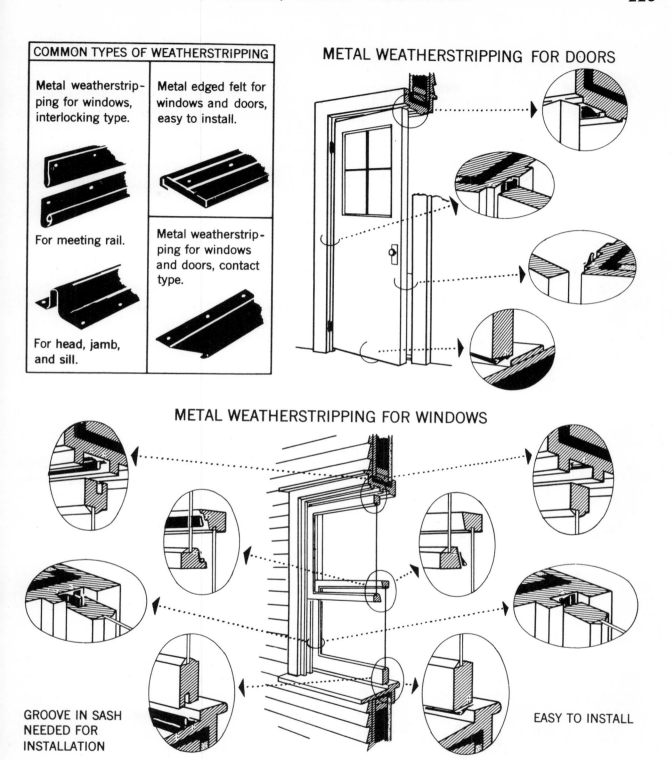

COMMON TYPES OF WEATHERSTRIPPING

Metal weatherstripping for windows, interlocking type.

For meeting rail.

For head, jamb, and sill.

Metal edged felt for windows and doors, easy to install.

Metal weatherstripping for windows and doors, contact type.

METAL WEATHERSTRIPPING FOR DOORS

METAL WEATHERSTRIPPING FOR WINDOWS

GROOVE IN SASH NEEDED FOR INSTALLATION

EASY TO INSTALL

J-24. Weatherstripping cuts heat losses through doors and windows.

Normal speech can be understood distinctly through a wall with a sound reduction factor of less than 25 DECIBELS.

Walls of 30 DECIBEL reduction will allow loud speech to be understood fairly well on the opposite side if conditions are quiet.

Loud speech is audible but not intelligible through walls of 35 DECIBELS.

Normal speech through walls of 40 DECIBELS is not audible. Loud speech can be heard faintly, but if there are some masking sounds in the room, such as a radio, nothing can be heard.

ACOUSTICS AND SOUND CONTROL

This material furnished by Practical Builder Magazine discusses principles of sound transmission; how it is measured; how transmitted through building materials; construction details on how to construct walls and ceilings with acoustical materials.

DEFINITIONS OF ACOUSTICAL TERMS

Decibel—The unit of measurement used to indicate the loudness or intensity of sound. Comparable to the degree as a measurement of heat or cold.

Reverberation Sounds — These are air-borne sounds which continue after the actual source has ceased; caused by reflections from floors, walls and ceiling.

Impact Sounds—These are the sounds that are carried through a building by the vibrations of the structural materials themselves. Footsteps heard through the floors of a structure are an example of impact sounds.

Decibels Reduction — An expression used to indicate the sound insulating properties of a wall or floor panel.

Masking Sounds—These are the normal sounds within habitable rooms which tend to "mask" some of the external sounds entering the room.

PRINCIPLES OF SOUND TRANSMISSION

The unit of measurement is called the DECIBEL and is indicative of the loudness or the intensity of the sound. Roughly speaking, the decibel unit is about the smallest change in sound that is audible to the human ear. It is important to understand this term but don't worry how it's calculated. Actually, the decibel has the same relation to a scale of loudness as the degree has to a thermometer. Reference to J-26 will show that the rustle of leaves or a low whisper is on the threshold of audibility; that is, the sound is just barely discernible to the ear. The top of the scale is a painfully loud sound of approximately 120 decibels, called the "threshold of feeling." Between these two limits is the range of ordinary sound. See Fig. J-25.

FALLACIES CORRECTED

One sound level is 10 decibels greater than another if its intensity is 10 times greater than the other. There is a logarithmic relation, on the decibel scale, to the amount of sound energy involved. If the sounds differ by 20 decibels, the ratio of their intensities is 10^2 or 100 times greater. If by 30 decibels, the ratio is 10^3 or 1,000 times greater, and so on up the scale.

There are two fallacies of sound insulation that exist in many builders' minds. One is that sound insulation depends primarily on the materials used (rather than the methods employed in construction) and the erroneous impression that materials that are good thermal insulators are therefore good sound insulators. Of course, there are exceptions in both cases.

There are two classes of sounds to be considered. The first is reverberation or air-borne sound. These are the everyday noises that are present wherever there are men, women or children. Telephone bells, typewriters, radios and machinery of all

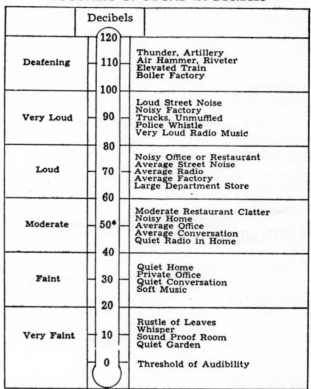

LOUDNESS OF SOUND IN DECIBELS

	Decibels	
Deafening	120 — 110 — 100	Thunder, Artillery Air Hammer, Riveter Elevated Train Boiler Factory
Very Loud	90 — 80	Loud Street Noise Noisy Factory Trucks, Unmuffled Police Whistle Very Loud Radio Music
Loud	70 — 60	Noisy Office or Restaurant Average Street Noise Average Radio Average Factory Large Department Store
Moderate	50* — 40	Moderate Restaurant Clatter Noisy Home Average Office Average Conversation Quiet Radio in Home
Faint	30 — 20	Quiet Home Private Office Quiet Conversation Soft Music
Very Faint	10 — 0	Rustle of Leaves Whisper Sound Proof Room Quiet Garden Threshold of Audibility

*Average working conditions—few places where people work are below this.

J-26. Scale showing the loudness of many typical sounds expressed in decibels. At the bottom of the scale is the threshold of audibility; that is, the degree of loudness at which sounds are barely heard; and at the top is the threshold of feeling, which is the point where sound vibrations are felt as well as heard. 130 decibels is painful to the ear and represents its limit of endurance.

kinds give off sound waves within a building. Street noises, such as whistles, automobiles and traffic, are carried into the building through the open windows or even through the walls, to a greater or lesser extent.

The other type of sound that is an important factor in all building construction is impact sound. Footsteps heard through the floors of multiple dwelling units are probably the most common of this type. However, the vibrations set up by machinery, motors, etc., may be in this classification as their sounds may often be transmitted to other portions of the structure by vibrations of the structural materials themselves.

The sound insulating properties, or resistance to sound transmission, of

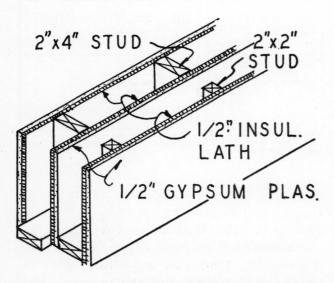

J-27. Frame construction panel has a decibel reduction factor of 51.3. On existing construction application of the 2 x 2 stud section would increase the sound insulation value of an ordinary stud wall.

walls, ceilings or floors are expressed in terms of decibels reduction. In other words, if a partition construction has a sound reduction of 40, it will reduce a sound of 60 decibels to an intensity equal to 20 decibels. There can be no percentage ratio of sound reduction, since such a partition may reduce the very loud sound by a small per cent, but, this same partition may completely reduce a much lower sound, thereby having a sound reduction of 100 per cent. An example of this is a partition with a decibel reduction of 40 which will reduce a sound of 30 decibels to the point of inaudibility.

REDUCING TO 15 DECIBELS

On this basis, it is important to have some estimate of the types of loudness of the sounds regarding insulation. If the problem is a wall between two apartments and ordinary conversation (taken as 65 decibels) is to be reduced, a wall with a 40 decibel reduction would only reduce the sound to 25 decibels. The conversation would still be quite audible, although probably unintelligible. In order to reduce this sound to 15 decibels (the point where the sound would be barely audible), it would be necessary to use a wall with a reduction factor of 50 decibels. In a case of this kind, the 10 decibel difference between the walls makes the difference of hearing or not hearing the sound on the other side. However, if the sound is a loud one, such as a loud radio (about 80 decibels) the poorer constructed wall would reduce it to 40 decibels; while the better wall would only reduce it to 30 decibels, which of course would make it still quite audible.

Actually there is a factor present in most cases which should be considered when designing any sound insulating panel. These are usually referred to as MASKING SOUNDS. In theory, an inaudible sound of zero (0) on the decibel scale is for a perfectly quiet room. Since there are noises in every habitable room which tend to mask the sound entering, it is only necessary to reduce sound to the level of the more or less maintained sound level within the space to be insulated. Assume that there is a radio playing soft music in the listening room (about 30 decibels). Thus, sound of less than 30 decibels entering the room would be completely masked.

THEORY OF
SOUND TRANSMISSION

When sound is generated within a room, the waves strike the walls, floor and ceiling. A large portion of this sound energy is reflected back into the room; the rest is "absorbed" by the surfaces. Actually, the amount absorbed is dependent on the porosity of the surface. If there are cracks or holes through the wall (no matter how minute), a part of these sound waves will travel through them as air-borne sounds. The important fact is that the sound waves striking the wall will cause it to vibrate as a diaphragm, reproducing these waves on the other side of the wall.

Sound transmission through theoretically air-tight partitions is almost entirely a matter of such diaphragm action. The sound insulation values of such homogeneous substances is therefore almost entirely a matter of their relative weight, thickness and area. In homogeneous partitions of normal dimensions, this value depends mostly upon weight. Every complex

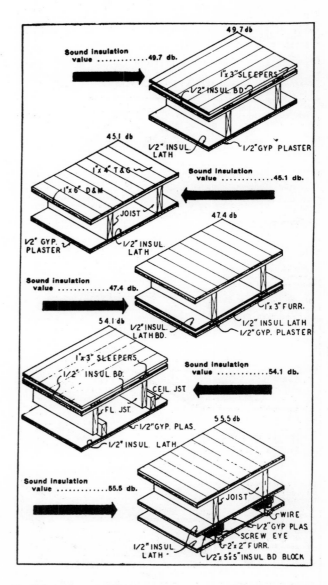

J-28. Sound insulation value of wood floor systems.

floor or wall structure, as distinguished from homogeneous construction, depends for any added sound in-

Combination floor panel constructed of 6" x 12" x 12" partition tile; the ceiling finished with plaster. Sound transmission loss—49.2 db.

Steel joist and concrete construction has sound transmission loss of 54.9 db. ¼" battleship linoleum helps absorb impact sounds.

Reinforced concrete slab with furring and gypsum plaster on insulating lath. Sound transmission loss—56.7 db.

Combination tile and concrete floor with wood floor anchored to resilient clips. Sound transmission loss—57.8 db. Same with sleepers embedded in concrete shows loss of 41 db.

Steel section floor with suspended metal lath and plaster ceiling. Approximately 4" between metal section and plaster. Sound transmission loss 61.2 db. Elimination of the ½" asphalt cut loss to 52.9 db.

Combination floor using insulating board and furring strips. Sound transmission loss —65.7 db. Suspending ceiling on wires gives 68.6 db. reduction.

J-29. Sound insulation value of masonry floor systems.

sulating properties it may possess upon the relative mechanical separation of its two surfaces. Good example—the double wall which has a complete separation of both surfaces.

Figs. J-28 and J-29 show the sound reduction factors of various types of floors and walls. A careful study shows that the weight of the material is an important factor in its sound reduction abilities. Staggered stud construction, covered with thin surfacing panels, does not have the sound reduction qualities of ordinary stud wall finished with three coats of plaster on heavy plasterboard.

DOUBLE WALLS

Since a double-wall plays an important part in sound insulation, it must be recognized that such a partition must possess a core or one surface of considerable weight and rigidity to be effective. This is why partitions of masonry cores with relatively lightweight isolated wall finishes, usually held in place with clips, show the best sound reduction factor.

IMPACT SOUNDS

Impact sounds, such as walking, moving furniture or direct transfer of vibration from machines or musical instruments, are more difficult to insulate than air-borne sounds. Often a machine may cause more annoyance in the room below than it does in the room where it is located. However, the sound insulation of machinery creates a special problem. Impact sounds of more general nature, such as walking, are of more concern to the builder and in most cases are confined to floor construction.

CARPET REDUCES SOUND

Generally these sounds can be reduced at their source by carpeting (or other types of resilient floor coverings) or by isolation of the floor from the ceiling below it. A floating floor is a partial solution towards insulation of impact noises. Experiments have shown that floors built with a wood sub-floor, a layer of insulation board and the finish floor nailed through the insulation into the subfloor, have practically no insulating value. If furring strips are placed over the insulation board and the finished floor nailed to them, conversation will be inaudible in the room below. Actually, there will be a reduction of from 40 to 50 decibels of air-borne sounds and a possible reduction of 20 decibels of impact sounds. Addition of carpeting or similar material on top of the wood floor in most cases will eliminate transmission of impact tools entirely.

FLOATING FLOOR

Floors constructed with separate wood joists for the ceiling below do not give results equal to the floating floor. The "wire" suspended ceiling and floor construction is the floating floor in reverse.

The solid masonry floor will transmit sound with practically no reduction in quantity. This insulating value can be increased by the use of suspended ceiling construction, being greater if resilient hangers are used. Adding a "floating" finish floor will also help. The combination of a floating floor (on resilient clips), the space filled with sound insulating material and the ceiling below hung on resilient hangers, will give a masonry floor a sound reduction factor of over 60 decibels. See Fig. J-30.

DOORS AND WINDOWS

Sound has a tendency to spread out after passing through an opening. Thus cracks and holes should be avoided in every type of construction if sound

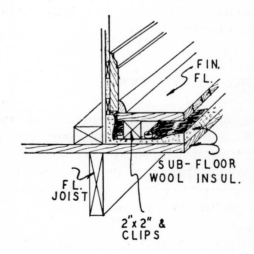

J-30. This floor system which uses insulation blanket and a resilient clip system has an average air-borne sound transmission reduction of 50.3 decibels. It is also an excellent way to treat existing floors for remodeling work.

insulation is to be achieved. Doors between rooms are probably the greatest factor in this category. A 1/4 in. crack around a wood door (2 in. thick) would admit four times as much sound of medium intensity as the door itself. Felt, rubber or metal strips around the jambs and head are desirable. Conditions can be further improved by some form of "draft excluder" at the sill, such as a threshold or felt weatherstop.

HOLLOW CORE DOORS

Ordinary well fitted, hollow-core interior doors will have a sound reduction value from 20 to 25 decibels. Similar double doors, hung with at least 6 in. air space between, will have a sound reduction factor as high as 40 decibels. This factor can be increased considerably by felt or rubber strips around the stops.

"SOUNDPROOF" DOORS

For special installations, "soundproof" doors are available and can be built to suit almost every condition. Special hardware is used on this type of door to prevent sound transmission through the doorknobs.

Similar precautions should be taken with glazed openings as with doors. Cracks around these openings may counteract other precautions to eliminate sound transmission. Windows or glazed openings should be as airtight as feasible. Double glazing also adds considerably to the sound reduction effect of the opening.

Ordinary double-strength glass or 1/4 in. plate glass has a sound reduction factor of 25 to 30 decibels. Two layers of 1/4 in. plate (1 1/2 in. space between) will have a reduction factor of around 40 decibels. Increasing the air space will increase the efficiency of the opening.

Glass block has a sound reduction factor of about 40 decibels; being effective where transparent glazing is not needed. Good mortar joints are necessary, just as they constitute good masonry practice.

NOISE REDUCTION WITHIN A SPACE

While it is important to design walls and floors that will reduce sound transmission between spaces, it is also advisable to treat the enclosure so that sound will be trapped or reduced at its source. Reducing the noise level within the room will not only have an appreciable effect on the transmission of sound, but will make living conditions within the room more desirable. Almost everyone has been aware of how acoustical treatment of restaurants has reduced the annoying clatter of dishes and conversation.

There are a number of different types of acoustical material available to the builder. Some are distinctly an applicator or "acoustical engineer" product. The latter requires either special equipment or trained men to install. The most common types and probably the most used methods are perforated or porous fiberboard units, perforated metal pan units, cork acoustical material and acoustical

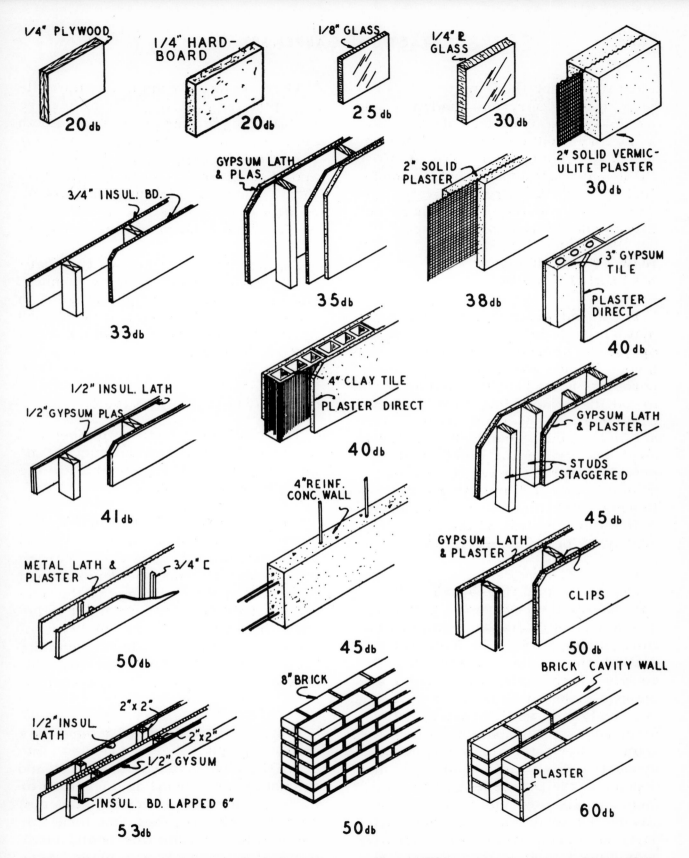

J-31. Sound insulation value of wall panels. The noise reduction factors given for these panels are average and conditions such as workmanship and quality of materials may raise or lower the efficiency of the panel.

plaster. All of these materials provide high absorption qualities and except for the acoustical plaster, have a factory applied finish. Since the sound absorbing properties of any of these materials depends on its sponge-like quality, they are relatively light and do not require any building reinforcement or structural changes.

HOW ACOUSTICAL MATERIALS WORK

The sound absorbing value of most materials is dependent to a greater or lesser degree on its porous surface. Sound waves entering these pores, or holes, get lost and are said to be dissipated into heat energy. Other materials depend on absorption action to reduce sound. The material used has a vibration point which approaches zero. Heavy draperies or hangings, hair felt and other soft flexible materials function in this manner. A brief description of the more general types being used follows.

The perforated fiberboard acoustical materials are made in tile shape of a low density fibrous composition. Holes about 3/16 in. in diameter are drilled almost through the tile. The sounds which strike these units are trapped in the holes as the walls, being relatively soft and fibrous in nature, form tiny pockets which absorb the sound. There are also some fibrous products which are not drilled, but depend on the porousness of the surface and its low vibration point to absorb the sound. Most of these products have a relatively smooth surface, providing a high degree of light reflection without glare.

They are usually applied to the ceiling or upper wall surface and may be installed by gluing over any smooth surface. Where the surface is in poor condition, furring strips can be used and the material nailed or glued to them. Each manufacturer has specifications on installation. Various methods are shown on these pages.

The perforated metal pan type performs in somewhat the same manner. The sound enters through the holes in the surface of the pans and is trapped by the backing material which is of soft resilient nature.

CEILING MAY BE REMOVED

These units are factory finished and are installed on suspended metal runners which are designed to allow the units to snap into place.

They also are used where suspended ceilings are advisable to conceal pipes, beams, etc. The entire ceiling or any part of it may be removed and relocated without damage to the material. This factor alone might influence the installation of this type of acoustical treatment where it had not been considered before because of the necessity of access to furred spaces.

Units are also made of ground cork and of glass fibers, pressed into acoustical units of various sizes and thickness, and installed by gluing or nailing. Because of the resistance of both to moisture, they are ideal for use in indoor swimming pools, commercial kitchens or any place where humidity is a problem.

Acoustical materials for plastic application narrows down to two types, namely acoustical plaster, and the sprayed on material which is usually applied by a special applicator.

The acoustical plasters are used where an unlined or plain surfaced wall or ceiling is desired or where curved or intricate planes make the use of unit types impractical.

To install acoustical plaster instead of plain plaster, omit the finish plaster coat and instead apply two coats of the acoustical plaster. The extra cost is difference between plaster finish coat and acoustical plaster coats.

INSTALLATION OF MATERIALS

Manufacturers' recommendations as to the manner of installation should be carefully followed on all acoustical materials. Many of these materials exhibit large variations in their properties when the method of installation has been changed from that recommended. In many cases, the amount of air space back of material is a factor in its sound absorption qualities.

Because of the relatively soft nature of most acoustical materials, it is the usual practice to install them on the ceiling or upper portion of sidewalls. For sounds originating in the average room, the ceiling offers necessary area.

SELECTION

The appearance or design of an acoustical product is difficult to judge from a sample. The material which might seem unsatisfactory in a small piece would actually be perfectly acceptable when in place. Beveled edges, tile patterns and perforated boards may be decorative when seen as a whole rather than as an individual piece, and the effect achieved by the many variations possible in installations allow design possibilities.

Where smooth unbroken surfaces are desired, plaster or sprayed-on materials are the logical solution. These may be finished in a relatively smooth and even-textured surface, and pre-tinted materials safeguard their sound absorption value and produce a uniform color.

Actually, acoustical materials serve a dual purpose; sound absorption and thermal insulation. While it is true that all thermal insulators do not have sound reduction virtues, conversely acoustical materials do have thermal insulation values because of their nature.

METHODS

Since ceiling structures are seldom level or true, it is advisable to level the ceiling beams with furring or gypsum lath. If furring strips are used, building paper should be applied under the tiles to prevent air circulation or "breathing" between the tiles. If gypsum lath is used as a base, the joints can be filled with spackle for the same reason. This, of course, would make the paper unnecessary.

The most economical method of application is spotting units with adhe-

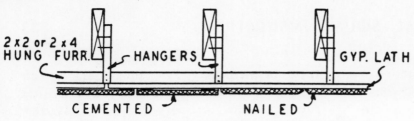

2 x 2 or 2 x 4 HUNG FURR. — HANGERS — GYP. LATH

CEMENTED   NAILED

Furring hung from joist with wood or metal hangers.

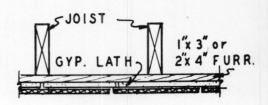

JOIST

GYP. LATH   1" x 3" or 2" x 4" FURR.

Wood furring strips and gypsum lath.

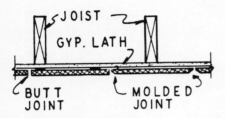

JOIST — GYP. LATH

BUTT JOINT   MOLDED JOINT

Joist bottoms must be level with this type of installation.

ACOUSTICAL UNITS
APPLIED TO WOOD FRAMING

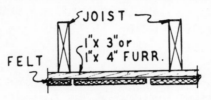

JOIST

1" x 3" or 1" x 4" FURR.

FELT

Felt prevents "breathing" of tiles.

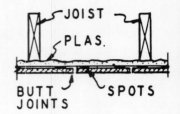

JOIST — PLAS.

BUTT JOINTS   SPOTS

On new work, scratch and brown coat of plaster is sufficient.

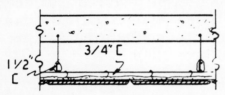

3/4" C

1 1/2" C

New work, scratch and brown coat plaster on metal lath.

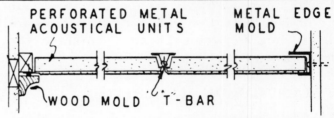

PERFORATED METAL ACOUSTICAL UNITS   METAL EDGE MOLD

WOOD MOLD   T-BAR

Wood molding or metal channel used to close work at intersection of walls.

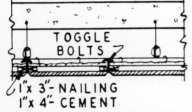

TOGGLE BOLTS

1" x 3"- NAILING
1" x 4"- CEMENT

Furring method used over old rough plaster ceiling.

METAL SUSPENDED CEILINGS
FOR ACOUSTICAL UNITS

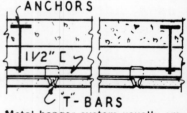

ANCHORS

1 1/2" C

T-BARS

Metal hanger system usually employed on new work.

HANGERS NEW WORK   EXPAN. BOLT OLD WORK   ❷

1" x 3" NAILING
1" x 4" CEMENT

1" x 3" DIRECT FURR.   ❶

1" x 3" CROSS FURR.
GYPSUM LATH
FELT FOR NAILING

SPOTS   ❸

TILE CEMENTED

1. Furring and cross-furring strips increase air space behind tiles.
2. Furring strips necessary where rough concrete exists.
3. Cemented direct, concrete must be smooth and level.
4. Two coats plaster used to level up rough concrete.
5. Same as No. 1 except that gypsum lath is eliminated.

ACOUSTICAL UNITS
APPLIED TO CONCRETE

❹

SCRATCH & BROWN COAT   CEMENT, NAIL, or BOTH

CONC. NAILS

❺

1" x 3" DIRECT FURR.
1" x 3" CROSS FURR.

J-32. Methods of installing acoustical units.

234

sive and cementing them to the surface, or nailing, or a combination of nailing and gluing.

Those units which have a tongue and groove lend themselves to blind nailing. Where cementing is used, generally the edges should be of the butt type. Most of the "perforated" units have short-drilled holes at the corners for face nailing.

METAL PANS

While some of the perforated metal pan type units are installed by applicators, the method used for almost all types is well standardized. The metal suspension systems consist of hangers and runner channels and the acoustical work attaches to the channels by clips or by having the units grooved to fit the mechanical requirements of the job.

Good workmanship is the most important factor in the application of any acoustical treatment. If the surface is made true and level and a good method of fastening is used, a workmanlike job will result.

PAINTING

Contrary to popular belief, painting of perforated boards does not lower their efficiency if properly done. The dirt clogging the pores of the material should be removed first. This may often be accomplished with a suction type vacuum cleaner or by brushing with a soft hair brush.

Spray painting is preferable to brush painting as a thinner mixture has less

tendency to clog the pores of the material. Naturally, improperly applied paint jobs would soon fill the material and thus destroy its efficiency.

Cementing of units to existing plaster is probably the most economical method of installation, and is also the market for the average builder. While use of acoustical units has been associated mostly with remodeling jobs, 65 per cent to 70 per cent of manufacturer's output goes into the new construction field.

GENERAL RULES

Care should be taken not to install too much acoustical material which can cause music and voices to sound muffled. Many other materials such as carpeting, and drapes will help absorb sounds. The average home living room with carpeted floor and the usual window hangings will find that ceiling treatment is sufficient.

TREAT ENTIRE CEILING

It is better practice to treat an entire ceiling with a material of a low noise reduction coefficient than partial areas with a material of high coefficient. It is customary not to treat ordinary beams in a ceiling because this work is usually more costly and little is to be gained.

Where ceiling heights are above normal, it is wise to use a material with a high noise reduction coefficient or, if this is not feasible, part of the sidewalls should also be covered.

High narrow spaces, such as halls, corridors, require special consideration because of the fact that there is a higher percentage of wall area in relation to ceiling area. Here it is advisable to cover a portion of the side wall.

SELECTION OF MATERIAL

The efficiency of an acoustical unit or product is measured by its ability to absorb sound waves. Since noise is a mixture of confused sounds of many frequencies, this efficiency is measured by the noise reduction coefficient of a material or the average middle range of sounds.

For the average installation this figure is used to compare the values of one material over another.

However, some materials are designed to do a better job for high or low frequency sounds and for special cases such as music studios, auditoriums and theaters, an acoustical engineer should be consulted. Most manufacturers will furnish this service.

Windows and Doors

INSTALLING WINDOW AND DOOR FRAMES

The present day building practice is to use window and door frames which were assembled at the mill or factory and brought to the job already put together or in knocked down form. Knocked down frames are easy to assemble.

Making up door and window frames on the job is time consuming and it's a job that is difficult to do well without adequate power-driven equipment.

Window and door frames should not be fitted into the openings until after wall sheathing has been completed. Ordinarily rough frame or grid openings as they are frequently called, for windows are 4 in. greater than window heights and 6 in. greater than window widths for frames with pulleys and sash weights and 3 in. greater where patent balances are used.

CASEMENTS AND DOUBLE-HUNG WINDOWS

The two most commonly used windows are double-hung, Fig. K-1, and casements or hinged windows, Fig. K-2. Some casements swing out and some swing in.

Details of framing for a typical double-hung window are illustrated in Fig. K-3. Sectional views of framing for typical casement windows are given in K-4 and K-5. Parts of a window are indicated in K-6.

On double-hung windows, strips which separate the top and bottom sash are called parting stops. Strips which hold windows in place in the frames are either inside or outside stops. Mullions are sections between windows used in pairs, triple windows, etc., Fig. K-7.

The exact procedure to follow in installing frames varies according to the frame at hand, but regardless of the frame to be installed all openings must be securely sealed.

An ideal arrangement is to use blind casings (shown in K-3) at the sides and top on both the outside and inside of the frame. These casings are nailed to the window studs at the sides and to headers at the top of the opening. Wall sheathing butts against the edge of the outside blind casing and the joint between the two is carefully sealed by using building paper and outside finish casing. The inside blind casing serves as a gauge for the plaster which is worked up to it. The joint between

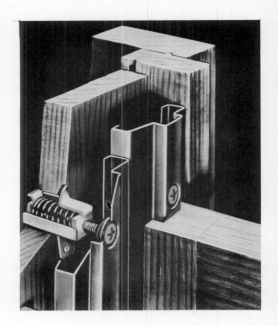

(Courtesy of Malta Mfg. Co.)

K-1. Typical double-hung window of modern design. Friction pressure between sash and weatherstripping holds the sash open at desired point. The sash may be removed by depressing it against one spring-activated side of weatherstripping. The cutaway view shows the construction of the unit and the friction adjusting screw.

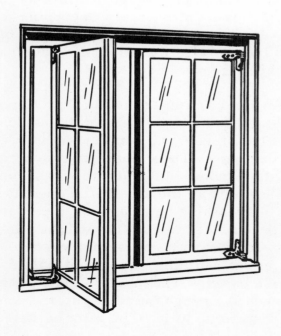

K-2. Casement window. Casement sash are sidehinged and usually of the outswinging type. Screens and storm sash are fitted on the interior.

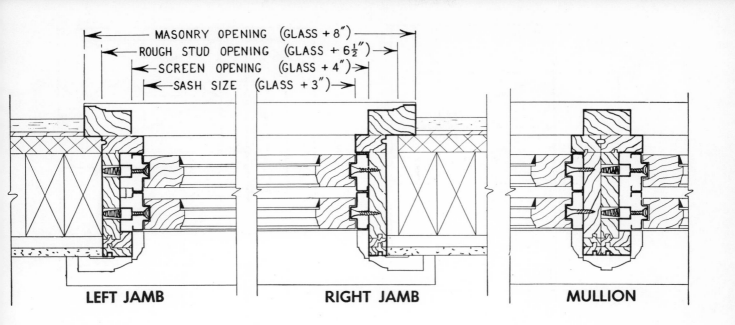

MASONRY OPENING (GLASS + 8")
ROUGH STUD OPENING (GLASS + 6½")
SCREEN OPENING (GLASS + 4")
SASH SIZE (GLASS + 3")

LEFT JAMB   **RIGHT JAMB**   **MULLION**

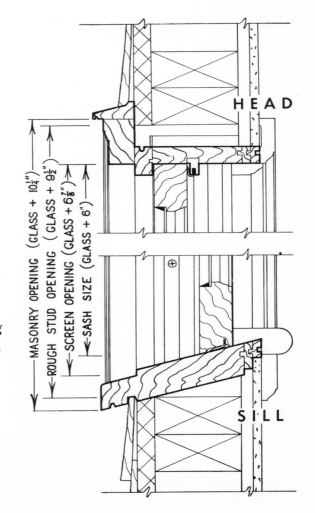

HEAD

MASONRY OPENING (GLASS + 10¼")
ROUGH STUD OPENING (GLASS + 9½")
SCREEN OPENING (GLASS + 6⅞")
SASH SIZE (GLASS + 6")

SILL

K-3. Installation details of double-hung
window, shown in Fig. K-1 - head,
jamb, mullion, and the sill.

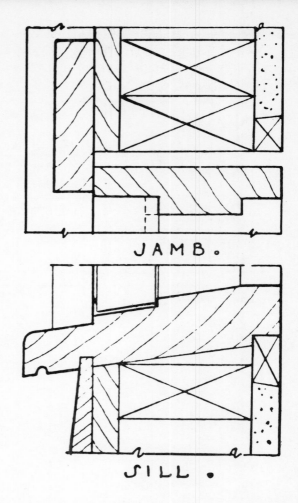

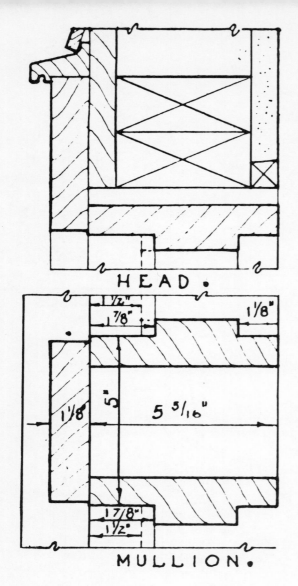

K-4. Sectional views of typical
out-swinging casement

the two is hidden by the inside finish casing.

Space between the sill at the bottom of the window and the header should be filled with calking material, then further sealed by letting the siding extend into a groove in the underside of the sill.

It is also important that the joint between the drip cap (molding across top of frame) and siding be made tight.

This may be done by the use of metal flashing nailed to the drip cap and bent to extend up under the siding.

Additional window frame installation details for frame houses are given in Fig. K-8. Figs. K-9 and K-10 show installation details for brick veneer and solid masonry construction.

Information on standard sizes of stock windows and sash is given in Figs. K-11 and K-12.

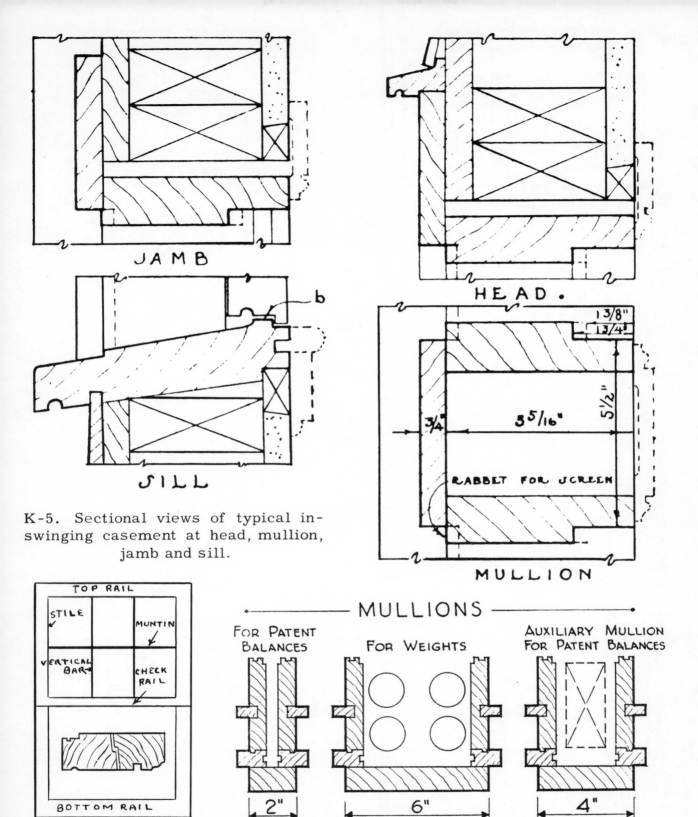

JAMB

HEAD.

SILL

b

MULLION

1 3/8"
1 3/4"

3/4"

3 5/16"

5 1/2"

RABBET FOR SCREEN

K-5. Sectional views of typical in-swinging casement at head, mullion, jamb and sill.

TOP RAIL

STILE

MUNTIN

VERTICAL BAR

CHECK RAIL

BOTTOM RAIL

K-6. Parts of a window.

MULLIONS

FOR PATENT BALANCES

FOR WEIGHTS

AUXILIARY MULLION FOR PATENT BALANCES

2"

6"

4"

K-7. Mullions form divisions between units of windows.

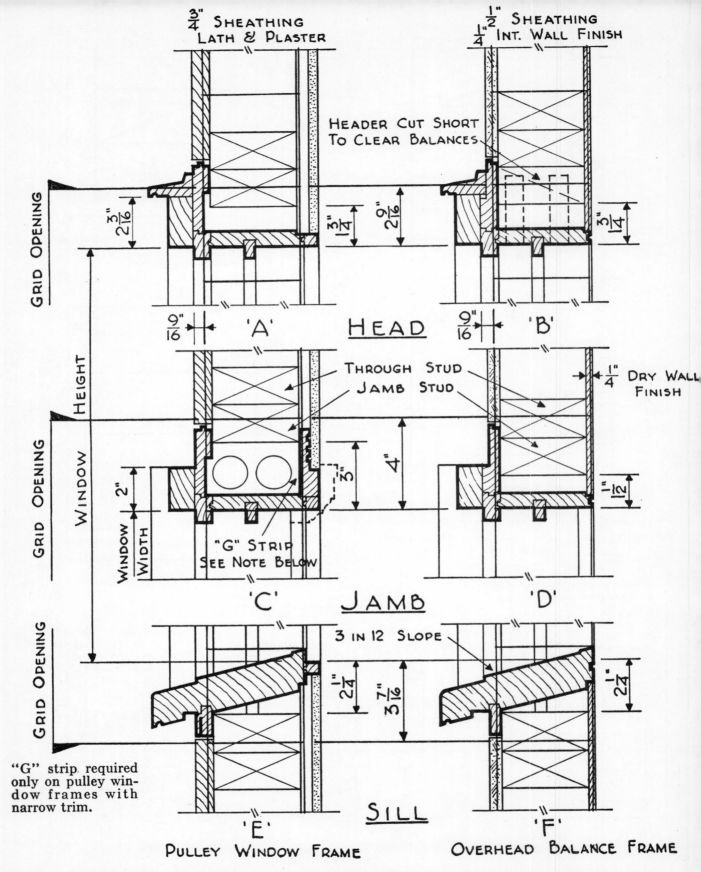

K-8. Window installation details—wood frame. Rough opening widths are 6 in. greater than window width for pulley window frames, 3 in. greater than window widths for patent balance frames. Rough opening heights are 4 in. greater than window heights.

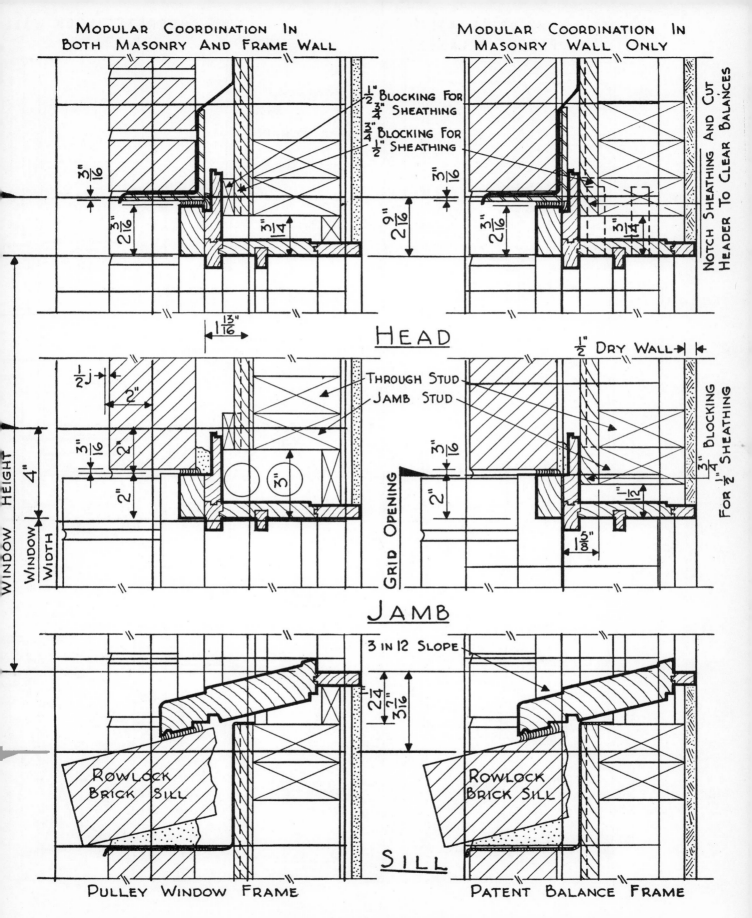

K-9. Window installation details—brick veneer construction. 243

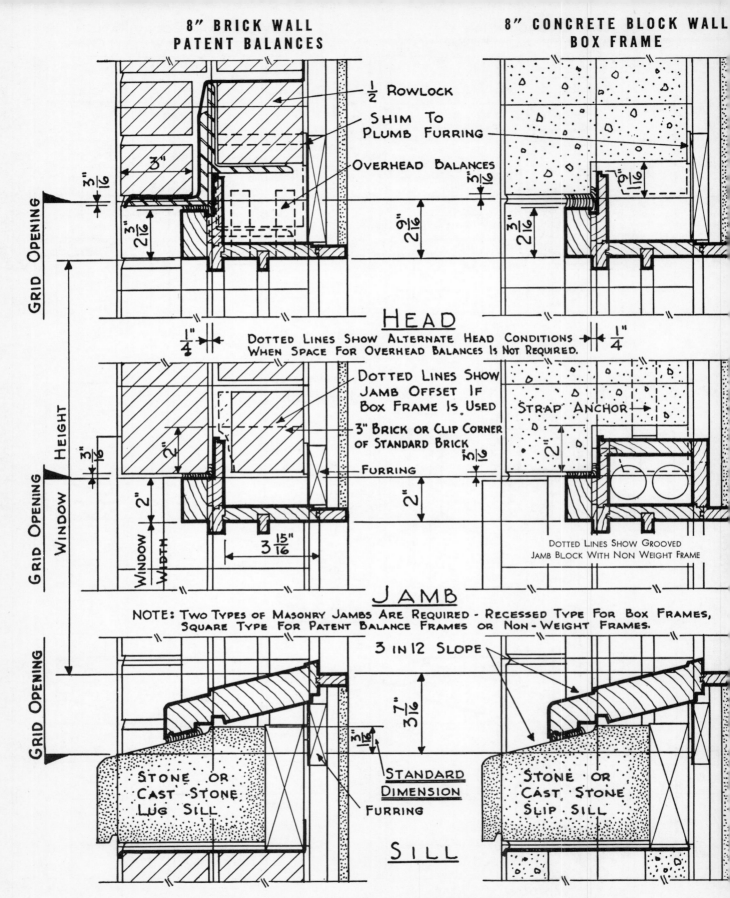

**8" BRICK WALL
PATENT BALANCES**

**8" CONCRETE BLOCK WALL
BOX FRAME**

½ ROWLOCK

SHIM TO
PLUMB FURRING

OVERHEAD BALANCES

3"
GRID OPENING

3"
2 9/16"

2 9/16"

3"
2 9/16"

HEAD
DOTTED LINES SHOW ALTERNATE HEAD CONDITIONS
WHEN SPACE FOR OVERHEAD BALANCES IS NOT REQUIRED.

¼"   ¼"

DOTTED LINES SHOW
JAMB OFFSET IF
BOX FRAME IS USED

STRAP ANCHOR

3" BRICK OR CLIP CORNER
OF STANDARD BRICK

FURRING

3"
GRID OPENING

HEIGHT

WINDOW

2"

WINDOW 2"

WINDOW WIDTH

3 15/16"

2"

2"

DOTTED LINES SHOW GROOVED
JAMB BLOCK WITH NON WEIGHT FRAME

JAMB
NOTE: TWO TYPES OF MASONRY JAMBS ARE REQUIRED - RECESSED TYPE FOR BOX FRAMES,
SQUARE TYPE FOR PATENT BALANCE FRAMES OR NON-WEIGHT FRAMES.

3 IN 12 SLOPE

GRID OPENING

7"
3 5/16"

3"

STONE OR
CAST STONE
LUG SILL

STANDARD
DIMENSION
FURRING

STONE OR
CAST STONE
SLIP SILL

SILL

K-10. Window installation details—solid masonry construction.

CHECK RAIL WINDOWS 1⅜" — POPULAR SIZES and DESIGNS

Prefit Face Measurements		
Stiles .... 1²⁹⁄₃₂"	Stiles .... 1²⁹⁄₃₂"	St. ..... 1²¹⁄₃₂" / St. ..... 1²⁹⁄₃₂"
Top Rail .... 1²⁹⁄₃₂"	Top Rail .... 1²¹⁄₃₂"	T.R. ... 1²¹⁄₃₂" / T.R. ... 1²¹⁄₃₂"
Bottom Rail .... 3"	Bottom Rail .... 3"	B.R. ... 2 ¾" / B.R. ... 2 ¾"
Vertical Bar .... ³⁄₁₆"	Vertical Bar .... ³⁄₁₆"	V.B. ... ³⁄₁₆" / V.B. ... ³⁄₁₆"
Horizontal Bar .... ⁷⁄₁₆"	Muntin .... ³⁄₁₆"	Mun. ... ³⁄₁₆" / Mun. ... ³⁄₁₆"
Check Rail .... 1 ³⁄₃₂"	Check Rail ...... 1 ³⁄₃₂"	C.R. ... 1 ³⁄₃₂" / C.R. ... 1 ³⁄₃₂"

Windows are made ⅛" narrower and ¹⁄₁₆" shorter than window opening sizes shown below

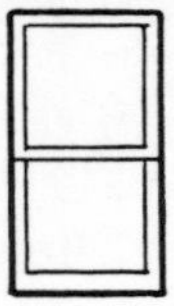

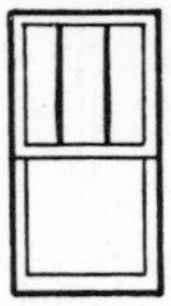

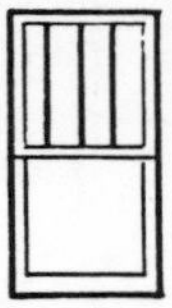

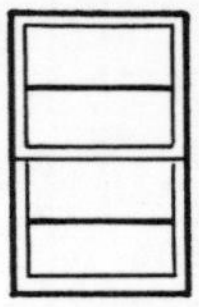

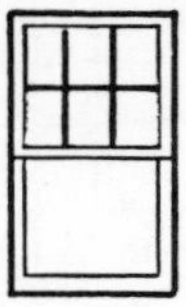

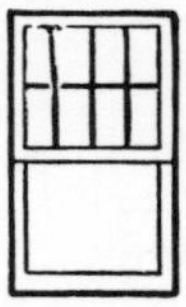

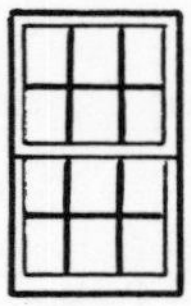

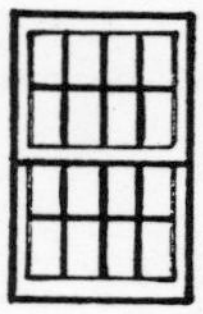

Prefit Face Measurements	2 Lt.	Top 3 Lt. W.	Top 4 Lt. W.	4 Lt. H.	Top 6 Lt.	Top 8 Lt.	12 Lt.	16 Lt.
1-8x3- 2	16x16	....	....	16x 7¾	....	....	....	....
3-10	20			9¾				
4- 6	24			11¾				
2-0x2-10	20x14	6 ½x14	....	20x6¾	6 ½x 7	....	....	....
3- 2	16	16		7¾	8		6²¹⁄₃₂x 8	
3- 6	18	18		8¾	9		9	
3-10	20	20		9¾	10		10	
4- 2	22	22		10¾	11		11	
4- 6	24	24		11¾	12		12	
4-10	26	26		12¾	13		13	
5- 2	28	28		13¾	14		14	
2-4x2-10	24x14	7²⁷⁄₃₂x14		24x 6¾	7²⁷⁄₃₂x 7		....	
3- 2	16	16		7¾	8		8x 8	
3- 6	18	18		8¾	9		9	
3-10	20	20		9¾	10		10	
4- 2	22	22		10¾	11		11	
4- 6	24	24		11¾	12		12	
4-10	26	26		12¾	13		13	
5- 2	28	28		13¾	14		14	
2-8x2-10	28x14	9 ⁵⁄₃₂x14		28x 6¾	9 ⁵⁄₃₂x 7		....	
3- 2	16	16		7¾	8			
3- 6	18	18		8¾	9			
3-10	20	20		9¾	10		9¹¹⁄₃₂x10	
4- 2	22	22		10¾	11			
4- 6	24	24		11¾	12		12	
4-10	26	26		12¾	13		13	
5- 2	28	28		13¾	14		14	
3-0x2-10	32x14	....	7¹³⁄₁₆x14	32x 6¾	....	7¹³⁄₁₆x 7	....	....
3-10	20	....	20	9¾		10		7¹³⁄₁₆x10
4- 6	24	....	24	11¾		12		12
4-10	26	....	26	12¾		13		
5- 2	28	....	28	13¾		14		14
3-4x4- 6	36x24	....	8¹³⁄₁₆x24	36x11¾		8¹³⁄₁₆x12		8¹³⁄₁₆x12
4-10	26	....	26	12¾		13		13
5- 2	28	....	28	13¾		14		14
3-8x4- 6	40x24	....	9¹³⁄₁₆x24	40x11¾		9¹³⁄₁₆x12		9¹³⁄₁₆x12
5- 2	28	....	23	13¾		14		14

K-11. Popular sizes and designs of check rail windows, including opening sizes, prefit layouts and glass sizes. No attempt has been made to list all the designs and sizes of windows that are available.

POPULAR SIZES and DESIGNS

CASEMENT SASH 1⅜"

Stiles.........1²¹⁄₃₂"   Bottom Rail......3"
Top Rail......1²⁹⁄₃₂"   Vertical Bar.......³⁄₁₆"
Muntin.........³⁄₁₆"

Prefit Face Measurements	1 Lt.	3 Lt. H.	4 Lt. H.	6 Lt. 2 W.	8 Lt. 2 W.
Sash are made ⅛" narrower and 1⁄₃₂" shorter than opening sizes given below	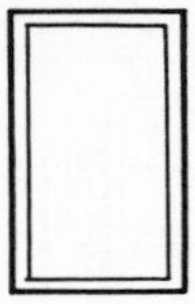	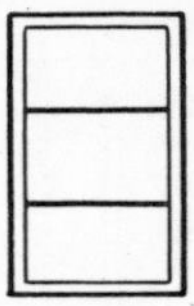	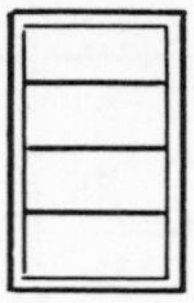	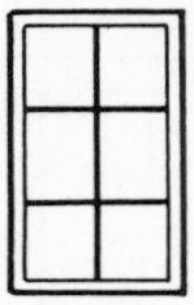	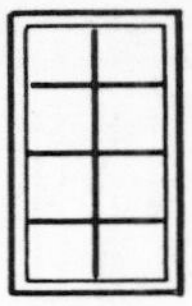
1-3½x3- 2	12x33	12x10¹³⁄₁₆	....	5⅞x10¹³⁄₁₆	....
3-10	41	13 ½	12x10¹⁄₁₆	13 ½	5⅞x10¹⁄₁₆
4- 6	49	....	12¹⁄₁₆	....	12¹⁄₁₆
1-7½x3- 2	16x33	16x10¹³⁄₁₆	....	7⅞x10¹³⁄₁₆	....
3-10	41	13½	16x10¹⁄₁₆	13 ½	7⅞x10¹⁄₁₆
4- 6	49	....	12¹⁄₁₆	....	12¹⁄₁₆

STORM SASH and SCREENS 1⅛"

Prefit Face Measurements

Storm Sash
St.....1²⁹⁄₃₂"
T.R....1²⁹⁄₃₂"
B.R....4 ¹⁄₁₆"
C.R.....⅞"

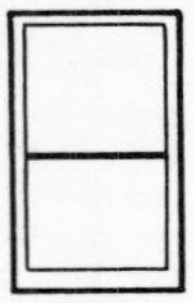

Screens
St.....1²⁷⁄₃₂"
T.R....1²⁷⁄₃₂"
B.R.....3"
C.R.....⅝"

Storm Sash or Screens

Storm Sash and Screens are available for all Standard Windows. The more popular sizes conform to the window sizes shown on the preceding page.

Storm Sash and Screens are made ⅛" narrower and 1" longer than window opening sizes.

CELLAR SASH 1⅛" and 1⅜"

St.....1²¹⁄₃₂" T.R.....1²⁹⁄₃₂" B.R.....1²⁹⁄₃₂" V.B.....⁷⁄₁₆"

St.....1²¹⁄₃₂" T.R.....1²⁹⁄₃₂" B.R.....1²⁹⁄₃₂" V.B.....³⁄₁₆"

St.....1²⁹⁄₃₂" T.R.....1²⁹⁄₃₂" B.R.....1²⁹⁄₃₂" V.B.....³⁄₁₆"

Prefit Face Measurements	2 Lt.	Prefit Face Measurements	3 Lt.	Prefit Face Measurements	4 Lt.
Sash are made ⅛" narrower and ⅛" shorter than opening sizes given below		Sash are made ⅛" narrower and ⅛" shorter than opening sizes given below		Sash are made ⅛" narrower and ⅛" shorter than opening sizes given below	
2-0x1-4	10x12	2-4x1-4	8 x12	3-8x1-4	9¹³⁄₁₆x12
2-4x1-4	12x12	2-8x1-0	9¹¹⁄₃₂x 8	1-8	16
1-8	16	1-4	12	4-4x1-4	11¹³⁄₁₆x12
2-0	20	1-8	16	1-8	16
....	.....	3-0x1-4	10²¹⁄₃₂x12	....	....
....	.....	1-8	16	....	....
....	.....	3-4x1-8	12 x16	....	....
....	.....	....	....	....	....

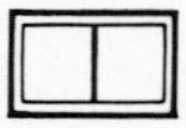

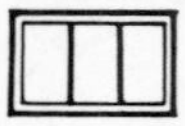

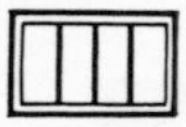

PLAIN RAIL WINDOWS 1⅛"

St.....1²¹⁄₃₂" T.R.....2 ³⁄₁₆" B.R.....2 ³⁄₁₆" M.R.....1 ³⁄₃₂" V.B.....¹⁵⁄₁₆" Mun....³⁄₁₆"

St.....1²¹" T.R.....2 ³" B.R.....2 ³" M.R.....1 ³" V.B.....³" Mun....³"

Prefit Face Measurements	8 Lt.	Prefit Face Measurements	12 Lt.
Windows are made ⅛" narrower and ¹⁄₁₆" shorter than opening sizes shown below	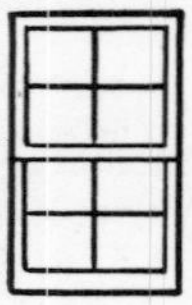	Windows are made ⅛" narrower and ¹⁄₁₆" shorter than opening sizes shown below	
1-8½x3-10	8x10	2-4x3-10	8x10
2-0½x4- 6	10x12	4- 6	12
2-4½x5- 2	12x14	2-7x4- 6	9x12
		2-10x4-6	10x12
		3-4x5- 2	12x14

BARN or UTILITY SASH 1⅛" and 1⅜"

Prefit Face Measurements—Stiles....1²¹⁄₃₂"   Top Rail....1²¹⁄₃₂"   Bottom Rail....3"   *Vertical Bar..³⁄₁₆" or ⁷⁄₁₆"   Muntin....³⁄₁₆"

	4 Lt.		6 Lt. 2 W.		6 Lt. 3 W.		9 Lt. 3 W.		12 Lt. 3 W.
Sash are made ⅛" narrower and 1⁄₃₂" shorter than opening sizes given below	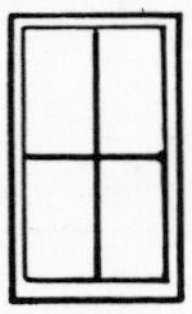	Sash are made ⅛" narrower and 1⁄₃₂" shorter than opening sizes given below	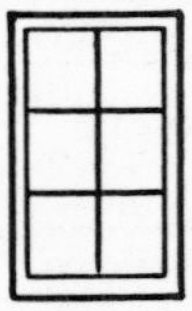	Sash are made ⅛" narrower and 1⁄₃₂" shorter than opening sizes given below		Sash are made ⅛" narrower and 1⁄₃₂" shorter than opening sizes given below		Sash are made ⅛" narrower and 1⁄₃₂" shorter than opening sizes given below	
1-8x2-1	8x10	1-8x2-11¼	8x10	2-1x1-11	7x 9	2-0x2- 8¼	6²¹⁄₃₂x 9	2-4x3-9½	8 x10
2-5	12	2-0x3- 5¼	10x12	2-4x2- 1	8x10	2-4x2-11¼	8 x10	2-8x4-5½	9¹¹⁄₃₂x12
2-0x2-1	10x10	....	.....	2- 5	12	3- 5¼	12	3-0x4-5½	10²¹⁄₃₂x12
2-5	12	....	.....	2-7x2- 5	9x12	2-8x3- 5¼	9¹¹⁄₃₂x12	....	....
2-9	14	....	.....	2- 9	14	....	....	....	....
3-1	16	....	.....	2-10x2- 5	10x12	....	....	....	....
2-4x2-5	12x12	....	.....	3-4x2- 5	12x12	....	....	....	....
2-9	14	....	.....	....	.....	....	....	....	....
3-1	16	....	.....	....	.....	....	....	....	....

*Vertical bar ⁷⁄₁₆" for Sash 2 lights wide; ³⁄₁₆" for Sash 3 lights wide.

K-12. Popular sizes and designs of casement sash, cellar sash, plain rail windows, storm sash and screens and barn sash.

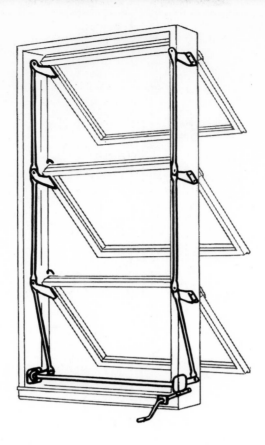

K-13. Wood awning window. Such windows have the sash hung from the top and are hinged by brackets attached to the jambs.

WOOD AWNING WINDOWS

Awning windows, Fig. K-13, have the sash hung from the top and are hinged by brackets attached to the jamb. The bottom rail of one window or tier interlocks with the top rail of the window below.

Opening and closing of awning windows is done by a worm and gear drive at the right hand side of the opening. Each tier operates independently. Multiple window openings are made possible by the use of muntins.

Awning windows permit wide latitude as to illumination and ventilation. The tilted sash deflect air currents upward and help keep the air at the ceiling moving.

Frames are usually set up by the manufacturer with sash and hardware installed, screens semi-prefit, wood stool and the apron furnished in cut lengths, KD (knocked down). Weather stripping is provided for jamb sections. Screens are used on the inside.

Installing of typical awning windows, on various types of construction, is shown in Figs. K-14 and K-15; standard sizes are given in Fig. K-16.

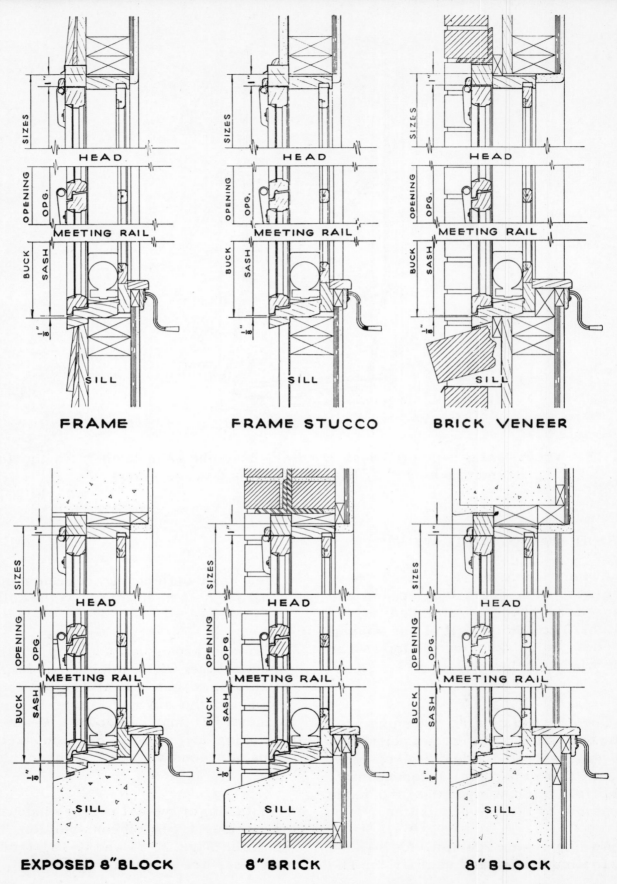

K-14. Installing awning windows in frame, stucco, brick veneer, block and brick types of construction.

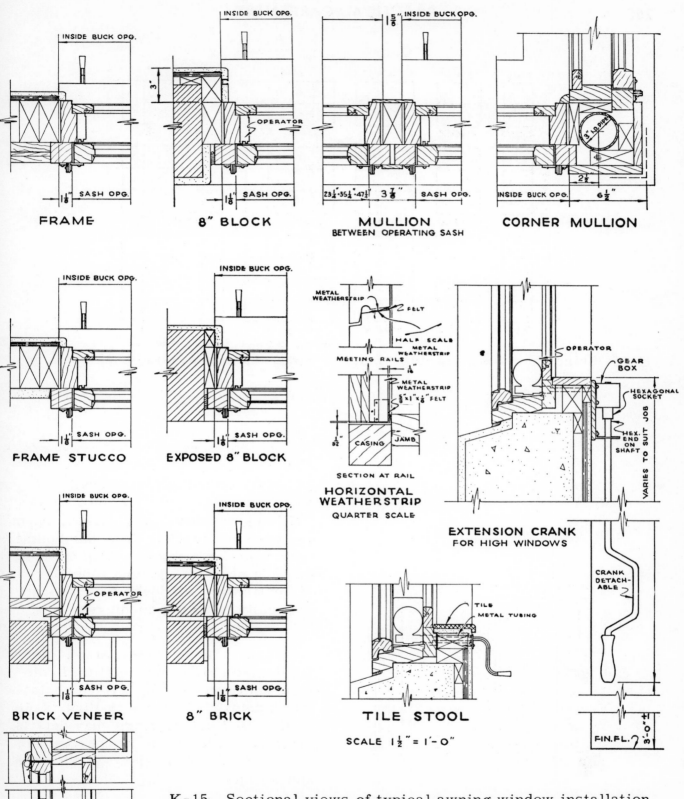

FRAME

8" BLOCK

MULLION
BETWEEN OPERATING SASH

CORNER MULLION

FRAME STUCCO

EXPOSED 8" BLOCK

HORIZONTAL
WEATHERSTRIP
QUARTER SCALE

SECTION AT RAIL

METAL
WEATHERSTRIP
FELT
HALF SCALE
METAL
WEATHERSTRIP
MEETING RAILS
METAL
WEATHERSTRIP
FELT
CASING
JAMB

EXTENSION CRANK
FOR HIGH WINDOWS

OPERATOR
GEAR
BOX
HEXAGONAL
SOCKET
HEX.
END
ON
SHAFT
VARIES TO SUIT JOB

CRANK
DETACHABLE

FIN.FL.

BRICK VENEER

8" BRICK

TILE STOOL

SCALE 1½" = 1'-0"

HEAD & MEETING RAIL
TOP VENT FIXED

K-15. Sectional views of typical awning window installation at jambs, mullions between operating sash and corner mullions, and buck openings.

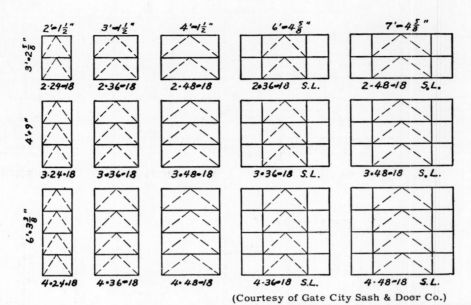

(Courtesy of Gate City Sash & Door Co.)

K-16. Standard sizes of awning windows. Sizes shown are inside buck openings.

GLIDING (SLIDING) WINDOWS

Gliding windows, Fig. K-17, open sidewise on tracks. The horizontal sliding action permits larger sizes than are practical in most other types of ventilating windows that operate vertically or swing on hinges.

Gliding window units are factory fabricated and are manufactured complete with parts fitted. Typical installation details are given in Figs. K-18 to K-27 inclusive. Angle bay details are given in K-28 and corner window details, K-29. K-30 shows stock sizes and layouts.

K-17. Gliding (sliding) window which opens sidewise. The horizontal sliding action permits large sizes of ventilating windows.

K-18. Sectional views of gliding window installation.

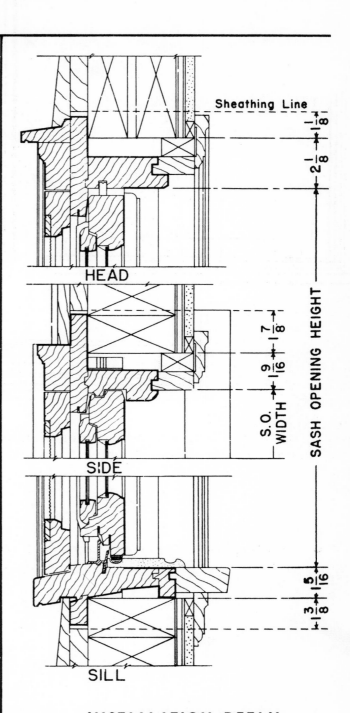

Sheathing Line

HEAD

SIDE

SILL

INSTALLATION DETAIL

G-10—Standard unit in frame wall with lath and plaster inside
finish and ¾" sheathing. The extension blind stop can be
rabbeted for ½" sheathing and this should be specified when
ordering the unit. Extension jambs and other trim should be
ordered separately to conform to individual requirements. Installation is similar for stucco or brick veneer or for dry wall inside.

ADAPTATION DETAILS
SCALE 1½" = 1'0"

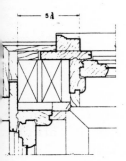

CORNER

etail shows corner construction
th standard two inch sill horns
d casing. Long sill horns can
e furnished for special corner
sings. This detail provides room
r a double 2x4 support.

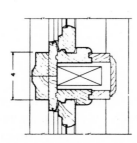

MULLION

Mullions are made by joining
single units. Detail shows typical
modular 4 inch mullion made by
placing two standard single units
together with sill horns butt jointed
and regular 2 inch casings back
to back.

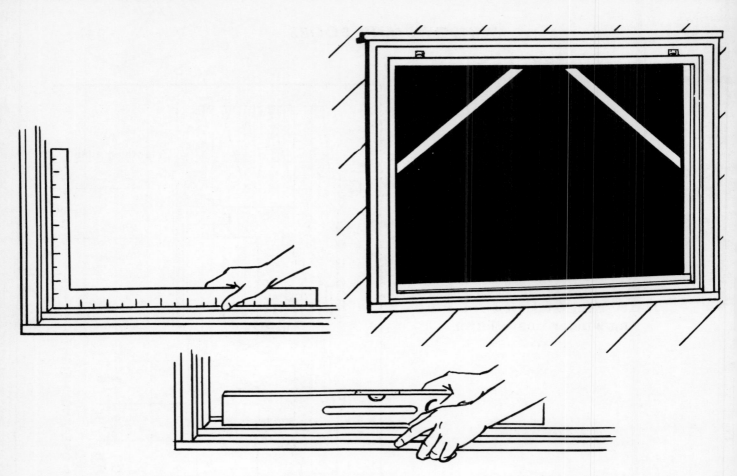

K-19. Gliding window frames should not be installed until sheathing is applied and the roof is on. Be sure frame is square and plumb in opening before nailing wide blind stops to studding.

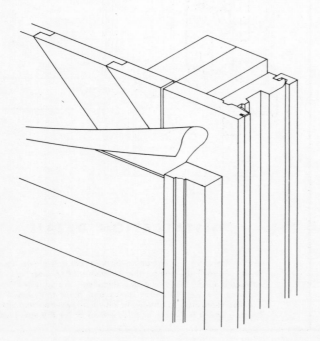

K-20. Gliding window installation. Lap building paper over wide blind stops and fit snugly up to casings. Use flashing where required. Note that sheathing is set back to allow for the wide blind stops.

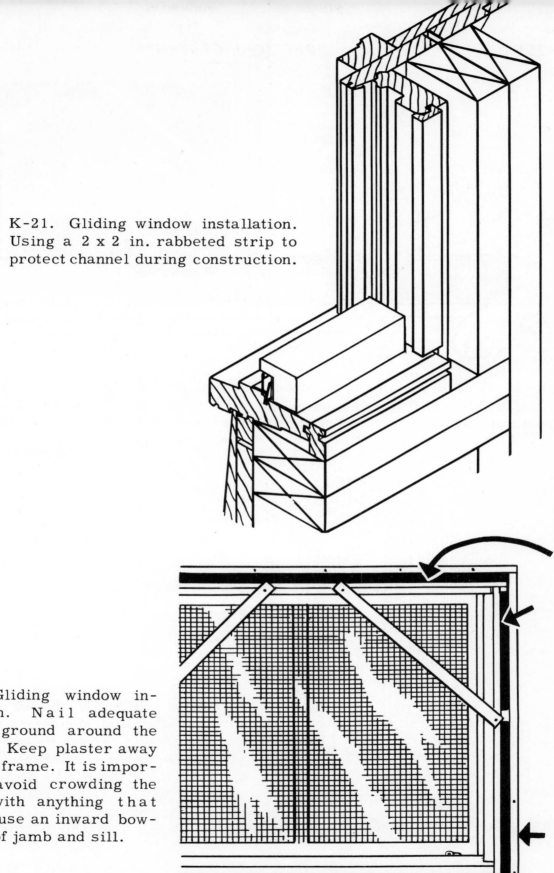

K-21. Gliding window installation. Using a 2 x 2 in. rabbeted strip to protect channel during construction.

K-22. Gliding window installation. Nail adequate plaster ground around the opening. Keep plaster away from the frame. It is important to avoid crowding the frame with anything that might cause an inward bowing of jamb and sill.

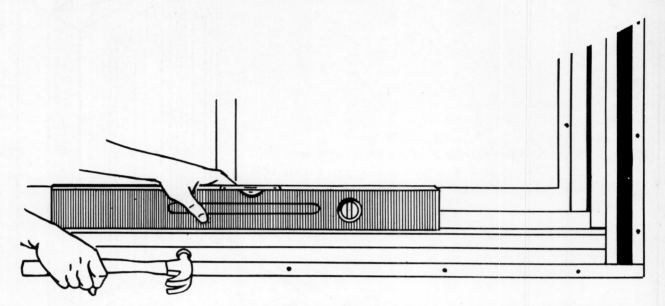

K-23. Gliding window installation. After plaster is dry and just before applying inside trim, the frame should be squared and leveled. Use blocking to straighten out any bowing of jambs or sill to insure these parts remaining straight and true.

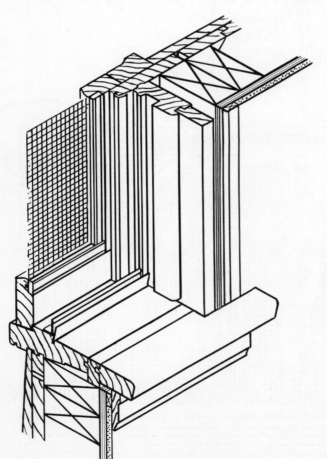

K-24. Gliding window installation. Apply extension jambs and stools. Remove protection strips from jambs. Clean dirt from sill and install sill track. Make sure stool is flush with window sill.

K-25. Gliding window installation. Install left hand sash first. Try sash in opening before applying trim. Make sure the side jamb and sash stile are in line as shown by the arrows. This is the proper time to check installation and blocking for adjusting and further block if needed.

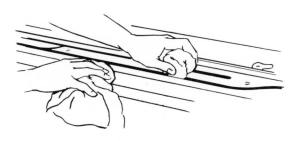

K-26. Gliding window installation. Remove dirt or paint from weatherstripping, wax lightly and buff with a dry cloth. Clean and wax sill channel and track.

K-27. Gliding window. Sash should be painted out of the opening and kept clean and free from exposure to dirt, moisture and damage. The putty needs the protection of one or more coats of paint before exposure to the weather. Lap the paint slightly on the glass to form a tight seal against moisture. When scraping dried paint be sure not to break the seal between the putty and the glass.

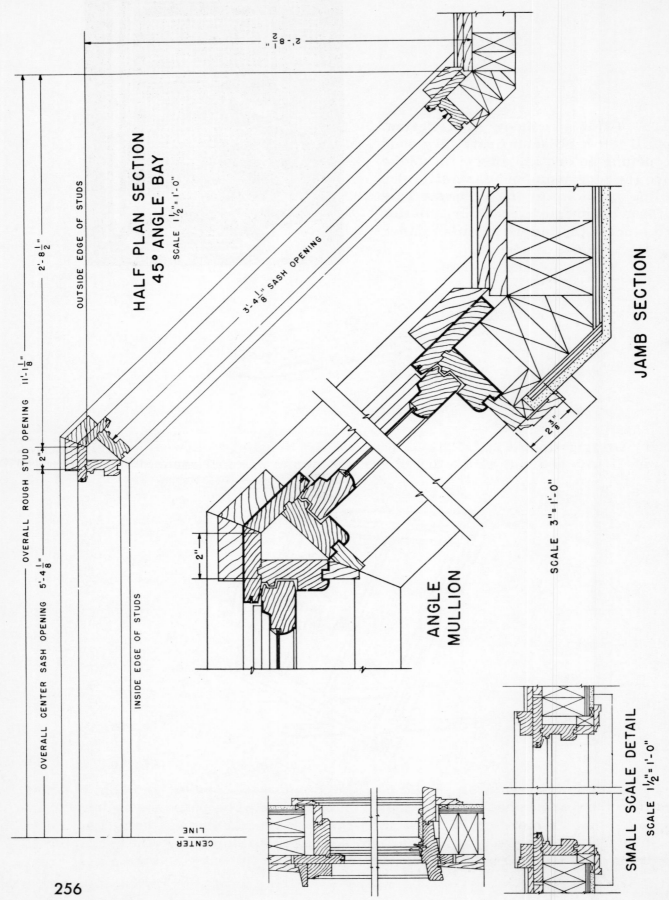

2'-8½"

2'-8½"

OUTSIDE EDGE OF STUDS

HALF PLAN SECTION
45° ANGLE BAY
SCALE 1½"=1'-0"

3'-4⅛" SASH OPENING

OVERALL ROUGH STUD OPENING 11'-1⅛"

2"

OVERALL CENTER SASH OPENING 5'-4⅛"

INSIDE EDGE OF STUDS

CENTER LINE

2"

ANGLE MULLION

2⅜"

JAMB SECTION

SCALE 3"=1'-0"

SMALL SCALE DETAIL
SCALE 1½"=1'-0"

K-28. Gliding window installation. Angle bay details.

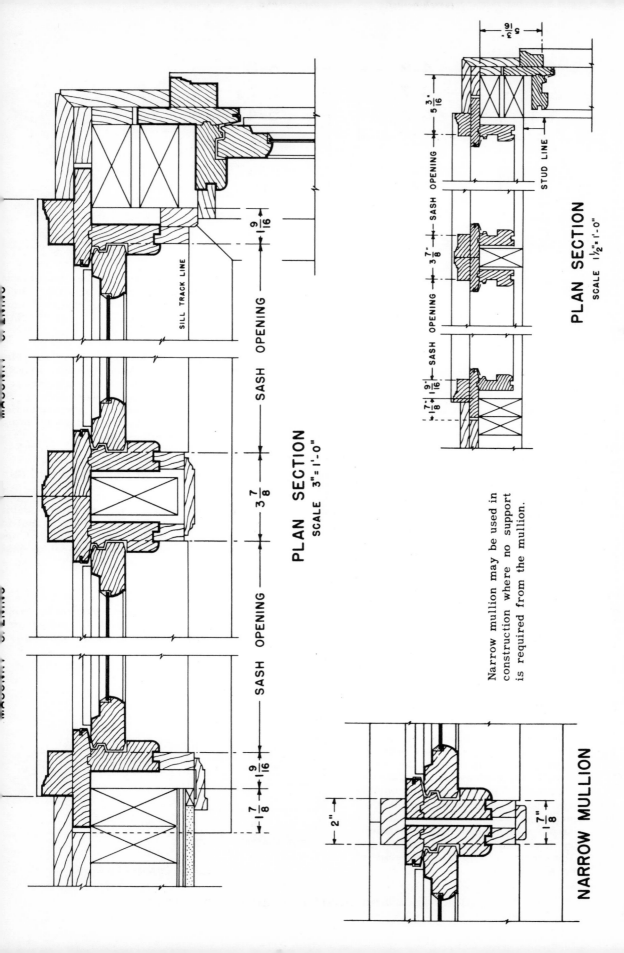

PLAN SECTION
SCALE 3" = 1'-0"

SASH OPENING

$3\frac{7}{8}$"

SASH OPENING

$1\frac{7}{8}$" $1\frac{9}{16}$"

$1\frac{9}{16}$"

SILL TRACK LINE

PLAN SECTION
SCALE $1\frac{1}{2}$" = 1'-0"

$5\frac{3}{16}$"

SASH OPENING

$5\frac{3}{16}$"

SASH OPENING

$3\frac{7}{8}$"

SASH OPENING

$1\frac{7}{8}$" $1\frac{9}{16}$"

STUD LINE

Narrow mullion may be used in construction where no support is required from the mullion.

NARROW MULLION

2"

$1\frac{7}{8}$"

K-29. Gliding window installation. Corner window details.

257

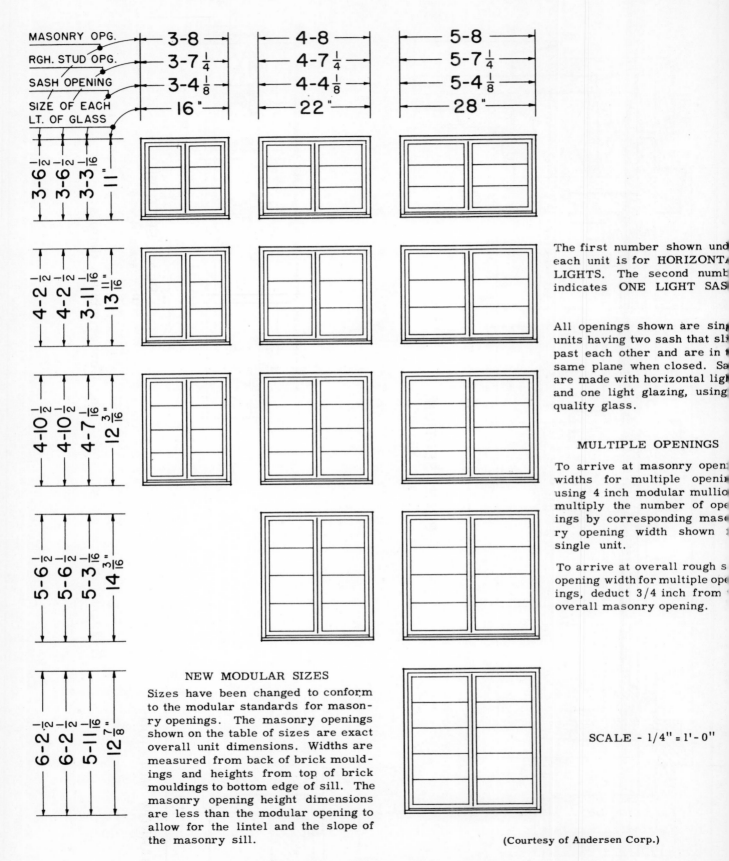

MASONRY OPG.
RGH. STUD OPG.
SASH OPENING
SIZE OF EACH LT. OF GLASS

3-8	4-8	5-8
3-7¼	4-7¼	5-7¼
3-4⅛	4-4⅛	5-4⅛
16"	22"	28"

3-6½   3-6½   3-3 6/16   11"

4-2½   4-2½   3-11 6/16   13 11/16"

4-10½   4-10½   4-7 6/16   12 3/16"

5-6½   5-6½   5-3 6/16   14 3/16"

6-2½   6-2½   5-11 6/16   12 7/8"

The first number shown und
each unit is for HORIZONT
LIGHTS. The second numb
indicates ONE LIGHT SAS

All openings shown are sin
units having two sash that sl
past each other and are in
same plane when closed. Sa
are made with horizontal lig
and one light glazing, using
quality glass.

MULTIPLE OPENINGS

To arrive at masonry open
widths for multiple openi
using 4 inch modular mullio
multiply the number of ope
ings by corresponding mase
ry opening width shown
single unit.

To arrive at overall rough s
opening width for multiple op
ings, deduct 3/4 inch from
overall masonry opening.

NEW MODULAR SIZES

Sizes have been changed to conform
to the modular standards for masonry openings. The masonry openings
shown on the table of sizes are exact
overall unit dimensions. Widths are
measured from back of brick mouldings and heights from top of brick
mouldings to bottom edge of sill. The
masonry opening height dimensions
are less than the modular opening to
allow for the lintel and the slope of
the masonry sill.

SCALE - 1/4" = 1'-0"

(Courtesy of Andersen Corp.)

258   K-30. Stock sizes and layouts of gliding windows.

INSULATING GLASS UNITS

Factory-built transparent insulating glass units, as shown in the cutaway view, Fig. K-31, are composed of two or more lights of glass separated by the usual practice to locate sources of heat near glass areas in buildings to offset both the conducted loss of heat from the room and the radiant loss from bodies of persons near such cold glass areas.

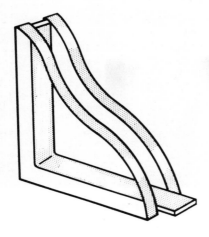 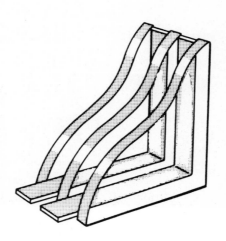

K-31. To the left is a cutaway view of double insulating glass. A metal-to-glass bond seals the edges of the two panes of glass. Triple insulating glass is shown at the right.

dehydrated air space, and hermetically sealed around the edges at the factory, with a metal-to-glass bond.

These factory-fabricated units, which cannot be altered without damaging them, come in different types of glass and in many sizes. Manufacturers also furnish them in special sizes to meet unusual conditions.

Insulating glass units serve several useful purposes: The warm side surface temperature is appreciably higher than that of single glazing. It has been

The higher glass surface temperature of insulating glass units reduces the amount of heat that must be supplied near such areas, permitting flexibility in room design.

A second important aspect of the warmer inside surface temperature is that insulating glass can be designed to reduce condensation otherwise resulting during cold weather, from interior humidification. The reduction of condensation on the warm side is important where visibility is desirable, and to prevent deterioration of sill, wall and floor by water drippage. See Fig. K-32.

Number of Panes	Thickness of Glass	Thickness of Air Space	Dry Bulb Air Temperatures on Cold Side													
			−30°		−20°		−10°		0°		+10°		+20°		+30°	
			Temp.	RH	Temp.	RH	Temp.	RH	Temp.	RH	Temp.	RH	Temp.	RH	Temp.	RH
Single Glass	1/8″	None	2°	5.5	9°	8.5	15°	12.0	22°	16.0	28°	21.0	35°	28.0	42°	36.5
	1/4″	None	5°	6.0	11°	9.5	18°	13.0	24°	17.0	30°	22.5	37°	29.5	43°	37.5
Double *Thermopane* (One Air Space)	1/8″	1/4″	35°	28.0	38°	31.5	41°	35.5	44°	39.5	47°	45.0	51°	50.0	54°	56.5
		1/2″	38°	31.0	41°	32.0	43°	38.0	46°	43.0	49°	48.0	52°	54.0	55°	60.0
	1/4″	1/4″	36°	28.5	39°	32.5	42°	36.5	45°	41.0	48°	47.0	51°	52.0	54°	58.0
		1/2″	39°	31.5	42°	33.0	45°	40.0	47°	45.0	50°	50.5	53°	56.0	56°	62.0
Triple *Thermopane* (Two Air Spaces)	1/8″ or 1/4″	1/4″	46°	41.5	48°	44.5	49°	49.0	52°	54.0	54°	58.0	57°	63.0	59°	68.5

The above chart is based on normal convection currents on the room side when unobstructed by curtains, drapes or heavy muntins.

K-32. Temperatures of glass surface on warm side and per cent relative humidity (RH) at which condensation occurs (dry bulb air temperature 70 degrees F. on warm side).

K-33. Typical installation of 1 in. insulating glass unit in picture window.

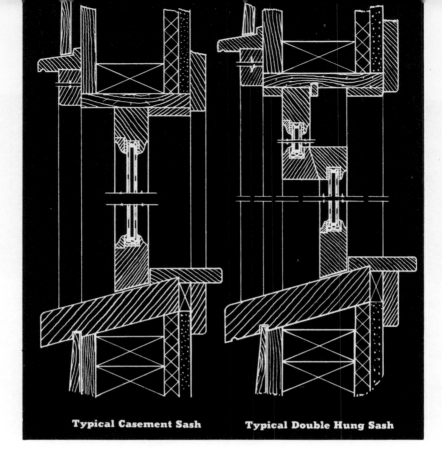

Typical Casement Sash   **Typical Double Hung Sash**

K-34. Typical installation of insulating glass units in casement sash and double hung sash.

In air conditioned space where it is desirable to control humidities accurately at all times, a condensate appearing on the glass surface indicates withdrawal of moisture from the air. Under such conditions an accurate control of humidity is difficult. Proper glazing with insulating glass will keep the inside glass surface temperature above the dew point and condensation will be greatly reduced.

Manufacturers of double-hung, casements, picture windows and windows for farm buildings and sash for double-pane insulating glass and ready-to-use windows are being offered in numerous sizes. A typical installation of 1 in. thick insulating glass unit in a picture window is shown in Fig. K-33. Typical casement sash and double-hung sash installations of 1/2 in. units are illustrated in K-34.

GLAZING DOUBLE-PANE GLASS

Insulating glass as required for, picture windows presents no difficult installation problems. However, it differs from glazing of single panes in several important ways. See Fig. K-35 for information on step-by-step installation procedure. Suggested framing details for window wall construction are given in K-36.

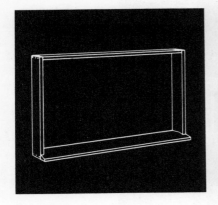

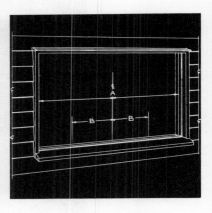

1. Make a simple frame of dressed lumber, preferably redwood, ponderosa pine, sugar pine, cypress or fir. Use 2 x 6's for sides and top, and 2 x 8 for sill. Rout out sill for drip and siding grooves; also, plane a bevel on outer portion of top surface of sill for water drainage. Inside dimensions of frame should be 1⅛" larger than size of *Thermopane* unit to be installed.

2. Nail on a spacer strip 5⁄16" thick x 1¼" wide (lattice strips may be suitable) around the inside of the frame to form an opening in which the *Thermopane* will be glazed. Heads of nails must not protrude.

3. Simple frame is placed in opening. Make sure that frame is square and plumb, that sill member is flat and level. A: Center of opening. B: Points midway from center to outer corners where setting blocks are placed.

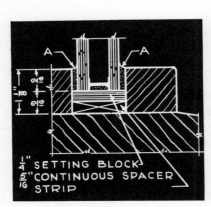

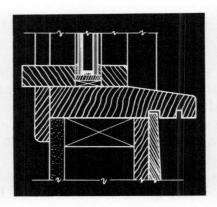

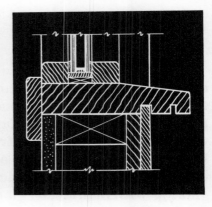

4. Section shows how *Thermopane* rests on setting blocks and is cushioned by ⅛" bed (A) of glazing compound on each surface of the glass.

5. Section above shows how stool can be used as back stop for the *Thermopane* unit. To the right is an alternate method.

6. Same section as illustration in 5 (left) but back stop does not double as stool. Plain trim is used to cover joint of sill at interior wall.

K-35. Step-by-step procedure for installing insulating glass in picture windows.

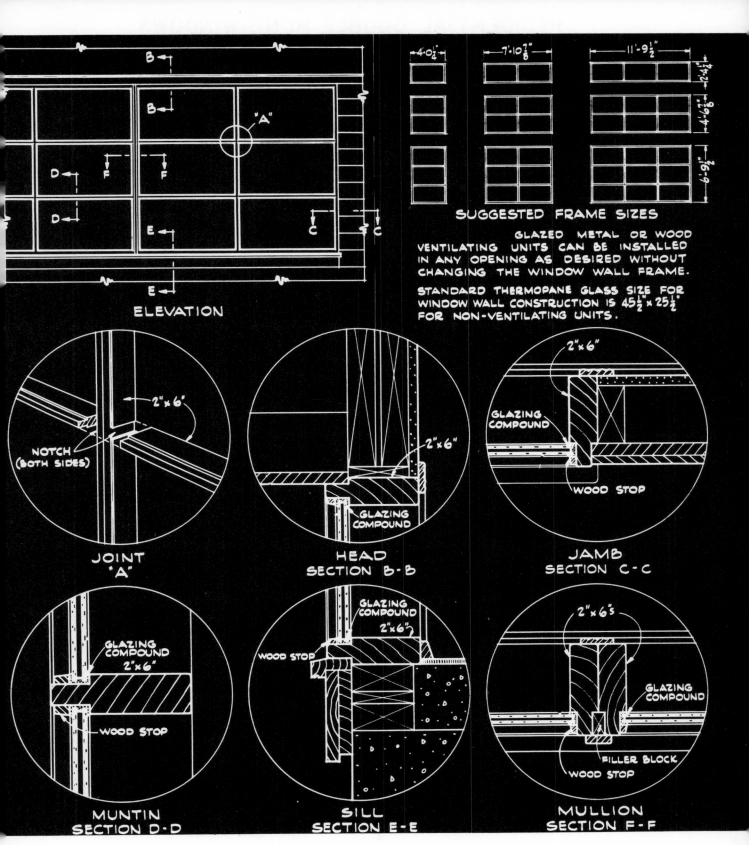

ELEVATION

SUGGESTED FRAME SIZES

GLAZED METAL OR WOOD VENTILATING UNITS CAN BE INSTALLED IN ANY OPENING AS DESIRED WITHOUT CHANGING THE WINDOW WALL FRAME.

STANDARD THERMOPANE GLASS SIZE FOR WINDOW WALL CONSTRUCTION IS $45\frac{1}{2}$" × $25\frac{1}{2}$" FOR NON-VENTILATING UNITS.

JOINT 'A'

HEAD SECTION B-B

JAMB SECTION C-C

MUNTIN SECTION D-D

SILL SECTION E-E

MULLION SECTION F-F

K-36. Framing details for insulating glass, window wall construction.

RESIDENTIAL DOUBLE HUNG WINDOWS

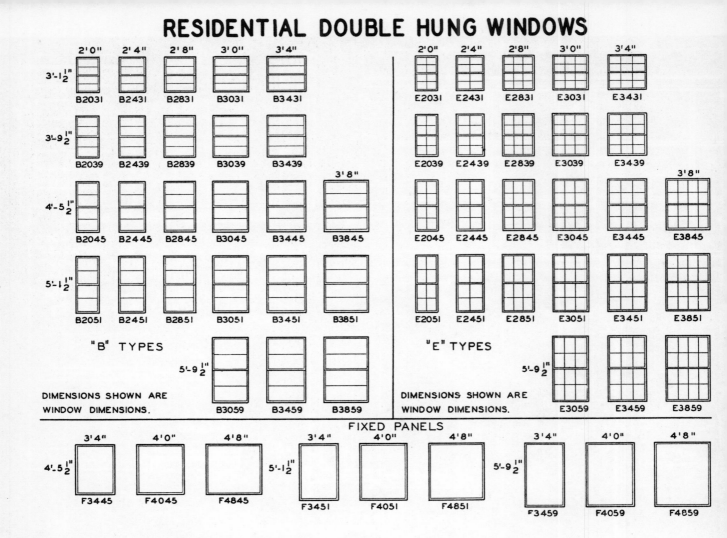

"B" TYPES

DIMENSIONS SHOWN ARE WINDOW DIMENSIONS.

"E" TYPES

DIMENSIONS SHOWN ARE WINDOW DIMENSIONS.

FIXED PANELS

RESIDENCE CASEMENTS

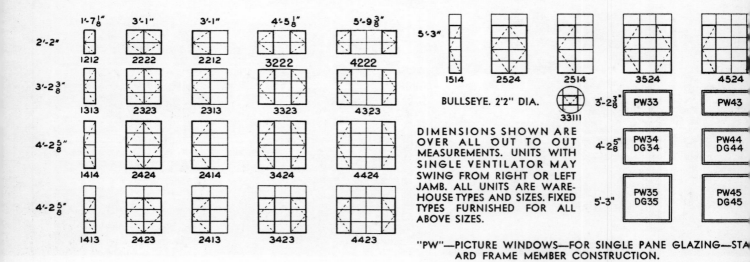

DIMENSIONS SHOWN ARE OVER ALL OUT TO OUT MEASUREMENTS. UNITS WITH SINGLE VENTILATOR MAY SWING FROM RIGHT OR LEFT JAMB. ALL UNITS ARE WAREHOUSE TYPES AND SIZES. FIXED TYPES FURNISHED FOR ALL ABOVE SIZES.

"PW"—PICTURE WINDOWS—FOR SINGLE PANE GLAZING—STARD FRAME MEMBER CONSTRUCTION.

"DG"—DOUBLE GLAZING—FOR 1" THICK, DOUBLE INSULAT GLASS, STOCK SIZES—SPECIAL SECTION FRAME CONSTRTION.

K-38. Popular sizes and types of steel residential casements and double hung windows.

METAL WINDOWS

Windows of steel are strong, enduring and offer considerable protection for window openings.

Some simple suggestions, as offered by the Metal Window Institute, if followed, will help assure longevity, ease of operation and minimum of maintenance expense:

1. Avoid unnecessary roughness in unloading windows at job site. Do not drop windows from conveyance.

2. Stand windows upright on pieces of lumber to keep them off the ground and cover to protect against the elements. Heavy objects should never be placed on a stack of windows.

3. Whenever it is necessary to remove wire or clips holding the ventilators closed, be sure to replace these clips or wires as soon as possible and until hardware is attached.

4. First field coat of paint should be applied before glazing windows. If shop coat of paint has become scratched or marred, "touch-up" the damaged surfaces before installation.

5. Protect ventilators and operating parts against accumulations of cement, lime and other building materials by keeping ventilators tightly closed whenever possible. Do not allow workmen to use ventilators for supporting scaffolding, or muntins for ladders.

6. Set windows plumb, level and square, and adjust all ventilators to close tightly and operate freely before surrounding masonry or other construction is started.

7. Attach hardware and glaze after all heavy construction work is completed. For glazing use a good grade of metal window putty or glazing compound. Be sure to "bed-putty" and use spring wire glazing clips which should be furnished by glazier.

8. A finish coat of good paint will then assure lasting satisfaction and economy of maintenance inherent in metal windows.

STEEL WINDOW INSTALLATION, POPULAR SIZES

Installation of residential steel casements—frame and brick veneer construction, is given in Fig. K-37.

Popular sizes and types of residential casements and double-hung windows are shown in Fig. K-38.

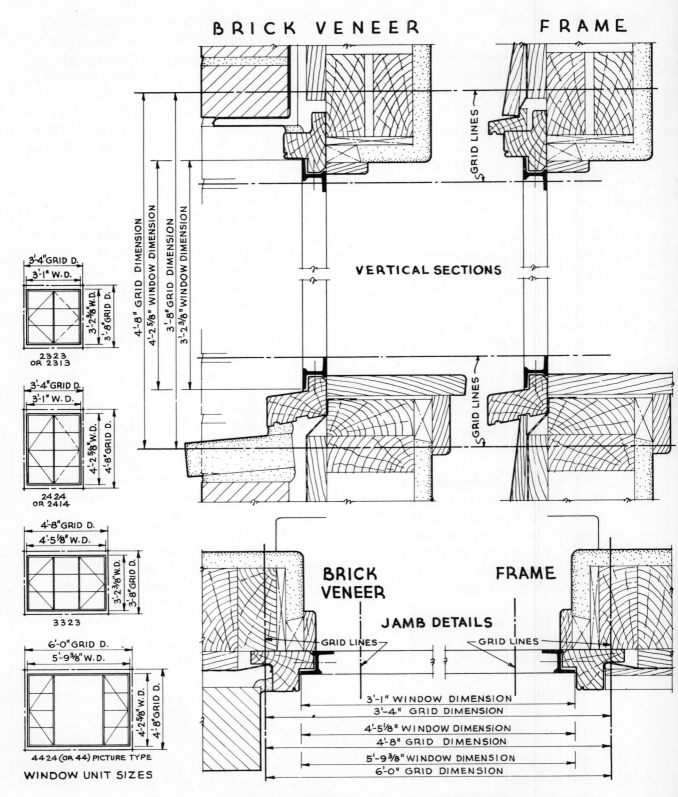

BRICK VENEER — FRAME

VERTICAL SECTIONS

BRICK VENEER — FRAME

JAMB DETAILS

3'-1" WINDOW DIMENSION
3'-4" GRID DIMENSION
4'-5⅛" WINDOW DIMENSION
4'-8" GRID DIMENSION
5'-9⅜" WINDOW DIMENSION
6'-0" GRID DIMENSION

WINDOW UNIT SIZES

2323 OR 2313
2424 OR 2414
3323
4424 (OR 44) PICTURE TYPE

K-37. Installing residential steel casements —
frame and brick veneer construction.

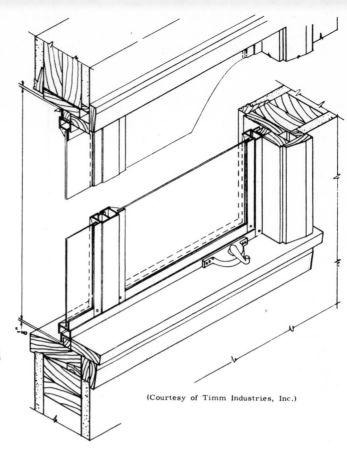

K-39. Typical installation of aluminum casement window in frame and stucco construction.

(Courtesy of Timm Industries, Inc.)

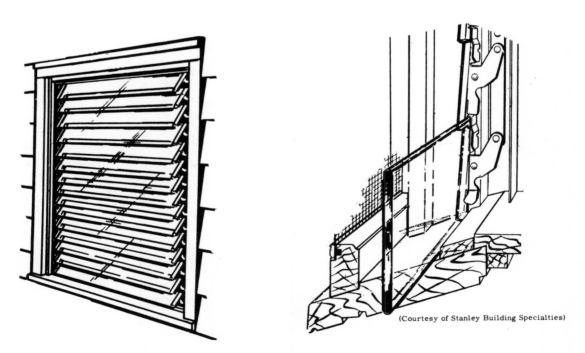

(Courtesy of Stanley Building Specialties)

K-39a. Left. Modern aluminum jalousie windows serve well as enclosures for breezeways, porches and garages. They are suitable for use as house windows, in warm climates. Right. Section view of typical jalousie window installation.

FITTING DOOR FRAMES

Door frames in exterior walls are usually fitted after the walls have been sheathed but before siding or other exterior finish is applied.

A door frame includes two side jambs, header and bottom sill, the top of which should be flush with the surface of the finish flooring.

The door jamb is the part of the frame which forms a lining for the opening and receives the door.

Some door frames are assembled on the job, others come to the job pre-assembled ready to fit into the rough openings.

TWO TYPES OF JAMBS

There are two principal types of door jambs—the rabbeted type in which stock about 1 3/8 in. in thickness is rabbeted on one or both sides to take doors, Fig. K-40, or the type with a separate door stop attached, Fig. K-41. The latter type is ordinarily made of 1 in. lumber and the stop bead attached by nailing. In some cases jamb is routed out to take a thicker stop, as shown by dotted lines.

The jambs should be tacked lightly on both sides, centered in the opening, as in K-42, and wedged with pieces of shingles or other tapered lumber.

Typical sill construction for outside

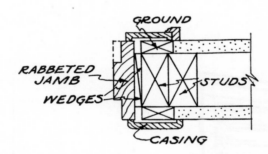

K-40. Door jamb which is rabbeted on both sides. In some cases the jamb is rabbeted on one side only, as indicated by the dotted lines.

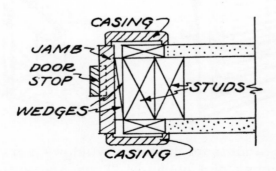

K-41. Door jamb to which stop is nailed. As an alternative the jamb may be routed out to receive the stop as indicated by the dotted lines.

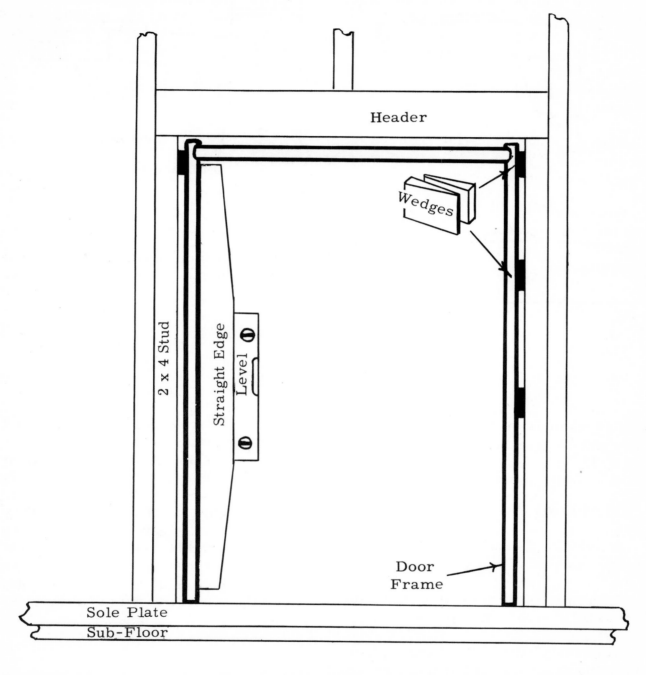

Header

Wedges

2 x 4 Stud

Straight Edge

Level

Door
Frame

Sole Plate

Sub-Floor

K-42. Fitting door frame. Jambs should be tacked lightly on both sides, centered in the opening, and wedged with pieces of shingles or other tapered lumber. Nails should not be driven completely into wood until all necessary adjustments have been made. Nails used should be regular casing nails. Nail heads should be countersunk and filled with putty.

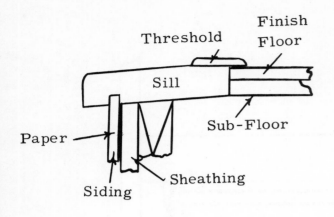

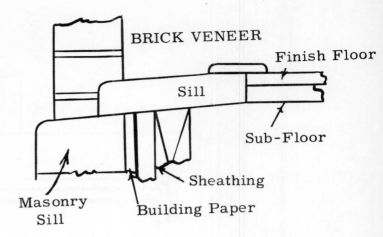

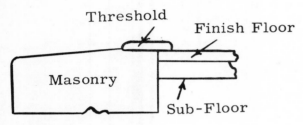

K-43. Entrance door sill construction —frame, brick veneer and masonry.

doors—homes of frame, brick veneer and masonry construction—is shown in K-43.

INSTALLING FRONT ENTRANCES

A typical factory-made front entrance is shown in K-44.

Such entrances generally come from the mill in semi-assembled form.

After the jambs and sill are in place, building paper should be tacked around the opening and the head casing installed over the head jamb. The head casing should be centered leaving 1/2 in. reveal (rabbet to receive screen or storm door).

Next, the side casings are placed over side jambs, allowing 1/2 in. reveal at sides, K-45, and butted against the head casing.

Cut notches at the bottom so they will fit over the ends of the sill. Take end pieces and butt them against ends of the head casing, lining them up with the bottom of the side casings. Keep these parallel with side casings.

Place pilaster base even with bottom edge of the side casings, fasten in place, then install pilaster with fluted side out, and pilaster caps. Entrance head should be placed on pilaster caps

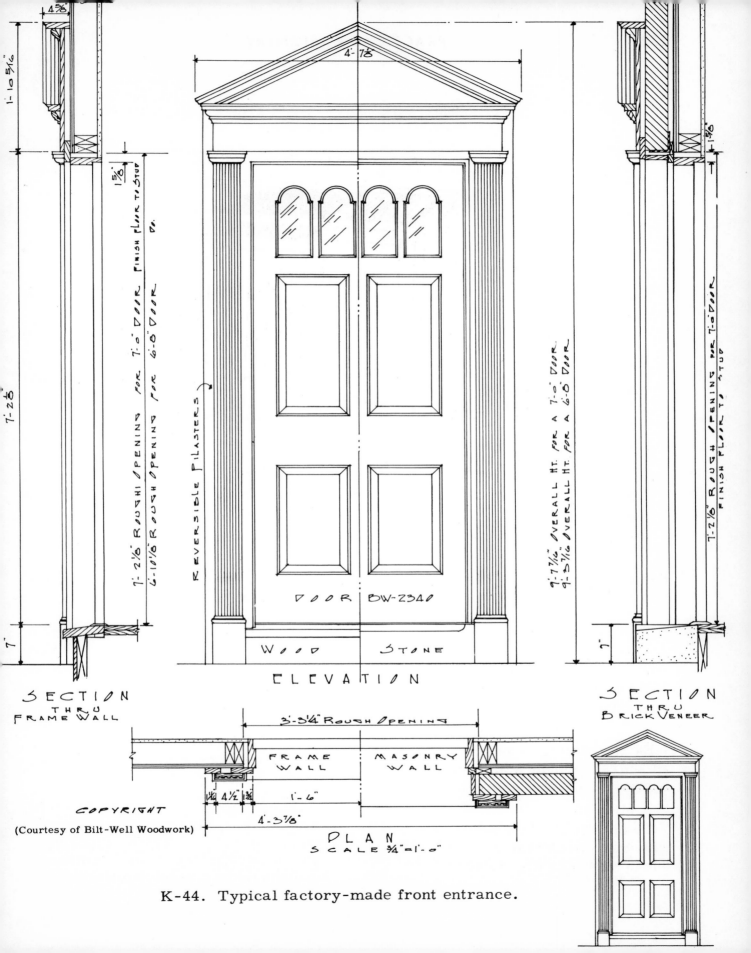

4⅝"

1'-10 5/16"

7'-2⅝"

7'-2⅝"

1⅝"

7'-2¼" Rough Opening for 7'-0" Door Finish Floor to Stud
6'-10⅝" Rough Opening for 6'-8" Door

7"

SECTION
THRU
FRAME WALL

4'-7⅞"

Reversible Pilasters

DOOR BW-2340

WOOD   STONE

ELEVATION

9'-7 7/16" Overall Ht. for a 7'-0" Door
9'-3 7/16" Overall Ht. for a 6'-8" Door

7'-2¼" Rough Opening for 7'-0" Door
Finish Floor to Stud

1⅝"

7"

SECTION
THRU
BRICK VENEER

3'-3¼" Rough Opening

FRAME
WALL

MASONRY
WALL

1½" 4½" 1¾"

1'-6"

4'-3⅞"

PLAN
SCALE ¾"=1'-0"

COPYRIGHT

(Courtesy of Bilt-Well Woodwork)

K-44. Typical factory-made front entrance.

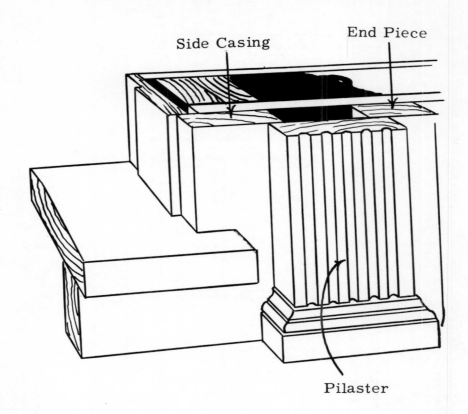

Side Casing

End Piece

Pilaster

K-45. Installing side casings and pilasters. Side casings are placed over side jambs, allowing 1/2 in. reveal at sides to receive screen or storm door.

and the ends should line up with outside edge of the pilasters.

Extra framing required to use such an entrance with a masonry wall is shown in the detail drawings, K-44.

Installation of a colonial entrance with framework that is slightly different is shown in Fig. K-46.

ADVANTAGE OF USING
STOCK DOORS

Doors illustrated in Fig. K-47 are made on a quantity production basis, through specialized machine operations and are ordinarily available for prompt delivery in all localities.

These doors may be adapted to all types of construction.

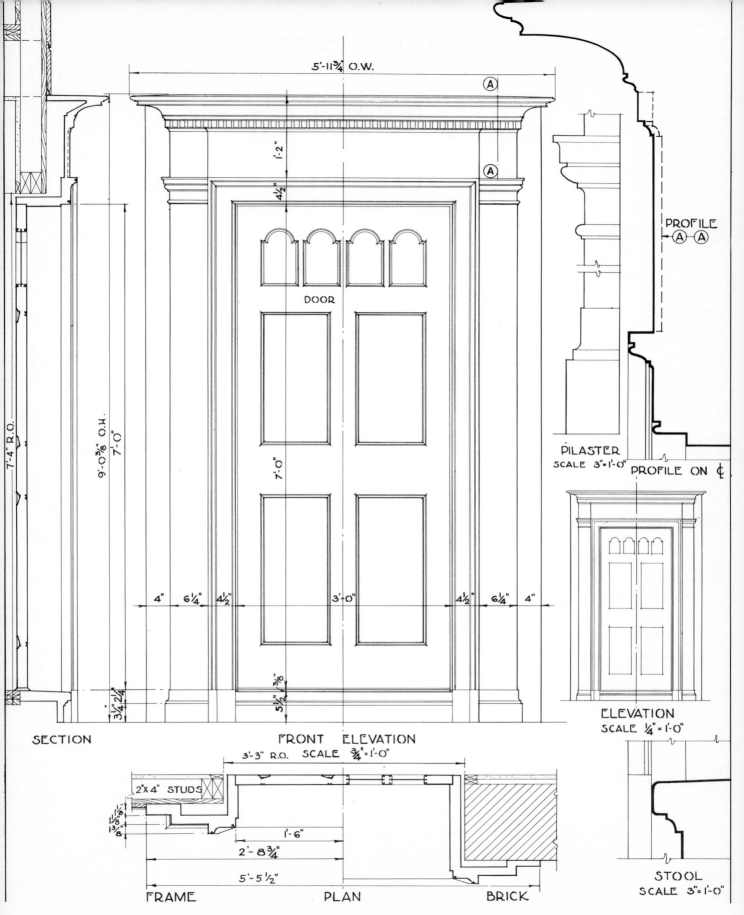

5'-11¾" O.W.

Ⓐ

Ⓐ

1'-2"

4½"

DOOR

7'-0"

9'-0⅜" O.H.

7'-0"

7'-4" R.O.

4" 6¼" 4½"   3'-0"   4½" 6¼" 4"

5½" ⅜"

3½" 2¼"

SECTION

FRONT ELEVATION
3'-3" R.O.   SCALE ¾" = 1'-0"

2"x 4" STUDS

1½"
1⅛"
1⅜"

1'-6"

2'-8¾"

5'-5½"

FRAME   PLAN   BRICK

PROFILE
Ⓐ Ⓐ

PILASTER
SCALE 3" = 1'-0"

PROFILE ON ₵

ELEVATION
SCALE ¼" = 1'-0"

STOOL
SCALE 3" = 1'-0"

K-46. Another typical installation of a factory-made front entrance.

POPULAR PATTERNS OF EXTERIOR DOORS

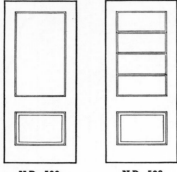

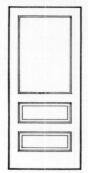
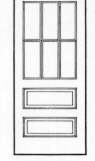

N.D. 500   **N.D. 506**   **N.D. 507**   **N.D. 508**   **N.D. 514**   **N.D. 516**

Above 1 light design N.D. 500 can be divided as in Design N.D. 506 or other divisions are available as listed below:
N.D. 501— 6 lts., 2 w.
N.D. 502— 9 lts., 3 w.
N.D. 505—12 lts., 3 w.

Above 1 light design N.D. 507 can be divided as in Design N.D. 508 or other divisions are available as listed below:
N.D. 509— 9 lts., 3 w.
N.D. 510— 8 lts., 2 w.
N.D. 511— 9 marg. lts.
N.D. 512—12 lts., 3 w.

Above 1 light design N.D. 514 can be divided as in Design N.D. 516 or other divisions are available as listed below:
N.D. 513— 3 hor. lts.
N.D. 515— 4 lts., 2 w.
N.D. 517— 9 lts., 3 w.
N.D. 519— 3 vert. lts.

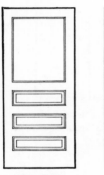
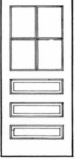
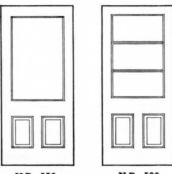

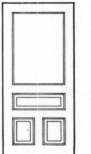
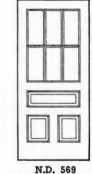

N.D. 537   **N.D. 538**   **N.D. 559**   **N.D. 563**   **N.D. 567**   **N.D. 569**

Above 1 light design N.D. 537 can be divided as in Design N.D. 538 or other divisions are available as listed below:
N.D. 536—3 hor. lts.
N.D. 539—6 lts., 3 w.
N.D. 542—3 vert. lts.

Above 1 light design N.D. 559 can be divided as in Design N.D. 563 or other divisions are available as listed below:
N.D. 560—4 lts., 2 w.
N.D. 561—6 lts., 2 w.
N.D. 562—9 lts., 3 w.

Above 1 light design N.D. 567 can be divided as in Design N.D. 569 or other divisions are available as listed below:

N.D. 570—9 lts., 3 w.

CONSTRUCTION DETAILS

Design No.	Stiles	Top Rail	Cross Rail	Lock Rail	Intermediate Rails	Mullions or Muntins	Bottom Rail	Panels	Approx. Glass Size 2'-8" x 6'-8" Door
*N.D. 500	5½"	5½"	......	9⅝"	......	......	9⅝"	Raised	22" x 40"
*N.D. 506	5½"	5½"	......	9⅝"	......	......	9⅝"	Raised	22" x 9⅝"
*N.D. 507	5½"	5½"	......	9⅝"	......	......	9⅝"	Raised	22" x 46"
*N.D. 508	5½"	5½"	......	9⅝"	......	......	9⅝"	Raised	10¾" x 15"
N.D. 514	4¾"	4¾"	......	4⅝"	4⅝"	......	9⅝"	Raised	23½" x 36"
N.D. 516	4¾"	4¾"	......	4⅝"	4⅝"	......	9⅝"	Raised	7½" x 17¾"
N.D. 537	4¾"	4¾"	4⅝"	......	......	......	9⅝"	Raised	23½" x 30"
N.D. 538	4¾"	4¾"	4⅝"	......	......	......	9⅝"	Raised	11½" x 14¾"
N.D. 559	4¾"	4¾"	......	8"	......	4⅝"	9⅝"	Raised	23½" x 40"
N.D. 563	4¾"	4¾"	......	8"	......	4⅝"	9⅝"	Raised	23½" x 13"
N.D. 567	4¾"	4¾"	4⅝"	......	......	4⅝"	9⅝"	Raised	23½" x 34"
N.D. 569	4¾"	4¾"	4⅝"	......	......	4⅝"	9⅝"	Raised	7½" x 16¾"

POPULAR SIZES: Nos. N.D. 500, 506, 507, 508 are 2'-8" x 6'-8", 3'-0" x 6'-8", 3'-0" x 7'-0"
Nos. N.D. 514, 516, 537, 538, 559, 563, 567, 569 are 2'-6" x 6'-6", 2'-8" x 6'-8", 3'-0" x 6'-8", 3'-0" x 7'-0'
*8" Lock Rail furnished when specified.

K-47. Popular sizes and designs of stock doors.

POPULAR PATTERNS OF EXTERIOR DOORS

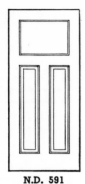

N.D. 591

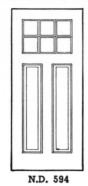

N.D. 594

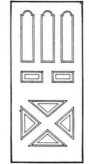

N.D. 608

N.D. 612

Above 1 light design N.D. 591 can be divided as in Design N.D. 594 or other divisions are available as listed below:

N.D. 592—3 vert. lts.
N.D. 593—4 vert. lts.

POPULAR SIZES

Nos. N.D. 591, 594, 608, 612
2'-8" x 6'-8", 3'-0" x 6'-8", 3'-0" x 7'-0"

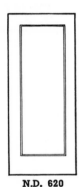

N.D. 620

N.D. 622

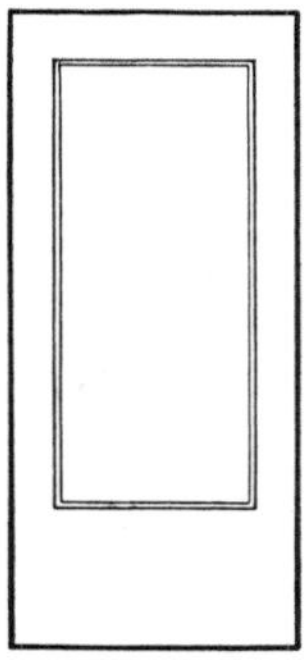

N.D. 635

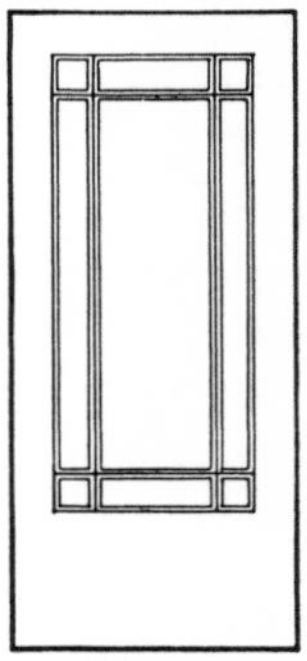

N.D. 638

Above 1 light design N.D. 620 can be divided as in Design N.D. 622 or other divisions are available as listed below:

N.D. 623— 9 marg. lts.
N.D. 625—10 lts., 2 w.
N.D. 626—12 lts., 3 w.
N.D. 627—15 lts., 3 w.
N.D. 630— 5 hor. lts.

POPULAR SIZES
Nos. N.D. 620, 622
2'-0" x 6'-8", 2'-6" x 6'-8", 2'-8" x 6'-8"

Above 1 light design N.D. 635 can be divided as in Design N.D. 638 or other divisions are available as listed below:

N.D. 636— 3 vert. lts.
N.D. 637— 8 lts., 2 w.
N.D. 640—10 lts., 2 w.
N.D. 641—12 lts., 3 w.
N.D. 642—15 lts., 3 w.
N.D. 644— 5 hor. lts.

POPULAR SIZES
Nos. N.D. 635, 638
2'-8" x 6'-8", 3'-0" x 6'-8", 3'-0" x-7'-0"

CONSTRUCTION DETAILS

Design No.	Stiles	Top Rail	Cross Rail	Lock Rail	Intermediate Rails	Mullions or Muntins	Bottom Rail	Panels	Approx. Glass Size 2'-8" x 6'- 8" Door
N.D. 591(1)	4¾" or 5½"	4¾" or 5½"	4⅝" or 5⅜"	......	......	4⅝" or 5⅜"	9⅝"	Raised	22" x 18"
N.D. 594(1)	4¾" or 5½"	4¾" or 5½"	4⅝" or 5⅜"	......	......	4⅝" or 5⅜"	9⅝"	Raised	7" x 8¾"
N.D. 608(2)	4¾"	4¾"	4⅝"	9⅝"	......	4⅝"	8"	Raised	6⅛" x 26⅞"
N.D. 612(3)	5½"	5½"	......	7"	......	5⅜"	8"	Raised	7" x 12"
*N.D. 620	4¾"	4¾"	......	......	......	......	9⅝"	......	23½" x 66½"
*N.D. 622	4¾"	4¾"	......	......	......	......	9⅝"	......	11½" x 16¼"
N.D. 635	5½"	6½"	......	......	......	......	18½"	......	22" x 56"
N.D. 638	5½"	6½"	......	......	......	......	18½"	......	5" x 5" (Cor. lts.)

NOTES: (1) Glass sizes shown are for doors with 5½" stiles. (2) Panel thickness 1⅛". Bars between glass 3½". (3) Panel thickness 1⅛"
*Also for interior use.

POPULAR PATTERNS OF EXTERIOR DOORS

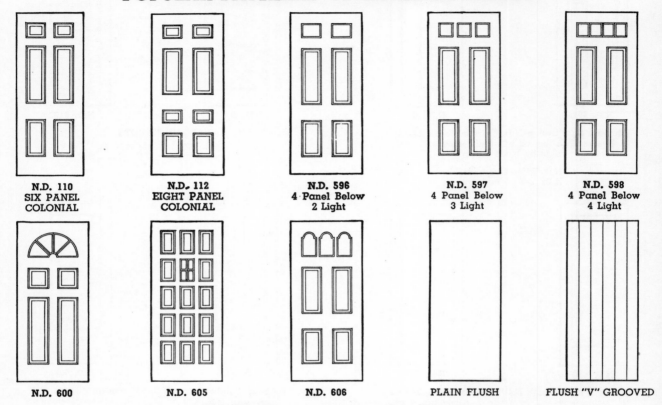

N.D. 110 SIX PANEL COLONIAL	N.D. 112 EIGHT PANEL COLONIAL	N.D. 596 4 Panel Below 2 Light	N.D. 597 4 Panel Below 3 Light	N.D. 598 4 Panel Below 4 Light
N.D. 600	N.D. 605	N.D. 606	PLAIN FLUSH	FLUSH "V" GROOVED

POPULAR SIZES: 2′-8″ x 6′-8″, 3′-0″ x 6′-8″, 3′-0″ x 7′-0″

CONSTRUCTION DETAILS

Design No.	Stiles	Top Rail	Cross Rail	Lock Rail	Intermediate Rails	Mullions or Muntins	Bottom Rail	Panels	Approx. Glass Size 2′-8″ x 6′-8″ Door
*N.D. 110(1)	5½″	5½″	....	8″	5⅜″	5⅜″	9⅝″	Raised	....
*N.D. 112(1)	5½″	5½″	....	8″	5⅜″	5⅜″	9⅝″	Raised	....
*N.D. 596(2)	5½″	5½″	5⅜″	8″	....	5⅜″	9⅝″	Raised	8¾″ x 7⅛″
*N.D. 597(2)(3)	5½″	5½″	5⅜″	8″	....	5⅜″	9⅝″	Raised	5¾″ x 7⅛″
*N.D. 598(2)(4)	5½″	5½″	5⅜″	8″	....	5⅜″	9⅝″	Raised	5⅛″ x 7⅛″
N.D. 600	5½″	5½″	Top 5⅜″	....	4⅝″	4⅝″	9⅝″	Raised	22″ x 11″
N.D. 605	4¾″	4¾″	2⅝″	....	....	2⅝″	9⅝″	Raised	6¾″ x 11⅞″
*N.D. 606(5)	5½″	5½″	5⅜″	8″	....	5⅜″	9⅝″	Raised	6³⁄₁₆″ x 9″
Flush Plain	If desired, light openings may be cut in these doors to suit wishes of purchaser.								
Flush "V" Grooved	If desired, light openings may be cut in these doors to suit wishes of purchaser.								

NOTES: (1) Panel thickness ¾″. Height of top panel over-all 7⅛″. (2) Panel thickness ¾″. (3) Bars between glass 3½″. (4) Bars between glass 1½″. (5) Bars between glass 1½″ to 3½″.
*Bottom and lock rails may be reversed when specified.

POPULAR PATTERNS OF INTERIOR DOORS

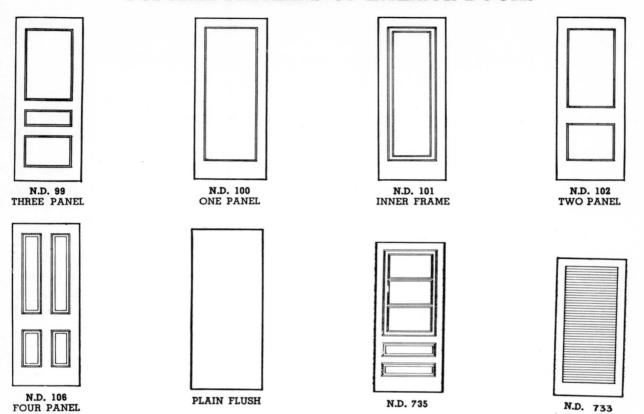

| N.D. 99 THREE PANEL | N.D. 100 ONE PANEL | N.D. 101 INNER FRAME | N.D. 102 TWO PANEL |

| N.D. 106 FOUR PANEL | PLAIN FLUSH | N.D. 735 | N.D. 733 |

CONSTRUCTION DETAILS

Design No.	Stiles	Top Rail	Cross Rail	Lock Rail	Intermediate Rails	Mullions or Muntins	Bottom Rail	Panels
N.D. 99	4¾″	4¾″	4⅝″	4⅝″	......	......	9⅝″	Flat
N.D. 100	4¾″	4¾″	......	......	......	......	9⅝″	Flat
N.D. 101	4¼″ Face	4¼″ Face	......	......	......	......	9¼″ or 9½″ Face	Flat
N.D. 102	4¾″	4¾″	......	8″	......	......	9⅝″	Flat
N.D. 106	4¾″	4¾″	......	8″	......	4⅝″	9⅝″	Raised
N.D. 107	4¾″	4¾″	......	......	4⅝″	......	9⅝″	Raised
N.D. 108 (1)(2)(3)	4¾″	4¾″	......	8″	3⅞″ or 4⅝″	3⅞″ or 4⅝″	9⅝″	Raised
N.D. 111 (1)(2)(3)	4¾″	4¾″	......	8″	3⅞″ or 4⅝″	3⅞″ or 4⅝″	9⅝″	Raised

NOTES: (1) Height of Top Panels Overall 7⅛″. (2) Doors 1′-6″ are made 1 Panel Wide.
(3) Bottom and lock rails may be reversed when specified.
*Also for exterior use.

POPULAR SIZES

1′-6″ x 6′-6″	2′-0″ x 6′-8″	2′-4″ x 6′-8″	2′-6″ x 6′-8″	2′-8″ x 6′-8″
1′-6″ x 6′-8″	2′-0″ x 7′-0″	2′-4″ x 7′-0″	2′-6″ x 7′-0″	2′-8″ x 7′-0″
2′-0″ x 6′-0″	2′-4″ x 6′-0″	2′-6″ x 6′-0″	2′-8″ x 6′-0″	3′-0″ x 6′-8″
2′-0″ x 6′-6″	2′-4″ x 6′-6″	2′-6″ x 6′-6″	2′-8″ x 6′-6″	3′-0″ x 7′-0″

(National Woodwork Manufacturers Association)

HOW TO HANG A DOOR

FITTING DOOR TO THE OPENING

The first step in fitting a door is to remove the protectors from the top and bottom and saw off the "horns" (side stiles which project beyond the top and bottom rails).

Take a look at the plans to make sure in which direction door is to open.

Check the door for warpage. On

Hold the door in the opening and mark from the inside to show exactly how much must be removed. Trim the lock side first, then the butt or back side so it will go into the opening. Clearance at the top and the sides should be about 1/16 in. (approximately the same as the thickness of a U. S. nickel). The cut at the top should be beveled slightly (about 1/16 in.) toward the inside or the stop, to allow for easy closing and to prevent binding.

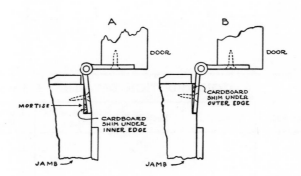

K-48. Hinge adjustments to correct ill-fitting doors.

interior doors slight warpage can usually be taken care of by placing the door so it will tend to straighten as it is closed. Excessively warped doors should not be used.

If the door is considerably oversize, some sawing will be required; if only minor fitting is required a jack plane (16 in. is a good size) will do the job satisfactorily.

Allow the approximate thickness of an 8d nail for clearance at the threshold. Floor clearance on inside doors will vary depending on whether linoleum or carpeting is used as a covering. The clearance for carpet is usually 3/4 in. and for tile or linoleum 3/8 in.

After fitting the door the hinges are attached. Two loose-pin butt hinges

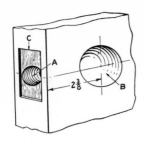

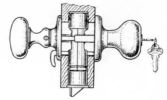

K-49. Installing cylinder lockset. Manufacturer's instructions show location and sizes of holes to be bored and mortises required.

are required for interior doors and three for heavy, exterior doors.

First, attach the hinges to the door. The top hinge is usually set about 7 in. from the top and bottom hinge about 10 in. from the bottom of the door. The third hinge on heavy doors should be installed midway between the other two hinges.

Take one of the hinges, place it on the edge of the door and mark around the leaf of the butt. Using a wood chisel, mortise out the marked area, being careful not to mar the surface or to cut too deep. Fasten this hinge to the door and follow the same procedure in fastening the other hinge or hinges as the case may be.

WEDGE DOOR IN POSITION

Now place the door in the opening, wedge it in the correct position and mark the jambs. To keep the door from binding on the jamb, keep the ends of the hinge leaves approximately 1/16 in. away from the stop or rabbet. Chisel out the wood which must be

removed. Fasten the jamb butt with only one screw so minor corrections can be made without removing the extra screws.

CORRECTING CLEARANCES

Minor clearance corrections on new and older doors as well can be made by applying cardboard shims back of the hinge butts at the proper place. If considerable space remains above the door and along the outside or lock edge, screws should be removed in the leaf of the bottom hinge fastened to the jamb, and a strip of cardboard inserted under the outer edge of that leaf, as shown in detail A, Fig. 48. Longer screws should be substituted for the original ones. After tightening the screws, the door should be closed to see whether the upper part has been pulled sufficiently close to the jamb. If it has, the trouble will have been corrected. If considerable space still remains above the door and along the outside or lock edge after the striking has been corrected, the screws should be removed in the leaf of the bottom

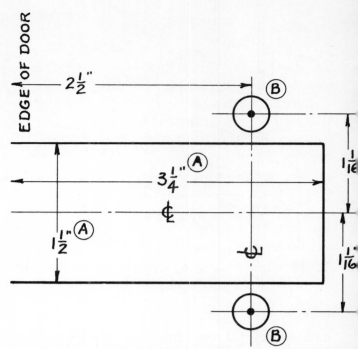

K-50. Unit lock installation. At right is a reproduction of installation sheet which accompanies this type of lock.

1 CUT OUT SECTION OF DOOR STILE $1\frac{1}{2}" \times$ DEEP AS SHOWN AT (A)

2 BORE TWO HOLES (B) - $\frac{3}{8}"$ DIA, $2\frac{1}{8}"$ CENTE TO CENTER, $2\frac{1}{2}"$ FROM EDGE OF DOOR. DRILL HOLES FROM OUTSIDE OF DOOR

3 TO APPLY LOCK TO DOOR, FIRST RELEASE THE SCREWS, THEN SPREAD ESCUTCHEC APART SO THAT LUGS ON OUTSIDE ESC'T WILL CLEAR THE DOOR. SLIDE LOCK IN CUTOUT FOR FRAME SO THAT FACE OF LOCK IS FLUSH WITH FACE OF DOOR. DRAW ESC'T AGAINST SIDE OF DOOR BY MEANS OF THE THRU BOLTS AND TIGHTEN SCREWS.

hinge which is fastened to the jamb. A strip of cardboard should be inserted under the outer edge of that leaf, detail B, Fig. K-48, and longer screws substituted for the original screws. If, after the screws have been tightened, the hinge pins do not move when the door is opened and closed and the crack or margin on all sides is even, the hinges have been properly adjusted. If the hinge pins do move when closing the door, the shims under the hinge leaves may need to be replaced by thinner ones.

If the crack or clearance margin around the door is not even and the door strikes along the outer edge, the door should be removed, the hinge leaves unscrewed from the jamb and some wood cut from the outer edge of the mortise in the jamb with a sharp chisel, being careful to taper the cut

STRIKE APPLICATION

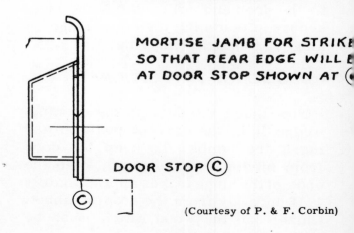

MORTISE JAMB FOR STRIKE SO THAT REAR EDGE WILL E AT DOOR STOP SHOWN AT (

DOOR STOP (C)

(Courtesy of P. & F. Corbin)

280

so that wood from the back edge is not removed. When the hinges are replaced, this beveled deepening of the mortise will tend to pull the door away from the lock jamb and toward the hinge jamb. If the hinge pins move as the door closes and there is still binding against the jamb, the mortises have been beveled too much. This can be remedied bv inserting thin shims under the outer edge of the jamb leaves.

INSTALLING LOCKS

Installing modern day locksets is not difficult, as complete instructions on where to mortise and where to bore holes in most cases is furnished by the manufacturer. Fig. K-49 shows a typical cylinder lockset installation, and K-50, a typical unit lock installation, including a reproduction of the manufacturer's instruction sheet.

SLIDING DOORS

By using sliding doors you add to the usable floor and wall space. Such doors are frequently installed in closets in small bedrooms and in space-saving cabinets.

Fig. K-51 shows a typical pocket (space where door slides into wall) assembly. Note that the rough opening is twice the door width plus 1 5/8 in. and that the stud width is 5 1/8 in.

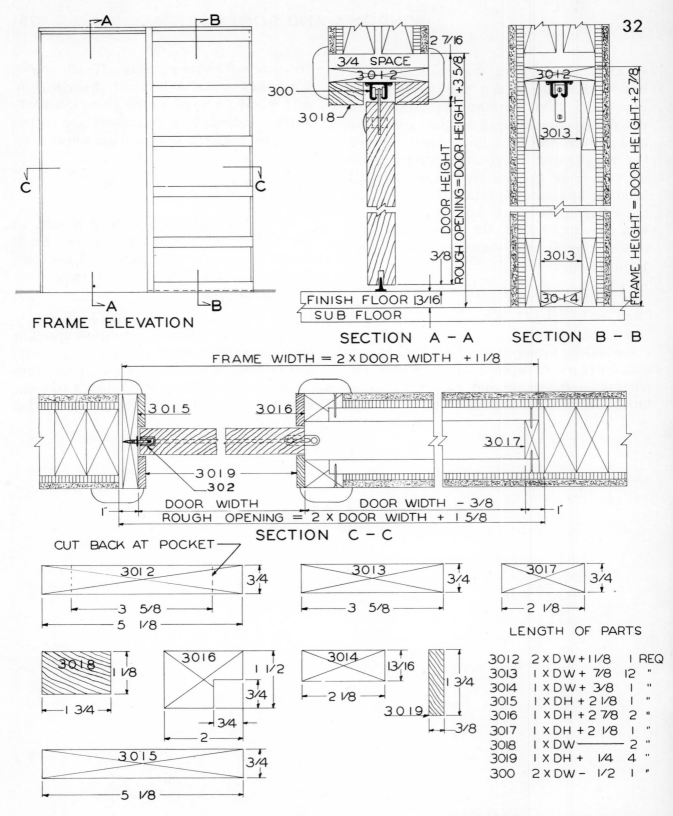

FRAME ELEVATION

SECTION A – A SECTION B – B

SECTION C – C

CUT BACK AT POCKET

LENGTH OF PARTS

3012	2 × DW + 1 1/8	1 REQ
3013	1 × DW + 7/8	12 "
3014	1 × DW + 3/8	1 "
3015	1 × DH + 2 1/8	1 "
3016	1 × DH + 2 7/8	2 "
3017	1 × DH + 2 1/8	1 "
3018	1 × DW———	2 "
3019	1 × DH + 1/4	4 "
300	2 × DW − 1/2	1 "

(Courtesy of Jay G. McKenna, Inc.)

K-51. Sliding door. Closed pocket (door slides into wall) assembly.

How To Build Staircases

A well designed modern staircase adds charm and dignity to a home. The factor of safety must receive consideration too because a lot of accidents happen on stairways.

The safest stairs are those built in straight flights with square landings at the turns. Winders (stairs with treads which are wide at the outside and narrow on the inside) although not considered as safe as straight flight stairs, are required where limited space prevents building stairs without them.

Stair risers (see Fig. L-1) are usually 6 3/4 to 8 in. and treads 10 to 11 in. wide in proportions that give 17 1/2 in. as sum of one riser and one tread.

Riser and tread dimensions should always be such that one can walk up and down with a normal, comfortable stride. This may be accomplished by using proper combinations of measurements for risers and treads. A stairway that is considered a typical "easy" stairway is one with 7 1/2 in. risers and 10 in. treads, Fig. L-2.

For convenient moving of furniture, stairs should be no less than 3 ft. wide. A 3 1/2 ft. width is better. The tread width does not include the nosing or the part projecting beyond the edge of the riser.

For safety, be sure to provide for

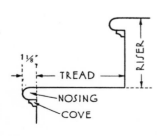

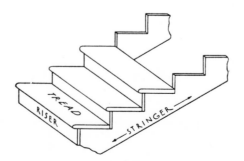

L-1. Parts of a staircase—tread, riser, stringer, nosing and cove.

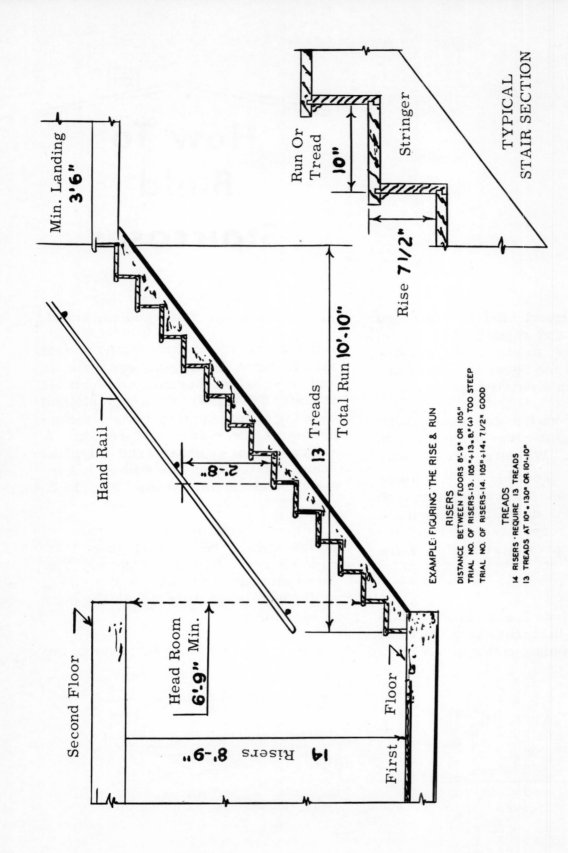

Min. Landing 3'6"

Hand Rail

2'-8"

13 Treads

Total Run 10'-10"

Second Floor

Head Room 6'9" Min.

14 Risers 8'-9"

First Floor

Run Or Tread 10"

Rise 7 1/2"

Stringer

TYPICAL STAIR SECTION

EXAMPLE: FIGURING THE RISE & RUN

RISERS

DISTANCE BETWEEN FLOORS 8'-9" OR 105"
TRIAL NO. OF RISERS-13. 105"÷13, 8."(+) TOO STEEP
TRIAL NO. OF RISERS-14. 105"÷14, 7 1/2" GOOD

TREADS

14 RISERS · REQUIRE 13 TREADS
13 TREADS AT 10" · 130" OR 10'-10"

L-2. Figuring number of stair risers and treads needed. A typical, "easy" staircase is one with 7 1/2 in. risers and 10 in. treads.

284

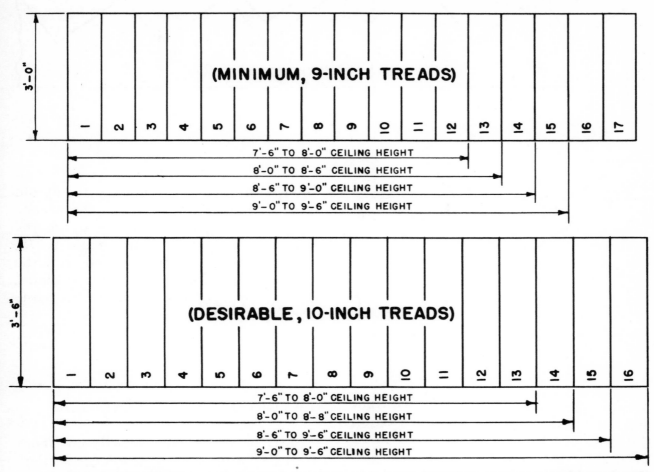

(MINIMUM, 9-INCH TREADS)

3'-0"

| 1 | 2 | 3 | 4 | 5 | 6 | 7 | 8 | 9 | 10 | 11 | 12 | 13 | 14 | 15 | 16 | 17 |

7'-6" TO 8'-0" CEILING HEIGHT

8'-0" TO 8'-6" CEILING HEIGHT

8'-6" TO 9'-0" CEILING HEIGHT

9'-0" TO 9'-6" CEILING HEIGHT

(DESIRABLE, IO-INCH TREADS)

3'-6"

| 1 | 2 | 3 | 4 | 5 | 6 | 7 | 8 | 9 | 10 | 11 | 12 | 13 | 14 | 15 | 16 |

7'-6" TO 8'-0" CEILING HEIGHT

8'-0" TO 8'-8" CEILING HEIGHT

8'-6" TO 9'-6" CEILING HEIGHT

9'-0" TO 9'-6" CEILING HEIGHT

IT USUALLY REQUIRES FROM 14 TO 16 RISERS (13 TO 15 TREADS) TO GET FROM ONE FLOOR TO ANOTHER, DEPENDING ON THE HEIGHT OF CEILING. IF A LANDING IS NECESSARY, THERE SHOULD BE AT LEAST ELEVEN RISERS FROM THE FLOOR TO THE LANDING TO ALLOW HEADROOM TO STAND OR PASS UNDERNEATH. BASEMENT STAIRS MAY BE STEEPER BUT SHOULD BE PROPORTIONED SO THAT SUM OF THE RISER AND TREAD (LESS THE NOSING) EQUALS APPROXIMATELY 17½ INCHES.

SUGGESTED ARRANGEMENTS

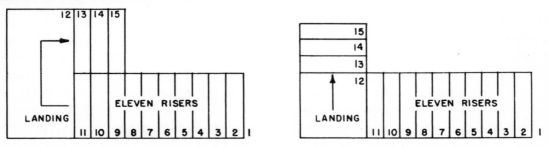

L-3. Number of 9 in. and 10 in. treads required with ceiling heights of 7 ft. 6 in. to 9 ft. 6 in.; also suggested landing arrangements.

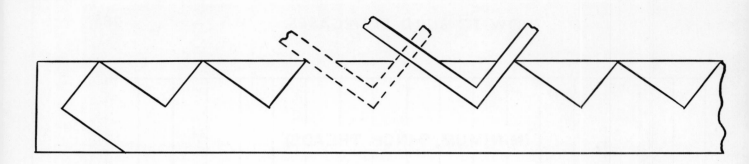

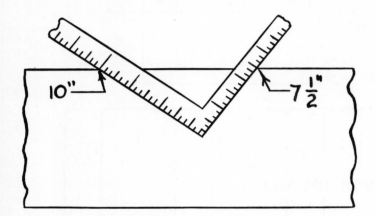

L-4. Using a steel square to lay out stair stringers. Length of the pieces required may be found by using the unit rise per step; in this case 7 1/2, on the tongue of the square and the tread dimension, 10 in., on the blade, and stepping off according to the number of risers.

plenty of natural and artificial light and include a hand rail. Hand rail on the rake or stairs should be 30 to 32 in. and on the landing 34 in. to 36 in. Hand rails should be continuous from floor to floor to provide security every step of the way.

HEAD ROOM

Head room over open stairs should be at least 6 ft. 9 in. Where the ceiling over a stairway is enclosed and sloped to follow the stairs, allow at least 7 ft. to 7 ft. 6 in. for head room. For convenience and to avoid waste hall space, stairs should lead to a rather central location on second floor. See Fig. L-3.

Space will be saved when the basement stairway is placed under the one to the second floor.

LAYING OUT STAIR STRINGERS

Stair stringers are usually cut from 2 x 12's. Sometimes the center stringer is made by nailing scrap blocks to a 2 x 6.

Select 2 x 12's that are straight and as free from knots as are available.

A practical way to lay out stair stringers is by using a steel square, Fig. L-4. Length of the stringers required may be found by using the unit rise per step, 7 1/2 in. in this case, on the tongue of the square, and the tread dimension 10 in., on the blade. Step off according to the number of risers. Shorten the rise of the first step at the bottom, the amount of the thickness of the tread and add this thickness to the top of the string-

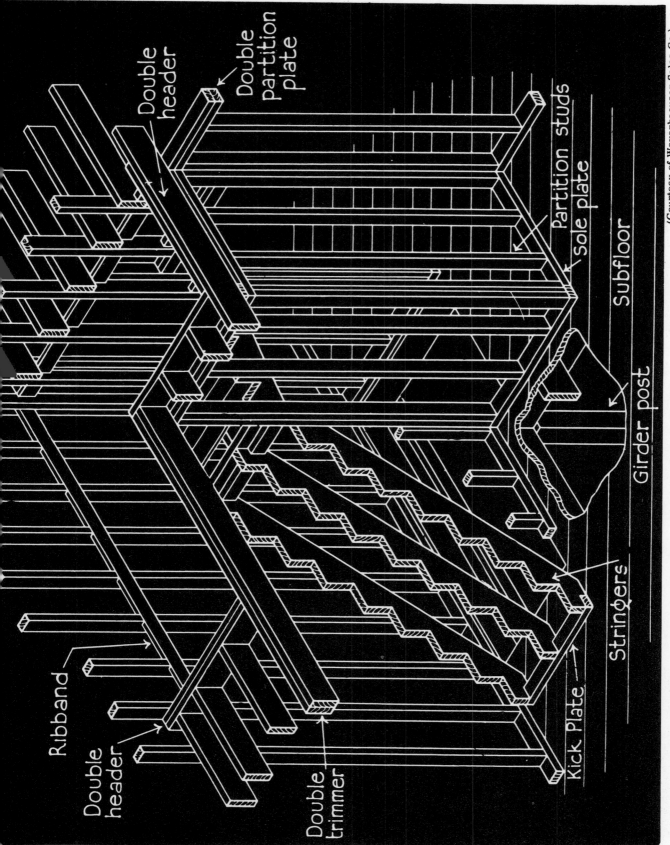

Double header

Double partition plate

Partition studs

Sole plate

Subfloor

Girder post

Stringers

Kick Plate

Double header

Ribband

Double header

Double trimmer

(Courtesy of Weyerhaeuser Sales Co.)

L-5. Framing for open stairway. Note how the stringers are fitted over plates at both ends.

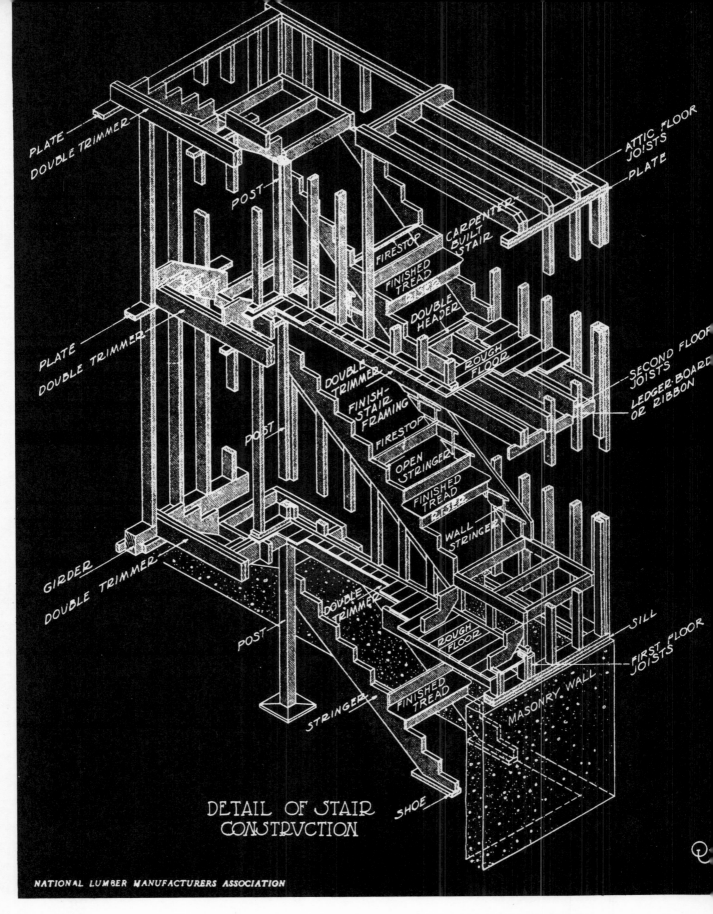

DETAIL OF STAIR
CONSTRUCTION

Labels on figure:
PLATE
DOUBLE TRIMMER
POST
PLATE
DOUBLE TRIMMER
POST
GIRDER
DOUBLE TRIMMER
POST
STRINGER
SHOE
DOUBLE TRIMMER
FINISHED TREAD
FIRESTOP
CARPENTER BUILT STAIR
FINISHED TREAD
DOUBLE HEADER
ROUGH FLOOR
DOUBLE TRIMMER
FINISH-STAIR FRAMING
FIRESTOP
OPEN STRINGER
FINISHED TREAD
WALL STRINGER
ROUGH FLOOR
FINISHED TREAD
MASONRY WALL
ATTIC FLOOR JOISTS
PLATE
SECOND FLOOR JOISTS
LEDGER BOARD OR RIBBON
SILL
FIRST FLOOR JOISTS

288   L-6. Typical stair framing from basement to the attic.

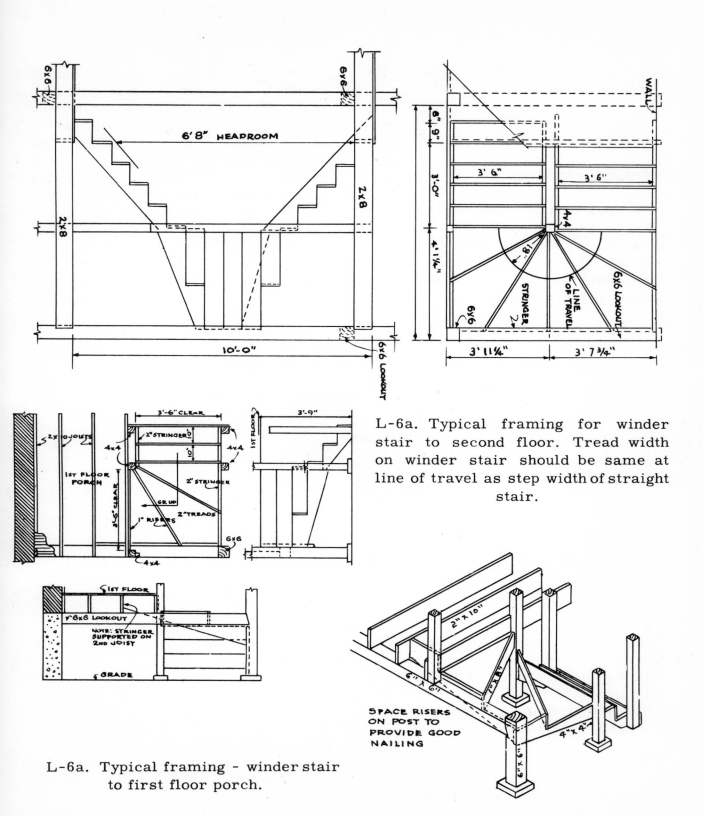

6x6

6'8" HEADROOM

2x8

2x8

2x8

10'-0"

6x6 LOOKOUT

WALL

6"
9"

3' 6"   3' 6"

3'-0"

4x4

4'1¼"

8'

STRINGER
LINE OF TRAVEL
6x6 LOOKOUT

6x6   2'

3' 11¼"   3' 7¾"

2x10 JOISTS

1ST FLOOR PORCH

4x4

3'-6" CLEAR

2" STRINGER

10'

4x4

2' STRINGER

6' UP

2" TREADS

2½'-5" CLEAR

1" RISERS

6x6

4x4

1ST FLOOR

3'-9"

L-6a. Typical framing for winder stair to second floor. Tread width on winder stair should be same at line of travel as step width of straight stair.

1ST FLOOR

6x6 LOOKOUT

NOTE: STRINGER SUPPORTED ON 2ND JOIST

GRADE

2" X 10"

6" X 6"

4" X 4"

6" X 6"

SPACE RISERS ON POST TO PROVIDE GOOD NAILING

L-6a. Typical framing - winder stair to first floor porch.

289

er, so it will fit snugly against the joist header.

Typical stair framing jobs are shown in Figs. L-5, L-6 and L-6a.

HOUSED STRINGERS

A plain stringer while suitable for use in the average home, does not provide the squeak free sturdiness or "finish" of a housed stringer, Fig. L-7, which is used to a considerable extent in the more expensive homes.

floors are commonly made of oak or birch, 1 1/8 in. or 1 1/4 in. in thickness. The nosing which extends beyond the risers is usually rounded, as in L-1. Treads and risers should be rabbeted together and glued and nailed securely. Well constructed stairs will not allow dirt to sift through joints and are less likely to squeak.

USING STOCK STAIRCASE PARTS

While stair parts can be cut out and shaped on the job, in most modern

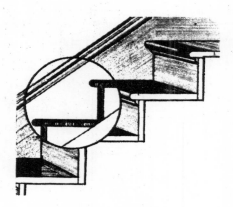

L-7. Housed stringer is made with horizontal and vertical grooves cut on the inside of the stringer to receive treads and risers which are wedged from beneath with glue covered wedges.

A housed stringer is made with horizontal and vertical grooves cut 1/2 in. deep on the inside of the stringer to receive the treads and risers which are wedged from beneath with glue covered wedges.

STAIR TREADS

Treads for basement stairs are usually cut from 2 x 12 in. stock. Treads for the main stairs from first to second

residence construction factory-built parts are used.

Parts required to build standard types of stairways are available from lumber and millwork dealers. The parts come to the job in heavy, protective cartons, along with directions for fitting.

Typical stock staircase parts are shown in Figs. L-8, L-9 and L-10.

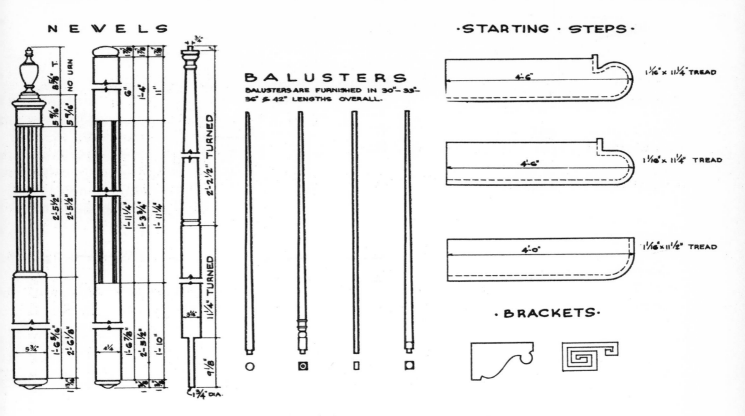

L-8. Stock parts dimensioned—newels, balusters, brackets, starting steps, treads.

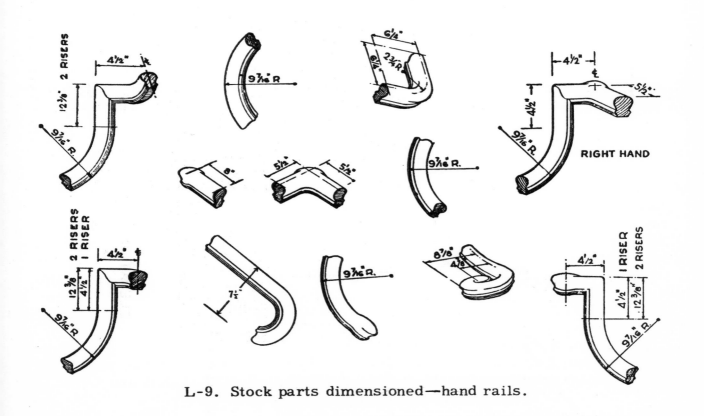

L-9. Stock parts dimensioned—hand rails.

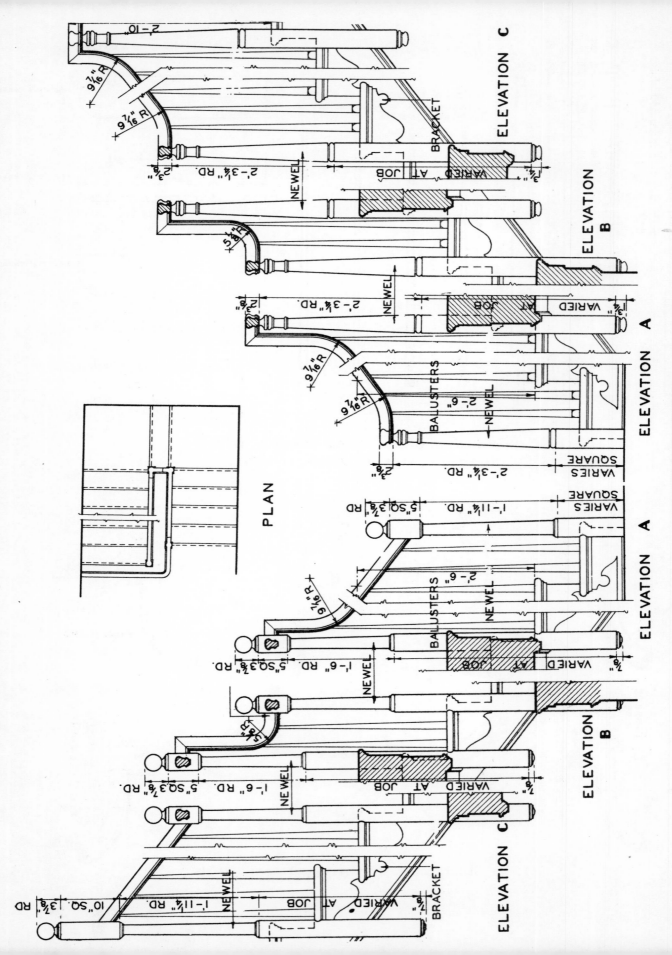

L-10. Typical assemblies of staircase parts.

DISAPPEARING ATTIC STAIRWAYS

Attic space may be made readily accessible for storage by providing a disappearing attic stairway as shown in Figs. L-11 to L-15 inclusive. When the stairway is closed all that can be seen is a neat plywood panel.

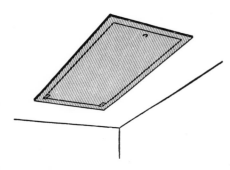

L-11. Folding attic stairway closed. Springs hold the unit tightly to the ceiling opening.

L-13. Unfolding stairway sections.

(Courtesy of EZ-Way Sales, Inc.)

L-14. Folding stairway ready for use.

L-12. Opening stairway.

STAIRWAY IS INSTALLED AS A UNIT

Folding stairways usually come already assembled. The jamb is generally included, making installation a matter of cutting the opening to size and nailing jamb, to ceiling joists.

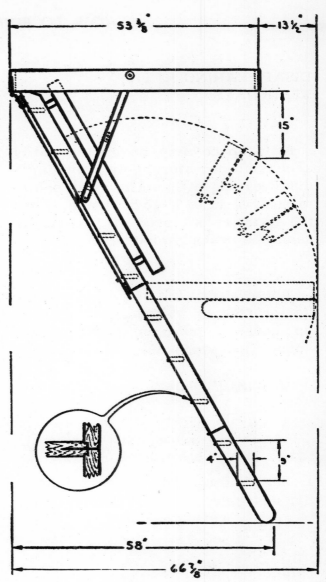

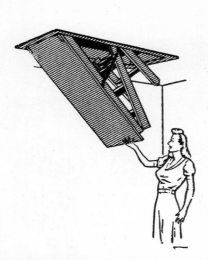

L-15. When not in use, steps are folded and the unit pushed upward to its original position.

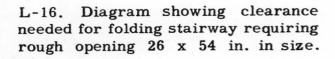

L-16. Diagram showing clearance needed for folding stairway requiring rough opening 26 x 54 in. in size.

Interior Walls, Finishes

Interior finishes which cover interior framed wall and ceiling areas in house construction are of two principal types, plaster and dry-wall.

PLASTER FINISH

A plaster finish requires a base upon which plaster can be spread. Wood lath at one time was commonly used, but the introduction of sheet or board-base materials has almost eliminated its use. Wood lath, if used, should be spaced not less than 3/8 in. apart to allow the plaster to form a good "key." A space of 1/4 in. should be left between lath ends, and joints should be broken every sixth to eighth lath. Wood lath should be nailed at all studs, using 3d wire nails.

GYPSUM BOARD LATH

A popular type of plaster base, which may be used on either side walls or ceilings, is gypsum-board lath, Fig. M-1a. Such lath is 16 x 48 in. and may be applied either horizontally or across the frame members. It has paper faces and a gypsum filler. For stud or joist spacing of 16 in. on center, 3/8 in. gypsum board is used. For 24 in. on center spacing, 1/2 in. thickness is needed. This material may be obtained with a foil back that serves as a vapor barrier. If it faces an air space it has some insulating value. It also comes with perforations which by improving the bond will lengthen the time the plaster will remain intact if exposed to fire.

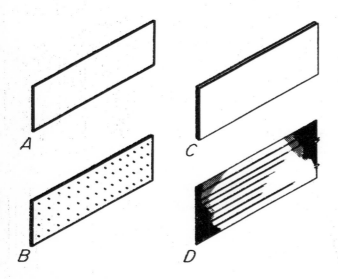

Fig. M-1a. Plaster base materials. A, Gypsum board; B, Gypsum board with perforation; C, Insulating fiberboard lath; D, Metal lath.

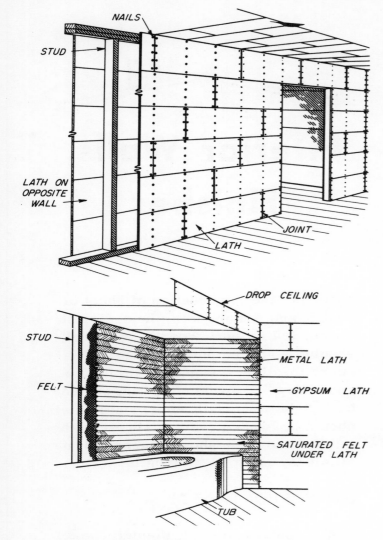

Fig. M-1b. Above. Application of gypsum lath. Below. Application of metal lath.

Insulating fiberboard lath, also shown in Fig. M-1a, may also be used as a plaster base. It usually comes in 1/2 in. thickness and 18 x 48 in. in size. It often has a shiplap edge. Fiberboard lath has a value as insulation and may be used on ceilings or walls adjoining exterior or unheated areas.

Expanded-metal lath, Fig. M-1b, consists of sheet metal slit and expanded to form openings for keying of plas-ter. Metal lath is usually 27 x 96 in. in size.

APPLYING GYPSUM LATH

Gypsum lath should be applied hor-izontally with joints broken, as in Fig. M-1b. Vertical joints should be made over centers of studs or joints. The gypsum board should be nailed with 13-gauge gypsum-lathing nails 1 1/8 in. long and with a 3/8 in. flat head. Nails should be spaced 4 in. on center, or 5 nails for the 16 in. height. The lath should be nailed at each stud or joist crossing.

Insulating lath should be installed much the same as gypsum lath, except that 13 gauge 1 1/4 in. blued nails should be used.

Expanded-metal lath applied around a tub recess for ceramic tile appli-cation, Fig. M-1b, should be used over a paper backing. Studs should be cov-ered with a 15-lb. asphalt-satured felt applied shingle style (unless the metal lath is paper backed). The scratch coat should be Portland ce-ment plaster of 5/8 in. thickness and integrally waterproofed, and must be scratched (roughened) thoroughly. The scratch coat should be dry before ceramic tile is applied.

PLASTER REINFORCING

Because drying usually takes place in wood framing members after a house is completed, some shrinkage can be expected, which, in turn may cause plaster cracks to develop in

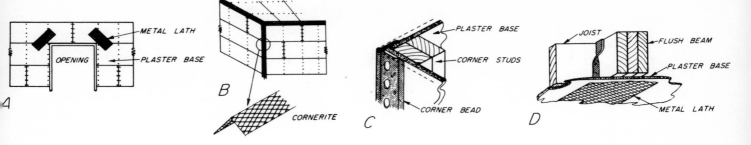

Fig. M-1c. Reinforcing plaster. A, At openings; B, At inside corners; C, At exterior corners; D, Under flush beams.

corners and around openings. To minimize this cracking, strips of expanded-metal lath are often used in key positions over the plaster-base material as reinforcement, Fig. M-1c. The metal lath should be tacked lightly in place. Corner beads of expanded-metal lath, or of perforated metal should be installed on all exterior corners. They should be applied plumb and level. The metal bead acts as a leveling edge when plastering and reinforces corners against mechanical damage.

Plaster grounds, which are strips of wood, usually the same thickness as the lath and plaster, are attached to the framing before the plastering operation. The grounds serve as leveling surfaces when plastering and as a nailing base for finish trim.

DRY WALL FINISH

Dry wall finish may be gypsum wallboard, fiberboard, plywood or wood in various sizes and forms.

GYPSUM WALLBOARD

Gypsum wallboard is a sheet material composed of a gypsum filler faced with paper. The sheets which are available in 3/8 and 1/2 in. are generally 4 ft. wide and come in lengths up to 12 ft. Edges along the length of the gypsum board are re-

Fig. M-1d. Dry-wall finish. Vertical and horizontal application of gypsum wallboard.

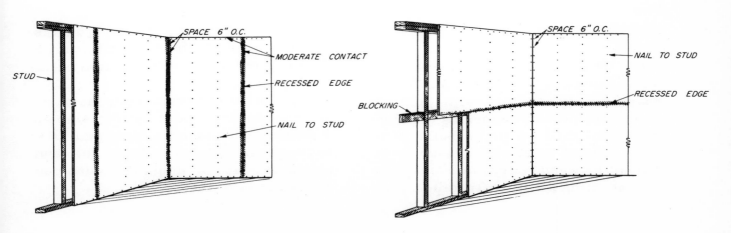

cessed to receive joint cement and tape.

Gypsum wallboard may be applied to walls either vertically or horizontally, Fig. M-1d.

USE CEMENT-COATED FLAT HEAD NAILS

Nails used in applying gypsum board should be long enough to penetrate about 3/4 into the wood stud or joist. Fig. M-2 shows the correct nail sizes to use when applying board over various bases.

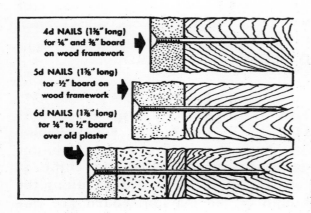

M-2. Cement-coated flat-head nails for applying gypsum board.

CONCEALING JOINTS

Fill channels formed by edges and ends (spaced 1/8 in. apart) of wallboard evenly and fully with joint cement. Mix cement according to directions furnished by the manufacturer. Next, center perforated tape over channel between boards and embed in cement, using a 4 in. putty knife. Tape

should be run the full length of joint.

Cement forced through tape perforations should be smoothed down. At this time, cement should also be applied to all nailheads.

After cement has dried for 24 hours, apply a thin coat of cement and feather out 3 to 4 in. on each side of the channel. When first coat of cement has dried thoroughly, apply second thin coat, feathering out 8 to 10 in. on each side of channel. After 24 hours, sand cement smooth and level with wallboard surface.

GYPSUM BOARD WITH FOIL BACKING

Gypsum board is available with aluminum foil applied to the back of each board, which provides an insulating value equivalent to approximately 1/2 in. thick insulating lath. The foil also serves as an effective barrier to the passage of vapor from the room into the wall space, eliminating the possibility of condensation trouble.

GYPSUM SHIPLAP FOR WARM CLIMATE

This product usually comes in 2 ft. width, is 3/8 or 1/2 in. thick, and is applied directly to the studding with 5d galvanized or cement-coated nails.

Gypsum shiplap construction is much more fireproof than nailing shiplap boards to studding and joists and covering them with light cotton cloth and wallpaper as is commonly done in many areas of the South.

USING FIBERBOARD

Two popular types of fiberboard which are used as interior finishes on walls and ceilings are insulating board and hardboard.

INSULATING BOARD

It may be said of the better types of insulating board that they build, insulate, decorate and help to quiet sound all with one material, applied in a single operation.

In cases where insulating board is to be used on walls in new construction particular care must be taken to see that the studs and joists are evenly spaced.

If the nailing faces of studs and joists are irregular and not in alignment, it may be necessary to use furring strips or shims to provide an even bearing for the board. Where furring strips are used, they should be not less than 1 x 2 in. strips, spaced not more than 16 in. apart and securely nailed.

Where old finishes are covered with insulating board the location of the studs should be marked before starting. Nails used to fasten the boards should be long enough to penetrate the studs at least 1 in. Panels should preferably cover the full height of the wall or entire length of the ceiling in single pieces. If unable to get board of that length, cross-stripping between furring strips should be provided for nailing at the joints.

On new work blocking between joists or studs with 2 x 4 in. lumber for end nailing of boards is recommended.

INSULATING TILE AND PLANK

Insulating tile ordinarily comes in sizes 12 x 12 in. and 16 x 16 in. Popular plank sizes are 12 x 24 in. and 16 x 32 in., Fig. M-3. Thickness is usually 1/2 in.

SUITABLE FOR BOTH OLD AND NEW WORK

Insulating tile and plank are suitable for both old and new construction. They may be fastened with nails, wire staples using an automatic trigger type stapler, or with adhesive. Adhesive is generally recommended for smooth continuous surfaces and nails or staples for fastening to furring strips, joists or studs. Tile and plank may be applied to continuous surfaces with nails if the surface is solid and true and capable of receiving and holding nails. If it won't hold nails, then it should be furred, using 1 x 2 in. or 1 x 3 in. strips cut from straight, uniform lumber.

Furring strips must, of course, be spaced properly to receive the tile. On 12 in. tile, for example, spacing of the furring should be 12 in. o. c. For 16 in. tile or plank the furring should be 8 in. on center.

APPLYING TILE TO OPEN FRAMING

In applying tile to open framing three methods are used. The open framing can be covered completely with a continuous surface such as plywood or wood sheathing, furred with 1 x 3 in. strips or applied directly onto properly spaced joists or studs.

Furring for side walls for tile or vertical plank should be across the studs in a horizontal position. Tile may be run diagonally too, by providing diagonal furring.

Nails should be driven through the thick part of the tongue, Fig. M-4. Care must be taken not to damage the joints. The use of a reinforcing strip of plywood 1/8 x 2 in. slipped under the tongue while nailing will protect the joint. Nailing tile which has a special joint permitting concealed nailing is shown in Fig. M-5. Note that the grooved part of the tile fits over the head of the nail.

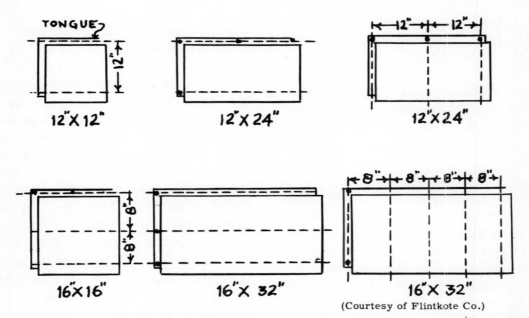

(Courtesy of Flintkote Co.)

M-3. Drawing which shows location and number of No. 16, 1 1/8 in. blued lath nails that should be used with tile of various sizes for concealed nailing. Dotted lines are center lines of furring strips.

TILE NAILING

Nails to be used with 1/2 in. tile or plank for concealed nailing should be 1 1/8 in. long No. 16 blued lath nails. The proper number of nails and location of the nails is shown in Fig. M-3.

START AT CENTER OF CEILING

In laying out ceilings first establish center lines. Run a line between the mid point (M-M in Fig. M-6) of each of the two short end walls. Next locate the mid point of the center line. At

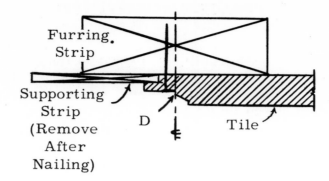

M-4. Nailing the tile to the furring strip. Edge of tile D fits over the center line of furring strip.

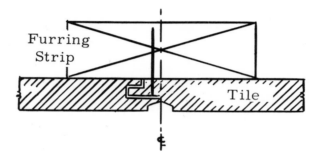

M-5. Groove of tile is slid into position with extending tongue of adjacent tile.

this point (C of Fig. M-6) establish an intersecting line (S-S) at right angles to the first center line M-M.

If the ceiling figures out so an even number of tiles are to be used the joint will occur on the center line. If an odd number of tiles the center line of the room will fall on the center line of the tile.

Use of a starting strip which is provided by most manufacturers, Fig. M-7, permits starting of the job in the center of the room with concealed nailing, Fig. M-7. Place this strip which supports tiles along the grooves so the nailing will always occur in the tongue and application can proceed

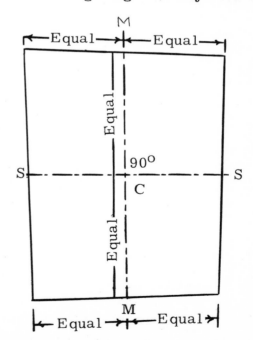

M-6. Locating center line of ceiling to be tiled.

outward in both directions, on center line of room.

Starting at center of room is best way to get same size blocks on sides of room near walls.

On side walls, all joints in vertical plank must be absolutely straight up and down. To do this, hang a plumb line at the mid point of each wall and use this line as a starting point.

In placing planks on side walls horizontally locate the lowest corner of the room, if there is a difference, and establish a level line at the ceiling perpendicular to the plumb line. Use this line for the first course. Always start at the ceiling level line. Cut pieces of tile or plank to fit at the top above the level line and work down. Nail all tile and plank so the tongue is on the lower side.

extent on accurate fitting, particularly around electrical fixtures, water pipes and other protruding obstructions.

A good way to get a tight fit around an odd-shaped obstruction is to saw or cut a hole in a tile large enough to slip over the obstruction without attempting to cut it to fit. Nail the tile in place temporarily, then place strips of gummed tape (cellophane tape is fine) across the corners and on the sides and ends until the opening is satisfactorily closed. Remove the tile with the tape still in place and use it as a pattern in cutting a tile for permanent installation.

APPLICATION WITH ADHESIVE

In using adhesive, Fig. M-8, the base must be in condition to receive the adhesive and the tile. It should be

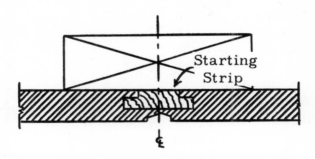

M-7. Application of starter strip, showing two joints (grooves) in place over tongue of starter strip.

FITTING AROUND LIGHTING FIXTURES, OTHER OBSTRUCTIONS

Neat and attractive appearance of a tile job depends to a considerable

clean, true and solid. Paint, wallpaper, whitewash, varnish, calcimine, etc. MUST be removed. If the surface is greasy, it should be washed clean with a solvent. The adhesive should make clean contact with the base material, without any intervening film.

Adhesive should be applied to the insulation board and not to the wall surface. A putty knife is excellent for the purpose.

First, spread a very thin film of adhesive as a prime coat, pressing well into insulating board over places where adhesive will finally be put. Adhesive used to hold the tile should be put on in spots, approximately 2 in. in diameter and about 1/2 in. thick.

Place spots near corners of tile or along outside edges, spaced about 1 1/2 in. from the edge to prevent it from squeezing out when tile is put in place.

In applying planks with adhesive, narrow lanes or strips of adhesive should be applied in a continuous band along edges about 1 1/2 in. from the edge. On large planks an additional lane should be placed in the middle of the plank.

After spots of adhesive have been put on tile or plank, it should be placed in the approximate position that it will occupy. Then, slide it back and forth pressing with the hands at the same time to work the adhesive into place to get good bond. Be sure the tiles are level and even.

REMOVE FIRST TILES

To make sure that the adhesive is sticking properly, it's a good idea to remove the first few units and see if the adhesive is sticking to both the tile and the wall. If not, make whatever corrections are necessary so the adhesive does stick to both surfaces.

PAINTING INSULATING TILE

The surface of most insulating tile can be decorated or redecorated by ordinary methods. There are several oil and casein base paints available.

Cleaning of tile and plank can be accomplished by rubbing carefully with a dry, clean uncolored rubber sponge. Before starting on the cleaning job, the surface should be brushed lightly with a whisk broom or cleaned with a vacuum cleaner having a brush attachment.

M-8. Application of adhesive to tile showing location of spots. Note that on rectangular tile, six spots are used.

HARDBOARD WALL COVERING

Hardboard is an all-wood fiber board made from exploded wood fiber, felted and pressed into board form and heated and shaped by flatbed hydraulic presses. Hardboard, although made from wood, has a slower combustion rate than wood because of the removal of turpentine, oil and certain other inflammable ingredients.

Untempered hardboard is intended for interior use exclusively. In making this product no chemical binders are added.

Tile hardboard is tempered hardboard (1/8 in. thick) which has had still further treatment and scored lines impressed on the surface to form squares. It resembles tile when properly finished.

APPLYING TILE AND PATTERNED HARDBOARD TO BATH OR KITCHEN

Plan the job in advance to use standard size panels wherever possible.

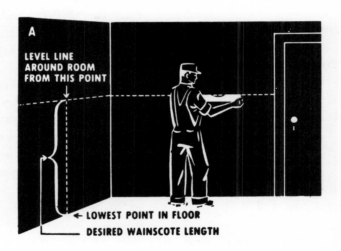

M-9. Applying hardboard. Measuring from lowest point on floor to desired height, to establish level line around room.

Tempered hardboard, which may be used for either interior or exterior use, is made by impregnating hardboard with a tempering compound and baking it. This increases tensile and flexural strength, resistance to abrasion and reduces moisture absorption rate. Standard thicknesses are 1/8, 3/16, 1/4 and 5/16 in.

Where cutting is necessary figure out a cutting schedule that will produce a minimum of waste.

Hardboard may be applied to smooth dry finished plaster, plaster board, wallboard, plywood, insulation board.

Remove wallpaper, scaly paint or

loose plaster. Reduce high spots and build up low spots with patching plaster to give smooth area. Be sure all patch-

around the room. Be sure to allow for base molding to overlap board at least 1/2 in.

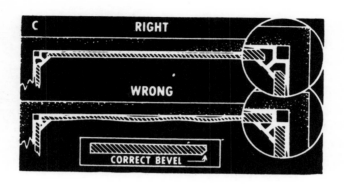

M-10. Edges of hardboard are slightly beveled and fitted into moldings at corners.

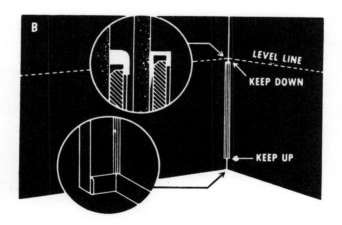

M-11. Be sure to keep top end of molding proper distance below level line to allow for neat fitting of cap molding and bottom end high enough from floor to allow for fitting of base molding.

ing is dry and solid before proceeding.

Next, measure up from lowest point in floor to desired height of hardboard, Fig. M-9, and establish a level line

Start applying panels from any inside corner and work around room. First wall to be covered should be one with the most cutouts for pipes and fixtures.

Nail corner molding in place, Fig. M-10. Be sure to keep top end of molding proper distance below level line to allow for neat fitting of cap molding and bottom end high enough from floor to allow for fitting of base molding, Fig. M-11.

USE ADHESIVE LIBERALLY

Apply liberal coating of adhesive over entire back of panel, using sawtooth spreader, Fig. M-13. Cover sawhorses with clean pad so surface won't be marred. Some manufacturers specify applying mastic to wall instead of panel. In either case panel should be pressed and kneaded firmly into place, beginning at the center and working toward the edges. Make sure the entire area is solidly fastened. Nailing if done at all should be used only on tile patterns or patterns with parallel lines. Countersink nail heads and fill with nail hole filler. If butt joints are desired, be sure they fall in a score line. Cut boards so a full score line develops when they are butted together. Fill joint with crack filler.

ALLOW FOR EXPANSION

Cut and fit panel, allowing for slight expansion of board, under molding. Bevel panels as required to fit molding used. Use a fine-tooth saw and always saw with finished surface toward you so you can change procedure if sawing damages edge of panel. Molding channels in areas where water splashes or stands should be filled with calking compound, Fig. M-12.

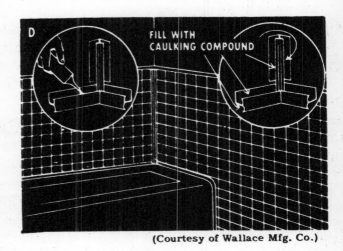

(Courtesy of Wallace Mfg. Co.)

M-12. Molding channels in areas where water splashes or stands should be filled with calking compound.

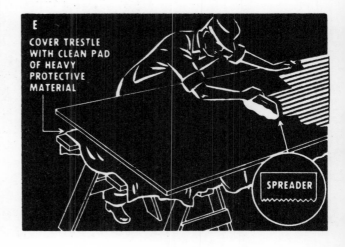

M-13. Using saw-tooth spreader to cover back of hardboard panel with liberal coating of mastic.

PLYWOOD FOR INTERIOR WALLS

Full information on using plywood for interior walls will be found in the special section of this book entitled, "Building With Plywood."

USING WALLBOARD

Wallboard is satisfactory for interior finishes where the added strength, hardness and abrasion resistance of tempered hardboards are not required. Standard-size panels are 4 x 8 ft., 4 x 10 ft. and 4 x 12 ft. Thickness is usually 3/16 in.

ASBESTOS-CEMENT BOARD

Asbestos-cement board is made from Portland cement and asbestos fiber, formed under high pressure to produce a hard, durable, noncombustible material.

Panels for interior finish are made in standard width of 4 ft. lengths of 4 and 8 feet and thickness of 1/8 and 3/16 in. The panels have a smooth, hard surface on the exposed side and may be obtained in plain or scored sheets, in their natural color of stone gray, or in colors produced by incorporating mineral pigments in the asbestos mixture at the time of manufacture, or by the application of baked-on enamel.

Because of the fact they have water-resistant qualities, asbestos-cement boards are frequently used for wainscots or complete finishes in bathrooms or kitchens. They are also appropriately used in building basement furnace enclosures where noncombustible material is required.

FURRING ALL-MASONRY WALLS

On all-masonry walls, 1 x 2 in. furring strips fastened to the walls with special nails or anchors, Fig. M-14, provide nailing surfaces for all kinds of interior finishes.

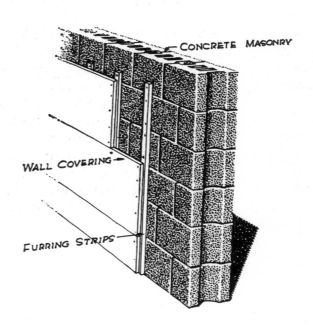

M-14. Furring strips on all-masonry walls provide nailing surface for interior finishes.

TILED WALLS

The advantages of tile walls as well as floors for bathrooms hardly need to be pointed out.

Good tile, properly applied on a foundation of sound framing is essential to satisfactory tile work.

Since the introduction of industry-approved adhesives, the installation of ceramic tile has been greatly facilitated.

Virtually any surface can now be tiled by the adhesive method as long as the surface is plumb and free from foreign materials which would interfere with the bond of the adhesive. Surfaces which may be tiled include concrete, plaster, wood, steel and wallboard.

In applying ceramic tile, it is important that the work of the carpenter be properly done. Selected wall studs should be used. All studs should be cross-braced midway in their height with 2 x 4 herringbone bridging cut between 15 and 30 degrees with the horizontal. In bathroom work the tub should rest on metal hangers securely fastened to the studs.

FLOOR TILE INSTALLATIONS

Floor surfaces to receive ceramic tile should be firm and true. Exterior grade plywood not less than 5/8 in. in thickness, nailed every six inches to joists spaced on 16 in. centers is usually recommended. Another acceptable base is 1/2 in. exterior grade plywood on 1 x 6 subflooring boards nailed diagonally to joists on 16 in. centers. A separation of 1/16 in. should be left between sheets of plywood and the walls for expansion. Nails should be flathead, preferably of the screw type and countersunk flush with the surface.

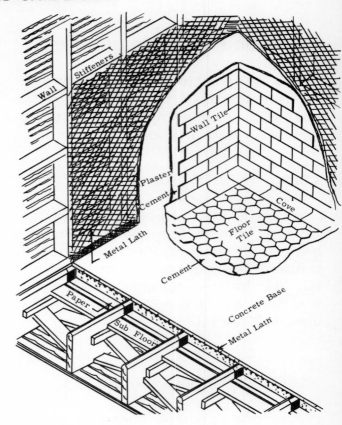

M-15. Providing concrete base or bed for ceramic tile on walls and floors. This method has been largely superseded by the use of industry-approved adhesives.

CONCRETE BED FOR CERAMIC TILE

Prior to the development of industry-approved adhesives, ceramic tile was applied to a concrete bed of adequate thickness, Fig. M-15. This method is still preferred by some contractors.

In preparing a concrete bed the minimum thickness of concrete base and tile should be not less than 1 1/4 in. To acquire sufficient space for the concrete bed, it is necessary to drop wood subflooring between the joists so the finish floor will be level with floors in adjoining rooms. A saturated felt should be applied over the wood subflooring.

On side walls, headers should be set between the studs at intervals of 12 to 16 in. and the concrete base

glass. This glass has sufficient structural strength to permit it to be used in large sheets held in place with a minimum of support. Walls may be made of translucent glass without a criss-cross of supporting members or mortar joints. See Fig. M-16.

The glass comes in pieces with a

M-16. Walls of structural corrugated glass may be used to separate various living areas of the home.

applied over metal lath securely nailed.

CORRUGATED GLASS

An interesting media of architectural expression is structural corrugated

maximum width of 50 in. and a maximum length of 12 ft. Thickness is approximately 3/8 in. Pitch of corrugations (center to center) is 2 1/2 in. as in Fig. M-17. Weight per square foot is approximately 5.3 lbs.

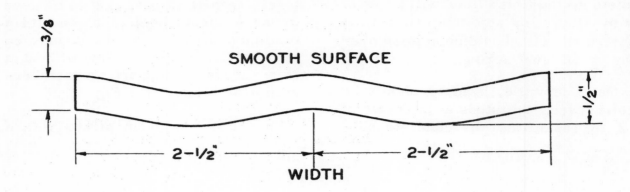

M-17. Corrugated glass is approximately 3/8 in. in thickness. The corrugations are usually about 2 1/2 in. center to center.

Suggested installation details are given in Fig. M-18.

Structural corrugated glass should never be glazed directly on metal, masonry, or other unyielding base. Where a base of this kind is necessary, wood setting blocks or other cushioning material of adequate size and shape should be used. It should never be set directly in concrete or wedged tightly into an opening. Not less than 1/8 in. should be allowed at each side jamb.

Where the glass is set edge to edge, sides of the abutting lights must be accurately ground. The appearance of the installation will be improved if the ground edges are painted with a clear cellulose acetate lacquer or transparent cellulose tape is applied. This helps to remove white, ground-glass edge, which is noticeable when the installation is viewed from an oblique angle.

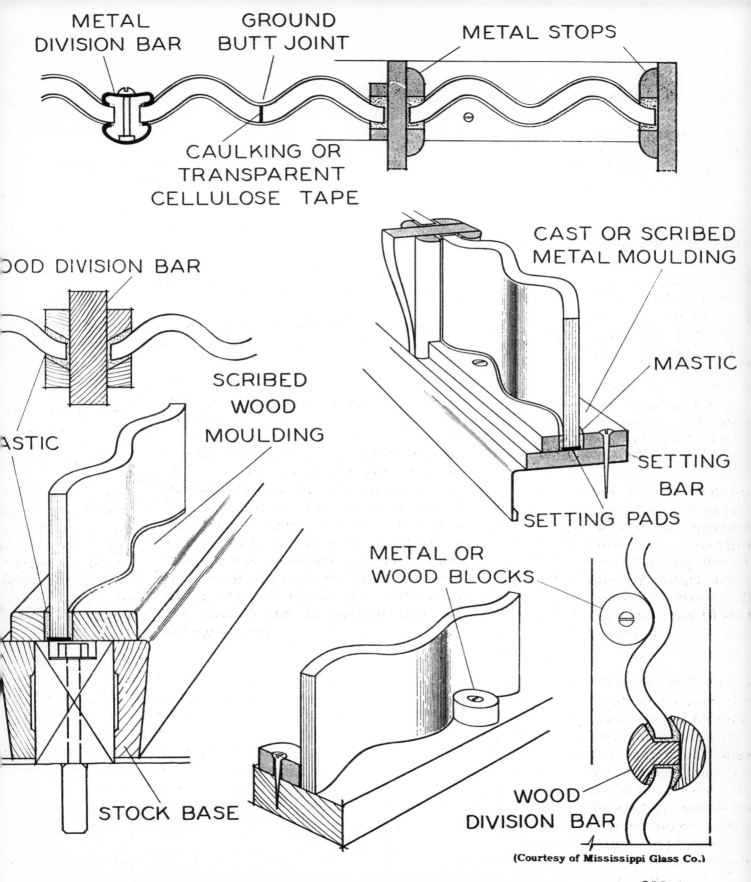

METAL
DIVISION BAR

GROUND
BUTT JOINT

METAL STOPS

CAULKING OR
TRANSPARENT
CELLULOSE TAPE

OOD DIVISION BAR

CAST OR SCRIBED
METAL MOULDING

SCRIBED
WOOD
MOULDING

MASTIC

ASTIC

SETTING
BAR

SETTING PADS

METAL OR
WOOD BLOCKS

STOCK BASE

WOOD
DIVISION BAR

(Courtesy of Mississippi Glass Co.)

311

M-18. Installing structural corrugated glass.

GLASS BLOCKS

Glass blocks are appropriately used as decorative features in many locations about the home.

In outer openings they have insulating properties which aid in heating and air conditioning, help prevent drafts, dampen disturbing noises, cut off unpleasant views yet insure privacy where it is most desired.

Inside the home, partitions and screens of glass blocks add a smart, modern touch to rooms they divide, yet provide plenty of light to show decorative schemes to the best advantage.

Glass blocks are made of two formed pieces of glass fused together to leave an insulating air space between. They come in several different patterns and are usually available in three sizes—6 x 6 in., 8 x 8 in. and 12 x 12 in. All are 3 7/8 in. thick. Special shapes are available for turning corners and for building of curved panels. The blocks come in both light-diffusing and light-directing types.

Installing glass blocks is not difficult. Tools required consist of trowel, plumb line and an old hoe for mixing the mortar.

INSTALLING GLASS BLOCK PANELS OF 25 SQUARE FEET OR LESS

Installation details for glass block panels of 25 sq. ft. and less are given in Fig. M 19. In such panels the height should not exceed 7 ft. and the width 5 ft.

Panels may be supported by "mortar key" at jambs in masonry, or by wood members in frame construction (no wall anchors required). No wall ties are required in the joints and expansion space is required at the head only.

INSTALLING GLASS BLOCK PANELS BETWEEN 25 AND 100 SQUARE FEET IN AREA HEIGHT OR WIDTH NOT TO EXCEED 10 FT.

On jobs of this size, Fig. M-20, expansion strips (strips of resilient material) are used to partially fill expansion spaces at jambs and head of larger panel openings.

Panels must be supported at jambs by use of wall anchors or wood members. A portion of each anchor is embedded in masonry and in glass block mortar joint. They should be crimped within expansion spaces and spaced 24 in. on centers to occur in same joints as wall ties. Anchors are corrosion-resistant, 2 ft. long and 1 3/4 in. wide.

Wall ties should be installed on 24 in. centers in horizontal mortar joints of larger panels and lap not less than 6 in. whenever necessary to use more than one length of tie. Do not bridge expansion spaces. Ties are corrosion-resistant, 8 ft. long and 2 in. wide.

FOR PANELS
25 SQ. FT. AND LESS

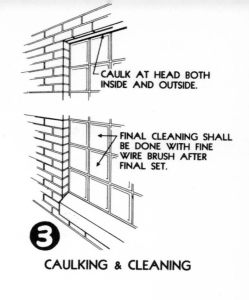

CAULK AT HEAD BOTH INSIDE AND OUTSIDE.

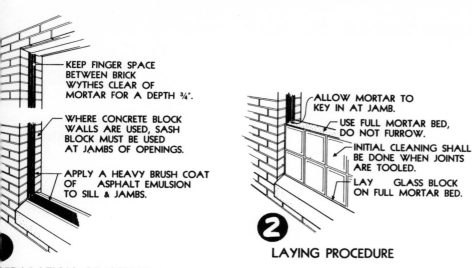

KEEP FINGER SPACE BETWEEN BRICK WYTHES CLEAR OF MORTAR FOR A DEPTH ¾".

WHERE CONCRETE BLOCK WALLS ARE USED, SASH BLOCK MUST BE USED AT JAMBS OF OPENINGS.

APPLY A HEAVY BRUSH COAT OF ASPHALT EMULSION TO SILL & JAMBS.

① PREPARATION OF OPENING

ALLOW MORTAR TO KEY IN AT JAMB.

USE FULL MORTAR BED, DO NOT FURROW.

INITIAL CLEANING SHALL BE DONE WHEN JOINTS ARE TOOLED.

LAY GLASS BLOCK ON FULL MORTAR BED.

② LAYING PROCEDURE

FINAL CLEANING SHALL BE DONE WITH FINE WIRE BRUSH AFTER FINAL SET.

③ CAULKING & CLEANING

TYPICAL INSTALLATION DETAILS

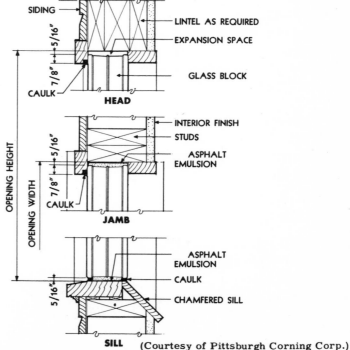

MASONRY CONSTRUCTION

5/16"

LINTEL AS REQUIRED
EXPANSION SPACE
CAULK
GLASS BLOCK

HEAD

5/16"

ASPHALT EMULSION

GLASS BLOCK

JAMB

OPENING HEIGHT
OPENING WIDTH

5/16"

ASPHALT EMULSION

CHAMFERED SILL

SILL

WOOD FRAME CONSTRUCTION

SIDING
7/8"
5/16"

LINTEL AS REQUIRED
EXPANSION SPACE
GLASS BLOCK
CAULK

HEAD

5/16"
7/8"
CAULK

INTERIOR FINISH
STUDS
ASPHALT EMULSION

JAMB

OPENING HEIGHT
OPENING WIDTH

5/16"

ASPHALT EMULSION
CAULK
CHAMFERED SILL

SILL

(Courtesy of Pittsburgh Corning Corp.)

M-19. Installing glass blocks—panels 25 sq. ft. and less.

FOR PANELS
BETWEEN 25 AND 100 SQ. FT.

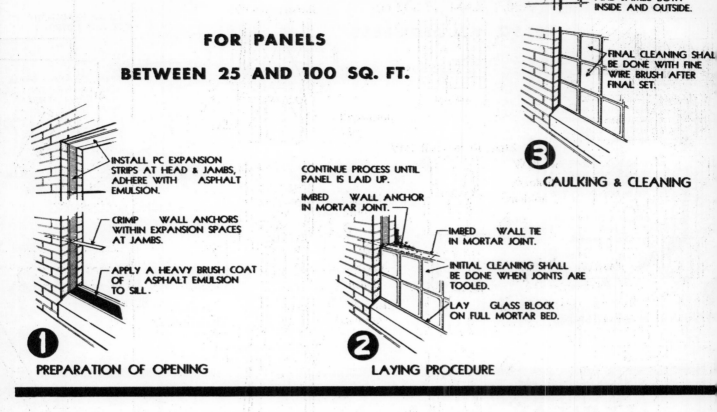

CAULK AT HEAD AND JAMBS BOTH INSIDE AND OUTSIDE.

FINAL CLEANING SHALL BE DONE WITH FINE WIRE BRUSH AFTER FINAL SET.

3 CAULKING & CLEANING

INSTALL PC EXPANSION STRIPS AT HEAD & JAMBS, ADHERE WITH ASPHALT EMULSION.

CRIMP WALL ANCHORS WITHIN EXPANSION SPACES AT JAMBS.

APPLY A HEAVY BRUSH COAT OF ASPHALT EMULSION TO SILL.

1 PREPARATION OF OPENING

CONTINUE PROCESS UNTIL PANEL IS LAID UP.

IMBED WALL ANCHOR IN MORTAR JOINT.

IMBED WALL TIE IN MORTAR JOINT.

INITIAL CLEANING SHALL BE DONE WHEN JOINTS ARE TOOLED.

LAY GLASS BLOCK ON FULL MORTAR BED.

2 LAYING PROCEDURE

TYPICAL INSTALLATION DETAILS

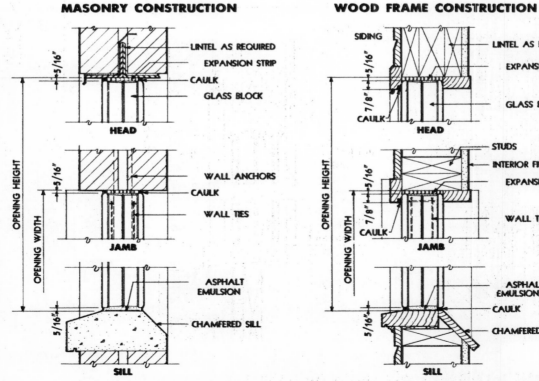

MASONRY CONSTRUCTION

5/16"

LINTEL AS REQUIRED
EXPANSION STRIP
CAULK
GLASS BLOCK

HEAD

5/16"

WALL ANCHORS
CAULK
WALL TIES

JAMB

OPENING HEIGHT

OPENING WIDTH

ASPHALT EMULSION

CHAMFERED SILL

5/16"

SILL

WOOD FRAME CONSTRUCTION

SIDING

5/16"

7/8"

CAULK

LINTEL AS REQUIRED
EXPANSION STRIP
GLASS BLOCK

HEAD

5/16"

7/8"

CAULK

STUDS
INTERIOR FINISH
EXPANSION STRIP
WALL TIES

JAMB

OPENING HEIGHT

OPENING WIDTH

ASPHALT EMULSION

CAULK

CHAMFERED SILL

5/16"

SILL

M-20. Installing glass blocks—panels of 25 to 100 sq. ft.

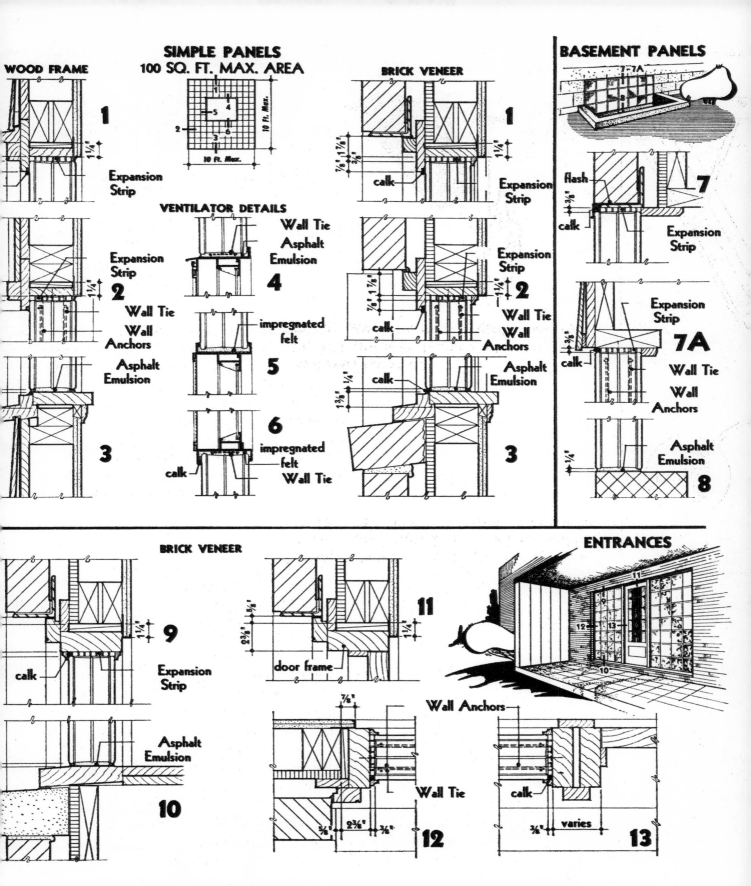

SIMPLE PANELS
100 SQ. FT. MAX. AREA

WOOD FRAME

1

Expansion
Strip

2

Expansion
Strip

Wall Tie

Wall
Anchors

Asphalt
Emulsion

3

VENTILATOR DETAILS

Wall Tie
Asphalt
Emulsion

4

impregnated
felt

5

6

impregnated
felt
Wall Tie

calk

BRICK VENEER

1

calk

Expansion
Strip

2

Expansion
Strip

Wall Tie
Wall
Anchors

Asphalt
Emulsion

calk

calk

3

BASEMENT PANELS

flash

calk

7

Expansion
Strip

Expansion
Strip

7A

calk

Wall Tie

Wall
Anchors

Asphalt
Emulsion

8

BRICK VENEER

9

calk

Expansion
Strip

Asphalt
Emulsion

10

door frame

11

ENTRANCES

Wall Anchors

Wall Tie

12

calk

varies

13

M-21. Installing glass blocks—details for exterior openings.

315

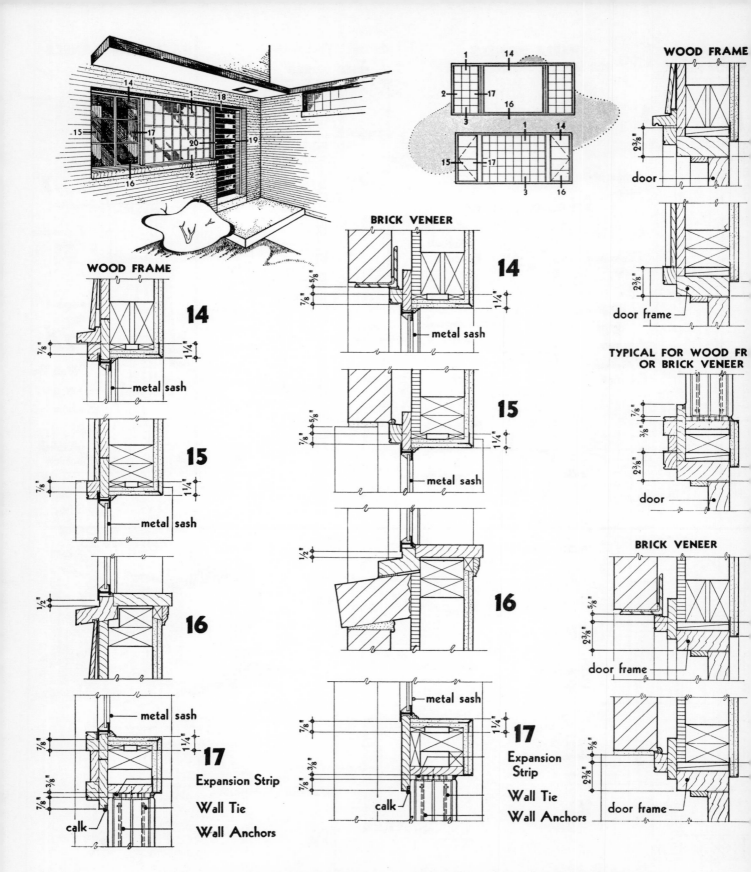

WOOD FRAME

BRICK VENEER

WOOD FRAME

14

15

16

metal sash

metal sash

metal sash

14

metal sash

15

metal sash

16

17
Expansion Strip
Wall Tie
Wall Anchors

door

door frame

TYPICAL FOR WOOD FR
OR BRICK VENEER

door

BRICK VENEER

door frame

door frame

metal sash

17
Expansion
Strip
Wall Tie
Wall Anchors

metal sash

calk

calk

M-22. Glass block panels combined with windows and doors.

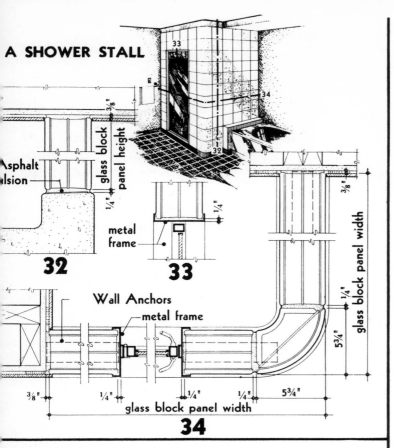

A SHOWER STALL

33

34

Asphalt Emulsion

glass block panel height

3/8"

1/4"

metal frame

32

1/4"

33

Wall Anchors

metal frame

glass block panel width

1/4"

3/8"

5 3/4"

glass block panel width

3/8"   1/4"   1/4"   1/4"   5 3/4"

glass block panel width

34

M-23. Glass block installation — details for special interior uses.

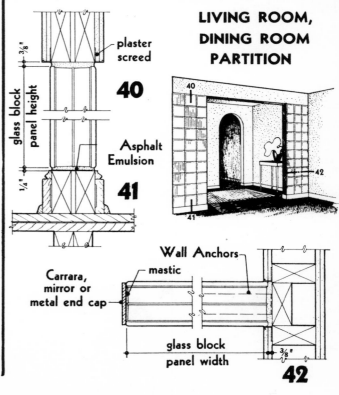

A BATH SCREEN

glass block panel height

3/8"

1/4"

35

plaster screed

Asphalt Emulsion

flash calk

Carrara Glass

mastic

36

35

37

36

Wall Anchors

mastic

Carrara, mirror or metal end cap

glass block panel width

3/8"

37

LIVING ROOM, DINING ROOM PARTITION

glass block panel height

3/8"

1/4"

plaster screed

40

Asphalt Emulsion

41

40

42

41

Wall Anchors

mastic

Carrara, mirror or metal end cap

glass block panel width

3/8"

42

ESTIMATING DATA

Blocks and mortar required for 100 sq. ft. panel:

Block Size	Blocks Required	Mortar Required
6 in.	400	4.3 cu. ft.
8 in.	225	3.2 cu. ft.
12 in.	100	2.2 cu. ft.

Materials required for 1 cu. ft. of mortar:

One bag of waterproofed prepared masonry mortar. Or, if 1:1:4 mix is used:

Waterproofed Portland Cement . . . . 1/4 bag
Hydrated lime . . . . . 1/4 bag
Plastering sand . . . . 1 cu. ft.

DETERMINING OPENING HEIGHTS AND WIDTHS

To determine height or width of opening required for panels, multiply number of units by nominal block size (6 in., 8 in. or 12 in.), then add 3/8 in. Example: What size opening will be required for an 8 in. block panel, 9 blocks high and 5 blocks wide?

Number of units times nominal size plus 3/8 in. equals opening size in inches:

9 x 8 equals 72 in. plus 3/8 in. equals 72 3/8 in. height.
5 x 8 equals 40 in. plus 3/8 in. equals 40 3/8 in. width.

Asphalt emulsion comes in 1 quart, 1 gallon and 5 gallon containers. Calking compound used should be of the non-staining waterproof type.

Interior Trim
Built-Ins

Interior trim, including lumber used for baseboards, picture and cornice moldings, door and window casings, is kiln dried and seasoned before it leaves the mill and should be protected from water and moisture until it has been nailed in place. If it is allowed to absorb moisture it will swell and warp. If nailed while wet, unsightly cracks are likely to develop as it dries out.

The trim is ordinarily nailed to framing members. In places where there are no framing members, nailing blocks of two-inch lumber should be set into the walls between studs before plastering, to provide a place to nail the trim.

It is very necessary to have a good tight joint between window stools and sills to keep the rain and cold from entering.

DOOR AND WINDOW TRIM

A typical interior door framing job is shown in Fig. N-1. Note that the casing is fastened directly onto the door jamb and ground (narrow strip of lumber which is fastened to the framework and provides a place to nail

trim and also aids the plasterer in getting the plaster the proper thickness.)

Three ways of making the joints at the upper corners of the door and window trim are shown in Fig. N-2. The modern tendency is toward using narrow trim. Most trim is concave or hollowed out slightly on the back so it will fit over unevenness in plaster. All trim should be primed on the back and particularly on the edges of mitered joints before it is assembled, to prevent it from absorbing moisture from the plaster or from the atmosphere.

BASEBOARDS

A baseboard is a flat board, usually 3 to 6 in. in width, which provides a finish at the junction of the floor and wall. It protects wall finish when the floor is being cleaned. A baseboard is usually accompanied by a mold or shoe at the bottom, called a shoe mold and sometimes a mold at the top, called a base mold, Fig. N-3. Fig. N-3 also shows three ways to join baseboards at the corners. Every attempt should be made to avoid joints in baseboards, other than the corners, as they are difficult to conceal. Where joints must be made it is well to locate them back of radiators or where large

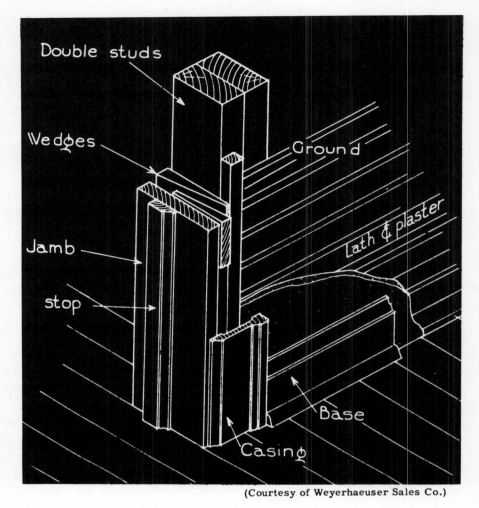

(Courtesy of Weyerhaeuser Sales Co.)

N-1. Typical interior door framing job.

pieces of furniture are likely to be set close to the wall. Baseboard joints should be cut at an angle rather than vertical with the floor. Such joints do not show up as much as square-cut joints.

As baseboards are nailed to studs after plastering has been completed, stud locations should be marked on the floor so that when the studs are concealed it will be possible to determine where nails should be driven. Baseboard 6 in. or less in height should have two nails, about 1 in. from the top and bottom. Nails should be set and holes puttied to match the finish.

INSTALLING BASE MOLDS

Base mold, if used, should be nailed to the studs, driving the nails diagonally downward in such a way as to draw it against the baseboard.

INSTALLING SHOE MOLD

When installing shoe mold, care should be taken to see that the nails go into the floor and not into the wall or baseboard. See Fig. N-4. The baseboard should be primed and finished before the shoe mold is installed; otherwise any shrinkage between the shoe and baseboard will leave a ridge or paint at the location of the original

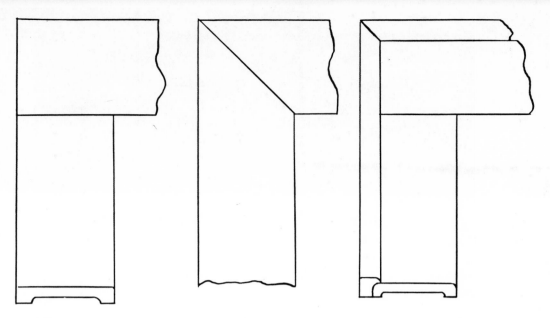

N-2. Joining trim at the corners. Left, square cut. Center, miter cut. Right, square cut modified by using back-band molding mitered at corner.

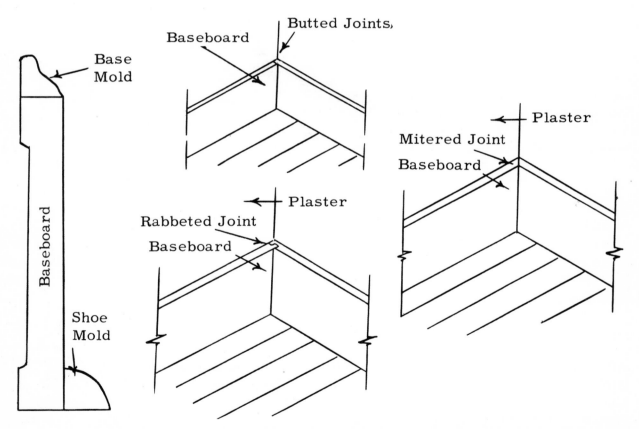

N-3. A baseboard is a flat board which provides a finish at the junction of the floor and wall. The drawings at the right show three ways to join baseboards at the corners: butt the ends together, miter them, form a rabbeted joint. The rabbeted joint is considered most satisfactory, and the mitered joint least desirable.

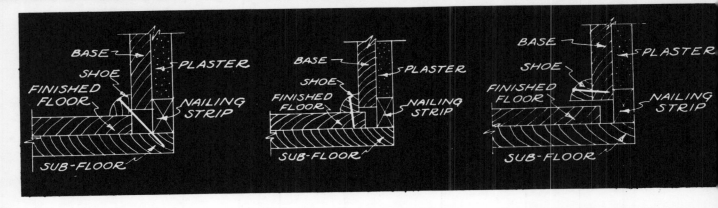

N-4. Fastening shoe mold. If subfloor extends between studs, nailing as shown at left is desirable. This takes care of any movement of floor or baseboard. Nailing to floor as shown in the center drawing is preferable to nailing to the baseboard as shown at the right. If the shoe mold is nailed to the baseboard, shrinkage may cause a space to open up between the floor and the mold.

N-5. Sectional views showing typical installation of interior window trim. The drawing at the right shows view at sill; below, left, view of top or head of window; below, right, fitting stool.

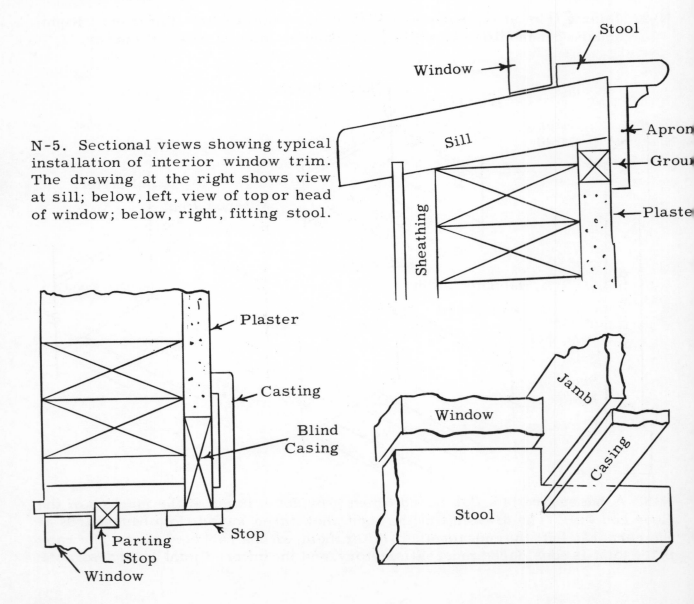

joint. It is common practice to finish the shoe mold to match the floor.

PLASTER GROUNDS

Wherever trim for windows and doors or baseboard is nailed against plaster, it is desirable that the adjacent plaster surfaces be flat and true. If not, the trim is likely to hit the high spots and cause ugly cracks.

Avoiding of both high and low spots can be accomplished to a considerable extent by using grounds, Fig. N-6.

The grounds, usually strips about 1 x 2 in. are nailed to the framework at critical points. These should, of course, be same thickness as finished plaster surface, usually 25/32 in.

Grounds are usually required for chair rail, picture mold, and wherever trim, such as required for fireplace mantels, may come in contact with plaster. They should be nailed securely at all studs and other supports.

WINDOW TRIM

Drawing N-5 shows sectional views of typical interior window trim. The first step is to install the stool between the jambs of the frame. This is notched at the ends as shown in one of the details. Next come the casings which should be cut to match door trim; then, the apron which fits below the stool and the stop strips. Remember that all joints must be cut accurately and neatly fitted, otherwise the job will appear to be amateurish.

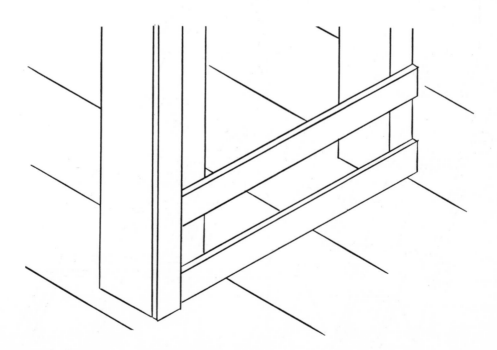

N-6. Grounds, usually 1 x 2 in. stock, help the plasterer get the plaster the proper thickness, also provide nailing strips for trim.

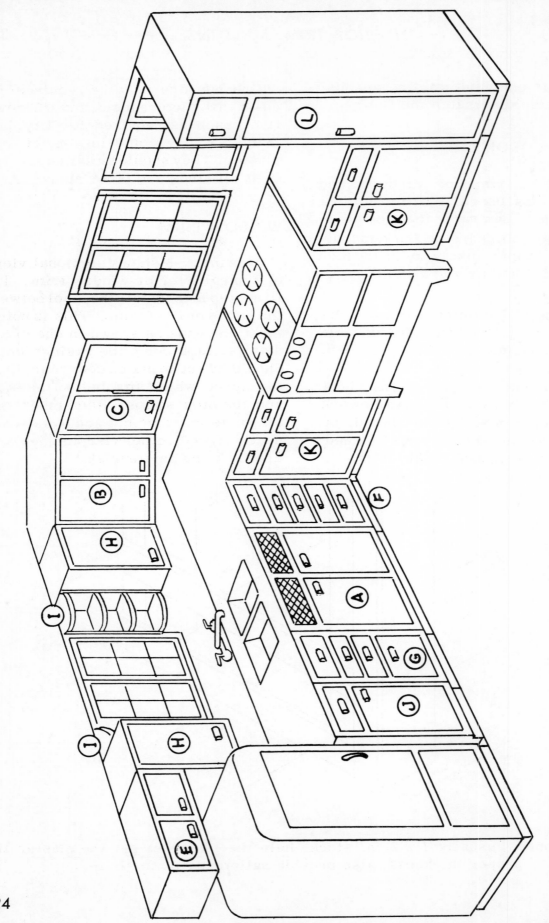

TYPICAL ASSEMBLY OF CABINET UNITS—Constructional details on the various units will be found on the following pages.

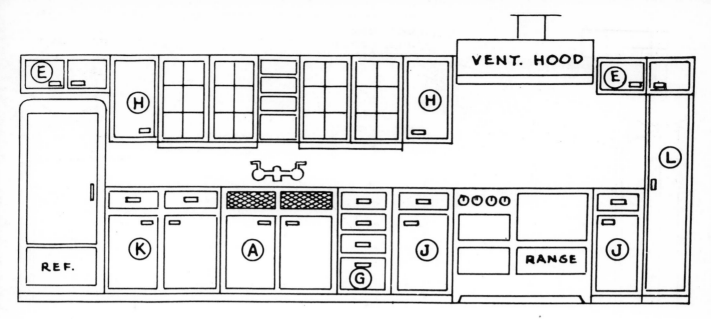

for a LONG WALL

TOWEL RACK

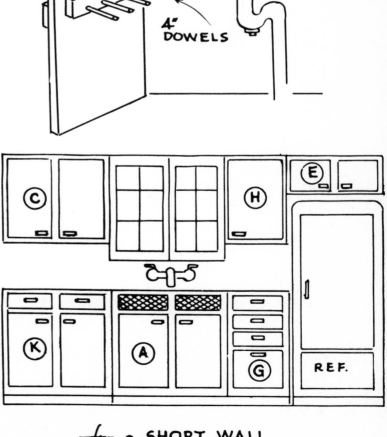

4" DOWELS

MODERN KITCHEN CABINETS

Individual units that may be formed into groups.

These drawings give constructional details on up-to-date kitchen cabinet units that are adaptable to any kitchen —large or small, new or old . . . any shape of kitchen, whether it is I, L or U.

for a SHORT WALL

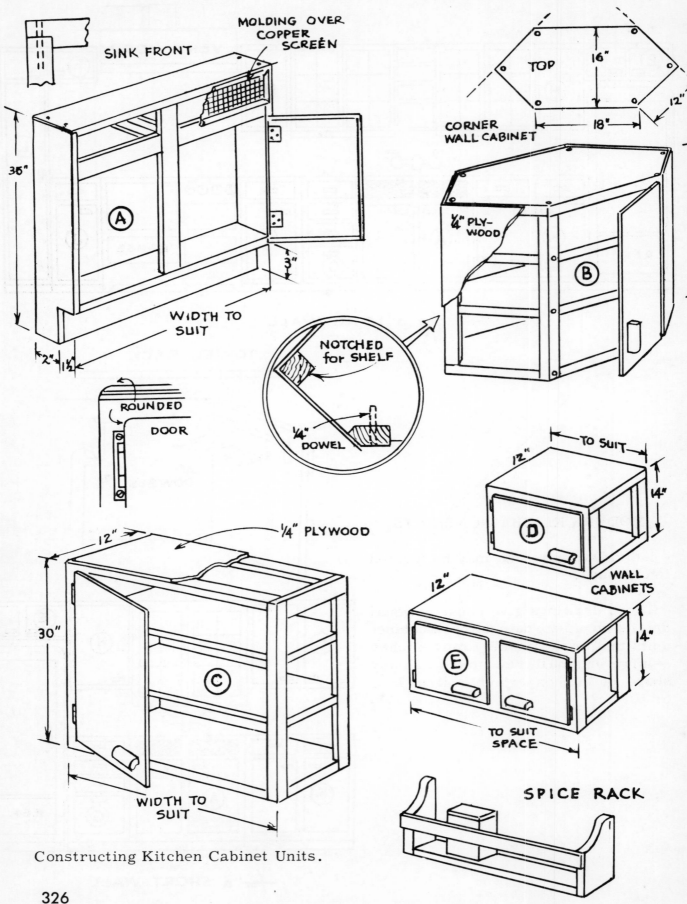

SINK FRONT

MOLDING OVER COPPER SCREEN

36"

Ⓐ

3"

2" 1½"

WIDTH TO SUIT

ROUNDED

DOOR

NOTCHED for SHELF

¼" DOWEL

TOP

16"

18" 12"

CORNER WALL CABINET

¼" PLY-WOOD

Ⓑ

¼" PLYWOOD

12"

30"

Ⓒ

WIDTH TO SUIT

TO SUIT

12"

14"

Ⓓ

WALL CABINETS

12"

14"

Ⓔ

TO SUIT SPACE

SPICE RACK

Constructing Kitchen Cabinet Units.

326

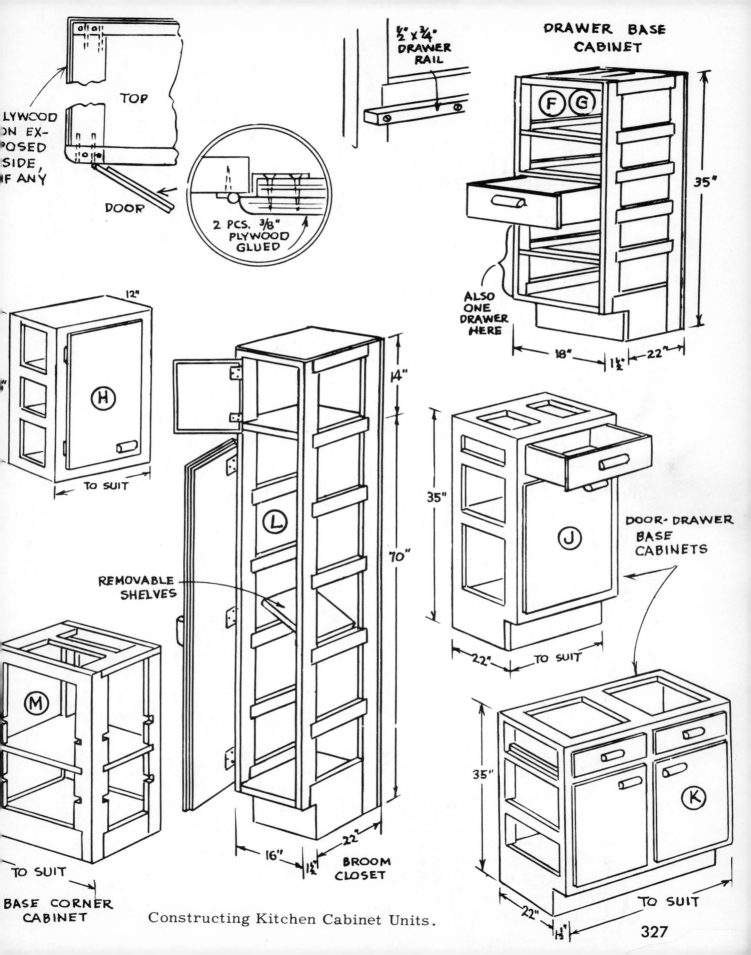

TOP

PLYWOOD
ON EX-
POSED
SIDE,
IF ANY

DOOR

2 PCS. ³/₈"
PLYWOOD
GLUED

½" x ¾"
DRAWER
RAIL

DRAWER BASE
CABINET

F G

35"

ALSO
ONE
DRAWER
HERE

18"   1½"   22"

12"

H

TO SUIT

14"

L

REMOVABLE
SHELVES

70"

16"   1½"   22"

BROOM
CLOSET

35"

J

22"   TO SUIT

DOOR-DRAWER
BASE
CABINETS

M

TO SUIT

BASE CORNER
CABINET

35"

K

22" 1½"   TO SUIT

Constructing Kitchen Cabinet Units.

327

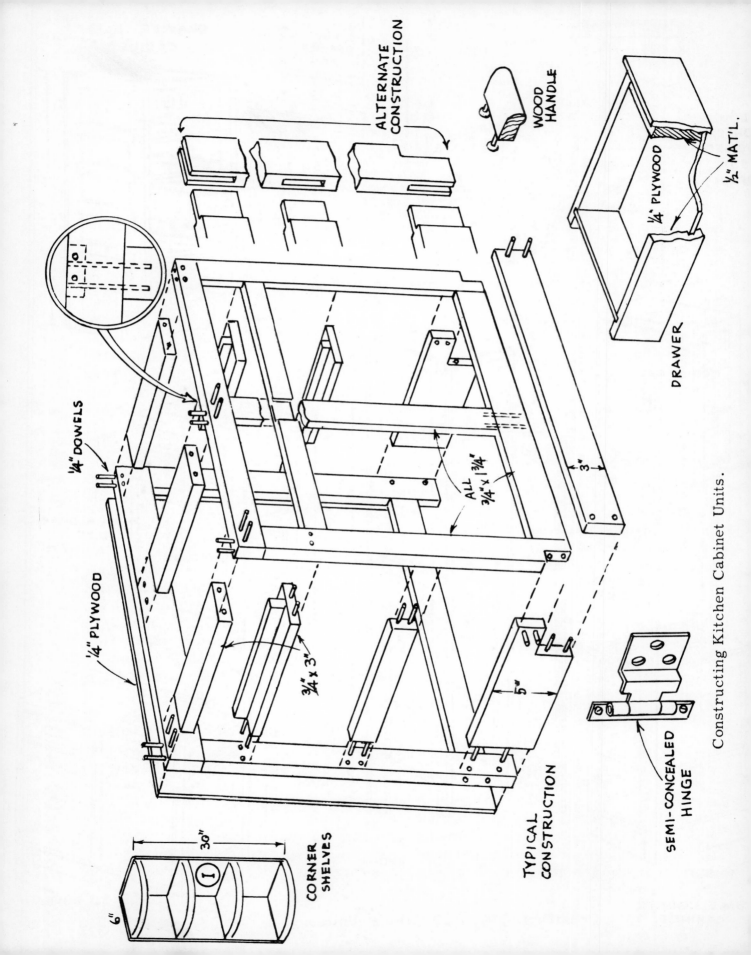

ALTERNATE CONSTRUCTION

WOOD HANDLE

½" MAT'L.

¼" PLYWOOD

DRAWER

¼" DOWELS

¼" PLYWOOD

ALL 3/4" x 1 3/4"

3/4 x 3"

3"

5"

SEMI-CONCEALED HINGE

TYPICAL CONSTRUCTION

CORNER SHELVES

30"

6"

I

Constructing Kitchen Cabinet Units.

Laying Finish Floors

The finish floor provides the wearing surface over the subfloor or over joists, if there is no subfloor.

Unless home is to be completely carpeted, hardwood floors are desirable.

Hardwoods most commonly used for flooring are oak, maple, beech, birch and pecan. Authorities estimate that oak constitutes about 80% of the residential flooring used in the U.S. today.

Softwood flooring (cedar, fir, hemlock, spruce and pine) is used to some extent and has fair lasting qualities if kept painted or varnished.

In cases where the floor is to be carpeted or covered with linoleum, plywood makes a satisfactory finish floor. Information on using plywood is contained in the "Building With Plywood" section of this book.

QUARTER AND PLAIN SAWED FLOORING

Wood flooring is frequently classified according to the method used in sawing it. When sawed from logs perpendicular or at an angle of not less than 45 degrees to the annual rings, it is classed as quarter-sawed, edge-grained or vertical-grained. Plain-sawed, flat-sawed, or flat-grained flooring is that which is sawed parallel to or less than an angle of 45 degrees from the annual rings. Oak is the only flooring that is ordinarily quarter-sawed.

SIZES OF HARDWOOD FLOORING

Strip flooring of oak, maple, beech, birch and pecan is manufactured in a variety of sizes ranging in width from 1 1/2 in. to 3 1/2 in. and in thickness from 5/16 in. to 17/16 in. The standard thicknesses for tongued and grooved strip flooring are 1/2 in., 3/8 in. and 25/32 in. Of these three, the 25/32 in. flooring is most widely used. This is made in four widths, 1 1/2 in., 2 in., 2 1/4 in. and 3 1/4 in. The 2 1/4 in. flooring is most popular.

Parquetry used in pattern floors (squares, rectangles, herringbone, etc.) is customarily tongued and grooved and end-matched and the pieces are laid separately either by nailing or setting in suitable mastic. Parquetry is made principally in 25/32 in. thickness. Standard lengths are in multiples of the face width. In strips 2 1/4 in. wide the lengths are 6 3/4 in., 9 in., 11 1/4 in., 13 1/4 in., 13 1/2 in.

GRADES OF OAK FLOORING

In unfinished flooring oak comes in grades as follows: Clear, Sap-clear, Select. In Plain Sawed: Clear, Select, No. 1 Common, No. 2 Common. In finished flooring white and red oak are separated according to: Prime grade, Standard grade, Standard and better grade and Tavern grade.

DETERMINING QUANTITY OF FLOORING NEEDED

To find out how much NOFMA flooring, (flooring made according to specifications of the National Oak Flooring Manufacturers' Association) is required for a room, first determine the area of the room by multiplying the width by the length. Then add one of the following percentages of that figure, depending upon the size of the flooring you intend to use:

50% for . . . . 25/32 x 1 1/2 in.
37 1/2% for . . . . 25/32 x 2 in.
33 1/3% for . . . . 25/32 x 2 1/4 in.
                              3/8 x 1 1/2 in.
                              1/2 x 1 1/2 in.
25% for . . . . 3/8 x 2 in.
                              1/2 x 2 in.
24% for . . . . 25/32 x 3 1/4 in.

Then add 5 per cent additional to compensate for floor layers' cutting and possible waste.

For example, assume you plan to lay 25/32 x 1 1/2 in. flooring in a room 12 feet wide by 15 feet long. The area of the room is 180 square feet. Adding 50 per cent, or 90 square feet, gives 270, the number of board feet of flooring. An additional 5 per cent for possible waste is 13 1/2 board feet, making a total of 283 1/2 board feet required.

This formula applies to flooring laid straight across a room. When the room has bay windows or other projections, extra allowance should be made to cover the additional space.

PROPER HANDLING OF OAK FLOORING

Certified hardwood flooring is kiln dried to a low moisture content. The moisture content equalizes itself to the moisture condition in the area where the flooring is to be used. For best results the flooring must be protected from the elements during storage and delivery.

Flooring should not be stored in a cold or damp building. Wait until the plaster and cement work have dried thoroughly and all but the final woodwork and trim have been installed before having it delivered.

Flooring should not be laid immediately after delivery. Especially in winter construction, the house should first be heated to 70 degrees F. Then the flooring should be piled loosely inside for at least 4 or 5 days before it is laid. This permits flooring to reach a moisture content equivalent to that of building where it is being used.

GETTING READY FOR FLOORING APPLICATION

For best results hardwood flooring, Fig. O-1, should be laid on a soundly constructed subfloor about 1 in. thick. Subfloor boards preferably should be no wider than 6 in. spaced about 1/4 in. apart and laid diagonally.

Flooring should ordinarily be laid to run lengthwise of a room and pass through from room to room without a break.

USING FURRING STRIPS

In some localities the finish floor is laid on furring strips, Fig. O-2, in-

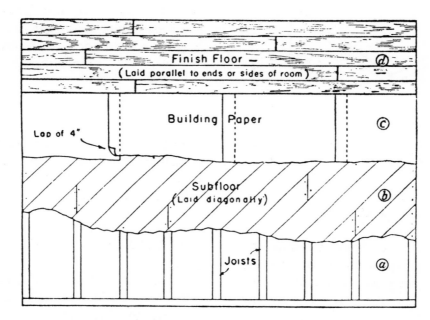

O-1. Cut-away view of floor, showing: A, joists; B, subfloor; C, building paper; D, finish floor.

The boards should be face-nailed solidly at every joist with two 10d nails. All end joints should rest on bearings. If boards wider than 6 in. are used, there should be extra nailing at each bearing.

Extra precaution should be taken to see that the subflooring is adequately nailed because inadequate nailing almost invariably results in squeaky floors.

stead of directly on the subfloor. The space thus provided serves as additional floor insulation and provides a place for running electrical conduit.

Furring strips, usually 1 x 2 in. stock, should be placed over each joist, or spaced 10 in. on centers and installed at right angle to the direction the finish floor is to be laid. Finish flooring should be nailed through fur-

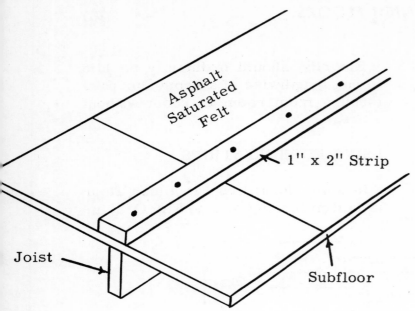

Asphalt Saturated Felt

1" x 2" Strip

Joist

Subfloor

O-2. Using furring strips to support finish floor. Space provided serves as additional floor insulation and provides place for running electrical conduit.

ring strips with nails one size larger than specified in the nailing schedule, Fig. O-3.

SOUNDPROOFING FLOORS

On furred floors as described in the preceding paragraphs sound insulation may be provided by placing insulating board over the floor before the strips are nailed in place.

Another way to provide sound insulation on double floors is to fill the space between the strips with loose fill insulation.

Fig. O-4 shows a method of sound insulating floors, Insulating in this way will also serve as thermal or heat insulation.

USE BUILDING PAPER

A good quality of building paper; that known as 15 lb. asphalt saturated felt, should be laid between the subfloor and the finish floor. Besides resisting moisture, the paper prevents dust from seeping through floor seams. For rooms directly over heating plants a double weight building paper or

NAIL SCHEDULE—Tongued and Grooved Flooring Must Be Blind Nailed

Flooring Dimension, In.	Size of Nails	Spacing of Nails	Following flooring must always be laid on a sub-floor, blind nailed:		
			$\frac{1}{2}$ x 2 or $\frac{1}{2}$ x 1$\frac{1}{2}$	6d bright wire casing nails	10 in. apart
$\frac{25}{32}$ x 3$\frac{1}{4}$	8d light flooring nail—wire nail or steel cut casing nail—(use cut nails when possible)	10 in. apart	$\frac{3}{8}$ x 2 or $\frac{3}{8}$ x 1$\frac{1}{2}$	4d bright wire casing nails	8 in. apart
			Square-edge flooring, as follows, face-nailed—through top face		
$\frac{25}{32}$ x 2$\frac{1}{4}$	Same nails as above	10 in. apart	$\frac{5}{16}$ x 2 or $\frac{5}{16}$ x 1$\frac{1}{2}$	1$\frac{1}{8}$-in. barbed wire flooring brad No. 16 heads countersunk and puttied	2 nails every 7 in.
$\frac{25}{32}$ x 1$\frac{1}{2}$	Same nails as above	12 in. apart			

O-3. Floor nailing schedule.

standard insulating board should be used instead of 15 lb. paper. Strips of building paper should be lapped at least 4 in.

EXPANSION SPACE

Finish flooring should not be laid tight against studding or walls. Be

Proper nails to use and spacing is shown in Fig. O-3.

Don't try to hammer each piece of tongued and grooved strip flooring into its final position as soon as it is nailed. After laying three or four pieces, place a short piece of waste flooring with the groove against the tongue of the

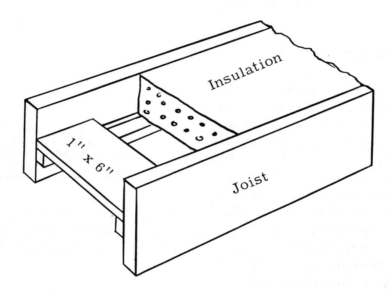

O-4. Insulating beneath a floor.

sure to leave an expansion space of not less than 1/2 in. See Fig. O-5.

FLOORING SHOULD BE TOE-NAILED

Tongued and grooved strip flooring should be fastened in place with the nails driven through the tongue at an angle of 45 to 55 degrees, Fig. O-6. The first couple of nails should be "toe-nailed" toward the preceding piece to make tight joints. The flooring should also be blind-nailed; that is, set with a nail set. Joints should be well distributed, preferably no two nearer than a foot.

outside piece and drive the pieces up snugly. Take care not to break the tongue. Repeat this after laying every three or four pieces of flooring.

When the floor has been brought to within 2 or 3 feet of the far wall, the room should be checked again to find out if the strips are parallel to the wall. If not, the grooved edges should be dressed off slightly at one end until the strips have been adjusted to run parallel to the wall. This is necessary in order that the last piece may show parallel to the baseboard.

If the room was found to be out of square at the start, it may be necessary to start adjustments at an early stage.

NAILING SHOE MOLDING

Fig. O-7 shows three ways to nail show molding. Method C, nailing molding to subfloor, is recommended.

FINISHING SUGGESTIONS

Although certified unfinished hardwood flooring is smoothly surfaced at the factory, scratches or other slight marks caused by handling usually appear when the floor has been laid. These may be removed by sanding or scraping. If available, an electrically operated sander should be used. For fine floors most manufacturers recommend at least four sandings, starting with No. 2 sandpaper and graduating down to No. 1/2, No. 0 and No. 00. The first coat of finish should be applied the same day the floor is laid.

PRE-FINISHED FLOORING

Some manufacturers produce flooring which is finished at the factory. In most cases such flooring is ready to use immediately after laying; in others the floor must be waxed before being used. Wax not only imparts a lustrous sheen to a floor, but forms a protective film that prevents dirt from penetrating the wood pores.

FINISH FLOORS ON JOISTS

The lack of a subfloor requires that more attention be given to locating

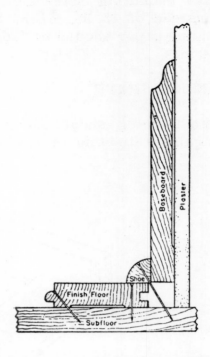

O-5. Laying first strip of finish flooring. Finish molding should not be placed until all flooring has been installed.

O-6. Nailing finish floor. Nails are driven at an angle of 45 to 55 degrees, through part where the tongue leaves the shoulder.

joists, especially on the first floor where heavy furniture is placed. Joists should be placed not more than 16 in. on centers.

Where subflooring is omitted entirely and workmen are required to walk around on joists or planks placed over the finish floor (softwood only), probably more loss of time and labor results than the amount saved by omitting the subfloor.

On jobs where softwood flooring is to be applied without subflooring, 25/32 in. flooring should be the minimum used. All joints in flooring should be made over joists.

Softwood floors are sometimes laid at the early part of the construction as they will scrape up and finish satisfactorily after being wet.

FLOOR VENTILATION

Where a basement is not provided, adequate provision should be made for free movement of cross currents of air beneath the building. Air circulation may be obtained by means of vents or other openings in foundation walls. The total area of such openings should be at least 1 1/2 per cent of the first floor area.

Additional information on floor ventilation and prevention of condensation will be found in chapter on Insulation.

FLOORING OVER CONCRETE

Flooring over concrete, either in a basement or over a concrete floor

slab, except in arid climate, should commence with a two-course waterproofing job, consisting of hot asphalt and 15-lb. asphalt felt. Hot asphalt should be mopped onto the concrete to form an adhesive for the first layer of asphalt felt, felt applied, and a second layer of felt applied.

On top of the second layer of waterproofing, 2 x 4 in. sleepers, (floor nailing pieces) should be laid in mastic 12 in. on centers.

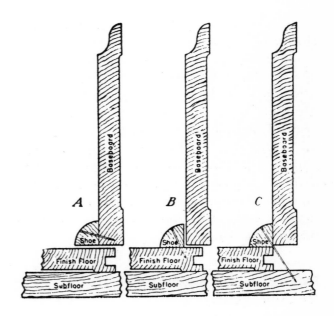

O-7. Nailing shoe molding. A, shoe molding nailed to baseboard; B, shoe molding nailed to finish floor; C, shoe molding nailed to subfloor. The latter method is recommended. The danger in method A is that a crack might develop between molding and finish floor; in B a crack may occur between shoe molding and baseboard. Method C virtually eliminates trouble.

Subflooring (square - edge boards) should be laid diagonally across the sleepers and fastened with 8d nails. Be sure to space the boards used in the subfloor at least 1/2 in. apart to allow for expansion.

Lumber for sleepers, before being installed, should be impregnated with an approved wood preservative.

Finish floor is applied the same as on other floors of the house.

SLAB FLOOR WITHOUT SUBFLOORING

On a concrete slab where the finish flooring is to be nailed directly onto wood sleepers, the sleepers may be set in the concrete when it is laid or attached to the concrete by means of sleeper clips or anchors. Sleepers should be spaced not more than 12 in. on centers. If the direction of the finish flooring has not been determined, sleepers may be laid diagonally to permit the finish floor to be laid either lengthwise or crosswise of the building.

INSTALLING ASPHALT FLOOR TILE

Asphalt tile can be installed over any dry, firm, smooth underfloor that is free from wax, oil and foreign matter.

Wood underfloors should be of double construction with the top boards not over 3 1/4 in. wide, or 1/4 in. plywood, well nailed. Over a wood underfloor

cement saturated felt with paste as specified by the manufacturer should be used. Edges of felt should be butted together, not lapped, and the felt rolled in both directions to eliminate air pockets.

PRECAUTIONS

Do not use weighted roller when installing asphalt tile. It is unnecessary. Asphalt tile cement should be spread with a notched trowel.

Remove all paint from concrete underfloors that are in direct contact with the ground. Dusty concrete underfloors should be primed with asphalt tile primer. Asphalt tile cement should be permitted to set-up before installing tile, according to the manufacturer's instructions.

Carefully place tile into position; avoid sliding as this may force cement up between the tiles. Excess cement can be removed with steel wool and linoleum cleaner. Don't use kerosene, gasoline or other solvents.

For straight border work asphalt tile can be cut by scoring deeply and snapping along scored line. For cutting along irregular lines tile can be heated on the reverse side sufficiently to be pliable and cut with hooked linoleum knife.

Tile exposed as in doorways and on stairs should have the edges protected with metal nosings or edgings.

For step-by-step installation procedure, refer to Fig. O-8.

1.

Determine the middle of both ends of room and strike a line through these points which will give you center line AA. Find the center of line AA, which gives point B. Measure 4′0″ from point B along line AA, which is point "C". 3′0″ from point B at a 90° angle to line AA, swing an arc at "D". Swing a 5′0″ arc from point "C" through arc "D". Snap a chalk line through the intersection of the two arcs at point "D", through point "B", which is line "EE". (Figure 1)

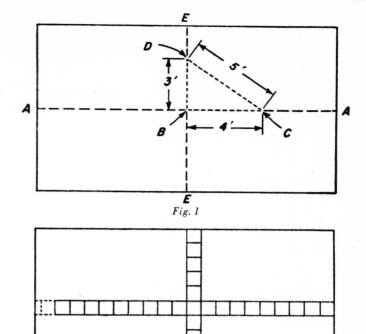

Fig. 1

2.

To determine the width of a border, lay a row of loose tiles across the room from wall to wall. The space between the last tile and the baseboard will constitute the border width for the room. Dividing this distance in half will result in the exact width of the border on either side of the room. Should this width be too narrow, deduct one tile from the layout and add the dimension of the tile to the double border width before dividing. Repeat this operation in the other direction of the room. (Figure 2)

Fig. 2

3.

Spread cement over lines AA and EE approximately 1′0″ wide leaving portions of the lines at intersection and ends open. Allow set-up time for adhesive and resnap chalk lines over cemented surface. (Figure 3)

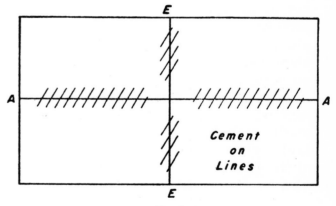

Fig. 3

4.

Spread cement over one-half of area and allow set-up time before starting installation of tile. Count the tiles in each row. If there is an even number of tiles, the two tiles in the center of each row, (Figure 4) (Tiles 1 and 2 and tiles 2 and 3) should meet exactly on center lines. If there is an odd number of tiles, the edges of the middle tile should fall at equal distances from the center lines. Install the tile in somewhat of a semi-circle around the first tile (Figure 4). It is important to remember the center lines are guide lines and must be followed or else the "field" will not square. After the entire field has been laid measure the space between the field tile and wall and cut border to fit snugly in place.

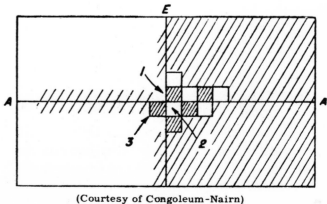

(Courtesy of Congoleum-Nairn)

Fig. 4

O-8. Installing asphalt floor tile.

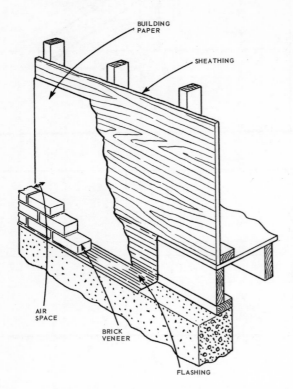

BUILDING
PAPER

SHEATHING

AIR
SPACE

BRICK
VENEER

FLASHING

Brick veneer over plywood sheathing.

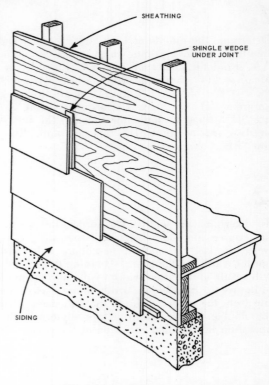

SHEATHING

SHINGLE WEDGE
UNDER JOINT

SIDING

Exterior plywood lap siding over plywood sheathing.

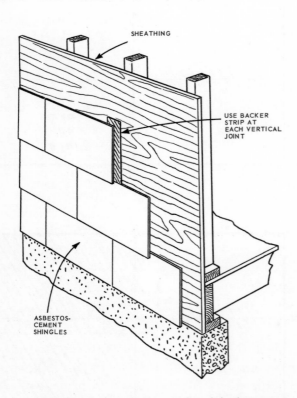

SHEATHING

USE BACKER
STRIP AT
EACH VERTICAL
JOINT

ASBESTOS-
CEMENT
SHINGLES

Asbestos-cement shingles over plywood sheathing.

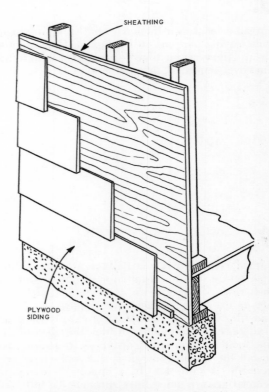

SHEATHING

PLYWOOD
SIDING

Exterior plywood bevel siding over plywood sheathing.

USING EXTERIOR PLYWOOD SIDING AND SHEATHING.

Building With Plywood

Because veneers (plies of wood) in plywood are rotary cut and are not sawn, Douglas fir plywood is available in large sizes. Plywood has great strength both lengthwise and cross-wise of the panel because of the cross-laminated construction.

For most building jobs panels only a fraction of an inch thick are required. Plywood may be cut, shaped and fastened easily with ordinary carpentry tools. Plywood deserves reasonable care, but no special attention is required as there is very little splitting, cracking and breaking. See Figs. P-1 and P-2.

ACCEPTABLE TO BUILDING CODES

Douglas fir plywood is accepted in the Uniform Building Code. Plywood is accepted too by the new Building Officials Conference of America Code, the Southern Building Code and many individual city codes.

In general, 3/8 in. exterior type fir plywood is accepted for siding, plywood 5/16 in. thick is accepted as structural sheathing without further bracing and plywood is accepted for both roof sheathing and subflooring.

PLYWOOD AND FHA

When FHA minimum property requirements are met for each use, FHA permits the use of plywood for all parts of a home . . siding (Exterior plywood), interior walls and ceilings, wall and roof sheathing and the sub-flooring.

MINIMUM FHA REQUIREMENTS

SIDING. Flat or lapped. For this use plywood must be of Exterior type and minimum of 3/8 in. thick with studs 16 in. o. c.

WALL SHEATHING. With the studs 16 in. o. c., 5/16 in. plywood; for studs 24 in. o. c. 3/8 in. plywood is acceptable. Corner bracing may be omitted. Nail with 6d nails, 6 in. o. c. on all edges and 12 in. o. c. at intermediate bearings. When 5/16 in. sheathing is used, barbed nails are required for applying asbestos cement shingles or siding, and barbed nails or nailing strips in applying wood shingles.

ROOF SHEATHING. Here too 5/16 in. plywood is accepted for rafter spacing 16 in. o. c. for both wood and asphalt shingles, but former must be applied

P-1. Cut-away view of house built of plywood showing where various grades are appropriately used. (1) Exterior type. (2) Interior grade A-A or A-B. (3) Interior type grade A-D. (4) Interior type grade B-D. (5) Interior type grade C-D. (6) Interior type grade B-B.

with nailing strips unless plywood 1/2 in. thick is used. The 1/2 in. plywood is accepted too, for rafters 24 in. o. c. Plywood should be installed with grain of outer plies across the rafters.

SUBFLOORING   A popular subflooring construction with Douglas fir plywood is that using 5/8 in. panels installed with outer plies of panels at right angles to joists spaced 16 in. o. c. When finish floor is 25/32 wood strip, no blocking is required. When finish floor is less than 25/32 in. wood or is block, linoleum, parquetry, composition rubber or ceramic tile, blocking is required under panel edges at right angles to joists. Nailing should be 6 in. o. c. at all the edges and 10 in. o. c. at intermediate members.

When all installation requirements are followed, FHA permits somewhat greater joist spacing than 16 in. o. c. with 5/8 in. plywood. Also permitted is 1/2 in. plywood subflooring.

INTERIOR FINISH. Minimum thickness of plywood accepted is 1/4 in.

If the studs are 16 in. o. c. If 3/8 in. plywood is used, spacing of studs may be 24 in. o. c.

FLOOR CONSTRUCTION WITH DOUGLAS FIR PLYWOOD

Fir plywood brings speed and economy in floor construction and provides a squeak-free base for finish flooring. The panels are used for subflooring, underlayment or base for linoleum and other coverings and combined subflooring and underlayment.

Plyscord is the grade of Douglas fir plywood intended for subflooring. It is unsanded.

As underlayment or when a single thickness is installed as a combination subflooring and underlayment, the Plypanel grade is suitable. Suitable also, is the Plybase grade having one surface slightly lower in appearance than the face of Plypanel.

Plyscord grade 5/8 in. thick, without any finish flooring, will sustain a load of 193 lbs. per sq. ft. with a deflection

of only .04 in. By contrast, many residences are designed for only a 40
lb. per sq. ft. floor load.

Smooth Plypanel underlayment is
ideal for new construction or over old
worn flooring.

is installed as combination subfloor
and underlay.

Plywood subflooring should be laid
with face grain of the panel across
the joists to provide maximum stiffness. Use 8d common nails for 5/8
in. plywood, 6d common nails for 1/2

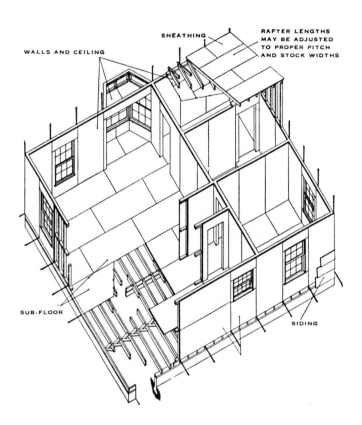

WALLS AND CEILING

SHEATHING

RAFTER LENGTHS
MAY BE ADJUSTED
TO PROPER PITCH
AND STOCK WIDTHS

SUB-FLOOR

SIDING

P-2. Lines extending beyond framework are guide lines or grid lines, 4 ft. apart,
to show how standard 4 x 8 ft. panels may be used in housing construction.

FLOOR APPLICATION

Grades and recommended thicknesses are shown in Fig. P-3. Note the
blocking along panel edges at right
angles to the joists when the plywood

in. thickness. Nail at 6 in. centers at
panel edges and 10 in. o. c. on other
bearings. Usually, installation is over
joists 16 in. o. c. but joist spacing up
to 24 in. is practical when 25/32 in.
strip floor is used.

Many home builders find it advantageous to use 5/8 in. Plyscord first to form smooth basement concrete walls and then to re-use the panels for the subflooring, roof sheathing, or wall sheathing. Glue bond in Plyscord sheathing grade is moisture-resistant, and will withstand initial use as form material as well as occasional wetting during construction.

As roof sheathing, plywood's inherent properties—large size, light weight, considerable strength, Fig. P-4, and stiffness—make it ideal for the purpose.

Plyscord, the unsanded construction grade of Douglas fir plywood will withstand occasional wetting such as might ordinarily be encountered during con-

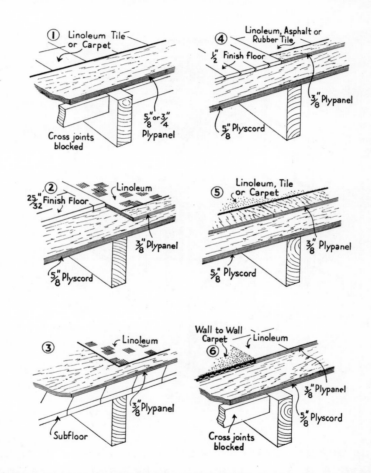

P-3. Floor construction details. Shown here are six details of typical construction practices using Douglas fir plywood. Detail 1 shows installation with a single thickness of plywood as combined subfloor and underlayment; detail 6 shows plywood underlayment below linoleum and carpeting over single thickness of plywood. Detail 3 is of plywood as underlayment only. Other sections show unsanded Plyscord as subfloor and sanded Plypanel as underlayment. For economy 1/2 in. thickness is acceptable anywhere 5/8 in. is shown, and similarly, 1/4 in. underlayment may be used in place of 3/8 in. Such construction generally meets FHA minimum requirements.

STRENGTH AND RIGIDITY OF FRAME WALLS
(From U.S. Forest Products Laboratory Tests, Wall with Openings)

Sheathing Material	Relative Rigidity	Relative Strength
1x8˝ DIAGONAL SHEATHING	1.0	1.3
29/32˝ FIBERBOARD (8d nails, spaced 3˝ at all vertical edges, 5½˝ to 6˝ elsewhere.)	1.6	2.1
HORIZONTAL SHEATHING (1x8 sheathing; 1x4 let in braces; 8d nails, 2 per stud crossing.)	1.5	2.2
1/4˝ PLYWOOD NAILED (6d nails spaced 5˝ at edges, 10˝ elsewhere.)	2.0	2.8
1/4˝ PLYWOOD GLUED TO FRAME	3.7	4.0

P-4. Plywood sheathing provides rigidity and strength as indicated in this table, based on tests by the U. S. Forest Products Laboratory.

Recommended Thickness for Plyscord Roof Sheathing
[Panels Lengthwise Across Rafters]

ROOF LOAD*	RAFTER SPACING	THICKNESS
20 lb./sq. ft.	18 in.	5/16 in.
	22 in.	3/8 in.
	27 in.	1/2 in.
	33 in.	5/8 in.
40 lb./sq. ft.	12 in.	5/16 in.
	16 in.	3/8 in.
	21 in.	1/2 in.
	24 in.	5/8 in.

* For deflection limited to 1/360 of span.

P-5. Spacing of rafters for 5/16 to 5/8 in. plywood sheathing.

struction. After the construction is completed, roof sheathing is normally dry and Plyscord will remain in good shape as long as the moisture content remains at less than 20%, which is a prerequisite to durability in any wood product.

Recommended thickness of Plyscord roof sheathing, as related to rafter spacing is given in Fig. P-5.

Plyscord roof sheathing should be installed with grain of the face plies across the rafters. Use 6d common nails for 5/16 in., 3/8 in. and 1/2 in. stock and 8d common nails for 5/8 in. panels. Space nails no more than 6 in. o. c. at panel edges and 12 in. on other bearings. Plyscord edges should be protected from weather at cornices and rakes by a strip of exterior type plywood, lumber or flashing. Normal precautions as to proper ventilation in attics should be taken to prevent excessive condensation.

INSULATION VALUES			Total Resistance (Inside to Outside Air)	U=Coefficient of Thermal Transmission in B.t.u.'s/hr./sq. ft./^{o}temp. difference
Wall Construction				
3/8" Plywood, single sheet			1.26	.79
3/4" Plywood, single sheet			1.74	.58
1/2" Fiberboard, single sheet			2.17	.46
Inside Lining	Insulation Between Studs	Outer Wall Materials		
1/4" Plywood		3/8" Ext. Plywood	2.49	.40
3/8" Plywood		3/8" Ext. Plywood	2.65	.38
1/4" Plywood	1/2" Blanket Insul.	3/8" Ext. Plywood	5.40	.19
1/4" Plywood		5/16" Plyscord furring, siding	4.32	.23
1/4" Plywood		5/16" Plyscord furring, 3/8" Ext. Plywood	3.80	.26
1/4" Plywood	1/2" Blanket Insul.	5/16" Plyscord furring, 3/8" Ext. Plywood	6.71	.15
3/4" Wood Lath & Plaster		5/16" Plyscord Paper, siding	3.49	.29
3/4" Wood Lath & Plaster	1/2" Blanket Insul.	5/16" Plyscord Paper, siding	6.40	.16

P-6. Plywood has the same rate of heat transmission as Douglas fir, i.e., 0.78 B. t. u's per inch. Plywood can be designed to meet any extreme requirement by using insulation materials. Simple panel construction, using exterior plywood outside studs (without sheathing) and plywood inside, usually requires added insulation in the wall, except in warm climates.

WALL SHEATHING WITH FIR PLYWOOD

As wall sheathing, the structural properties of fir plywood simplify and speed the building project and introduce savings in application time. Plywood sheathed walls are tight, draft-free and contribute to overall warmth of the house. Insulation values of all-plywood walls and plywood in combination with other materials are given in Fig. P-6.

When walls are plywood sheathed, no building paper is required.

WALL SHEATHING APPLICATION

Minimum thickness of Plyscord wall sheathing is 5/16 in. for 16 in. stud spacing and 3/8 in. for 24 in. stud spacing. Install with face grain either parallel or across studs. Use 6d common nails for 5/16 in., 3/8 in. and 1/2 in. Plyscord and 8d common nails for 5/8 in. thickness stock. Nails should be spaced not more than 6 in. o. c. at edges of the panels and 12 in. o. c. on the other bearings.

Plywood makes a suitable backing for wall materials including all panel materials, acoustical tile and other tiles, cork, metals and asbestos. In some cases the unsanded Plyscord grade is okay and most economical; for other backing jobs one of the sanded grades should be used. In cases where considerable moisture is likely, as back of a shower stall, exterior

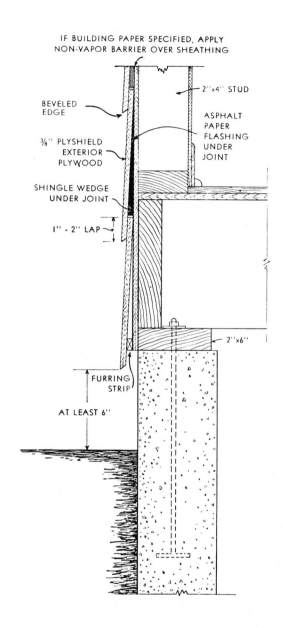

IF BUILDING PAPER SPECIFIED, APPLY
NON-VAPOR BARRIER OVER SHEATHING

2''x4'' STUD

BEVELED EDGE

ASPHALT PAPER FLASHING UNDER JOINT

3/8'' PLYSHIELD EXTERIOR PLYWOOD

SHINGLE WEDGE UNDER JOINT

1'' - 2'' LAP

2''x6''

FURRING STRIP

AT LEAST 6''

P-7. Section showing plywood lap siding. Shingle or tapered wood wedge and asphalt paper flashing under vertical joints. If plywood sheathing is used with the plywood lap siding, place good vapor barrier on inside wall.

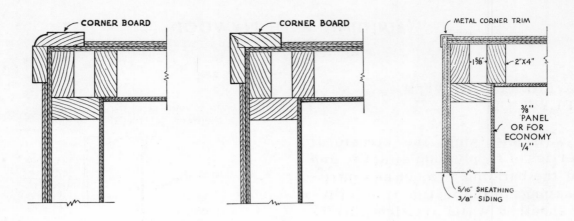

P-8. Three ways to treat corners when using plywood siding.

type plywood with waterproof adhesive should be used.

SIDING WITH FIR PLYWOOD

Plyshield is the siding grade of Douglas fir plywood; Fig. P-7. It is made with waterproof adhesive; one side is smooth for painting, while on the other characteristics such as restricted knotholes are permitted.

In using Plyshield panels; a wide variety of decorative treatments may be attained. Large panels make possible large, unbroken areas for pleasing results. Decorative treatments are obtained with horizontal or vertical moldings, including the vertical "board and batten" effect.

Wide lapped siding, either with shallow or deep shadow line and wide siding with inset moldings are also practical. Panels are easily cut with a power saw into 12 in., 16 in. or 24 in. siding.

Plywood may be used to advantage to complement other building materials being used for gable ends, en-

trance treatments, paneling above or below windows, for an upper or lower band on walls, for dormers and bays.

HOW SIDING IS APPLIED

When Plyshield siding is applied over plywood sheathing, ordinarily no building paper is needed. If building paper is specified, it should be a non-vapor barrier type.

Use non-corrosive (hot-dipped) galvanized nails; 6d common for 3/8 in. plywood siding and 8d for thicker plywood.

PANEL SIDING

Plyshield of 3/8 in. is the minimum thickness recommended, although for economy in certain construction, 1/4 in. may be used. Space nails not more than 6 in. o. c. at panel edges and 12 in. elsewhere.

LAP SIDING

Plyshield 3/8 in. thick is used for studs up to 16 in. o. c.; thicker

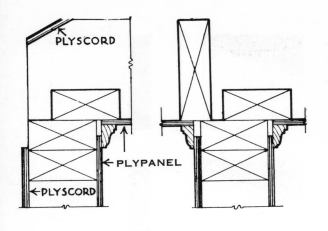

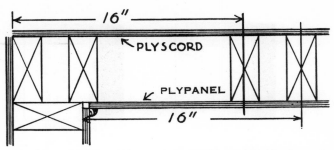

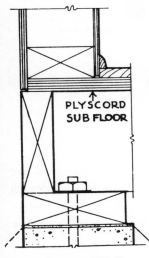

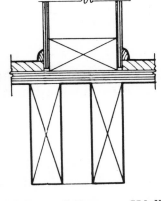

Section of Partition Wall running parallel to floor joists.

Above is a plan at the corner of a typical Dri-Bilt with Plywood house. With Plyscord sheathing or sub-flooring, the wall stud nearest the corner post should be centered 16″ from the outside edge of this post, so that with 16″ stud spacing beyond, all panels will have their edges fall at stud or joist centers.

With Plywood interiors, the 16″ stud spacing should start from the corner, at the face of the abutting wall. This will center the third stud exactly 48″ along the wall, to coincide with the edge of the 48″ panel.

Section Exterior Wall running across joists. Joists or header is set 5/16″ outside of stud line to provide for 5/16″ Plyscord. This simplifies use of standard 4′ x 8′ sheathing, either horizontally or vertically.

Plan where partition and outer wall meet.

Door Jamb Details

"Stock" window frames, with 4-1/2″ jamb widths, are readily adapted to Dri-Bilt with Plywood walls.

Simplest procedure is to have jobber or dealer, or builder at the job, rip the jambs and sills to desired width with a power saw.

Many builders and architects prefer to use furring strips to secure the building paper to the wall sheathing. These strips build out the wall to full frame thickness, and have added advantage of creating a double air space for still greater insulation value.

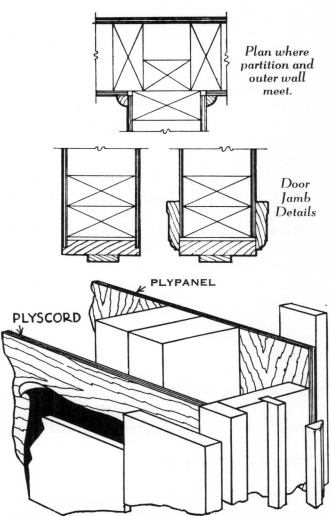

P-9. Plywood construction details.

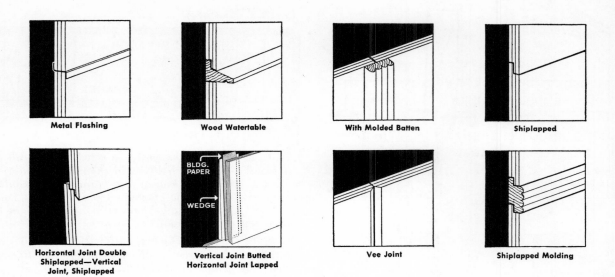

| Metal Flashing | Wood Watertable | With Molded Batten | Shiplapped |

| Horizontal Joint Double Shiplapped—Vertical Joint, Shiplapped | Vertical Joint Butted Horizontal Joint Lapped | Vee Joint | Shiplapped Molding |

P-10. Plywood siding joint details. All edges of plywood siding should be sealed with a heavy coat of exterior house primer or lead and oil paste.

if stud spacing is greater. A bevel of at least 30 degrees upward is recommended to provide a drip at the outer edge. The lap should be at least 1 1/2 in. Vertical joints should be butted over a shingle and centered over a stud unless wood sheathing 3/4 in. thick is used. Nail siding to each of the studs along bottom edge and not more than 4 in. o. c. at vertical joints. Nails should penetrate studs or wood sheathing at least 1 in. If plywood lap siding is wider than 12 in., wood shingle strip should be used at all stud bearings with intermediate vertical nailing. Outside corners should butt against corner molding or be covered, Fig. P-8. Wall sections of typical plywood construction are shown in P-9.

TYPES OF JOINTS

Fig. P-10 shows several simple and attractive ways for handling the joints between the plywood panels. All edges of plywood siding—no matter whether butted, V-shaped, lapped, covered or exposed — should be sealed with a heavy application of high-grade exterior house primer, aluminum paint or heavy lead and oil paint.

INTERIOR PANELING WITH DOUGLAS FIR PLYWOOD

Plywood walls, partitions and ceilings offer a means of speeding up house construction. Such walls may be finished in a variety of ways including light stain-glaze, wallpaper or paint.

Plypanel is the paneling grade of Douglas fir plywood. The use of 3/8 may be installed either vertically or horizontally. Backing at joint is recommended and may be built to serve as a firestop. Panels 3/8 in. thickness should be fastened with 6d finishing or casing nails spaced 6 in. o. c. Panels 1/4 in. in thickness which are sometimes used for economy should be installed with 4d finish nails

348

Fig. P-11 shows typical joint details which may be used to achieve the distinctive appearance of real wood paneled interiors. Fig. P-12 shows suggested panel arrangements. Whenever grain patterns are to be preserved, selection of panels for pattern and appearance prior to installation will assure the most pleasing effect.

V-shaped grooves, easily made with a portable electric router, may be employed to simulate narrower panel-

construction. All grades of Douglas fir plywood are offered in this size; however, other sizes. . . both smaller and larger . . . meet economically many building needs.

Fir plywood is manufactured in several stock widths and lengths. Stock sizes of Plypanel, Plybase, Plyshield and other grades include: Widths— 30 in., 36 in., 42 in. and 48 in. Lengths —60 in., 72 in., 84 in., 96 in., 108 in., 120 in. and 144 in. Plyscord is of-

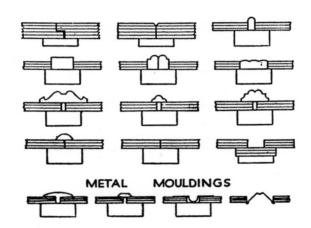

METAL   MOULDINGS

P-11. Suggestions for joint treatment on interior plywood walls, utilizing both wood and metal moldings.

ing or designs on the panel face. Lapping of panels in many cases, is effective. Application of plywood over various walls is shown in Fig. P-13.

SUGGESTED TIME-SAVERS

SIZES:

Plywood panels 48 in. x 96 in. are popular for broad surfaces in home

fered in the 48 in. width and in lengths of 96 in., 108 in., 120 in. and 144 in.

The stock panel width of 48 in. as well as the popular 8 ft. lengths, are multiples of 16 in., the accepted spacing for studs and joists.

Consequently, edges of panels will naturally meet at centers of studs and joists, when spacing is regular and

DESIGN 1	DESIGN 2	DESIGN 3

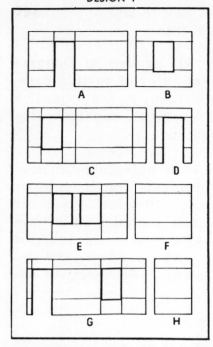 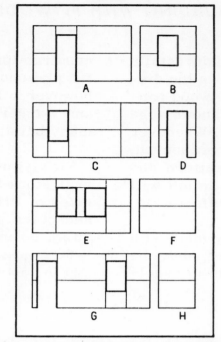 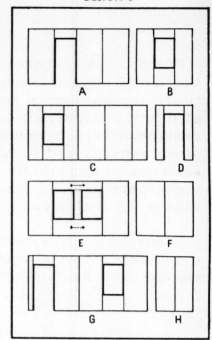

Shown above are three plywood wall paneling design suggestions for each of eight typical wall elements. The basic rule followed in each is to "work from the openings," i.e., first line up vertical joints above doors, above and below windows, then divide the plain wall space into an orderly pattern.

DESIGN 1 is a horizontal pattern obtained by placing panels in three pieces so that continuous horizontal joints are at 1.) window and door head level, and 2.) window sill or other level in proportion to the upper joint. If the height of window and door tops are not the same, choose the lower to establish joint line.

Note that the panel arrangement is keyed by vertical joints placed on either side of the top of the door and above and below windows as shown in Elevations A, C, E and G. Where panel length exceeds wall-element width, as shown in Elevations B and D, vertical joints above openings may be omitted.

DESIGN 2 is a simple two-panel horizontal arrangement. The single continuous horizontal joint is placed midway between door and ceiling. Vertical joints at openings (elevations A, C, E and G) again key panel design, except that they may be omitted where panel length ex-

ceeds wall element width as in Elevations B and D.

DESIGN 3, a vertical panel arrangement is another illustration of the basic principle of initiating panel design by lining up vertical joints with wall openings. The plain wall space is then divided vertically in widths proportionate to that of openings. In a vertical panel arrangement where width of a door or window opening exceeds panel width, panels may be placed horizontally as shown by arrows in Elevation E. Such combinations of vertical and horizontal arrangements may be used in the same room with pleasing effect.

P-12. Plywood panel arrangements for interior walls. When grain patterns are to be preserved, selection of panels for pattern and appearance prior to installation is desirable.

PROVIDED one or two simple steps are taken.

By spotting window and door openings between grid lines, i. e., within 4 ft. panels, only one panel instead of two need be cut. This permits all headers through the house to have same length, allowing quick, economical cutting.

Furthermore, the extra cost of jogs and offsets in a floor plan can be min-

imized by planning so that the face of the wall comes at a grid line.

Grid lines at inside face of walls are desirable when interiors are built with plywood.

This means 4 ft. x 8 ft. panels will cover ceilings with little or no cutting; the same thing applies to wall panels. Also stock cupboards can be fitted into such a layout.

FINISHING EXTERIOR PLYWOOD

Tests indicate that the best paint job for regular wood siding is also the best for exterior type Douglas fir plywood. High grade outside house paints of either TLZ (titanium-lead-zinc) foundation or white lead and oil give excellent service. Be sure to avoid paints which set to a hard, brittle film.

For complete compatibility (no harmful chemical action) between coats, be sure to use prime and finish coats produced by the same manufacturer and formulated as companion products. Allow each coat to dry before the following coat is put on, but keep in mind that painting should be completed as soon as practicable to obtain good adhesion between coats.

Prior to erection, all edges should be sealed with a heavy application of high-grade exterior house primer, aluminum paint or heavy lead and oil paint. FHA recommendations for paint for sealing edges are: 100 lbs. white lead paste, 1 3/4 gal. raw linseed oil and 1 pint dryer, mixed and applied without thinning. This applies to all exposed edges and edges of panels that are lapped, butted and covered with moldings.

In unusually damp locations panels should be primed on the back with a coat of exterior house primer.

THREE COAT SYSTEM RECOMMENDED

A three-coat system is suggested as providing the best conventional protective coating.

The initial coat is important. A high grade exterior primer, thinned with 1 pt. of pure raw linseed oil per gal. of paint and brushed on is recommended. Also, an aluminum primer, compounded from aluminum paste and high quality long oil spar varnish, makes an excellent primer. Use about 1 3/4 lbs. paste or powder in 1 gal. of varnish, mixed just before application. Greater opacity of finish coats may be required, however, to mask the aluminum primer. Over the primer apply the second and third coats of paint according to the manufacturer's instructions.

OTHER SUITABLE FINISHES

Top quality two-coat TLZ house paints, in most cases, will also be quite satisfactory. However, the same dry film should be the same thickness as the three coats.

Textured finishes, using oil or synthetic resin base paints containing mineral particles, asbestos fiber, etc. as part of the pigment have proved popular and are generally satisfactory.

Stains, when applied to plywood, fail to provide a protective film, unless covered with high grade spar varnish.

FINISHING INTERIOR PLYWOOD

Attractive light stain-glaze finishes for walls of Plypanel grade fir plywood have been developed. These subdue the grain contrast yet preserve the natural beauty of the wood. Basic finishing steps are as follows:

1. To White Panel: A coat of interior white undercoat thinned 1 part undercoat to 1 part turpentine or thinner. This may be wiped on with a rag or brushed for more grain show-through. When dry, sand lightly with fine sandpaper.

2. To Seal Wood: One coat of thinned white shellac or clear resin sealer (this seal coat may be thinned more if greater color penetration is wanted). Sand lightly when thoroughly dry.

3. To Provide Color: One color coat. This may be interior undercoat or enamel, thinned as for step No. 1, or color in oil. Light stains may also be used. The color is applied thinly or dry-brushed to proper color tone. When dry sand lightly with fine paper.

4. For Wearing Surfaces: Use one coat flat varnish. A desirable effect may be obtained by steel-wooling, being sure to work with the grain of the wood.

INEXPENSIVE "BLOND" FINISH

An inexpensive "blond" finish may be obtained by using, first, a coat of interior white undercoat thinned so the wood pattern shows through. The undercoat may be tinted if color is desired. Then, a coat of clear shellac, lacquer or flat varnish to protect the surface.

Attractive and economical one-coat stain-wax finishes in various colors are on the market.

When using conventional oil or spirit stain on fir plywood, first apply clear resin sealer, or thinned white shellac to subdue the contrast.

COVERING PLYWOOD WITH WALLPAPER

Plywood panels should be closely butted, primed with a thin flat white paint and all joints filled with Swedish putty. Then, coat surface with a wheat flour paste to which has been added a gelatin glue size.

Over the plywood apply smooth wall liner, blank stock or smooth 3/4 in. deadening felt treated with the same paste and size. The wall liner, blank stock or building felt, should be butted neatly and rolled out smooth. Following this, wallpaper may be hung in the usual way.

ENAMELING PLYWOOD WALLS

Best results may be obtained by first covering the smooth Plypanel with painter's canvas or inexpensive unbleached muslin. Fill nail holes or

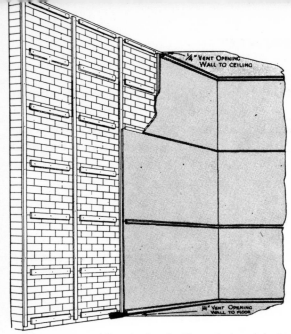

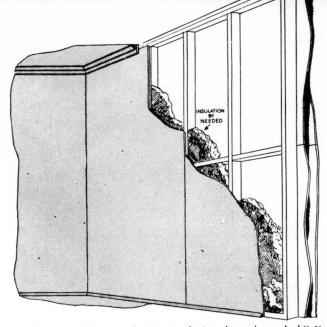

Over masonry walls. Apply 1" x 2" vertical and horizontal strips nailed to wood or cinder nailing blocks set in wall; to wood laths set in mortar joint; to wood or metal plug insets.

Over wood framework. Use stock size plywood panels (4'x8' is common size) and let panel joints occur over studs (usually 16" on centers).

When basement walls are actually damp, paint them with a waterproof paint before installing recreation room. Do not put nailing strips against wet wall; in cases where wall may become damp, the strips should first be treated with a preservative or given a heavy coat of asphalt paint. Any basement wall occasionally may become damp and this dampness must be taken out from behind the paneling by use of a continuous air space with top and bottom openings.   It is preferable to place a screen over the bottom vent. Plywood panels should be back-primed with resin sealer or other good primer where condensation may occur on the masonry.

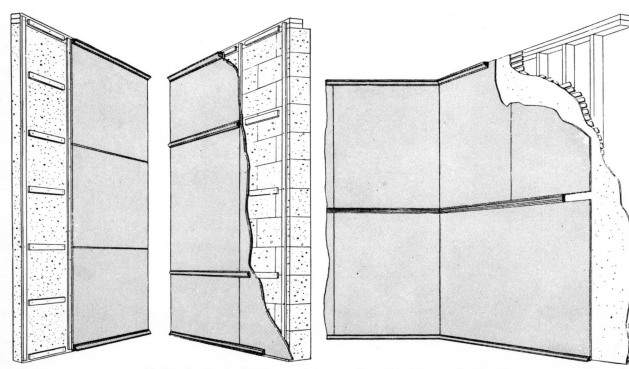

Over concrete or cement-block walls. Apply 1" x 2" vertical and horizontal strips nailed to wood nailing blocks or plugs set in holes driven in cement blocks or concrete.

Over old plaster walls. Usually no stripping required as plaster has 2" x 4" studs usually 16" on centers. When old surface is badly broken up, nail furring strips over studs.

P-13.   Installing plywood panels over masonry walls, wood framework, cement-block walls and over old plaster walls.

hammer marks and joints with Swedish putty. Prime wood with thin flat white oil paint. Hang muslin like wallpaper with regular paste. When dry, apply coat of glue size. Over this any conventional enamel finish may be applied with beautiful results.

REGULAR PAINT FINISHES

A more economical finish consists of using wall and woodwork paints. Panels should be primed well and high grade paints used. Before applying water thinned paints, plywood should be sealed with a clear resin sealer, shellac or a flat white paint. For textured surfaces, prime with regular undercoat and follow with a heavy coat of stippling paint.

BUILT-IN CONVENIENCES

No matter whether the floor plan is liberal or restricted . . . built-in plywood conveniences are recognized as an important part of the modern, livable home.

Chimneys and Fireplaces

A well-built, fire-safe chimney is an asset to a home, and if well designed, will add a touch of distinction to its appearance.

Whether a chimney will work properly depends on flue size, wall construction, smoothness of linings; also its height and its direction (without sharp bends or offsets).

CHIMNEY SHOULD BE SELF SUPPORTING

The chimney should be self-supporting and so constructed that it is independent of the house framing. Soil conditions determine the size of the footing needed, but a footing should never be less than 12 in. thick and it should extend at least 6 in. beyond each face of the chimney. Walls of a chimney with fire clay flue lining should be at least 4 in. thick if built of brick, not less than 8 in. thick if built of stone.

Combustible materials such as wooden framing members should be at least 2 in. from the chimney wall, Fig. R-1. The open space between the floor framework and the chimney should be filled with mortar, mineral wool or other incombustible material, Fig.

R-2. Plastering directly on chimney brickwork is not recommended because plaster cracks are most certain to develop.

CONCRETE CHIMNEY CAP

The chimney should be capped with stone, terra cotta, concrete or cast iron and should extend at least 3 ft. above a flat roof and 2 ft. above a ridge roof.

Construction of a concrete chimney cap is shown in Fig. R-3. The outside dimensions of the cap should be slightly greater than the outside dimensions of the chimney. Side forms may be of 1 x 4 or 2 x 4 lumber. Core dimensions should be the same as the outside of the chimney flue.

A 1:2 1/4:2 1/2 concrete mix (1 part Portland cement, 2 1/4 parts sand and 2 1/2 parts gravel not over 3/4 in.) is about right. A 1/4 in. round reinforcing bar should be bent to form a square, then placed in the center of the concrete section. Lap the bar ends about 10 in.

An edging tool can be used to round the top edges of the cap if desired.

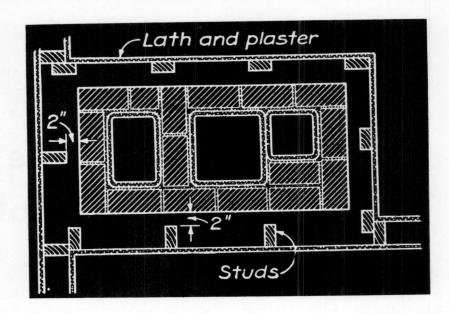

R-1. Cross section of chimney showing the proper arrangement for three flues. The division wall should be well bonded with the sidewalls by staggering the joints of successive courses. Note the studs are 2 in. away from brickwork.

After the concrete hardens for 2 or 3 days, forms may be removed, the inner form being withdrawn first. Portland cement mortar consisting of 1 part Portland cement to 3 parts of mortar sand should be used in setting the cap on the top of the chimney.

FLUES SHOULD BE SEPARATED AT LEAST 4 IN.

A division wall of at least 4 in. of brick should separate one flue from others in the same chimney.

Sizes of rectangular and round flue lining commonly used are shown in Fig. R-4.

To make the junction between the chimney and the roof water tight, flashing is required, Fig. R-5.

The term "flashing" is applied to the pieces of metal—tin, copper, sheet iron, or lead—that are nailed onto the roof along with the shingles and bent up against the chimney wall, while "counter flashing" means the pieces of metal are set into the chimney brickwork and bent down over the flashing to form a water-tight joint.

Copper is the best metal to use on flashing jobs. It costs more than ordinary sheet metal but will be permanent. Ordinary sheet iron rusts out and is difficult to replace.

A metal covered "cricket" or "chimney saddle" is frequently used back of the chimney to shed the water. These are ordinarily available from building supply houses.

EIGHT INCH WALLS ARE DESIRABLE

Building the exposed upper section of a chimney with 8 in. walls, Fig. R-6,

356

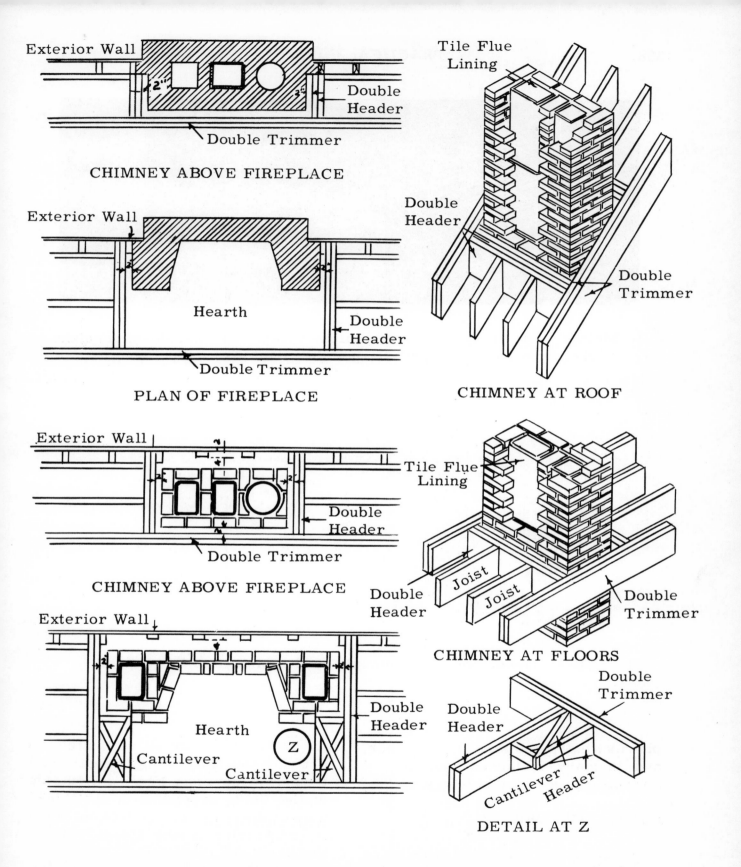

Exterior Wall

2"

Double Header

Double Trimmer

CHIMNEY ABOVE FIREPLACE

Exterior Wall

2"

Hearth

Double Header

Double Trimmer

PLAN OF FIREPLACE

Exterior Wall

2"

2"

Double Header

Double Trimmer

CHIMNEY ABOVE FIREPLACE

Exterior Wall

2"

Hearth

Cantilever

Z

Cantilever

Double Header

Tile Flue Lining

Double Header

Double Trimmer

CHIMNEY AT ROOF

Tile Flue Lining

Double Header

Joist

Joist

Double Trimmer

CHIMNEY AT FLOORS

Double Header

Cantilever Header

Double Trimmer

DETAIL AT Z

R-2. Fireplace with alternate flue designs; framing around chimney.

357

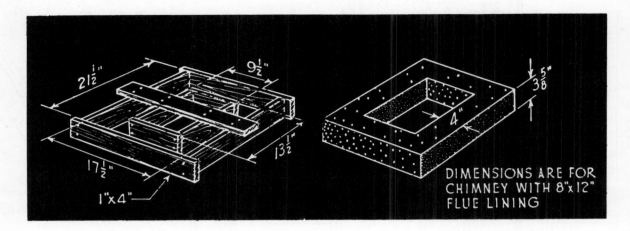

R-3. Method of building a concrete chimney cap. The outside dimensions of the cap should be slightly larger than the top of the chimney.

Rectangular linings [1]				Round linings [2]			
Outside dimensions (inches)	Cross-sectional area		Wall thickness	Inside diameter (inches)	Cross-sectional area		Wall thickness
	Inside	Outside			Inside	Outside	
	Square inches	Square feet	Inches		Square inches	Square feet	Inches
4½ by 8½	23.6	0.26	5⁄8	6	28.3	0.29	5⁄8
4½ by 13	38.2	.41	5⁄8	8	50.3	.49	3⁄4
7½ by 7½	39.1	.39	5⁄8	10	78.5	.75	7⁄8
8½ by 8½	52.6	.50	5⁄8	12	113.0	1.07	1
8½ by 13	80.5	.78	3⁄4	15	176.7	1.62	1⅛
8½ by 18	109.7	1.10	7⁄8	18	254.4	2.29	1¼
13 by 13	126.6	1.20	7⁄8	20	314.1	2.82	1⅜
13 by 18	182.8	1.70	7⁄8	22	380.1	3.48	1⅝
18 by 18	248.1	2.30	1⅛	24	452.3	4.05	1⅝
20 by 20	297.6	2.60	1⅜	27	572.5	5.20	2

[1] All rectangular flue lining is 2 feet long.
[2] Round flue lining, 6 to 24 inches in diameter, is 2 feet long; that 27 to 36 inches in diameter is 2½ or 3 feet long.

R-4. Dimensions of commonly used commercial flue lining.

provides extra resistance to weather, and in many instances adds to the attractiveness of the chimney.

ESTIMATING BRICK

The quantity of standard-size brick (8 x 3 3/4 x 2 1/4 in.) required to build a straight chimney having only two or three flues can be estimated by drawing the flue lining to scale and then drawing lines 4 to 8 in. outside of the lining depending on the thickness of the brick walls. Lay out 4 x 8 in. rectangles in the space between the lining and the outside lines to determine how many bricks are needed for one course.

For example, if 15 1/2 bricks are needed for each course, Fig. 1, the height is 30 ft. and 1/2 in. mortar joints are used, there would be 4 1/2 courses per foot or 135 courses for the 30 ft. chimney. Multiplying 15 1/2 by 135 equals 2,092 bricks. Assuming that about 100 more bricks will be needed to make the lower portion solid, 2,200 bricks will be needed altogether.

ed lime and 6 parts clean sand. Firebrick is best laid in fire clay cement.

FIREPLACE CONSTRUCTION

In order that satisfactory results may be obtained from an open fireplace it is essential that the flue have the proper area, that the throat be correctly proportioned and located, that a properly constructed smoke shelf

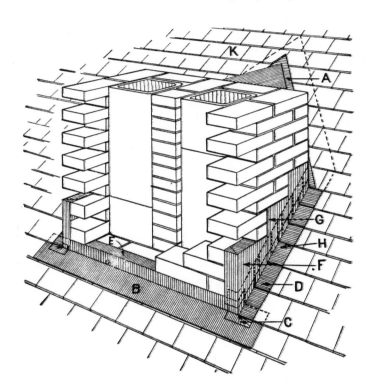

R-5. Flashing to make junction between chimney and roof water tight. Sheet metal A should extend under shingles K at least 4 in. Apron B is bent as at E with base flashings C, D and H and cap flashings F and G, lapping over base flashings. When chimney contains two flues, joints should be separated as shown.

MORTAR TO USE

A mortar that is quite satisfactory for setting flue linings and all chimney masonry, except firebrick, consists of 1 part Portland cement, 1 part hydrat-

and chamber be provided. The chimney must be carried high enough to avoid interference with the draft and the shape of the fireplace be such as to direct the maximum amount of radiated heat into the room.

FLUE AREA

The sectional area of the flue bears a direct relation to the area of the opening in the fireplace. Area of lined flues should be a tenth or more of that of the fireplace opening. If the flue is unlined proportion should be slightly more because of greater friction.

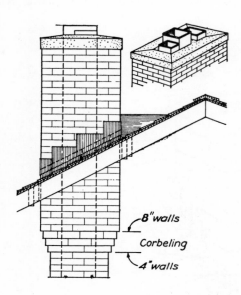

8" walls

Corbeling

4" walls

R-6. Greater resistance to weather is provided by building the exposed upper section of a chimney with 8 in. walls. The mortar joint is not so likely to fail as it is when the wall is only 4 in. thick, and in many cases a larger chimney is more attractive.

A good rule to follow is to allow thirteen square inches of area for the chimney flue to every square foot of fireplace opening. For the fireplace shown in Fig. R-7, the opening of which has an area of 8.25 square feet, there is required a flue having an area of 107 square inches. If this flue were built of brick and unlined, it would probably be made 8 in. x 16 in., or 128 square inches, because brickwork can be laid to better advantage if the dimensions of the flue are multiples of 4 in. If the flue is lined, and lining is strongly recommended, the lining should have an inside area of approximately 107 square inches.

Not providing a chimney flue of sufficient sectional area is in many cases the cause of an unsatisfactory fireplace. The cross section should be the same throughout the entire length of the chimney. If necessary to change the direction of the flue, the full area should be preserved through all turns and bends and the change should be made as gradual as possible, Fig. R-8.

THROAT

In Fig. R-7 is shown the throat, the narrow opening between the fireplace and the smoke chamber. Correct throat construction contributes as much or more to efficiency of a fireplace than any other feature except proper flue design. A flue twice as large as is necessary brought straight down to the fireplace without constriction at the throat would result in a poor draft, for the draft does not depend upon the largeness of the flue but upon its proper proportioning to the fireplace and throat. Arrows indicate upward flowing currents of warm air which are thrown forward at the throat and pass through the smoke chamber into the flue on the inner side. The rapid upward passage of

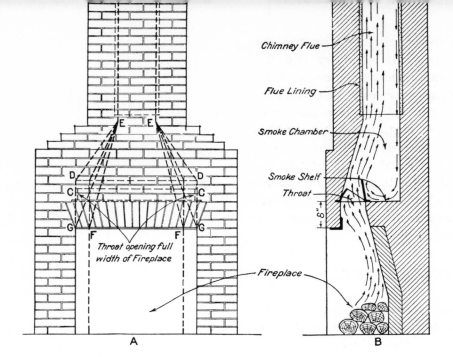

R-7. A, top of throat damper is at DD, smoke shelf at CC. Side wall should not be drawn in until height of DD is passed. This assures full area. If drawing in is done as indicated by lines EF and EG, the width of the throat becomes less than the width of the opening and causes air currents to pile up in corners of the throat, resulting frequently in a smoky fireplace. B, correct fireplace construction.

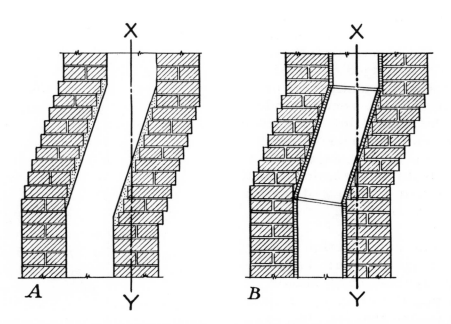

R-8. For structural safety the amount of offset must be limited so that the center line, XY, or the upper flue will not fall beyond the center of the wall of the lower flue. A, offsetting of the left wall of an unlined flue is started two brick courses higher than on the right wall so that the area of the sloping section will not be reduced after plastering; B, a lined flue showing method of cutting tile.

air causes a down current on the opposite side, as indicated by the descending arrows. Down current is not as strong as up current, but may be of such force that if there is no throat in the fireplace, Fig. R-9, to increase the velocity of the upward current by constricting it, the meeting of the two currents will result in smoke being forced out into the room. This explains why some fireplaces have ample flue area, yet smoke badly.

THROAT CONSTRUCTION

Throat area should not be less than that of the flue. Its length should always be equal to the width of the fireplace opening. Sides of the fireplace should be vertical until the throat is passed. Above the throat sides should be drawn in until the desired flue area is obtained. The throat should be set 8 in. above the location of the lintel, also indicated in Fig. R-7. If a damper is installed, the width of the brick opening at the throat will depend upon the width of the frame of the damper, the width of the throat proper being regulated by the hinged cover of the damper. If the throat damper is omitted, which is seldom recommended, the opening should be 4 in. The smoke shelf should not be bricked up, but should conform to the dotted lines, Fig. R-10. Depth of the smoke shelf should be the same for a 2 ft. as for a 10 ft. fireplace opening.

Proper throat construction is very necessary to successful fireplace operation so special care should be taken to see that the width is not made more than 4 in. and that the side walls are carried up perpendicularly until the throat is passed, so the full length of opening is provided. In many cases trouble experienced in an existing

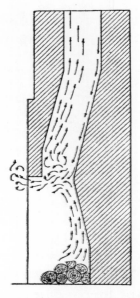

R-9. Fireplaces constructed like this without throat will very likely smoke.

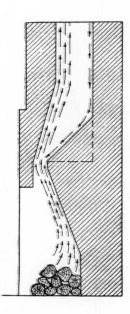

R-10. This construction without a throat damper directs the down draft so that it meets the up draft almost at the throat. This is a serious fault.

fireplace with ample flue area is caused by incorrect formation of the throat.

The smoke chamber is the space extending from the top of the throat up to the bottom of the flue proper

Opening		Depth,	Mini-mum back (hori-zontal)	Vertical back wall,	Inclined back wall,	Outside dimensions of standard rectangular flue lining	Inside diameter of standard round flue lining
Width,	Height,						
Inches	Inches	Inches	Inches	Inches	Inches	Inches	Inches
24	24	16–18	14	14	16	8½ by 8½	10
28	24	16–18	14	14	16	8½ by 8½	10
24	28	16–18	14	14	20	8½ by 8½	10
30	28	16–18	16	14	20	8½ by 13	10
36	28	16–18	22	14	20	8½ by 13	12
42	28	16–18	28	14	20	8½ by 18	12
36	32	18–20	20	14	24	8½ by 18	12
42	32	18–20	26	14	24	13 by 13	12
48	32	18–20	32	14	24	13 by 13	15
42	36	18–20	26	14	28	13 by 13	15
48	36	18–20	32	14	28	13 by 18	15
54	36	18–20	38	14	28	13 by 18	15
60	36	18–20	44	14	28	13 by 18	15
42	40	20–22	24	17	29	13 by 13	15
48	40	20–22	30	17	29	13 by 18	15
54	40	20–22	36	17	29	13 by 18	15
60	40	20–22	42	17	29	18 by 18	18
66	40	20–22	48	17	29	18 by 18	18
72	40	22–28	51	17	29	18 by 18	18

R-11. Recommended dimensions for finished fireplaces from Farmers' Bulletin 1889.

SMOKE SHELF AND CHAMBER

A smoke shelf and chamber are very essential. The shelf is formed by setting the brickwork back at the top of the throat to the line of the flue wall. The shelf should be the full length of the throat. Depth of the shelf should not be less than 4 in., but it may vary from 4 in. up to 12 or more, depending upon the depth of the fireplace.

The purpose of the smoke shelf is to change the direction of the down draft so the hot gases at the throat will strike it approximately at a right angle instead of head-on. Therefore the shelf should be made as wide as the construction will permit at a height of 8 in. above the top of the fireplace opening.

and between the side walls, which may be drawn in after the top of the throat is passed. The area at the bottom of the chamber is quite large, since its width includes that of the throat plus the depth of the smoke shelf. This space holds accumulated smoke temporarily if a gust of wind across the top of the chimney momentarily cuts off the draft. Without this chamber smoke would likely be forced out into the room. A smoke chamber also lessens the force of the down draft by increasing the area through which it passes. If the walls are drawn inward one foot for each 18 in. of rise, friction is reduced and interference with the draft lessened. Walls of the smoke chamber should be plastered smoothly with cement mortar at least one-half inch thick. Roughness im-

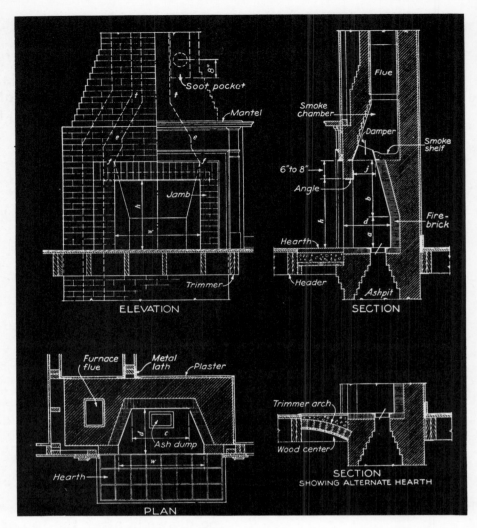

R-12. A typical fireplace, illustrating practical details of construction. An alternate method of supporting the hearth is given in the lower right-hand corner of the drawing.

pedes the upward movement of the air currents.

FIREPLACE SHAPE

Information on the shape of the fireplace proper may be obtained by again referring to R-7; the back should pitch forward from a point a little less than half way from the hearth to the top of the opening and the sides should be beveled as indicated. Straight back and sides do not radiate as much heat out into the room.

THROAT DAMPER

A correctly designed throat damper provides a way to regulate the fire. The damper usually consists of a cast-iron frame with a lid hinged so the width of the throat opening may be varied. Regulating the size of the opening according to the kind of fire helps prevent waste of heat up the chimney when the fireplace is in use and closes the opening when the fireplace is not in use. The placing of the damper varies with the type, but generally the bottom of the frame is built into the brickwork at the level of the top of the fireplace opening, forming the throat and supporting the masonry above it.

FIREPLACE SIZES

Fig. R-11 gives recommended dimensions for fireplaces of various widths and heights.

THE HEARTH

The hearth should be flush with the floor, so wood chips, bark from logs, etc. can be brushed into the fireplace, Fig. R-12. An ash dump located in the hearth near the back of the fire-

pivoted cover. The basement ash pit should be of tight masonry and provided with a clean-out door, Fig. R-13.

FIREPLACE JAMBS

The jambs of a fireplace should be of sufficient width to give stability to the structure both structurally and in appearance. For a fireplace opening 3 ft. wide or less, 16 in. is generally sufficient; for wider openings similar proportions should be kept. Also to be taken into consideration are the proportions of the room.

BACK AND SIDES

Back and sides of a fireplace should

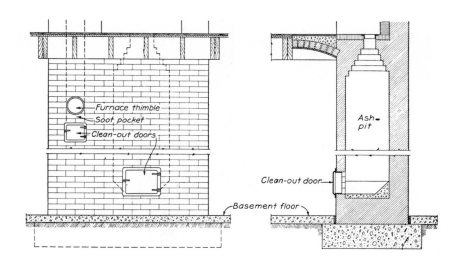

R-13. The fireplace ashpit should be of tight masonry and it should be provided with a tight fitting iron clean-out door and frame about 10 x 12 in. in size. A clean-out for the furnace flue as shown is also recommended.

place is handy for clearing ashes and other refuse, provided there is space below for an ash pit. The dump consists of a cast-iron metal frame with

be constructed of firebrick. Bricks should be laid flat with the long sides exposed, as there is danger of their falling out if they are placed on edge.

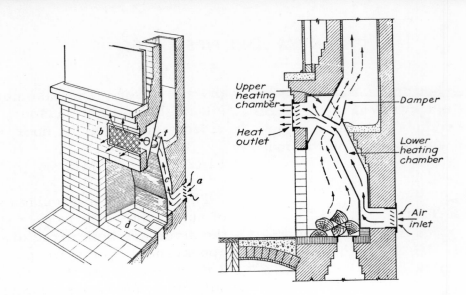

R-14. In this modified fireplace air enters the inlet, "a," from outside and is heated as it rises by natural circulation through the back chamber, "c," and the tubes, "t," being discharged into the room from the register, "b." Air for supporting combustion is drawn into the fire at "d" and passes between the tubes up the flue. A damper is also provided to close the air inlet.

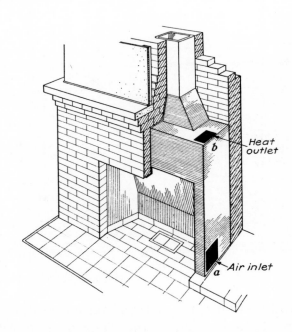

R-15. In this fireplace the air is not drawn in directly from outdoors but through the inlet, "a," from the room that is being heated. The air is heated by contact with the metal sides and back of the fireplace, rises by natural circulation, and is discharged back into the room from the outlet, "b," or to another room on the same floor or in the second story. The inlets and outlets are connected to registers which may be located at the front of the fireplace, ends of the fireplace, or on the wall of an adjacent room.

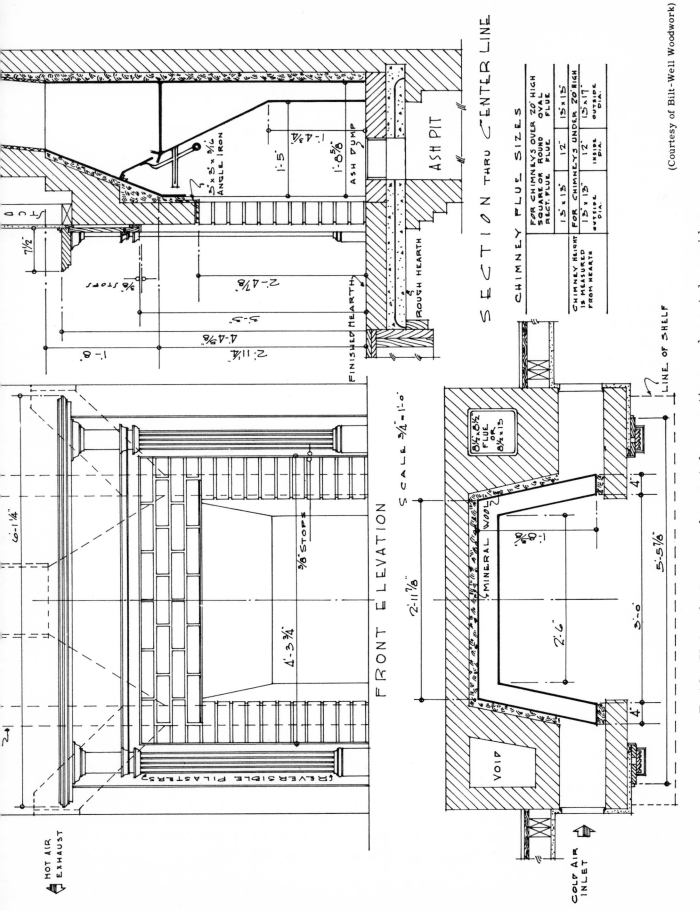

SECTION THRU CENTER LINE

CHIMNEY FLUE SIZES

	FOR CHIMNEYS OVER 20' HIGH		FOR CHIMNEYS UNDER 20' HIGH	
CHIMNEY HEIGHT IS MEASURED FROM HEARTH	SQUARE OR RECT. FLUE	ROUND OR OVAL FLUE		
	OUTSIDE DIA.	OUTSIDE DIA.	INSIDE DIA.	OUTSIDE DIA.
	13"×13"	12"	12"	13"×17"
	13"×13"	15"×15"	15"×15"	

FRONT ELEVATION

SCALE ¾" = 1'-0"

ASH PIT

ASH DUMP

3"×3"×³⁄₁₆" ANGLE IRON

ROUGH HEARTH

FINISHED HEARTH

⅜" STOPS

HOT AIR EXHAUST

(REVERSIBLE PILASTERS)

⅜" STOPS

LINE OF SHELF

8¼"×6¼" FLUE OR 8½"×13"

MINERAL WOOL

VOID

COLD AIR INLET

(Courtesy of Bilt-Well Woodwork)

R-16. Using factory-made mantel saves time and mantel provides worthwhile room decoration.

SUPPORTING IRONS

In small fireplaces sagging of the arch over the opening seldom occurs, but in larger fireplaces it is common. Such trouble may be prevented by using a heavy flat iron bar or a T-shaped bar, the wider the opening the heavier the iron required.

MODIFIED FIREPLACES

Modified fireplaces of today are of various types. See Figs. R-14 and R-15. Such fireplaces consist of units of heavy metal, set into place and con-cealed by brickwork or other con-struction.

An advantage claimed for modified fireplace units is that the correctly designed and proportioned firebox, manufactured with throat, damper, smoke shelf and chamber, provides a form for the masonry, thus reducing the risk of failure and assuring a smokeless fireplace. But it must be kept in mind that even though unit is properly designed, it will not operate efficiently if chimney is inadequate.

Using a factory-made mantel, Fig. R-16, provides a means of saving time and a worthwhile room decoration.

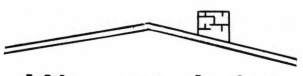

Misc. Helpful Information

USING ESSEX TABLE ON SQUARE TO FIND NUMBER OF BOARD FEET

The Essex board measure table appears on the steel square on the back of the blade. It is easy to use and once its essentials are understood, it may be used to quickly find the number of board feet in a piece of lumber.

THREE DIMENSIONS MUST BE KNOWN

To find the number of board feet in a piece of lumber, its three dimensions — width, thickness and length must be known. Two of these dimensions are taken care of at one time by the inch markings on the outer edge of the blade. These figures represent the width in inches of a board 1 in. thick. The third dimension of the board or timber is found in the vertical column of figures under the inch mark

12 (12 is the base number of the table). The figures under the number represent lengths in feet. All the other figures in the table represent totals of board feet.

FIND LENGTH FIRST

To find the number of board feet in a piece of wood, find its length in the column under 12 and guide laterally (sidewise) along this line until the figure under the width of the board is reached. This figure is the number of board feet, in feet and inches, of a piece of lumber 1 in. thick. To find the result for lumber of other thicknesses, multiply the first result by the thickness of the piece. In the answer table, figures to the left of the vertical lines represent feet, the figures to the right represent inches.

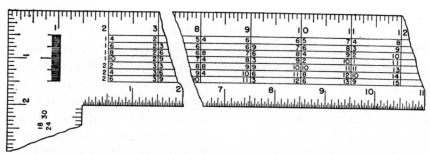

Essex board measure table on steel square.

LET'S TAKE AN EXAMPLE

For example: How many board feet of lumber are there in a piece 8 in. wide, 3 in. thick and 13 ft. long?

First, find the length, 13 ft. under the inch figure 12.

Move along the line to the left until directly under the figure 8, which represents the width of the piece.

Read the figure in the table: 8/8 or 8 8/12 (8 2/3) feet. This figure is for a board 1 in. thick.

Multiply 8 2/3 x 3 which gives us 26, the number of board feet in a piece 8 in. wide, 3 in. thick and 13 ft. long. A board half this length would contain 13 board feet, one twice this length twice 26, or 52 board feet.

In this way the scale can be used to determine the number of board feet in any size of timber.

HOW TO BUILD SCAFFOLDING

In building a house or other structure above the reach of workmen standing on the ground, scaffolding should be provided so the job may be carried on without unnecessary loss of time.

The type of scaffold required depends to a considerable extent on how many men will be on it at one time, distance above the ground, whether it will be required to support building materials, etc. Special care should be taken to see that the scaffold built is adequate to carry the required load with safety.

Typical single-pole and double-pole scaffolds are shown in Fig. S-1. Uprights may be of straight-grain 2 x 4's. The lower ends should be placed on pieces of boards to prevent them from settling into the ground. Cross ledgers should be 2 x 6's about 4 ft. long. Use at least three 16d nails at each end of cross ledgers to fasten them to the

uprights, or in the case of the single-pole scaffold one end of the cross ledger is fastened to a 2 x 6 block securely nailed to the wall. Braces may be made of 1 x 6 lumber, fastened to uprights with 10d nails, and with 8d nails where they cross. For the platform 2 x 10 planks free from objectionable knots should be used. Spike them to cross ledgers to prevent possibility of slipping.

LADDER JACK SCAFFOLDS

Ladder jacks, Fig. S-2, can be used to good advantage in providing scaffolding on many building jobs, particularly on jobs where a single workman is employed, and on repair jobs. In using these ladder jacks you need two ladders of the same size and a strong plank. As the work progresses height of the scaffold is adjusted by standing on one ladder, supporting the

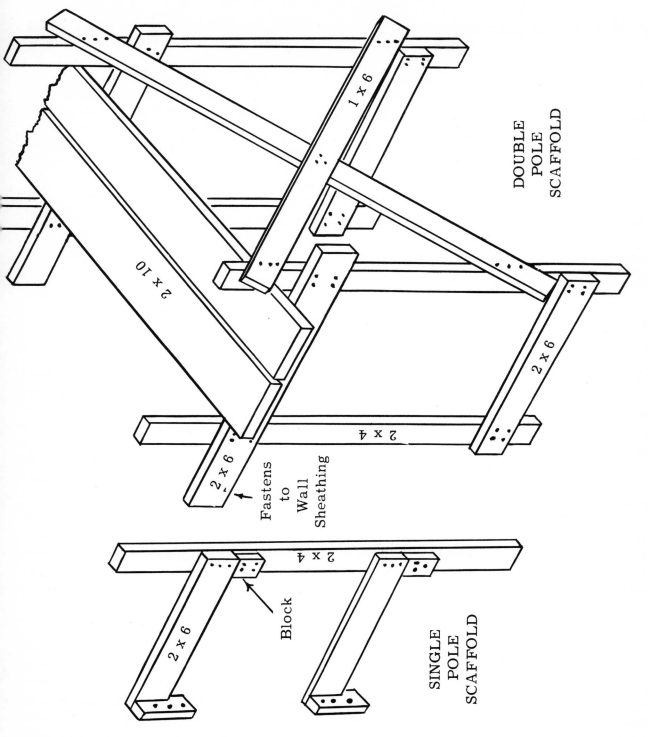

1 x 6

2 x 10

2 x 6

2 x 4

2 x 6

Fastens
to
Wall
Sheathing

DOUBLE
POLE
SCAFFOLD

2 x 4

Block

2 x 6

SINGLE
POLE
SCAFFOLD

S-1. Single-pole and double-pole scaffolds.

371

S-2. Ladder jacks used in providing scaffold.

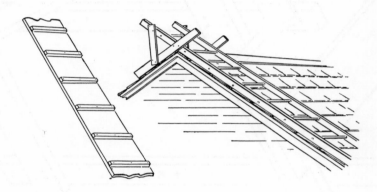

S-3. Two types of supports that may be used in
roof construction and repairing.

plank with one arm, raising the ladder jack to desired position and placing plank back on the jack.

Fig. S-3 shows two types of supports that may be used to good advantage in roof construction and repairing.

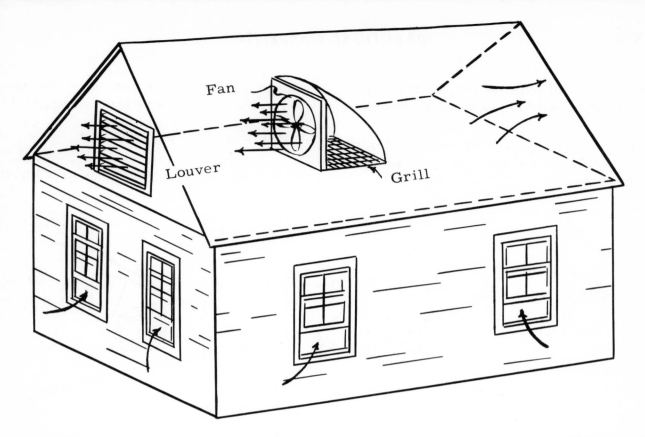

Fan

Louver

Grill

S-4. Installing attic fan. The opening should be centrally located so that good circulation of air can be obtained from all parts of the house.

INSTALLING ATTIC FANS

In most parts of the country, artificial circulation of night air may be used to reduce the day temperature of a house several degrees, as well as to increase night comfort.

Artificial circulation of night air serves two purposes. One is to draw into the house cooler air from outdoors and provide immediate comfort to the occupants during evening and sleeping hours. Hot air that has accumulated within the home during the day is replaced with night air and a constant circulation of air is provided.

The second purpose is to remove heat from walls, objects in rooms and from the attic by passing cooler outside air over and through them. Walls and furnishings have been absorbing heat all day. By removing this stored heat the temperature of the walls and objects is lowered so that a cooler interior temperature can be maintained during the next day. To get the maximum benefit from such operation, the house must be kept closed during the hot daytime.

One disadvantage of bringing large

quantities of outside air into the house at night is the dust and pollen nuisance.

However, by means of some filtering material, this may be partially corrected.

extremely hot weather, one change per minute is sometimes required.

USE OF ATTIC FANS

One of the best ways to circulate

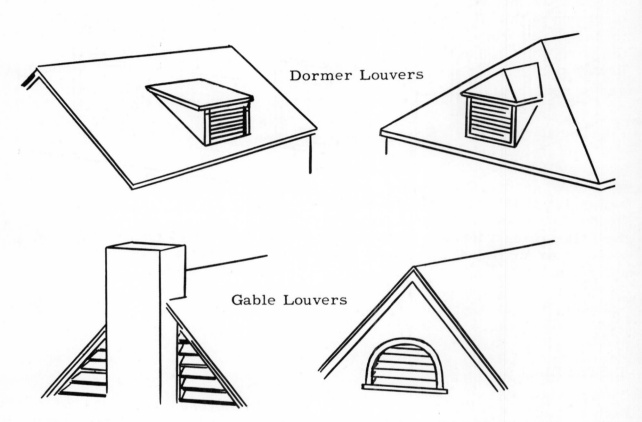

Dormer Louvers

Gable Louvers

S-5. Attic fan discharges air to the outside through open windows or louvers in the attic walls or dormers.

AMOUNT OF AIR
CHANGE NEEDED

Having enough night air passed through the house is important. In studies made by the Kansas State College, Manhattan, Kan., 15 to 30 changes per hour were found to be necessary to provide satisfactory results. In

outside night air in through the house and out through the attic is by the use of a large electrically operated attic fan. This is usually a slow speed, large diameter fan, built especially for the purpose. These fans move large volumes of air through the house. An attic is an excellent location for such a unit.

FAN LOCATION

The fan should be installed near an opening through the ceiling into the attic, Fig. S-4. The opening should be centrally located so that good circulation of air can be obtained from all parts of the home. The attic fan discharges the air to the outside through open windows or louvers in the attic walls or dormers, Fig. S-5. Installation of ready-made gable sash and louvers is shown in Fig. S-6.

The attic fan brings in cooler air and forces out the hot air that has accumulated in the attic. These temperatures during the daytime go as high as 140 to 150 degrees Fahrenheit. Open all windows of the home to cool the entire house, or only those to a given room for more rapid cooling in one room.

Locate the fan over or near a partition wall or other solid support to prevent undue sagging of the ceiling and excessive vibration. An excellent location is over a closet or just back from an attic door or ceiling opening. Do not install the fan less than three feet from the nearest side of the ceiling grille or opening. If the fan is located too close to the grille opening, air and fan noises may prove objectionable. For greatest economy, place the fan the distance of its diameter from the nearest side of the ceiling opening. If possible, locate the fan in the attic so that light coming through the louver or window cannot shine through the fan and grille and flicker in the room below. The fan should be placed in the attic so that the air will be circulated as much as possible be-fore it escapes through the exhaust openings. Construct the housing around the fan to create good suction for the fan. The mounting of the fan on rubber cushions or pads will be very helpful in keeping noise and fan vibration to a minimum.

SELECTION OF FAN

Fans of varying sizes are now available on the commercial market with the proper speed and design for successful air circulation through the attic. Fig. S-7 gives a list of some typical ones with the pertinent data for each indicated. The major factors to consider in the selection of an attic fan are quietness of operation, simplicity of installation, and the capacity to move a large volume of air economically.

FREE CIRCULATION OF AIR REQUIRED

Due to the large volume of air that the attic fan will move per minute, there must be a sufficiently large opening into the attic for the air to enter. If this opening is not sufficient, back pressure develops causing poor circulation and excessive noise. The recommendation for Kansas conditions is to design the installation for 30 complete air changes per hour. On this basis, the ceiling inlet opening for air circulation should be that as indicated in Fig. S-7 under recommended size of opening to attic. In like manner to prevent back pressure, the outlet from the attic through the outside wall must be large, as also indicated.

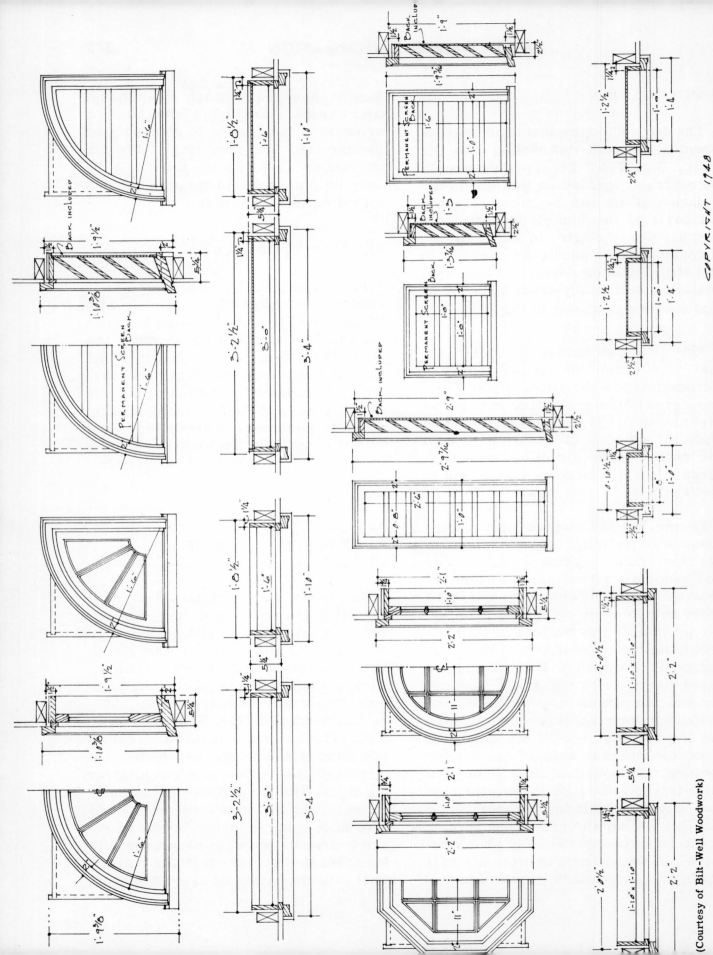

S-6. Installing factory-made gable sash and louvers.

The attic inlet is usually through what is called a ceiling grille. It may be, however, just an open stairway or hole in the ceiling. The outlet for the air to leave the house is called the exhaust opening. It is usually a louver constructed right in the wall. It may, however, be windows.

CEILING GRILLES OR FAN INLET OPENINGS

Two points should be kept in mind in planning the ceiling opening. It should be located so that air can be readily pulled through it from any or all of the rooms as desired. Second,

sufficient size to assure air velocity through the grille of not more than 750 cubic feet per minute. For general practice, 500 to 750 cubic feet per minute is satisfactory.

Ceiling fan openings can be installed so that when the fan is turned on, the grille opens automatically, and when the fan is turned off the grille closes. This type of grille requires metal shutter equipment for best results. The air discharge rate for these metal grilles is usually around 80 per cent, as compared to only 50 to 60 per cent on the wood type.

Volume of House in Cu. Ft.	Fan Size Inches Dia.	Free Air Discharge Cu. Ft. Per Min.	Normal H.P.	Recommended Fan Speed	Recommended Size of Opening to Attic in Sq. Ft. Free Air Opening	Wood Grille 60 %	Metal Grille 80 %	Recommended Size of Opening from Attic in Sq. Ft. Wood Louver 50 %	Metal Louver 80 %
7,400	24	3,700	1/6	675	6.2	10.3	7.8	12.4	7.8
11,000	30	5,500	1/6	480	9.2	15.3	11.5	18.4	11.5
16,000	36	8,000	1/4	410	13.3	22.2	16.6	26.6	16.6
24,000	42	12,000	1/3	300	20.0	33.3	25.0	40.0	25.0
30,000	48	15,000	1/2	290	25.0	41.7	31.2	50.0	31.2
34,000	54	17,000	1/2	260	28.3	47.2	35.4	56.6	35.4
46,000	60	23,000	3/4	245	38.3	63.8	48.0	76.6	48.0

S-7. Table showing size of exhaust area required for various attic fan installations.

the opening or the open part of the grille should never be less than the size of the fan. The opening into the attic must be at least as large as the fan. If you have a grille opening, the opening must be larger to provide for the lack of air flow through the partially obstructed area. Generally for homes, where quiet operation is desired, the net grille area should be of

ATTIC EXHAUST OPENINGS

Successful fan operation depends upon adequate exhaust openings from the attic. Where possible, these exhaust openings should be built into the side of the house away from the prevailing winds. These openings can be open windows or louvers. To secure adequate outlet capacity, it is usually easiest to construct louvers. Louver openings are usually constructed of wood, galvanized sheet iron or copper. Metal louvers offer less obstruction to air flow and consequently their over-all size may be less than that of other types.

In every installation, it is necessary to provide a definite amount of free air space in the attic openings so that the air may be expelled easily. The free air space required for the louver openings is the free air space between the louver slats. This area depends upon the amount of air to be moved and upon the size of the fan. Because of the obstruction to air flow caused by the slats or louvers, their gross area will need to be more than the actual free area required. Sometimes the net area of the exhaust opening is too large for one louver or window and so two or more such openings will be needed. Information as to the size of exhaust area required is given in Fig. S-7. Wire screen, if placed inside the exhaust louver, will keep out birds, leaves, etc., but will retard the air flow. At least one-fourth additional

louver area should be provided.

WIRING RECOMMENDATIONS

Connect the fan motor to a circuit of sufficient size to carry the increased load. A separate circuit is desirable in the average installation, using not smaller than No. 12 size wire. Locate the switch as centrally and conveniently as possible. In a two-story house, two three-way switches may be installed so that the fan can be controlled from either floor. This is not necessary, but may be desired for convenience.

The cost of operation varies depending upon the rate per kilowatt hour. Usually the additional electricity used by the average fan installation falls in the lower bracket rate, and accordingly the cost of operation is quite small.

OPERATION COST

From a test and survey made by the Dallas Power and Light Company in Texas, the following data were derived from 55 installations:

Size of Fan	No. Fans In Test	Ave. KW Hours Used Per Fan Per Season	Total Cost Per Season, May 1 - October 1, at 3 cents per KW Hour
30	6	149	$4.47
36	16	274	8.22
42	20	331	9.93
48	10	400	12.00

HOW TO READ HOUSE PLANS

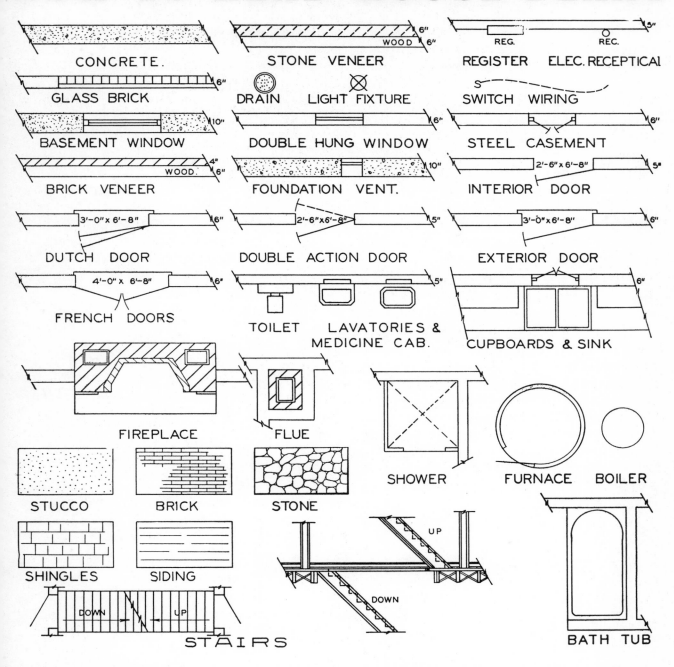

CONCRETE.

STONE VENEER

REGISTER ELEC. RECEPTICAL

GLASS BRICK

DRAIN LIGHT FIXTURE

SWITCH WIRING

BASEMENT WINDOW

DOUBLE HUNG WINDOW

STEEL CASEMENT

BRICK VENEER

FOUNDATION VENT.

INTERIOR DOOR

DUTCH DOOR

DOUBLE ACTION DOOR

EXTERIOR DOOR

FRENCH DOORS

TOILET LAVATORIES & MEDICINE CAB.

CUPBOARDS & SINK

FIREPLACE FLUE

SHOWER FURNACE BOILER

STUCCO BRICK STONE

SHINGLES SIDING

STAIRS

BATH TUB

A house plan, usually in the form of a blueprint, is in a sense a picture of the home to be built. It is made up of views such as the front view, rear view and end views. The views are made up of lines which are visible when the building is viewed from various positions; for example, a front view or elevation, consists of the lines which can be seen clearly if you view the structure from the front.

A blueprint shows clearly and distinctly all essential dimensions of a structure and it indicates the surface from which they are taken.

Several types of lines are used in blueprints: Working lines represent the edges of surfaces. Dotted lines indicate a surface that is hidden from sight when the object is viewed from the side shown. Dimension lines are drawn between two working lines to indicate measurements between two points. Section lines, which are parallel lines drawn close together at an angle to working lines, represent what would be seen if a cut were made through the part being shown and a portion removed.

Plans are usually drawn to an accurate scale. By scale we mean that lines on the drawing have an accurate proportion to the line of the work. The scale ⅛th in. to the foot, for example, means that ⅛th in. on the drawing would equal 1 ft. in the structure being erected.

Since it is not practical to show details on a scale blueprint exactly as they would appear on a full-size drawing, symbols, as shown in the accompanying drawing identifying a definite material or structure, are used.

While most of the symbols are self-explanatory there are a couple which the writer feels could stand a little explanation: One is the symbol for stone veneer. In this type construction, a 6 in. wall of stone is used on the outside of a regular frame wall as a covering material. It is not designed to carry weight of the building and is held in place by ties to the framework of the building. The same applies to brick veneer, except that on a brick veneer wall, one width of brick is usually used, which makes a wall facing 4 in. thick.

The showing of a stairs marked "down" on floor plans indicates there is a basement under the house. A stairs marked "up" leads either to second-floor rooms or to attic storage space which is often sufficient to convert into usable rooms.

Specifications which accompany the blueprints, describe in words many things that cannot conveniently be shown on the drawings. This includes information on the quality of material or fixture to be used and how installation is to be made.

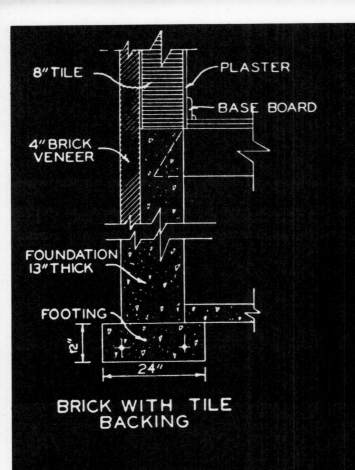

8" TILE

PLASTER

BASE BOARD

4" BRICK VENEER

FOUNDATION 13" THICK

FOOTING

12"

24"

BRICK WITH TILE BACKING

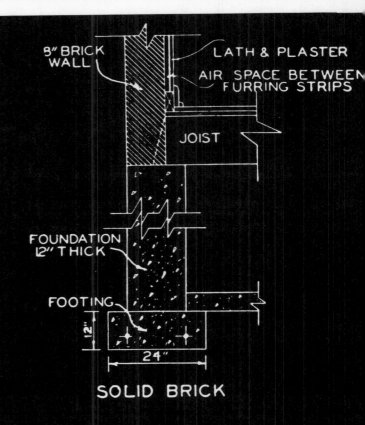

8" BRICK WALL

LATH & PLASTER

AIR SPACE BETWEEN FURRING STRIPS

JOIST

FOUNDATION 12" THICK

FOOTING

12"

24"

SOLID BRICK

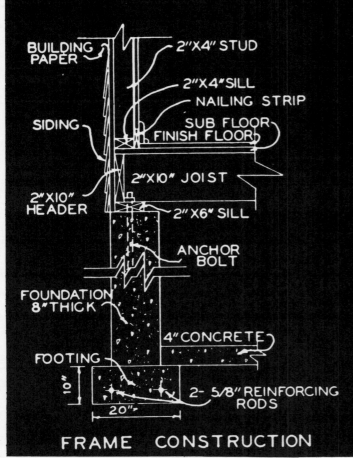

BUILDING PAPER

2"X4" STUD

2"X4" SILL

NAILING STRIP

SUB FLOOR

FINISH FLOOR

SIDING

2"X10" JOIST

2"X10" HEADER

2"X6" SILL

ANCHOR BOLT

FOUNDATION 8" THICK

4" CONCRETE

FOOTING

10"

20"

2- 5/8" REINFORCING RODS

FRAME CONSTRUCTION

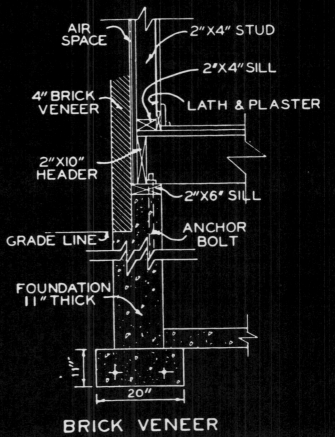

AIR SPACE

2"X4" STUD

2"X4" SILL

4" BRICK VENEER

LATH & PLASTER

2"X10" HEADER

2"X6" SILL

GRADE LINE

ANCHOR BOLT

FOUNDATION 11" THICK

FOOTING

11"

20"

BRICK VENEER

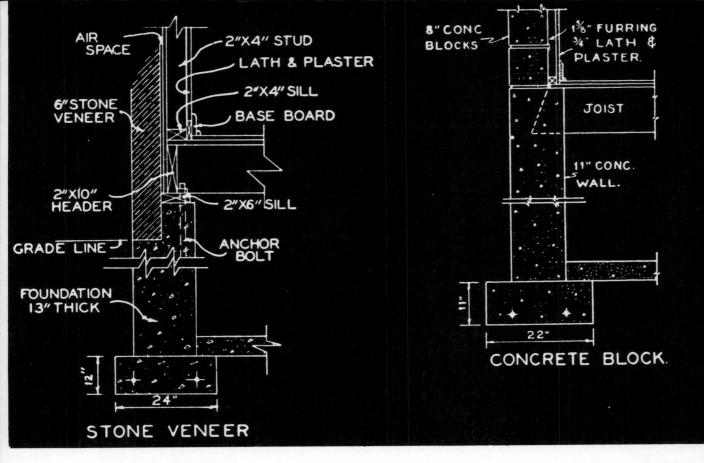

AIR SPACE
2"X4" STUD
LATH & PLASTER
6" STONE VENEER
2"X4" SILL
BASE BOARD
2"X10" HEADER
2"X6" SILL
GRADE LINE
ANCHOR BOLT
FOUNDATION 13" THICK
12"
24"

STONE VENEER

8" CONC BLOCKS
1⅜" FURRING
¾" LATH & PLASTER.
JOIST
11" CONC. WALL.
11"
22"

CONCRETE BLOCK.

MINOR PLAN ALTERATIONS CAN BE HANDLED BY BUILDER

Minor changes in design and material substitutions can be handled by any competent builder or carpenter who is familiar with various types of construction, without going to the expense of making up special plans or supplements.

Let's assume, for example, that plans on the home you want to build specify frame construction instead of brick veneer, for exterior walls. A brick veneer wall is made by applying one course of brick to the outside of a frame wall, instead of wood siding. Typical sections of both frame and brick veneer walls are shown in the accompanying drawings. The drawings show the foundation walls are the same thickness, but since the brick is on the outside of the frame the foundation should be set out the thickness of the

brick, all around, in order to provide a base for the veneer.

Perhaps you would like to add an extra window to the living room, dormer to an upstairs room, or move the partition between the kitchen and dining room to increase the size of the kitchen. Such changes are simple to handle, and may be added to the stock plans by the builder, using a colored pencil, and will serve as a guide to the carpenters on the job.

Filling in blank spaces in the Specification and Contract Form, which usually accompanies working plans, will serve as a written confirmation of all verbal understandings, notations on plans required to meet local ordinances, minor alterations, etc. between the owner and builder, and will form the legal basis upon which their relationship is established.

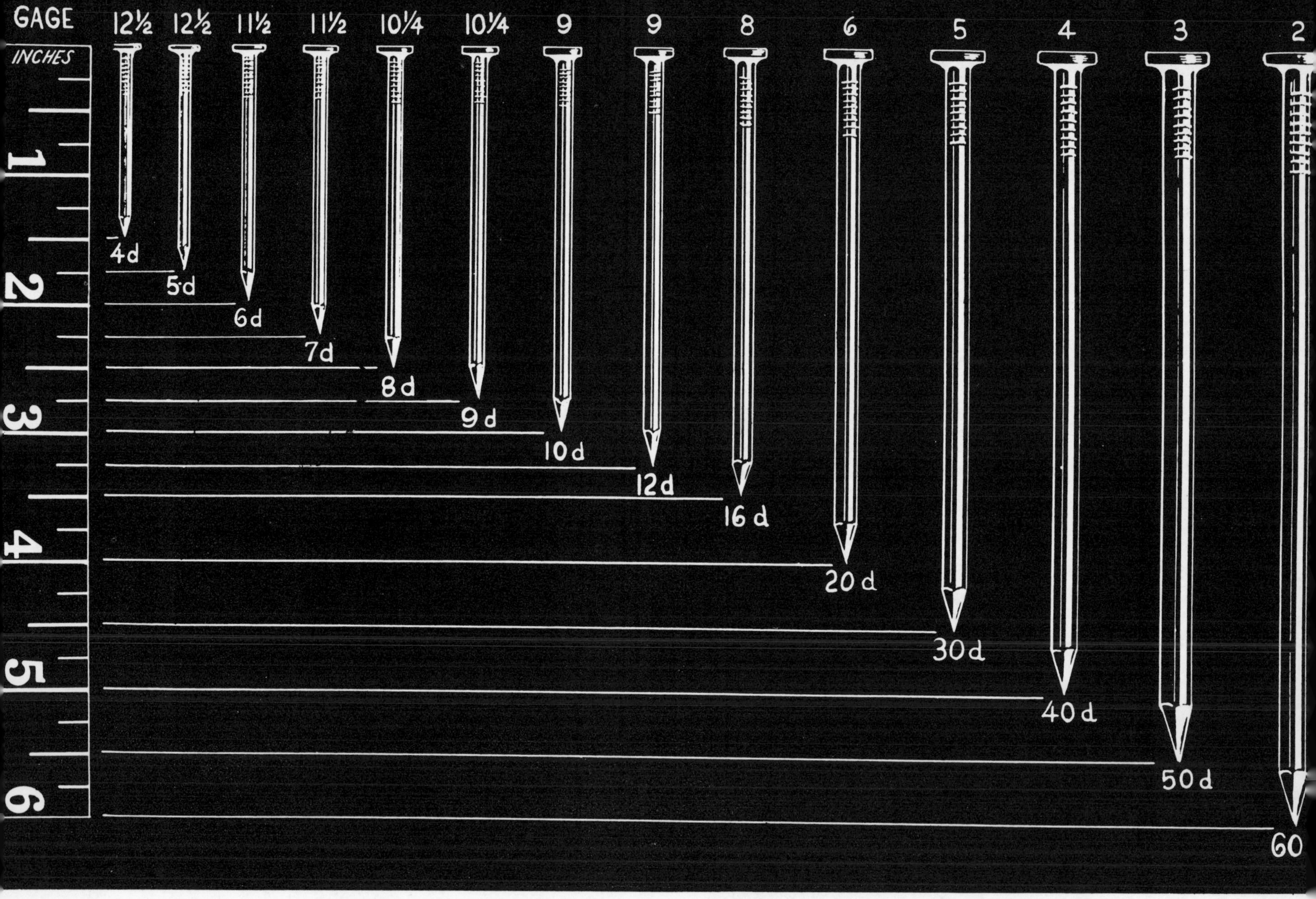

SIZES OF COMMON WIRE NAILS

GAGE

2	60
3	50 d
4	40 d
5	30 d
6	20 d
8	16 d
9	12 d
9	10 d
10¼	9 d
10¼	8 d
11½	7 d
11½	6 d
12½	5 d
12½	4 d

INCHES

1   2   3   4   5   6

BUILDING TERMS YOU SHOULD KNOW

A

Acoustic Tile:—Tile designed and constructed to absorb sound.

Adobe Construction:—A type of construction in which the exterior walls are built of blocks that are made of soil mixed with straw and hardened in the sun. This type of construction is employed chiefly in the warm, dry climate of the Southwest.

Air Conditioning:—The simultaneous control of temperature, humidity, movement, and purity of air in buildings.

Air-dried or Air Seasoned:—Dried by exposure to the air, usually in a yard, without artificial heat.

Alcove:—A large recess connected with or opening off a room.

Alteration:—Any change in exit facilities, structural parts, or mechanical equipment which does not increase the cubic content of a building.

Alternating Current:—A flow of current which constantly changes direction at a fixed rate.

Amortization: — In accounting: The scheduled liquidation of a long-term debt.

Ampere:—A measure of electric current.

Anchor:—Irons of special form used to fasten together timbers or masonry.

Appendage:—Any structure attached to the outside of a building and not essential to its stability.

Apron:—The flat member of the inside trim of a window placed against the wall immediately beneath the stool.

Ashlar Masonry:—Masonry of sawed dressed, tooled, or quarry-faced stone with proper bond.

B

Back Vent:—A branch vent installed primarily for the purpose of protecting fixture traps from self-siphonage.

Balloon Framing:—A system of framing a building in which all vertical structural elements of the bearing walls and partitions consist of single pieces extending from the top of the foundation sill to the roof plate and to which all floor joists are fastened.

Balloon-Payment Mortgage Loan: — A mortgage loan which, by its terms, provides for partial liquidation of the load by periodic payments of the debt and the remainder at the maturity of the loan.

Baluster:—A small column used to support a rail.

Balustrade:—A row of balusters with the rails, generally used for porches, balconies, etc.

Band:—A low, flat molding.

Base:—The bottom of a column; the finish of a room at the junction of the walls and floor.

Basement: — A story partly underground, but having less than half its clear height below grade.

Batter:—The slope, or inclination from the vertical, of a wall or other structure or portion thereof.

Batter Board:—A temporary framework used to assist in locating the corners when laying out a foundation.

Bay:—One of the intervals or spaces into which a building plan is divided by columns, piers, or division walls.

Bay Window:—A rectangular, curved, or polygonal window, or group of windows, supported on a foundation extending beyond the main wall of a building.

Beam:—An inclusive term for joists, girders, rafters, and purlins.

Bearing Partition:—A partition which supports any vertical load in addition to its own weight.

Bearing Wall:—A wall which supports any vertical load in addition to its own weight.

Bed:—A molding used to cover the joint between the plancier and frieze; also used as a base molding upon heavy work and sometimes as a member of a cornice.

Bedding:—A filling of mortar, putty, or other substance in order to secure a firm bearing.

Belt Course:—A horizontal board across or around a building, usually made of a flat member and a molding.

Bevel:—One side of a solid body is said to be on a bevel with respect to another when the angle between the two sides is greater or less than a right angle.

Bevel Board (pitch board):—A board used in framing a roof or stairway to lay out bevels.

Bevel Siding (lap siding):—Used as the finish siding on the exterior of a house or other structure. It is usually manufactured by "resawing" dry, square surfaced boards diagonally to produce two wedge-shaped pieces. These pieces commonly run from 3/16 in. thick on the thin edge to 1/2 to 3/4 in. thick on the other edge, depending on the width of the siding.

Birdseye:—A small central spot with the wood fibers arranged around it in the form of an ellipse so as to give the appearance of an eye.

Blind Nailing:—Nailing in such a way that the nailheads are not visible on the face of the work.

Board:—Lumber less than 2 in. thick.

Board Foot:—The equivalent of a board 1 ft. square and 1 in. thick.

Boarding In:—The process of nailing on the outside studding of a house.

Boards:—Yard lumber less than 2 in. thick, 8 in. or more in width.

Braced Framing:—A system of framing a building in which all vertical structural elements of the bearing walls and partitions, except corner posts, extend for one story only, starting at the foundation sill for the first-story framing and at the top plate of the story below for all stories above the first. Corner posts extend from foundation sill to roof plate and are braced by diagonal members usually extending the full height of each story and crossing several of the studs in each outer wall.

Bracket:—A projecting support for a shelf or other structure.

Break Joints:—To arrange joints so that they do not come directly under or over the joints of adjoining pieces, as in shingling, siding, etc.

Brick Construction:—A type of construction in which the exterior walls are bearing walls made of brick or a combination of brick and tile masonry.

Brick-Veneer Construction:—A type of construction in which a wood-frame construction has an exterior surface of brick applied.

Bridging:—Pieces fitted in pairs from the bottom of one floor joist to the top of adjacent joists, and crossed to distribute the floor load; sometimes pieces of width equal to the joist and fitted neatly between them.

Built-up Timber:—A timber made of several pieces fastened together and forming one of larger dimension.

C

Carriages:—The supports of the steps and risers of a flight of stairs.

Casement:—A window in which the sash opens upon hinges.

Casing:—The trimming around a door or window, either outside or inside, or the finished lumber around a post or beam, etc.

Catch Basin:—A small underground structure for surface drainage in which sediment may settle before water reaches the drain lines.

Center-hung Sash:—A sash hung on its centers so that it swings on a horizontal axis.

Cesspool:—A covered pit with open-jointed linings into which raw sewage is discharged, the liquid portion of which is disposed of by seepage or leaching into the surrounding porous soil, the solids or sludge being retained in the pit.

Chamfer:—A beveled surface cut upon the corner of a piece of wood.

Clapboards:—A special form of outside covering of a house; siding.

Coarse-grained Wood:—Wood with wide and conspicuous annual rings; that is, rings in which there is considerable difference between spring wood and summer wood. The term is sometimes used to designate wood with large pores, such as oak, ash, chestnut, and walnut, but in this sense the term "coarse textured" is more often used.

Collar Beam:—A tie beam connecting the rafters considerably above the wall plate. It is also called a rafter tie.

Combination Frame:—A combination of the principal features of the full and balloon frames.

Common Wall:—A wall owned by one party but jointly used by two parties, one or both of whom is entitled to such under the provisions of a lease.

Conductors:—Pipes for conducting water from a roof to the ground or to a receptacle or drain; downspout.

Conduit, Electrical:—A pipe, usually metal, in which wiring is installed.

Convenience Outlet:—An outlet into which may be plugged portable equipment such as lamps.

Coping:—A capping at the top of a wall, serving to shed water.

Cornice:—A decorative element made up of molded members usually placed at or near the top of an exterior or interior wall.

Coursed Rubble:—Masonry composed of roughly shaped stones fitting approximately on level beds and well bonded.

Cross-connection:—Any connection between two water-piping systems whereby water may flow from one system to the other, the direction of flow depending on the direction of the pressure differential between the two systems.

Cross Ventilation (natural):—Ventilation through openings in adjacent outside walls. (Sometimes called "corner ventilation.")

Cubic Content of a Building:—As determined by any prescribed method for use in estimating total construction costs, such as method used by Rental Housing Division, Federal Housing Administration, viz, the volume of a building is derived by multiplying the area of a building by the height figured as follows: Where flat roofs with parapets occur, a point 6 in. above the roof is taken. Where sloping roofs occur, one-half the height of the slope is used. Where basements occur, a point 6 in. below the basement slab is used. Where no basements occur, the point varies depending upon the depth of the foundation walls. For example, with a 2 ft. 6 in. foundation wall, a point 6 in. below the floor construction is used. Where the foundation walls are 4 ft. deep, a point 2 ft. below the first floor construction is used. Other depths are figured in proportion. Dormers, chimneys, and other protrusions from the building proper are figured separately.

Curb: (or curbed) Roof:—A roof in which the slope is broken on two or more sides; so called because a horizontal curb is built at the plane where the slope changes.

Curtain Wall:—A nonbearing wall between columns or piers which is not supported by girders or beams.

D

Dead Load:—The weight of all permanent stationary construction included in a building.

Dimension:—All yard lumber except boards, strips, and timbers; that is, yard lumber 2 in. and less than 5 in. thick, and of any width.

Direct Nailing:—To nail perpendicular.to the initial surface, or to the junction of the pieces joined. Also termed face nailing.

Dormer:—An internal recess the framing of which projects from a sloping roof.

Dormer Window:—A vertical window, in a relatively small internal recess, projecting from a sloping roof. (See Dormer.)

Double Dwelling:—A two-family dwelling in which the living units are side by side, each unit having open spaces on at least three sides.

Dressed Size:—The dimensions of lumber after planing; usually 3/8 in. less than the nominal or rough size; for example, a 2 in. x 4 in. stud actually measures 1 5/8 in. x 3 5/8 in. (See Nominal Size.)

Drip:—The projection of a window sill or water table to allow the water to drain clear of the side of the house below it.

Drop Siding:--Usually 3/4 in. thick and 6 in. wide, machined into various patterns. Drop siding has tongue and groove or shiplap joints, is heavier, and has more structural strength than bevel siding.

Dry Rot:—A term loosely applied to many types of decay but especially to that which, when in an advanced stage, permits the wood to be easily crushed to a dry powder. The term is actually a misnomer for any decay, since all fungi require considerable moisture for growth.

Dry Wall:—A wall of stone or other durable material, laid without mortar.

Dry - Wall Construction:—A type of construction in which the interior wall finish is of a material other than plaster or material similar to it.

Duplex Dwelling: — A two-family dwelling in which the living units are one above the other but may or may not have separate outside entrances as in flats.

Dwarf Partition: — A partition that does not extend from floor to ceiling.

E

Enclosure Wall: — An exterior non-bearing wall in skeleton construction anchored to columns, piers, or floors, but not necessarily built between columns or piers.

Exterior-protected Construction: — That type of building construction in which the exterior walls, party walls, and fire walls are of incombustible materials and self-supporting, and interior structural framing is wholly or partly of wood or similar materials.

Exterior Wall: — Any outside wall or vertical enclosure of a building other than a party or common wall.

F

Facade: — The face of a building.

Faced Wall: — A masonry wall faced on one or both sides with a material different from the body of the wall, in which the facing and the body are bonded so that they will act as a unit under loads.

Factor of Safety: — The ratio of the ultimate strength of a material to its working stress.

Factory and Shop Lumber: — Lumber intended to be cut up for use in further manufacture. It is graded on the basis of the percentage of the area which will produce a limited number of cuttings of a specified, or a given minimum, size and quality.

Fascia: — A flat member of a cornice or other finish, generally the board of the cornice to which the gutter is fastened.

Fire-division Wall: — A wall which subdivides a building to restrict the spread of fire, but is not necessarily continuous through all stories not extended through the roof.

Fire Stop: — A solid, tight closure of a concealed space, placed to prevent the spread of fire and smoke through such a space.

Fire Wall: — A wall which subdivides a building to restrict the spread of fire. It starts at the foundation and extends continuously through all stories to and above the roof.

Flight of Stairs or Steps: — A run of stairs or steps between landings.

Flashing: — Sheet metal or other material used in roof and wall construction to protect a building from seepage of water.

Flat Roof: — A roof which is flat or one which is pitched only enough to provide for drainage.

Floor Area: — In building regulations: The floor space enclosed by exterior walls, fire walls, or fire partitions, or by a combination of them.

Flue: — The space or passage in a chimney through which smoke, gas, or fumes ascend. Each passage is called a flue, which together and including the surrounding masonry make up the chimney.

Flush: — Adjacent surfaces even, or in same plane (with reference to two structural pieces).

Footing: — The spreading course or courses at the base or bottom of a foundation wall, pier, or column.

Footing Courses: —The bottom and heaviest courses of a piece of masonry.

Foundation: —The supporting portion of a structure below the first-floor construction, or grade, including the footings.

Foundation Wall: —Any bearing wall or pier below the first-floor construction.

Framing: —The rough timber structure of a building, including interior and exterior walls, floor, roof, and ceilings.

Furring: — Narrow strips of board nailed upon the walls and ceilings to form a straight surface upon which to lay the laths or other finish.

G

Gable: —That portion of a wall contained between the slopes of a double-sloped roof or that portion contained between the slope of a single-sloped roof and a line projected horizontally through the lowest elevation of the roof construction.

Gabled Roof: —A ridge roof which terminates in a gable.

Gambrel: —A symmetrical roof with two different pitches or slopes on each side.

Gambrel Roof: —A gable roof each slope of which is broken into two planes.

Girder: —A large or principal beam used to support concentrated loads at particular points along its length.

Girt (ribband): —The horizontal member of the walls of a full or combination frame house which supports the

floor joists or is flush with the top of the joists.

Gross Floor Area: —The total area of a floor of a building or building unit, measuring from inside surfaces of enclosing walls.

Ground: —A strip of wood assisting the plasterer in making a straight wall and in giving a place to which the finish of the room may be nailed.

Grout: —Mortar made so thin by the addition of water that it will all run into the joints and cavities of the masonwork and fill them up solid.

Gypsum Board: —Wallboard made of gypsum, with a covering of paper.

H

Half Story: —That part of a building situated wholly or partly within the roof frame finished for habitation.

Header: —In carpentry: A beam placed perpendicular to joists and into which joists are framed in framing a chimney, stairway, or other opening.

Headroom: —The clear space between floor line and ceiling, as in a stairway.

Heart, Heartwood: —The wood, extending from the pith to the sapwood, the cells of which no longer participate in the life processes of the tree. Heartwood may be infiltrated with gums, resins, and other materials which usually make it darker and more decay-resistant than sapwood.

Heel of a Rafter: —The end or foot that rests on the wall plate.

Height of Ceiling: —The vertical distance from the finished floor to the finished ceiling in any room, exclusive of projecting ceiling beams. (Note: —In instances where ceilings are not level over the full area of a room, special rulings must control.)

Height of a Story:--The vertical distance from the surface of a floor to the surface of the next floor above.

Height of Wall:—The vertical distance to the top of the wall (mean height of gable) measured from the foundation walls, or from a girder or other immediate support of such wall.

Hip Rafter:—A rafter which forms the intersection of an external roof angle.

Hip (or hipped) Roof:—
1. In general, a roof which has one or more hips.
2. A roof which has four sloping sides that meet at four hips, or at four hips and a ridge.

Hip Roof:—A roof which slopes up toward the center from all sides, necessitating a hip rafter at each corner.

I

Incinerator:—A device which consumes usual household waste by burning.

Indirect Cross-connection:—A cross-connection, frequently referred to as a potential cross-connection, in which the interconnection is not continuously inclosed and the completion of the cross-connection depends on the occurrence of one or more abnormal conditions. Examples: Water-closets with direct flush-valve supply, bathtubs and lavatories with faucet openings that may become submerged, and other plumbing fixtures and equipment whose supply inlets may become partially or wholly submerged.

Interior Stairway:—A stairway within the exterior walls of a building.

J

Jack Rafter:—A short rafter framing between the wall plate and a hip rafter.

Jamb:—The side piece or post of an opening; sometimes applied to the door frame.

Joist:—One of a series of parallel beams used to support floor and ceiling loads, and supported in turn by larger beams, girders, or bearing walls.

K

Kiln-dried Lumber:—Lumber dried by artificial heat to a moisture content which is less than can normally be obtained through the natural process commonly known as air seasoning.

Knot:—That portion of a branch or limb that has become incorporated in the body of a tree.

L

Lath:—A building material of wood, metal, gypsum, or insulating board, that is fastened to the frame of a building to act as a plaster base.

Lean-to Roof:—
1. A roof which has a single sloping surface that is supported at the top by a wall that is higher than the roof.
2. A roof which has a single sloping surface.

Ledger Strip:—A strip of lumber nailed along the bottom of the side of a girder on which joists rest.

Lintel:—A horizontal structural member which supports the load over an opening such as a door or window.

Lip:—A molding with a lip which over-laps the piece against which the back of the molding rests.

Live Load:—The total of all moving and variable loads that may be placed upon a building.

Lumber:—The product of the saw and planing mill not further manufactured than by sawing, resawing, and passing lengthwise through a standard planing machine, crosscutting to length and working.

M

Mansard Roof:—A type of curb roof in which the pitch of the upper portion of a sloping side is slight and that of the lower portion steep. The lower portion is usually interrupted by dormer windows.

Masonry:—Stone, brick, hollow tile, concrete block or tile, and sometimes poured concrete and gypsum block, or other similar materials, or a combination of same, bonded together with mortar to form a wall, pier, buttress, etc.

Matched Lumber:—Lumber that is edge dressed and shaped to make a close tongue-and-groove joint at the edges or ends when laid edge-to-edge or end-to-end.

Mechanical Equipment:—In architectural and engineering practice: All equipment included under the general heading of plumbing, heating, air conditioning, gasfitting, and electrical work.

Meeting Rail:—The bottom rail of the upper sash, and the top rail of the lower sash of a double-hung window. Sometimes called the check rail.

Millwork:—The finished wood portions of a building which are cus-tomarily obtained from a planing mill, such as doors, window and door frames, sash, panelwork, etc. It does not include lumber used for structural purposes or siding, which are items of yard lumber.

Moisture Content of Wood:—Weight of the water contained in the wood usually expressed in percentage of the weight of the oven-dry wood.

Molding—Base:—The molding on the top of a base board.

Monitor Roof:—A type of gable roof commonly used on industrial buildings, which has a raised portion along the ridge with openings for light and/or air.

Mortise:—The hole which is to receive a tenon, or any hole cut into or through a piece by a chisel, generally of rectangular shape.

Mullion:—A slender bar or pier forming a division between units of windows, screens, or similar frames—generally nonstructural.

Muntin:—The vertical member between two panels of the same piece of panel work. The vertical sash-bars separating the different panes of glass.

N

Net Floor Area:—The gross floor area, less the area of the partitions, columns, and stairs and other floor openings.

Newel:—The principal post at the foot of a staircase; also the central support of a winding flight of stairs.

Nominal Size:—As applied to timber or lumber, the ordinary commercial size by which it is known and sold in the market.

Nonbearing Partition: — A partition extending from floor to ceiling which supports no load other than its own weight.

Nosing: — The part of a stair tread which projects over the riser, or any similar projection; a term applied to the rounded edge of a board.

O

Open-grained Wood: — Common classification of painters for woods with large pores, such as oak, ash, chestnut, and walnut. Also known as "coarse" textured.

Open Stairway: — A stairway the floor landings of which are a part of the public hallways.

Oriel Window: — A window or group of windows that projects from the main line of an enclosing wall of a building and is carried on brackets, corbels, or a cantilever.

P

Panel Wall: — A nonbearing wall in skeleton construction built between columns or piers and wholly supported at each story.

Parapet Wall: — That part of an exterior, party, or fire wall extending above the roof line.

Parge Coat or Parget: —
1. Coarse plasterwork applied over masonry as a protection or decoration.
2. A base coat or protective coat for dampproofing.

Partition: — A wall that subdivides space within any story of a building.

Party Wall: — A wall used jointly by two parties under easement agreement and erected at or upon a line separating two parcels of land that may be held under different ownership.

Penny: — As applied to nails it originally indicated the price per hundred. The term now serves as a measure of nail length and is abbreviated by the letter "d."

Pent Roof: — A roof, other than a lean-to roof, which has a single sloping surface.

Personal Property: — All property other than real property.

Pier: — A column of masonry, usually rectangular in horizontal cross section, used to support other structural members. (Note: — In building codes, the horizontal cross-sectional area is usually specified as "not exceeding 4 square feet."

Pilaster: — A part of a wall that projects not more than one-half of its own width beyond the outside or inside face of a wall, acting as an engaged pier.

Pile: — A heavy timber, or pillar of metal or concrete, forced into the earth or cast in place to form a foundation member.

Pitch: — Inclination or slope, as of roofs or stairs, or the rise divided by the span.

Pitch Board: — A board sawed to the exact shape formed by the stair tread, riser, and slope of the stairs and used to lay out the carriage and stringers.

Plain Concrete: — Concrete containing not more than two-tenths of 1 per cent of reinforcement.

Plan: — A drawing representing any one of the floors or horizontal cross-sections of a building, or the horizontal plane of any other object or area.

Plan:—A horizontal geometrical section of a building, showing the walls, doors, windows, stairs, chimneys, columns, etc.

Planks or Lumber:—Material 2 or 3 in. thick and more than 4 in. wide, such as joists, flooring, etc.

Plaster:—A mixture of lime, hair, and sand, or of lime, cement and sand, used to cover outside and inside wall surfaces.

Plat:—A map, plan, or chart of a city, town, section, or subdivision indicating the location and boundaries of individual properties.

Plate:—

1. A horizontal structural member placed on a wall or supported on posts, studs, or corbels to carry the trusses of a roof or to carry the rafters directly.

2. A show or base member, as of a partition or other frame.

3. A small relatively flat member usually of metal placed on or in a wall to support girders, rafters, etc.

Platform Framing:—A system of framing a building on which floor joists of each story rest on the top plates of the story below (or on the foundation wall for the first story) and the bearing walls and partitions rest on the subfloor of each story.

Plumbing:—The work or business of installing in buildings the pipes, fixtures, and other apparatus for bringing in the water supply and removing liquid and water-borne wastes. This term is used also to denote the installed fixtures and piping of a building.

Plumbing Stack:—A general term for the vertical main of a system of soil, waste, or vent piping.

Plumbing System:—A system of pipes including the water-service line and building drainage lines from their several connections within the building to their connections with the public mains or individual water-supply and sewage-disposal systems, together, with fixtures, traps, vents, and other devices connected thereto. Storm-water drainage pipes may be considered a part of the plumbing system when connected to a public sewerage system.

Plywood:—A piece of wood made of three or more layers of veneer joined with glue and usually laid with the grain of adjoining plies at right angles.

Pointing:—

1. The treatment of joints in masonry for appearance or protectection by filling with mortar under tool pressure and usually to a definite form.

2. The filling placed in joints of roofing of slate, tile, etc., as a closure.

Porch:—A floor extending beyond the exterior walls of a building. It may be enclosed or unenclosed.

Portico:—An open space having a roof supported by columns, located outside an entrance to or exit from a building.

Power Circuit:—A circuit transmitting electric energy to a motor or to a heating unit too large to be served by an ordinary circuit.

Prefabricated Construction:—A type of construction so designed as to involve a minimum of assembly at the site, usually comprising a series of large units manufactured in a plant.

Preservative:—Any substance that, for a reasonable length of time, will prevent the action of wood-destroying fungi, borers of various kinds, and similar destructive life when the wood has been properly coated or impregnated with it.

Prevailing Wage: —On work other than public work of the United States Government: The wage paid the majority of workers in a specific class of occupation in a particular community.

Property Line: —A recorded boundary of a plot.

Property-line Wall: —A wall built to and along a property line.

Protective Covenant: —
1. A written agreement restricting the use of real property and intended to protect and benefit the property.
2. A restriction appearing in a conveyance instrument affecting the use of real property.

Purlin: —A horizontal member usually laid at right angles to main rafters or trusses of a roof to support elements of the roof framing.

Pyramid Roof: —A hip roof which has four sloping surfaces, usually of equal pitch, that meet at a peak.

Q

Quarter-sawed: —Another term for edge grain.

Quitclaim Deed: —A deed whereby the grantor conveys to the grantee whatever interest he possesses in the property granted without warranty.

R

Rabbet: —A rectangular longitudinal groove cut in the corner of a board or other piece of material.

Radio Outlet: —An outlet having connected thereto an aerial and ground for the use of a radio.

Rafter: —One of a series of structural members of a roof designed to support roof loads. The rafters of a flat roof are sometimes called roof joists.

Rake: —The trim of a building extending in an oblique line, as rake dado or molding.

Rammed-earth Construction: —A type of construction in which the exterior walls are bearing walls composed of a controlled combination of sand, clay, coarse aggregate, and moisture compacted by pressure into forms.

Ramp: —An inclined plane connecting separate levels.

Reinforced Concrete: —Concrete containing more than two-tenths of 1 per cent of reinforcement and in which the reinforcement is so embedded that the two materials act together in sustaining the load.

Reinforced-concrete Construction: — A type of construction in which the principal structural members, such as floors, columns, and beams, are made of concrete poured around isolated steel bars or steel meshwork in such manner that the two materials act together in resisting force.

Retaining Wall: —
1. Any wall subjected to lateral pressure other than wind pressures.
2. A wall built to support a bank of earth.

Ridge Roof: —A roof which has one or more ridges.

Roof: —The entire construction used to close in the top of a building.

Roof Hip: —The sloping line at the junction of two roof surfaces where an external angle greater than 180 degrees is formed.

Roofing:—The materials applied to the structural parts of a roof to make it watertight.

Roof Ridge:—The horizontal line at the junction of the top edges of two roof surfaces where an external angle greater than 180 degrees is formed.

Roughing-in:—The work of installing all pipes in the drainage system and all water pipes to the point where connections are made with the plumbing fixtures.

Rough Lumber:—Lumber undressed as it comes from the saw.

S

Saddle Board:—The finish of the ridge of a pitch-roof house. Sometimes called comb board.

Sapwood:—The layers of wood next to the bark, usually lighter in color than the heartwood, 1/2 in. to 3 or more in. wide that are actively involved in the life processes of the tree. Under most conditions sapwood is more susceptible to decay than heartwood; as a rule, it is more permeable to liquids than heartwood. Sapwood is not essentially weaker or stronger than heartwood of the same species.

Sash:—The framework which holds the glass in a window.

Sawing, plain:—Lumber sawed regardless of the grain, the log simply squared and sawed to the desired thickness; sometimes called slash or bastard sawed.

Scaffold or staging:—A temporary structure or platform enabling workmen to reach high places.

Scale:—A short measurement used as a proportionate part of a larger dimension. The scale of a drawing is expressed as 1/4 in. equals 1 ft.

Scantling:—Lumber with a cross section ranging from 2 in. x 4 in. to 4 in. x 4 in.

Scarfing:—A joint between two pieces of wood which allows them to be spliced lengthwise.

Scotia:--A hollow molding used as a part of a cornice, and often under the nosing of a stair tread.

Seasoning:—Removing moisture from green wood in order to improve its serviceability.

Seat Cut or Plate Cut:—The cut at the bottom end of a rafter to allow it to fit upon the plate.

Seat of a Rafter:—The horizontal cut upon the bottom end of a rafter which rests upon the top of the plate.

Second Growth:—Timber that has grown after the removal by any means of a large portion of the previous stand.

Section:—A drawing showing the kind, arrangement, and proportions of the various parts of a structure. It is assumed that the structure is cut by a plane, and the section is the view gained by looking in one direction.

Septic Tank:—A sewage-settling tank intended to retain the sludge in immediate contact with the sewage flowing through the tank, for a sufficient period to secure satisfactory decomposition of organic sludge solids by bacterial action.

Sheathing:—The structural covering, usually of boards · or wallboards, placed over exterior studding or rafters of a structure.

Sheathing Paper:—A building material used in wall, floor, and roof construction to resist the passage of air.

Shiplapped Lumber:—Lumber that is edge dressed to make a close rabbetted or lapped joint.

Sill:—

1. The lowest member of the frame of a structure, usually horizontal, resting on the foundation and supporting the uprights of the frame.

Sizing:—Working material to the desired size; a coating of glue, shellac, or other substance applied to a surface to prepare it for painting or other method of finish.

Skeleton Construction:—A type of construction in which all external and internal loads and stresses are transmitted to the foundations by a rigidly connected framework of metal or reinforced concrete. The enclosing walls are supported by the frame at designated intervals; usually at each story.

Skylight:—Any cover or enclosure placed above a roof opening to provide for the admission of natural light.

Sleeper:—A timber laid on the ground to support a floor joist.

Soffit:—The underside of the members of a building, such as staircases, cornices, beams, arches, etc., relatively minor in size as compared with ceilings.

Softwoods:—The botanical group of trees that have needle or scalelike leaves and are evergreen for the most part, cypress, larch, and tamarack being exceptions. The term has no reference to the actual hardness of the wood. Softwoods are often referred to as conifers, and botanically they are called gymnosperms.

Sound Knot:—A knot which is solid across its face and which is as hard as the surrounding wood.

Space Heating:—The method of heating individual rooms or living units by means of equipment located entirely within these rooms or living units.

Span:—The distance between structural supports such as walls, columns, piers, beams, girders, and trusses.

Specification:—A written document stipulating the kind, quality, and sometimes the quantity of materials and workmanship required for any construction or work.

Specific Gravity:—The ratio of the weight of a body to the weight of an equal volume of water at some standard temperature.

Splash Block:—A small masonry block laid with the top close to the ground surface to receive roof drainage and carry it away from the building.

Square:—A unit of measure--100 sq. ft.—usually applied to roofing materials.

Square:—A tool used by mechanics to obtain accuracy; a term applied to a surface including 100 square feet.

Stair Landing:—A platform between flights of stairs or at the termination of a flight of stairs.

Stair Rise:—The vertical distance from the top of one stair tread to the top of the one next above.

Stairs, box:—Those built between walls, and usually with no support except the wall strings.

Stairway, Stair, or Stairs:—A series of steps, with or without landings, or platforms, usually between two or more floors of a building.

Standing Finish:—Term applied to the finish of the openings and the base, and all other finish necessary for the inside of the house.

Steel-frame Construction:—A type of construction in which the structural parts are of steel or dependent on a steel frame for support.

Stoop:—A small porch, veranda, or platform, or a stairway, outside an entrance to a building.

Story:—That part of a building comprised between any floor and the floor or roof next above

Strip Kitchen:—Kitchen Equipment located along the wall of a room or of a space designed or used primarily for other purposes.

Structure:—Anything erected which requires permanent location on the ground or is attached to something having a permanent location on the ground.

Structural Timber:—Pieces of wood of relatively large size in which strength is the controlling element in their selection and use. Trestle timbers (stringers, caps, posts, sills, bracing, bridge ties, guard rails); car timbers (car framing, including upper framing, car sills); framing for buildings (posts, sills, girders, framing joists); ship timbers (ship timbers, ship decking); and cross arms for poles are examples of structural timbers.

Studding:—The framework of a partition or the wall of a house; usually referred to as 2 x 4's.

Subfloor:—Boards or matched lumber laid on joists over which a finish floor is to be laid.

Subsurface Utilities:—The public services underground, including sewers, gas, water lines, and sometimes telephone and electric-light conduits.

Surfaced Lumber:—Lumber that is dressed by running it through a planer.

T

Tail Beam:—A relatively short beam or joist supported in a wall on one end and by a header on the other.

Termite Shield:—A shield usually of sheet metal, placed in or on a foundation wall or other mass of masonry or around pipes to prevent the passage of termites.

Thermostat:—An instrument that controls automatically the operation of heating or cooling devices by responding to changes in temperature.

Three-way Switch:—A switch designed to operate in conjunction with a similar switch to control one outlet from two points.

Threshold:—The beveled piece over which the door swings; sometimes called a carpet strip.

Through Ventilation (natural):—Ventilation through openings in opposite outside walls. (Sometimes called "cross ventilation.")

Tie Beam (collar beam);—A beam so situated that it ties the principal rafters of a roof together and prevents them from thrusting the plate out of line.

Timber:—Lumber with cross section over 4 in. x 6 in., such as posts, sills, and girders.

Timbers:—Lumber 5 in. or larger in least dimension.

Tin Shingle:—A small piece of tin used in flashing and repairing a shingle roof.

Toenailing:—To drive a nail at a slant with the initial surface in order to permit it to penetrate into a second member.

To the Weather:—A term applied to the projecting of shingles or siding beyond the course above.

Transformer:—A device for transforming the voltage characteristics of a current supply.

Trap:—A fitting or device so designed and constructed as to provide a liquid trap seal which will prevent the passage of air through it.

Tread:—The horizontal part of a step.

Trim:—The finish materials in a building, such as moldings applied around openings (window trim, door trim) or at the floor and ceiling of rooms (baseboard, cornice, picture molding).

Trimmer:—The beam or floor joist into which a header is framed.

U

Unprotected-metal Construction:—A type of construction in which the structural parts are of metal unprotected by fireproofing.

V

Valley:—The internal angle formed by the two slopes of a roof.

Valley Rafter:—A rafter which forms the intersection of an internal roof angle.

Veneer:—Thin sheets of wood.

Veneered Wall:—A wall with a masonry facing, which is attached to but not bonded so as to form an integral part of the wall for purposes of load bearing and stability.

Vent:—A pipe installed to provide a flow of air to or from a drainage system or to provide a circulation of air within such system to protect trap seals from siphonage and back pressure.

Ventilation:—The process of supplying

and removing air by natural or mechanical means to or from any space. (Such air may or may not have been conditioned.)

Vent Stack:—A vertical vent pipe installed primarily for the purpose of providing circulation of air to or from any part of the building drainage system.

Verge Boards:—The boards which serve as the eaves finish on the gable end of a building.

Vertical Grain:—Another term for edge grain.

Vestibule:—

1. A minor enclosed space at the entrance of a building.
2. An entry.

Vestibule:—An entrance to a house; usually enclosed.

Voltage:—A measure of electric pressure between any two wires of an electric circuit.

W

Wainscoting:—Matched boarding or panel work covering the lower portion of a wall.

Wall, bearing:—A wall which supports any vertical load in addition to its own weight.

Wallboard:—Wood pulp, gypsum, or similar materials made into large, rigid sheets that may be fastened to the frame of a building to provide a surface finish.

Warp:—Any variation from a true or plane surface. Warp includes bow, crook, cup, and twist, or any combination thereof.

Water-closet:—

1. A plumbing fixture consisting of a bowl for the reception of fecal

discharges and equipment for flushing the bowl with water.

Water Table:—The finish at the bottom of a house which carries the water away from the foundation.

Weathering: — The mechanical or chemical disintegration and discoloration of the surface of wood that is caused by exposure to light, the action of dust and sand carried by winds, and the alternate shrinking and swelling of the surface fibers that come with the continual variation in moisture content brought by changes in the weather. Weathering does not include decay.

Weephole:—A small hole, as in a retaining wall, to drain water to the outside.

Well: — An open, unoccupied minor area bounded on all sides by the walls of a building passing through at least one floor, commonly used to supply light and air for stairways and minor interior spaces.

Wind ("i" pronounced as in kind):—

A term used to describe the surface of a board when twisted (winding) or when resting upon two diagonally opposite corners, if laid upon a perfectly flat surface.

Wing:—A lateral extension of a building from the main portion thereof or one of two or more coordinate portions of a building which extends from a common junction.

Wire Glass:--Glass having a layer of meshed wire incorporated approximately in the center of the sheet.

Wooden Brick:—Piece of seasoned wood, made the size of a brick, and laid where it is necessary to provide a nailing space in masonry walls.

Wood-frame or Frame Construction:—A type of construction in which the structural parts are of wood or dependent upon a wood frame for support. In codes, if brick or other combustible material is applied to exterior walls, the classification of this type of construction is usually unchanged.

Garages
One, Two-Car

Garage construction is not difficult, and the one-car and two-car garage designs covered in this section may be varied to meet almost any garage need.

CONSTRUCTING ONE-CAR GARAGE

The one-car garage, Fig. V-1, provides the compactness of a one-car garage and sufficient extra space for a workbench, and storage for lawn mower, garden tools, etc. This garage may be built with a gable roof or a hip roof, as shown in Fig. V-14. If desired the front overhang may be omitted to reduce the overall length from 24 ft. to 22 ft.

Much of the success in building a serviceable, sturdy garage depends on paying close attention to details of construction as shown in Fig. V-2.

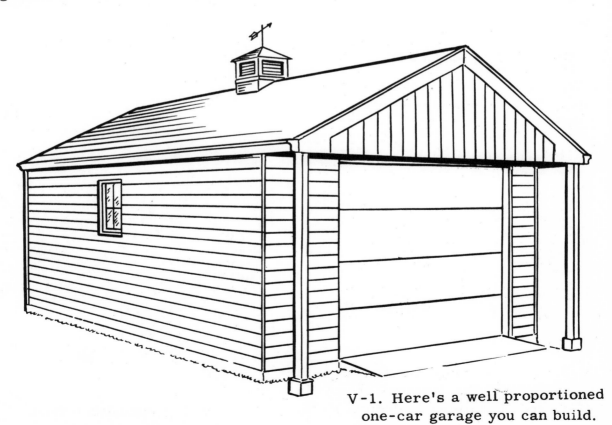

V-1. Here's a well proportioned one-car garage you can build.

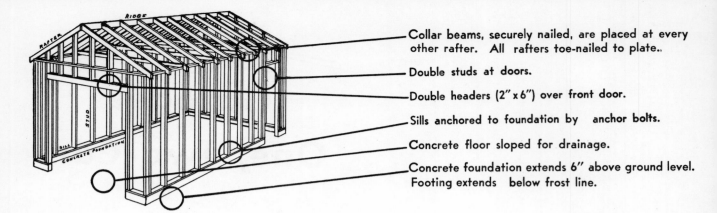

Collar beams, securely nailed, are placed at every other rafter. All rafters toe-nailed to plate..

Double studs at doors.

Double headers (2" x 6") over front door.

Sills anchored to foundation by anchor bolts.

Concrete floor sloped for drainage.

Concrete foundation extends 6" above ground level. Footing extends below frost line.

V-2. Much of the success of building a durable, attractive garage depends on paying close attention to details of construction as shown in this drawing.

GABLE ROOF		HIP ROOF		
Quan.	Size	Quan.	Size	Used for
18 -	1/2" x 8" Carriage bolts	18 - 1/2" x 8" Carriage bolts		Anchor bolts
1 -	2" x 4" x 8'	1 - 2" x 4" x 8'		" "
1 -	2" x 4" x 10'	1 - 2" x 4" x 10'		" "
1 -	2" x 4" x 12'	1 - 2" x 4" x 12'		Sills
1 -	2" x 4" x 14'	1 - 2" x 4" x 14'		"
1 -	2" x 4" x 18'	1 - 2" x 4" x 18'		"
4 -	2" x 2" x 8'	4 - 2" x 2" x 8'		Cornice trim
4 -	2" x 4" x 10'	4 - 2" x 4" x 10'		Plates
6 -	2" x 4" x 14'	6 - 2" x 4" x 14'		"
45 -	2" x 4" x 7'	45 - 2" x 4" x 7'		Studs
2 -	4" x 4" x 8'	2 - 4" x 4" x 8'		Posts
2 -	2" x 4" x 12'			Gable studs
5 -	1" x 4" x 12'	5 - 1" x 4" x 12'		Wind bracing
1 -	1" x 4" x 8'	1 - 1" x 4" x 8'		" "
1 -	2" x 4" x 8'	1 - 2" x 4" x 8'		" "
4 -	2" x 6" x 14'	4 - 2" x 6" x 14'		Headers
1 -	2" x 4" x 12'	1 - 2" x 4" x 12'		Window & door head & sill framing
5 -	2" x 4" x 14'	5 - 2" x 4" x 14'		Rafter ties
26 -	2" x 4" x 8'	26 - 2" x 4" x 8'		Rafters
		4 - 2" x 6" x 12'		Hip rafters
2 -	2" x 6" x 12'	1 - 2" x 6" x 12'		Ridge board
460 B.M. 1" x 6" Boards		460 B.M. 1" x 6" Boards		Roof sheathing
4 Squares asphalt shingles		4 Squares asphalt shingles		Roofing
534 B.M. 1" x 6" Drop siding		534 B.M. 1" x 6" Drop siding		Siding
70 B.M. 1" x 8" Vertical siding				Siding
64 Lin. ft. 1" x 6"		78 Lin. ft. 1" x 6"		Fascia
36 Lin. ft. 1" x 6"				Barge board
1 - 2" x 4" x 12'				Gable end shelf
28 B.M. 1" x 6" Boards				" "
32 Sq. ft. 1/4" Hard board		32 Sq. ft. 1/4" Hard board		Soffit
2 - 1'-10" x 2'-5" Barn sash		2 - 1'-10" x 2'-5" Barn sash		Windows
16 Lin. ft. 2" x 2"		16 Lin. ft. 2" x 2"		Window trim
1 - 2" x 4" x 6'		1 - 2" x 4" x 6'		Window sill
20 Lin. ft. - 3/4" x 1 1/4" Stop		20 Lin. ft. 3/4" x 1 1/4" Stop		Window stop
1 - 2'-6" x 6'-8" Ext. door		1 - 2'-6" x 6'-8" Ext. door		Service door
1 - 3/4" x 4" x 10'		1 - 3/4" x 4" x 10'		Door jamb
1 - 3/4" x 4" x 8'		1 - 3/4" x 4" x 8'		" "
1 - 2" x 6" x 3'		1 - 2" x 6" x 3'		Door sill
1 - 9' x 7' Garage door		1 - 9' x 7' Garage door		Garage door
1 - 3/4" x 4" x 10'		1 - 3/4" x 4" x 10'		Door jamb
2 - 3/4" x 4" x 8'		2 - 3/4" x 4" x 8'		" "
32 - Lin. ft. 1" x 2"		32 - Lin. ft. 1" x 2"		Door trim
44 - Lin. ft. 1/2" x 1 5/8" Stop		44 - Lin. ft. 1/2" x 1 5/8" Stop		Door stop
1 - Bundle Wood lath		1 - Bundle Wood lath		
1 - Roll 15 lb. Felt		1 - Roll 15 lb. Felt		Roof felt
25 lbs. 16d Common nails		25 lbs. 16d Common nails		Hardware
25 lbs. 8d " "		25 lbs. 8d " "		"
18 lbs. 7d Galv. box nails		18 lbs. 7d Galv. box nails		"
12 lbs. 1" Roofing nails		12 lbs. 1" Roofing nails		"
5 lbs. 8d Casing nails		5 lbs. 8d Casing nails		"
1 1/2 Pairs 3 1/2" x 3 1/2" Butt Hinges		1 1/2 Pairs 3 1/2" x 3 1/2" Butt Hinges		"
1 Mortise Lock		1 Mortise Lock		"
1 Gallon Ext. Primer		1 Gallon Ext. Primer		Paint
1 Gallon Ext. House Paint		1 Gallon Ext. House Paint		Paint
1 20" x 20" Cupola with Weather vane		1 20" x 20" Cupola with Weather vane		Cupola

V-3. List of material required in constructing the garage shown in V-1, and the alternate design, V-15.

CONCRETE FOUNDATION RECOMMENDED

A few dollars may be saved by using creosoted posts as a garage support, but a concrete foundation, Fig. V-4, is much more substantial and is recommended. Or, the garage may be put on a concrete slab--4 in. if reinforced, 6 in. if no reinforcing is used. The slab provides a floor and also serves as a foundation.

Information on forms, mixing and pouring concrete may be obtained from the first chapter of this book.

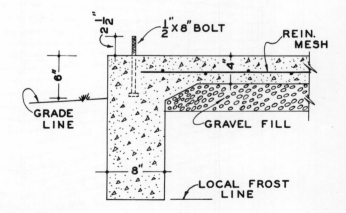

V-4. Foundation detail.

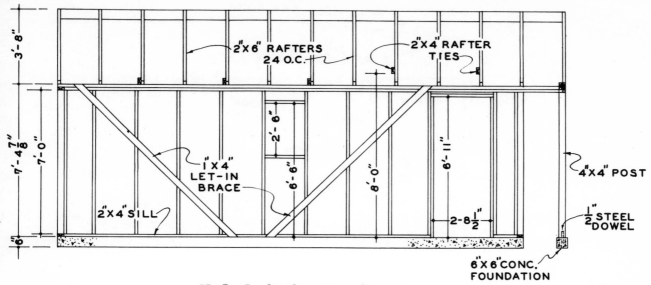

V-5. Left elevation framing.

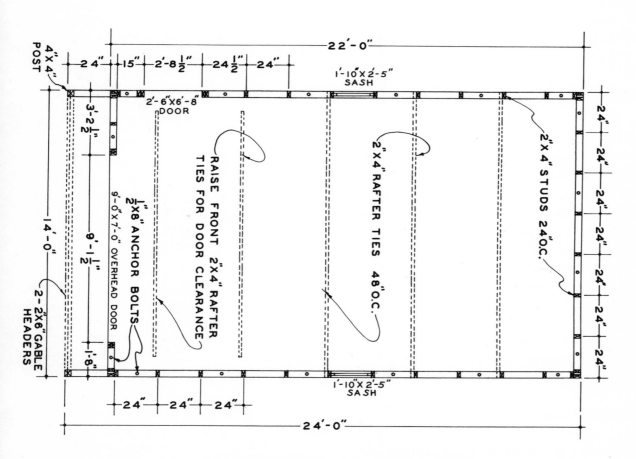

V-6. Floor plan of one-car garage.

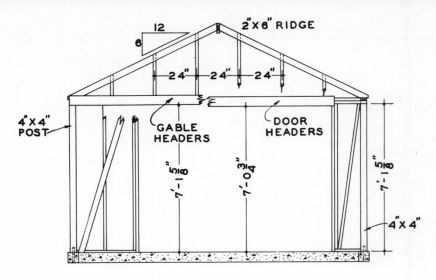

V-7. Front elevation framing.

Material required to build the garage shown in Fig. V-1, and the alternate design, Fig. V-14, is listed in Fig. V-3.

FRAMING

Framing of the garage starts with the side walls. Spacing of the wall studs for the left elevation is shown in V-5 and V-6. The right elevation is the same except there is no door opening. It is advisable to assemble the side wall framing on the ground or concrete floor if the floor has been laid. Bore holes in the sills to take anchor bolts, raise the frame and run braces from stakes to temporarily support the framing. Use a level to check the plumb before fastening the braces.

FRAMING GARAGE ENDS

The front elevation framing is shown in Fig. V-7. Make whatever minor framing changes are needed to take the door which is to be used. Note that there are double studs on

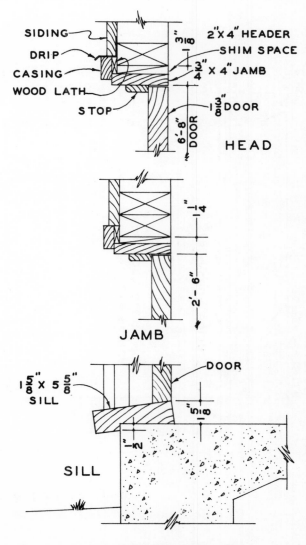

V-8. Side door details.

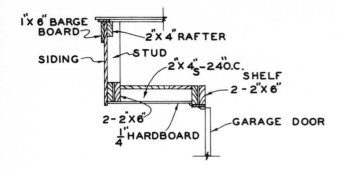

V-9. Section through front gable.

the sides of the door opening and that a double 2 x 6 header is specified.

Assemble the front elevation framing, raise into place and nail the corners securely. Then, proceed with the framing of the other end.

ROOF CONSTRUCTION

Details on roof framing may be obtained from V-5 and V-7. Additional information on roof construction, which will be found helpful in connec-

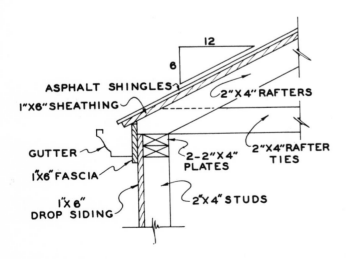

V-10. Cornice section for one-car garage.

tion with this part of the job, will be found in the chapter on Roof Framing.

To offset the outward thrust of the roof cross ties should be fitted 48 in. o. c. as shown in the floor plan.

Roof sheathing specified for this garage is 1 x 6 boards. The sheathing should be laid solid as it is to be covered with asphalt shingles. Information on how to apply asphalt shingles will be found in the Roofing section of this book.

ADDITIONAL DETAILS

The window trim, window sills, corners and door sills can be cut from common lumber on circular saw. Using a rabbeted 2 x 2 on the corners is preferable to the common practice of nailing boards over the drop siding, as this will eliminate water storage pockets at the ends of the siding.

Siding specified for this particular garage is 1 x 6 drop siding. The siding job should be started at the bottom. Put on the first strip flush with the underside of the sill. Use 8d casing nails, setting nail heads in slightly for calking. Tar paper may be used under the siding if desired. Unroll the paper, tack it to studs to keep the strip upright while the siding is being nailed. The second strip of tar paper should overlap the first about 4 in.

See Figs. V-8 to V-12 inclusive, for details on framing around doors, windows, cornices and corners. A cupola may be purchased ready-made

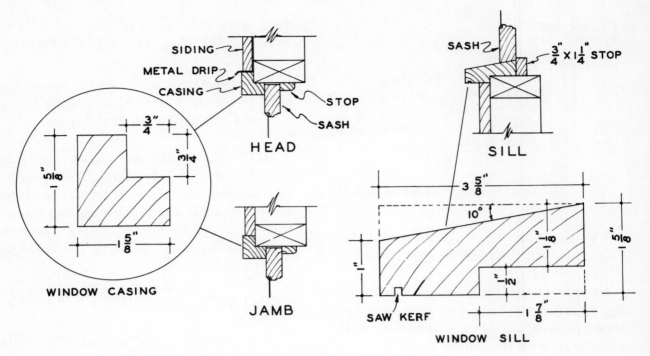

V-11. Window details.

or constructed from information given in Fig. V-13.

INSTALLING LARGE DOOR

When installing a large garage door instructions provided by the manufacturer should be carefully followed. The door selected should be one that is modern in design and operates easily.

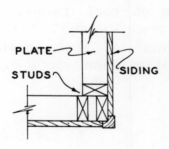

V-12. Corner detail.

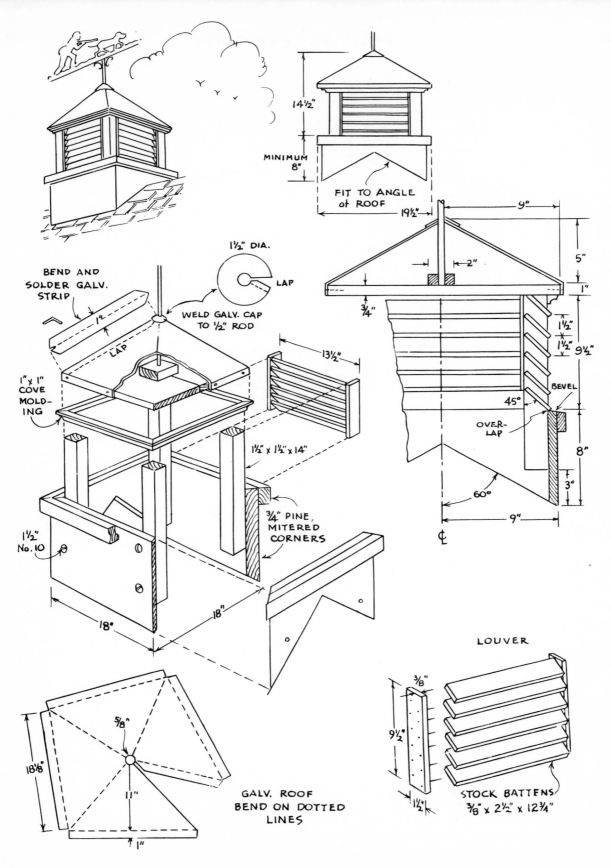

MINIMUM 8"

14½"

FIT TO ANGLE of ROOF

19½"

BEND AND SOLDER GALV. STRIP

1½" DIA.

LAP

WELD GALV. CAP TO ½" ROD

1"

LAP

1"×1" COVE MOLD-ING

9"

5"

1"

2"

¾"

1½"

1½"

9½"

13½"

1½" × 1½" × 14"

BEVEL

45°

OVER-LAP

8"

3"

¾" PINE, MITERED CORNERS

60°

9"

℄

1½" No. 10

18"

18"

18⅛"

5/8"

11"

1"

GALV. ROOF BEND ON DOTTED LINES

LOUVER

3/8"

9½"

1½"

STOCK BATTENS 3/8" × 2½" × 12¾"

V-13. Constructional details on garage cupola.

405

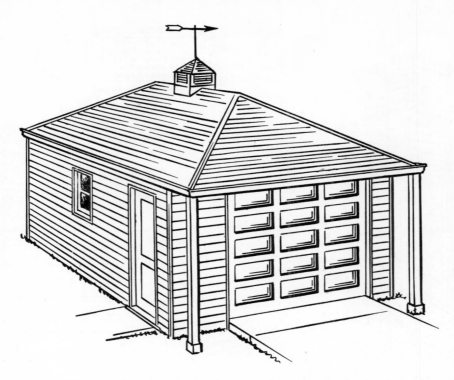

V-14. Alternate design--one-car garage with hip roof.

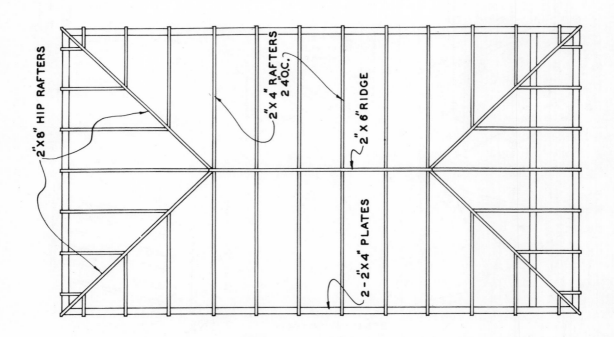

2"x8" HIP RAFTERS

2"x4" RAFTERS 24 O.C.

2"x6" RIDGE

2-2"x4" PLATES

V-14a. Hip roof framing for one-car garage.

V-15. Two-car garage 20 x 22 ft. in size with gable roof.

TWO-CAR GARAGES

A well-built two-car garage of modern design 20 x 22 ft. in size, is shown in Fig. V-15.

The material list, Fig. V-16, indicates the items that will be needed. Notes concerning construction procedure given for the one-car garage are in most cases, applicable to the construction of a two-car garage. The two-car garage floor plan is shown in V-17. Elevation framing is shown in V-18 and V-19. A cornice section for the two-car garage is detailed in V-20.

The two-car garage may be built with a hip roof, Fig. V-21, if desired. Fig. V-22 shows how to frame the hip roof.

GABLE ROOF		HIP ROOF		
Quan.	Size	Quan.	Size	Used for
1 -	2" x 4" x 6'	1 -	2" x 4" x 6'	Sills
3 -	2" x 4" x 10'	3 -	2" x 4" x 10'	"
1 -	2" x 4" x 12'	1 -	2" x 4" x 12'	"
1 -	2" x 4" x 18'	1 -	2" x 4" x 18'	"
7 -	2" x 4" x 8'	7 -	2" x 4" x 8'	Plates
2 -	2" x 4" x 12'	2 -	2" x 4" x 12'	"
4 -	2" x 4" x 14'	4 -	2" x 4" x 14'	"
47 -	2" x 4" x 7'	47 -	2" x 4" x 8'	Studs
4 -	2" x 4" x 10'			Gable studs
6 -	1" x 4" x 12'	6 -	1" x 4" x 12'	Wind bracing
2 -	2" x 4" x 8'	2 -	2" x 4" x 8'	Wind bracing
2 -	2" x 10" x 18'	2 -	2" x 10" x 18'	Headers
1 -	2" x 4" x 12'	1 -	2" x 4" x 12'	Window & door head & sill framing
5 -	2" x 4" x 20'	5 -	2" x 4" x 20'	Rafter ties
24 -	2" x 6" x 12'	24 -	2" x 6" x 12'	Rafters
		4 -	2" x 8" x 16'	Hip rafters
1 -	2" x 6" x 10'	1 -	2" x 6" x 4'	Ridge boards
1 -	2" x 6" x 12'			" "
608 B.M.	1" x 6" Boards	608 B.M.	1" x 6" Boards	Roof sheathing
5 1/3 Squares asphalt shingle		5 1/3 Squares Asphalt shingles		Roofing
580 B.M.	1" x 6" Drop siding	672 B.M.	1" x 6" Drop siding	Siding
240 B.M.	1" x 8" Vertical siding			Siding
46 Lin. ft. 1" x 6"		86 Lin. ft. 1" x 6"		Fascia
48 Lin. ft. 1" x 6"				Barge board
2 -	1'-10" x 2'-5" Barn sash	2 -	1'-10" x 2'-5" Barn sash	Windows
16 Lin. ft. 2" x 2"		16 Lin. ft. 2" x 2"		Window trim
1 -	2" x 4" x 6'	1 -	2" x 4" x 6'	Window sill
20 Lin. ft. 3/4" x 1 1/4" Stop		20 Lin. ft. 3/4" x 1 1/4" Stop		Window stop
4 -	2" x 2" x 8'	4 -	2" x 2" x 8'	Corner trim
1 -	2'-6" x 6'-8" Ext. door	1 -	2'-6" x 6'-8" Ext. door	Service door
1 -	3/4" x 4" x 10'	1 -	3/4" x 4" x 10'	Door jamb
1 -	3/4" x 4" x 8'	1 -	3/4" x 4" x 8'	" "
1 -	2" x 6" x 3'	1 -	2" x 6" x 3'	Door sill
1 -	16' x 7' Garage door	1 -	16' x 7' Garage door	Garage door
1 -	3/4" x 4" x 16'	1 -	3/4" x 4" x 16'	Door jamb
2 -	3/4" x 4" x 8'	1 -	3/4" x 4" x 8'	" "
50 L in. ft. 1" x 2"		50 Lin. ft. 1" x 2"		Door trim
50 Lin. ft. 1/2" x 1 5/8"		50 Lin. ft. 1/2" x 1 5/8"		Door stop
1 Bundle wood lath		1 Bundle wood lath		
1 Roll 15 lb. felt		1 Roll 15 lb. felt		Roof felt
19 - 1/2" x 8" Carriage bolts		19 - 1/2" x 8" Carriage bolts		Hardware
40 lbs. 16d Common nails		40 lbs. 16d Common nails		"
30 lbs. 8d Common nails		30 lbs. 8d Common nails		"
16 lbs. 1" Roofing nails		16 lbs. 1" Roofing nails		"
20 lbs. 7d Galv. box nails		20 lbs. 7d Galv. box nails		Hardware
6 lbs. 8d Casing nails		6 lbs. 8d Casing nails		"
1 1/2 Pairs 3 1/2" x 3 1/2" Butt Hinges		1 1/2 Pairs 3 1/2" x 3 1/2" Butt Hinges		"
1 Mortise lock		1 Mortise Lock		"
1 1/2 Gallons Ext. primer		1 1/2 Gallons Ext. primer		Paint
1 1/2 Gallons Ext. house paint		1 1/2 Gallons Ext. house Paint		"
1 - 20" x 20" Cupola with Weather vane		1 - 20" x 20" Cupola with Weather vane		Cupola

V-16. List of material required for two-car garage.

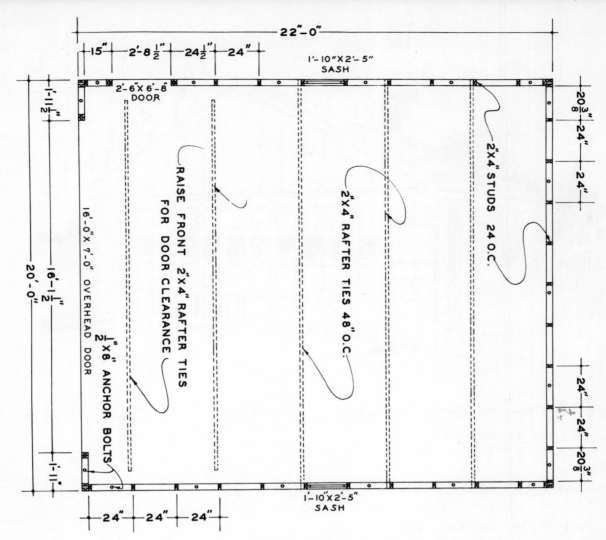

V-17. Floor plan of two-car garage.

V-18. Two-car garage, left elevation framing.

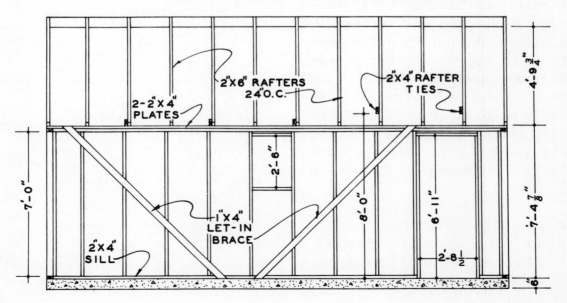

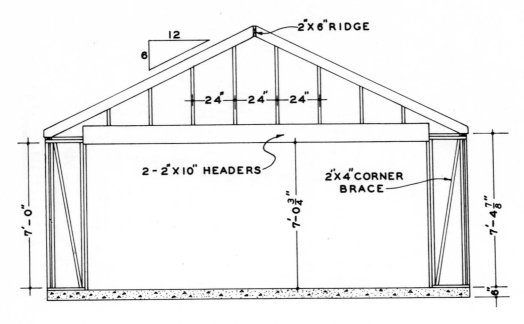

V-19. Two-car garage, front elevation framing.

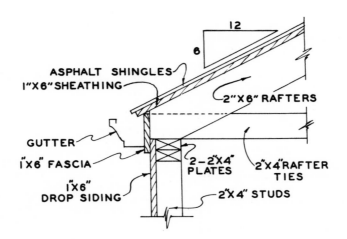

V-20. Cornice section for two-car garage.

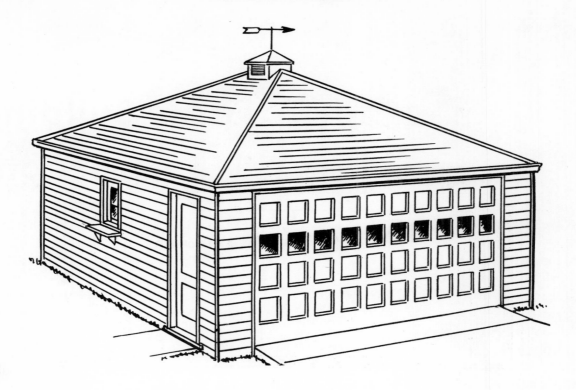

V-21. Alternate design for two-car garage, with hip roof.

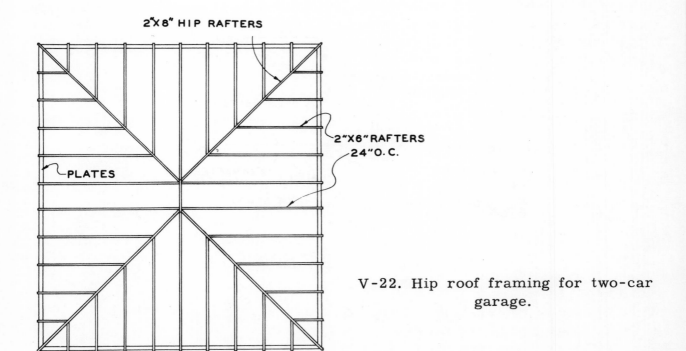

2"X8" HIP RAFTERS

2"X6" RAFTERS 24" O.C.

PLATES

V-22. Hip roof framing for two-car garage.

Farm Building Construction

FARM BUILDING PLANNING

In erecting new farm buildings or remodeling old ones, it's well to keep the designs simple. Buildings of simple design are less costly to construct and they are more easily converted for purposes other than originally intended, as building space requirements change.

Proper housing of farm animals has a definite relation to profitable production. Dry, sanitary, comfortable quarters, well lighted and well ventilated are of foremost importance. Good construction is also important,

as it reduces upkeep and assures a better building investment.

Farm buildings should be planned for efficiency—to reduce labor of feeding, cleaning and general daily chores.

DATA FROM AGRICULTURAL COLLEGES

Factual data on the farm buildings included in this section of Practical Carpentry have been drawn from agricultural colleges and building material manufacturers.

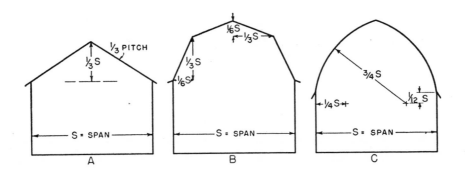

W-1. Shapes of roofs. A, Gable roof. In a 1/3 pitch gable roof the height from walls to ridge is 1/3 the width or span (S) of the building. B, Gambrel roof. Various proportions are used. C, Curved or Gothic roof. Various rates of curvatures are used.

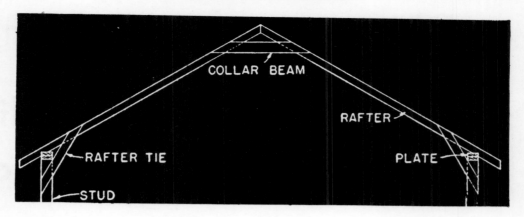

W-2. Roof tied together at top with collar beam. The rafters of gable roofs should be tied to the studs or wall posts at intervals of 6 to 8 ft.

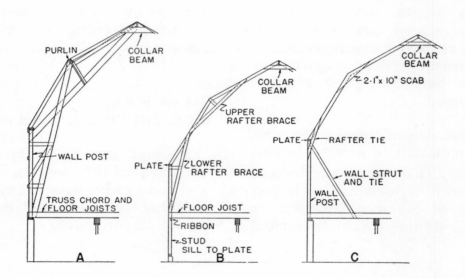

W-3. Three types of framing in common use for gambrel roof. A, Truss; B, Braced rafter; C, Self-supporting roof with wall strut and tie.

Buildings covered are practical, serviceable and conservative in material requirements. In most cases the constructional details are applicable to buildings of different size than the examples shown.

Information on form construction, concrete work, wall framing, sheathing, roofing materials, building with plywood, constructing scaffolds, etc., much of which is applicable to farm building construction, will be found in the sections of this book covering these particular subjects.

ROOF CONSTRUCTION

Gable and gambrel roofs (A and B in Fig. W-1) are the most usual on farm buildings. The curved or so-called Gothic roof is, however, coming into use for large barns in many localities, because of the development of glued, factory-built laminated rafters.

GABLE ROOF

The gable roof is simplest to build. For a building of given size it has, of the three types shown in W-1, the least area. It is therefore the least costly to maintain.

The chief objection to a gable roof for a dairy or hay barn is that it provides a relatively low loft with inadequate space for hay storage.

Gable roofs are built with a variety of pitches. The 1/4 and 1/3 pitch are the most usual. In a 1/3 pitch roof, for example, the height from walls to ridge of the roof is 1/3 the width or span of the building. Additional information on roof pitch will be found in the section on Roof Framing.

Rafters of gable roofs are usually spaced 24 in. on centers. The usual wooden roof sheathing provides adequate strength when laid on rafters thus spaced. Rafters spaced 24 in. o. c. should be of 2 x 6 in. lumber unless the clear, unsupported span is less than 6 ft.

It is essential that all rafters be securely tied together at the top with 1 x 8 in. or 2 x 6 in. collar beams, Fig. W-2, and that bottoms of rafters be well anchored to the plate and side walls. Well-nailed wooden rafter ties at intervals of 6 to 8 ft. from rafter to

stud or post are satisfactory.

Studies of farm buildings damaged by wind indicate that the most usual ways in which a building fails in a high wind is by spreading and opening at the ridge and rising from the plate.

GAMBREL ROOF

A great variety of designs or combinations of rafter lengths are used in gambrel roofs. In the one shown in Fig. W-1, all the rafters are the same length and the angle of all the end cuts is the same.

GOTHIC OR CURVED ROOF

The curved or so-called Gothic roof is built in various heights and curvatures, and is made in various ways. It may be built up of boards or laminations, bent to the desired radius and nailed together in sufficient numbers to provide adequate strength.

In a barn 36 ft. wide, the ridge of a gambrel roof of these proportions is 6 ft. higher above the plate than in one with 1/3 pitch and 9 ft. higher than in one with a 1/4 pitch gable roof.

The usual gambrel roofs do not have posts in the loft areas or ties that extend all the way across the loft. Considerable space is, however, used along the sides by bracing.

Three methods of framing gambrel roofs for barns from 34 to 38 ft. wide are shown in Fig. W-3.

Curved, laminated rafters in which the individual strips of laminations are bent and glued together at the factory are available in many localities.

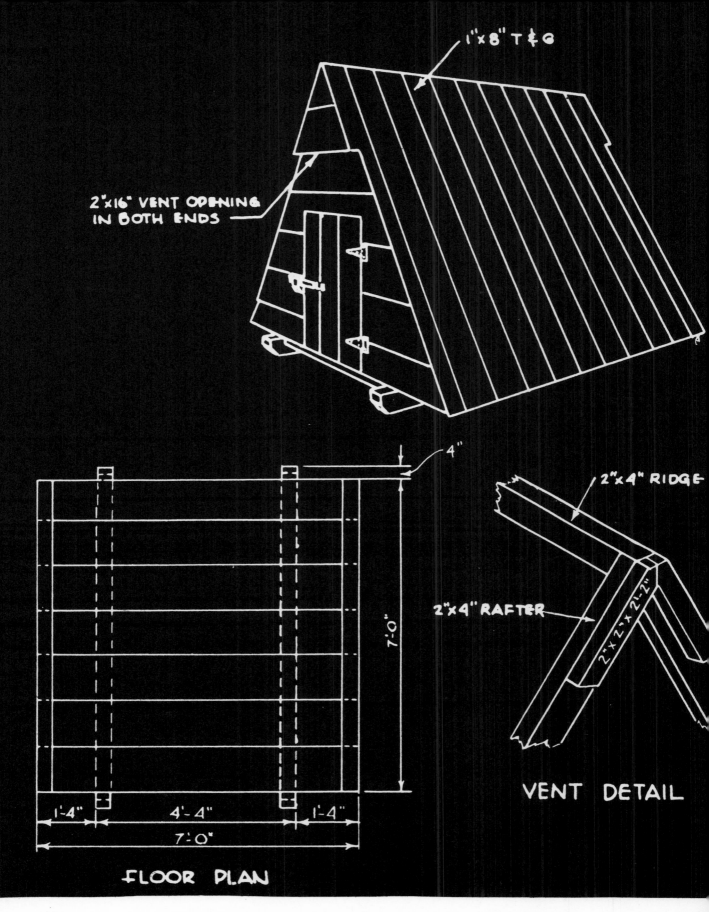

1"x8" T&G

2"x16" VENT OPENING
IN BOTH ENDS

2"x4" RIDGE

2"x4" RAFTER

2"x 2" x 2'-2"

4"

7'-0"

1'-4"   4'-4"   1'-4"

7'-0"

FLOOR PLAN

VENT DETAIL

MICHIGAN STATE COLLEGE A-TYPE HOG COT
Completed cot, floor plan, detail of vent

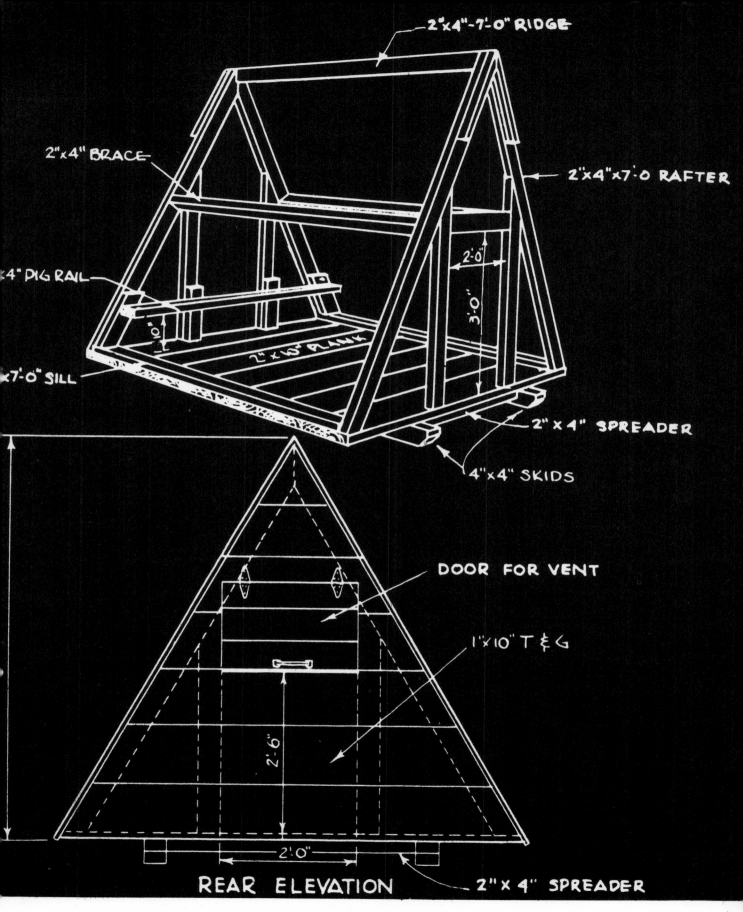

2"x4"-7'-0" RIDGE

2"x4" BRACE

2"x4"x7'-0 RAFTER

2'-0"

3'-0"

4" PIG RAIL

2"x10" PLANK

7'-0" SILL

2" x 4" SPREADER

4"x4" SKIDS

DOOR FOR VENT

1"x10" T&G

2'-6"

2'-0"

REAR ELEVATION

2" x 4" SPREADER

MICHIGAN STATE COLLEGE A-TYPE HOG COT
Framing details, rear elevation

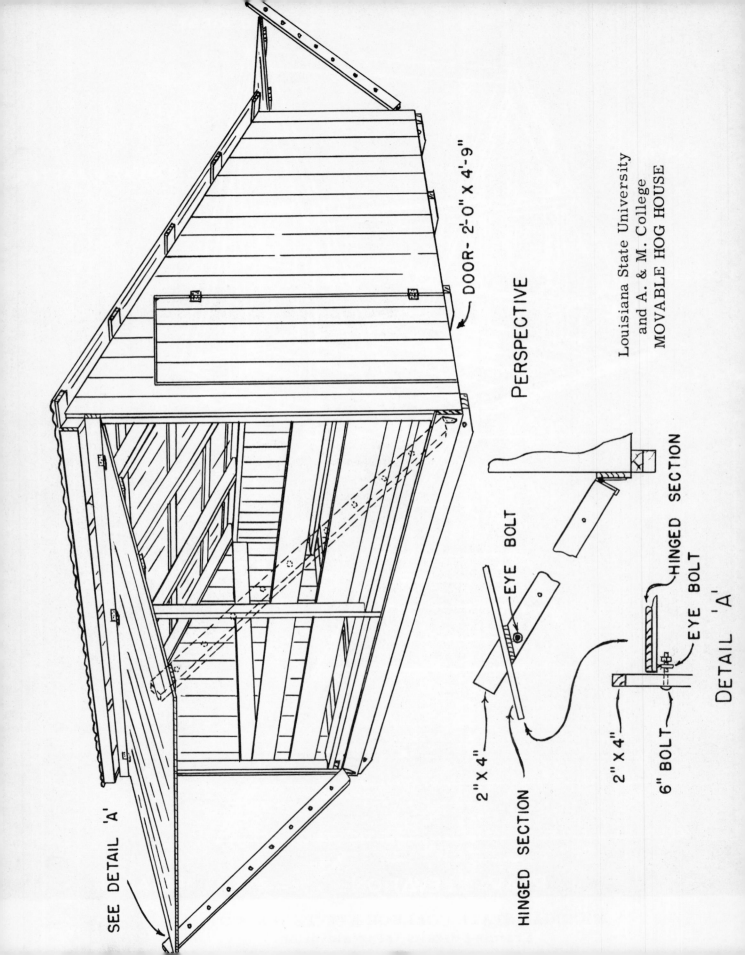

SEE DETAIL 'A'

DOOR- 2'-0" X 4'-9"

PERSPECTIVE

Louisiana State University
and A. & M. College
MOVABLE HOG HOUSE

HINGED SECTION

2" X 4"

EYE BOLT

HINGED SECTION

EYE BOLT

2" X 4"

6" BOLT

DETAIL 'A'

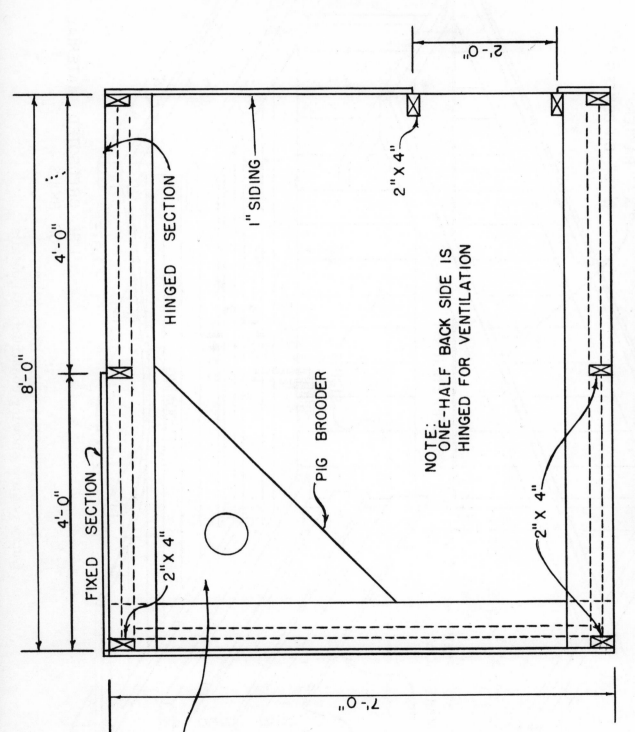

LOUISIANA MOVABLE HOG HOUSE—Floor Plan

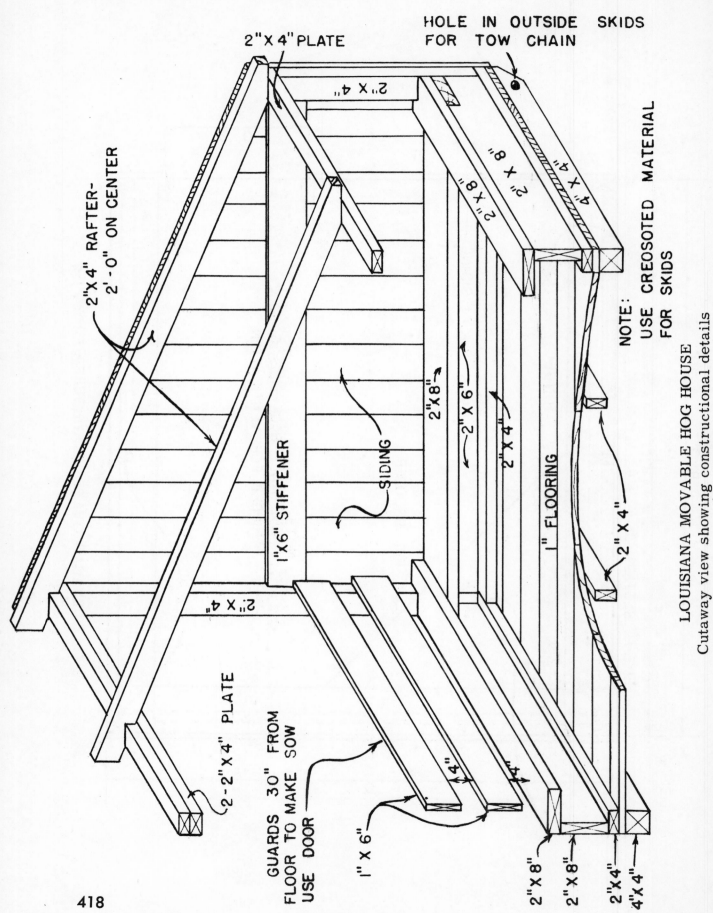

2"X 4" PLATE

HOLE IN OUTSIDE SKIDS FOR TOW CHAIN

2" X 4"

2" X 8"

2" X 8"

4" X 4"

NOTE: USE CREOSOTED MATERIAL FOR SKIDS

2"X 4" RAFTER— 2'-0" ON CENTER

1"X 6" STIFFENER

SIDING

2"X 8"

2" X 6"

2" X 4"

1" FLOORING

2" X 4"

2"X 4"

2-2" X 4" PLATE

GUARDS 30" FROM FLOOR TO MAKE SOW USE DOOR

1" X 6"

4"

4"

2" X 8"

2" X 8"

2" X 4"

4" X 4"

LOUISIANA MOVABLE HOG HOUSE
Cutaway view showing constructional details

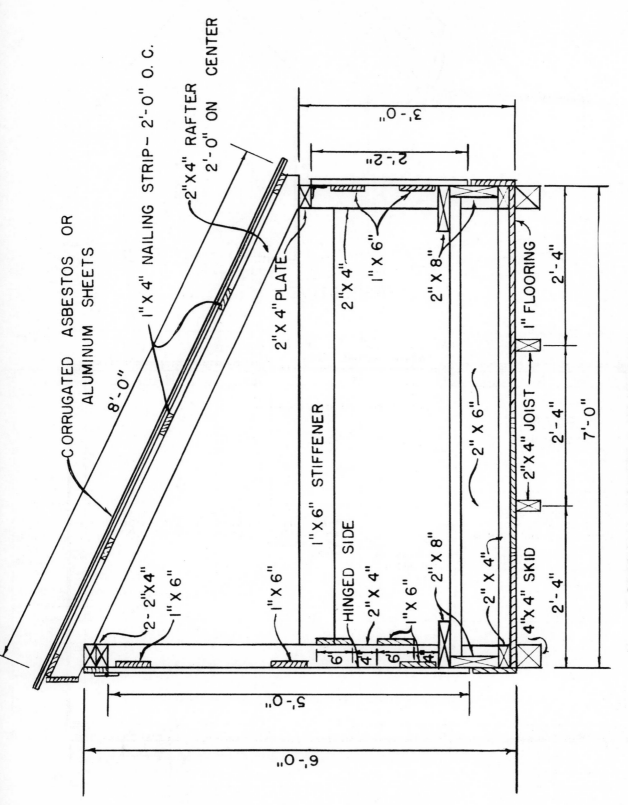

CORRUGATED ASBESTOS OR ALUMINUM SHEETS

1"x 4" NAILING STRIP—2'-0" O.C.

2"x 4" RAFTER 2'-0" ON CENTER

8'-0"

2"x 4" PLATE

1"x 6" STIFFENER

HINGED SIDE

2"x 4"

1"x 6"

2-2"x 4"

1"x 6"

1"x 6"

2"x 4"

1"x 6"

2"x 8"

2"x 8"

2"x 4"

2"x 6"

2"x 6"

4"x 4" SKID

1" FLOORING

2"x 4" JOIST

3'-0"

2'-2"

2'-4"

2'-4"

2'-4"

2'-4"

7'-0"

6"

4"

6"

4"

5'-0"

6'-0"

LOUISIANA MOVABLE HOG HOUSE—Section view

419

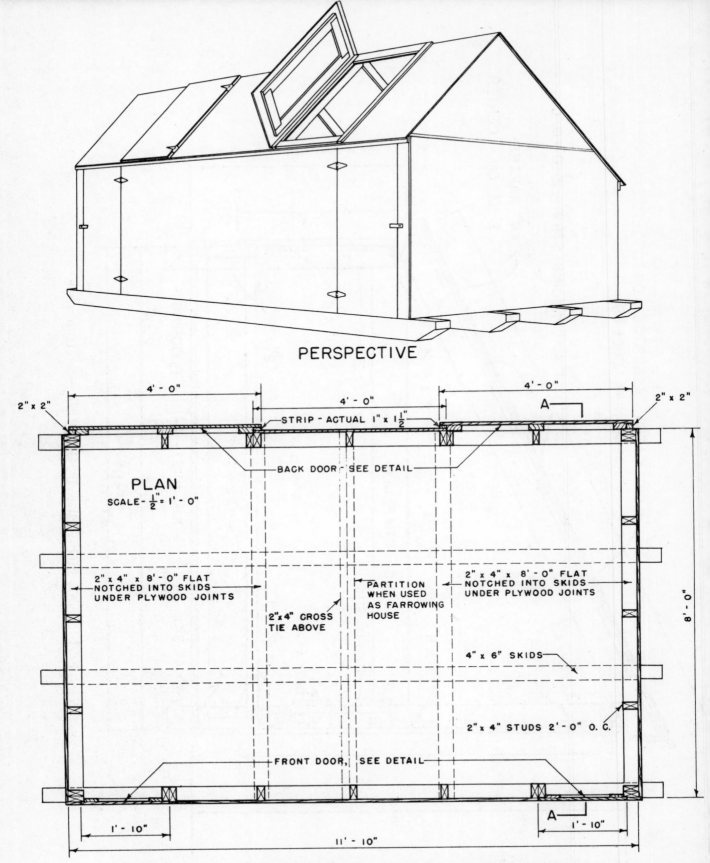

PERSPECTIVE

PLAN
SCALE- $\frac{1}{2}$" = 1'-0"

4'-0"

4'-0"

4'-0"

2" x 2"

2" x 2"

STRIP - ACTUAL 1" x 1$\frac{1}{2}$"

A

BACK DOOR - SEE DETAIL

2" x 4" x 8'-0" FLAT
NOTCHED INTO SKIDS
UNDER PLYWOOD JOINTS

2" x 4" x 8'-0" FLAT
NOTCHED INTO SKIDS
UNDER PLYWOOD JOINTS

2"x 4" CROSS
TIE ABOVE

PARTITION
WHEN USED
AS FARROWING
HOUSE

4" x 6" SKIDS

2" x 4" STUDS 2'-0" O. C.

8'-0"

FRONT DOOR, SEE DETAIL

A

1'-10"

1'-10"

11'-10"

DOUBLE MOVABLE FARROWING HOUSE CONVERTIBLE TO 300
BUSHEL GRAIN BIN (from Midwest College Plan Service)

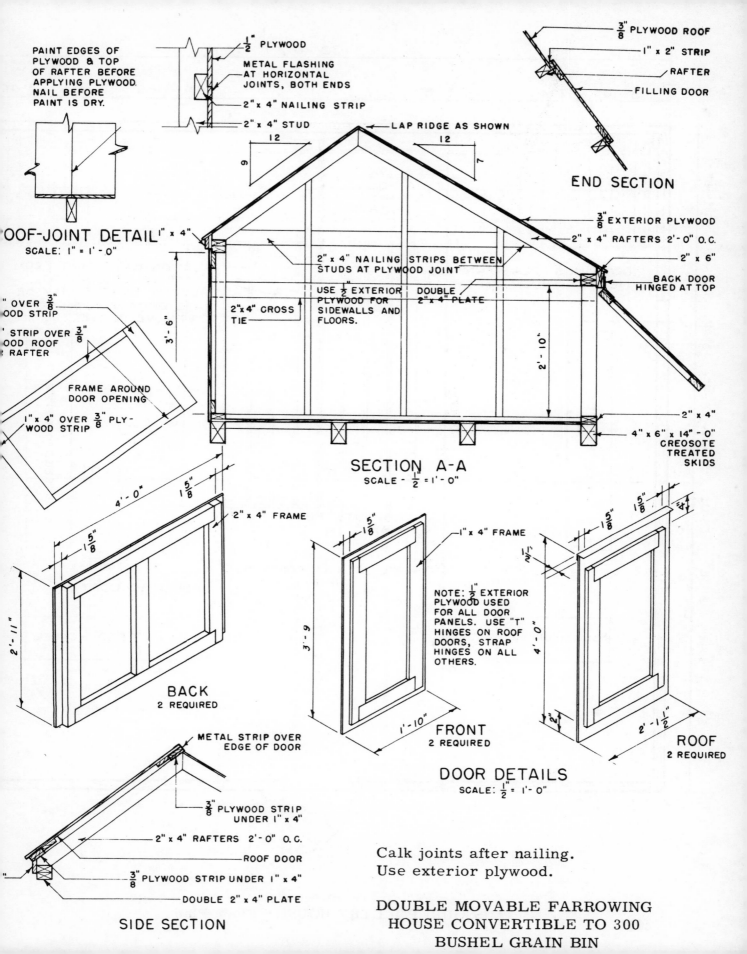

PAINT EDGES OF PLYWOOD & TOP OF RAFTER BEFORE APPLYING PLYWOOD. NAIL BEFORE PAINT IS DRY.

½" PLYWOOD

METAL FLASHING AT HORIZONTAL JOINTS, BOTH ENDS

2" x 4" NAILING STRIP

2" x 4" STUD

⅜" PLYWOOD ROOF

1" x 2" STRIP

RAFTER

FILLING DOOR

END SECTION

OOF-JOINT DETAIL
SCALE: 1" = 1'-0"

1" x 4"

LAP RIDGE AS SHOWN

12   9   12   7

⅜" EXTERIOR PLYWOOD

2" x 4" RAFTERS 2'-0" O.C.

2" x 6"

BACK DOOR HINGED AT TOP

" OVER ⅜" OOD STRIP

' STRIP OVER ⅜" OOD ROOF RAFTER

2" x 4" NAILING STRIPS BETWEEN STUDS AT PLYWOOD JOINT

USE ½" EXTERIOR PLYWOOD FOR SIDEWALLS AND FLOORS.

DOUBLE 2" x 4" PLATE

2"x 4" CROSS TIE

FRAME AROUND DOOR OPENING

1" x 4" OVER ⅜" PLY-WOOD STRIP

3'-6"

2'-10"

2" x 4"

4" x 6" x 14"-0" CREOSOTE TREATED SKIDS

SECTION A-A
SCALE - ½" = 1'-0"

4'-0"   1⅝"

1⅝"

2" x 4" FRAME

2'-11"

BACK
2 REQUIRED

1⅝"

1" x 4" FRAME

3'-9"

NOTE: 1" ½ EXTERIOR PLYWOOD USED FOR ALL DOOR PANELS. USE "T" HINGES ON ROOF DOORS, STRAP HINGES ON ALL OTHERS.

1'-10"

FRONT
2 REQUIRED

1⅝" 1⅝"

½"

2½"

4'-0"

2"

2'-1½"

ROOF
2 REQUIRED

DOOR DETAILS
SCALE: ½" = 1'-0"

METAL STRIP OVER EDGE OF DOOR

⅜" PLYWOOD STRIP UNDER 1" x 4"

2" x 4" RAFTERS 2'-0" O.C.

ROOF DOOR

⅜" PLYWOOD STRIP UNDER 1" x 4"

DOUBLE 2" x 4" PLATE

SIDE SECTION

Calk joints after nailing.
Use exterior plywood.

DOUBLE MOVABLE FARROWING HOUSE CONVERTIBLE TO 300 BUSHEL GRAIN BIN

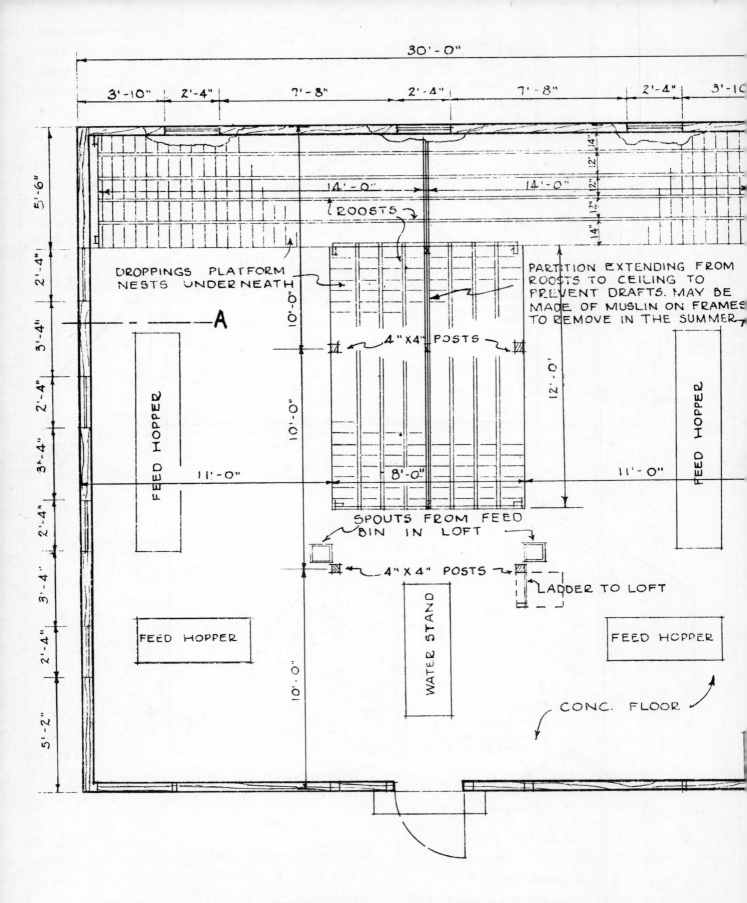

30'-0"

3'-10" 2'-4" 7'-8" 2'-4" 7'-8" 2'-4" 3'-10

5'-6"

2'-4"

3'-4"

2'-4"

3'-4"

2'-4"

3'-4"

2'-4"

5'-2"

14'-0" 14'-0"

1¼" 12" 12" 1¼"

14"

ROOSTS

DROPPINGS PLATFORM
NESTS UNDERNEATH

PARTITION EXTENDING FROM
ROOSTS TO CEILING TO
PREVENT DRAFTS. MAY BE
MADE OF MUSLIN ON FRAMES
TO REMOVE IN THE SUMMER

A

4" X 4" POSTS

FEED HOPPER

10'-0"

10'-0"

12'-0"

11'-0"

8'-0"

11'-0"

FEED HOPPER

SPOUTS FROM FEED
BIN IN LOFT

4" X 4" POSTS

LADDER TO LOFT

FEED HOPPER

10'-0"

WATER STAND

FEED HOPPER

CONC. FLOOR

MISSOURI POULTRY HOUSE—Floor Plan

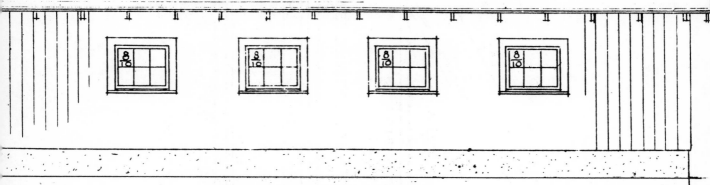

CEDAR SHINGLES

SIDE ELEVATION
SCALE ¼" = 1'-0"

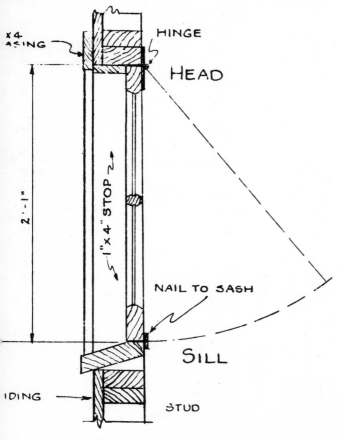

HINGE

x4
ASING

HEAD

1"x4" STOP

2'-1"

NAIL TO SASH

SILL

IDING

STUD

TYPICAL
WINDOW DETAIL
SCALE 1½" = 1'-0"

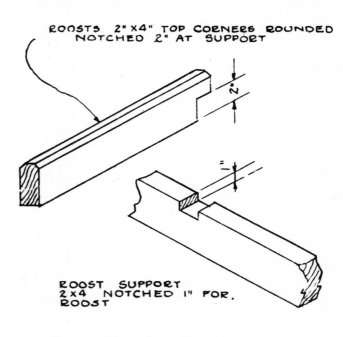

ROOSTS 2"x4" TOP CORNERS ROUNDED
NOTCHED 2" AT SUPPORT

2"

1"

ROOST SUPPORT
2x4 NOTCHED 1" FOR
ROOST

ROOST & SUPPORT
·DETAIL·

MISSOURI POULTRY HOUSE
Side Elevation, Window and Roost
Support Details

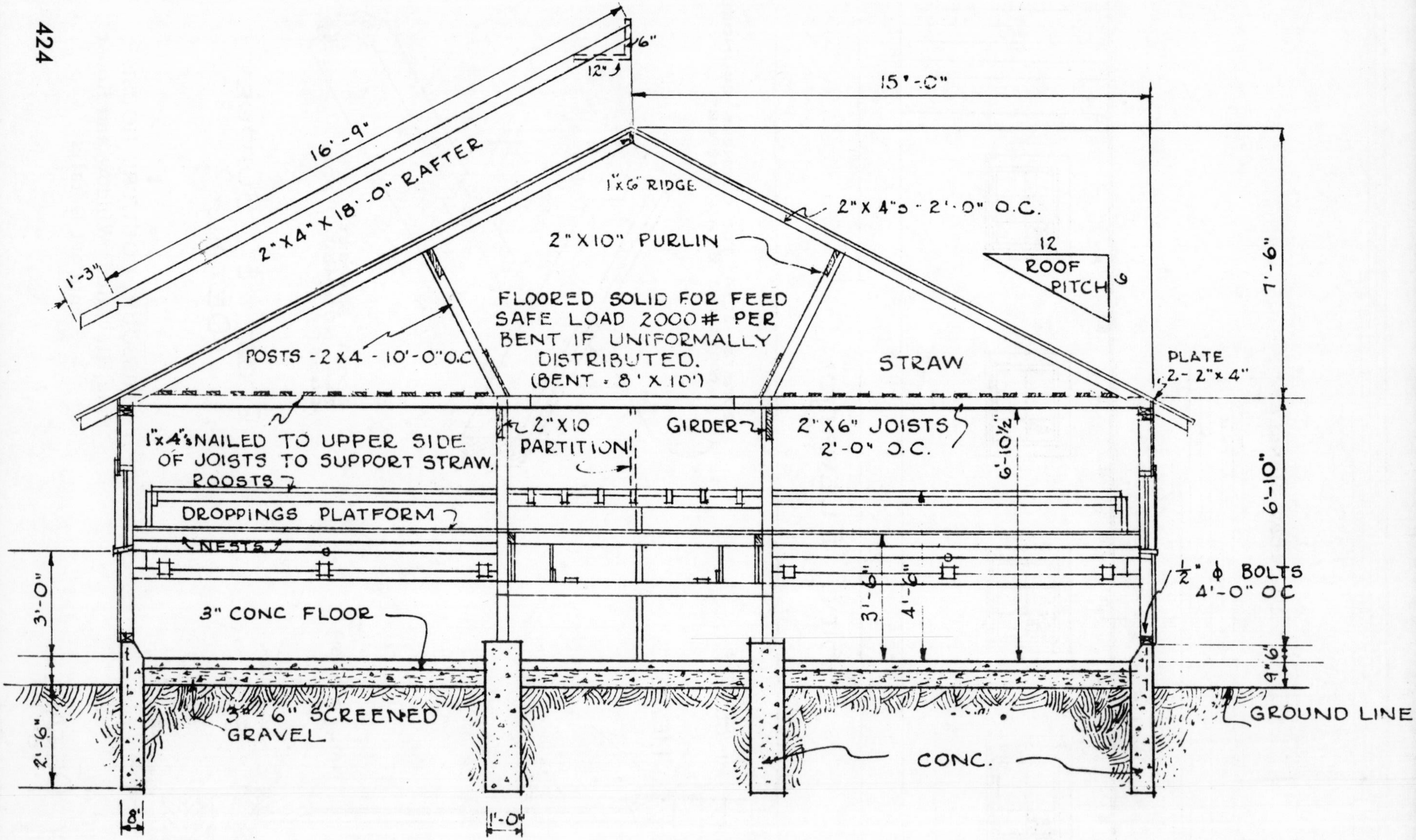

MISSOURI POULTRY HOUSE—Section A—A

7'-6"

6'-10"

15'-0"

12
ROOF
PITCH

PLATE
2-2"X4"

½"φ BOLTS
4'-0" O.C.

GROUND LINE

STRAW

2"X4"s - 2'-0" O.C.

6

1X6 RIDGE

CONC.

6"

12

2"X10" PURLIN

FLOORED SOLID FOR FEED
SAFE LOAD 2000# PER
BENT IF UNIFORMLY
DISTRIBUTED.
(BENT = 8'X10')

2"X6" JOISTS
2'-0" O.C.

6'-10"

4'-6"

3'-6"

POSTS - 2"X4" - 10'-0" O.C.

2"X10
PARTITION

GIRDER

16'-0"

2"X4"X18'-0" RAFTER

1"X4"s NAILED TO UPPER SIDE
OF JOISTS TO SUPPORT STRAW.

POSTS

DROPPINGS PLATFORM

NESTS

3" CONC FLOOR

3"-6" SCREENED
GRAVEL

1'-0"

1'-3"

8"

3'-0"

2'-6"

1'-6"

424

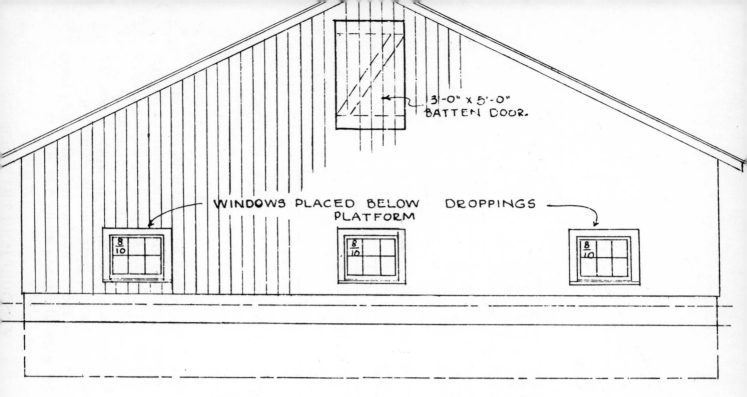

3'-0" x 5'-0" BATTEN DOOR.

WINDOWS PLACED BELOW PLATFORM

DROPPINGS

8/10

8/10

8/10

· END (NORTH) ELEVATION ·

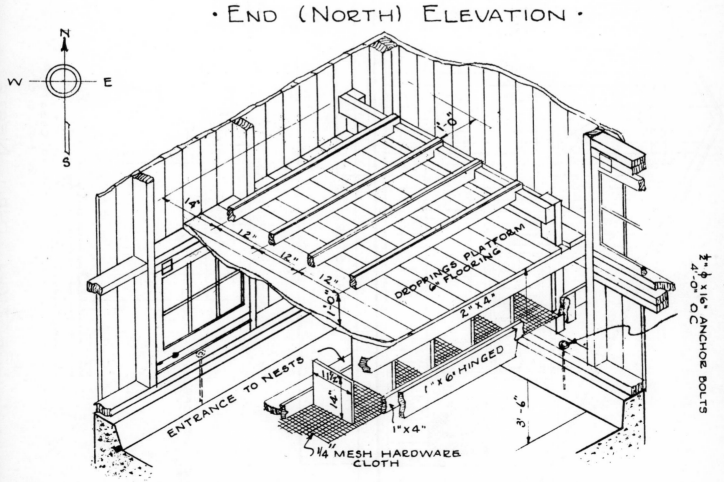

N
W   E
S

1'-0"

13"

12"

12"

12"

12"

1'-0"

DROPPINGS PLATFORM
6" FLOORING

2" x 4"

½"φ x 16" ANCHOR BOLTS
4'-0" O.C.

ENTRANCE TO NESTS

11½"

14"

1" x 4"

1" x 6" HINGED

3'-6"

¼" MESH HARDWARE CLOTH

MISSOURI POULTRY HOUSE—End elevation, details of roosts and nests

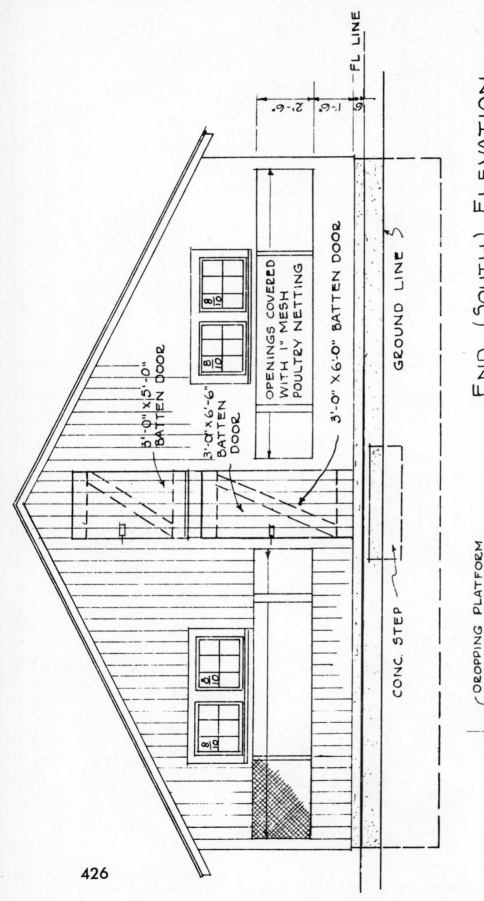

3'-0"×5'-0" BATTEN DOOR

3'-0"×6'-6" BATTEN DOOR

8/10

8/10

OPENINGS COVERED WITH 1" MESH POULTRY NETTING

3'-0"×6'-0" BATTEN DOOR

2'-6"

1'-6"

.6"

FL LINE

GROUND LINE

CONC. STEP

8/10

8/10

426

END (SOUTH) ELEVATION

Note: Walls may be sided with car siding placed vertically or with boards and battens placed vertically or with drop siding placed horizontally. For vertical siding place studding not more than 8 ft. apart and nail siding to sills, girts and plates not more than 3 ft. apart. For horizontal siding leave out girts and place studs 2 ft. apart.

DROPPING PLATFORM

1" PARTITION BOARDS PLACED 1'-0" O.C.

2 × 4

BUTTON

1×6

11½"

14"

1"× 4"

1"× 4"

¾" HARDWARE CLOTH

1"×4" CLEATS @ 3'-0" O.C.

SECTION THRU NESTS

MISSOURI POULTRY HOUSE

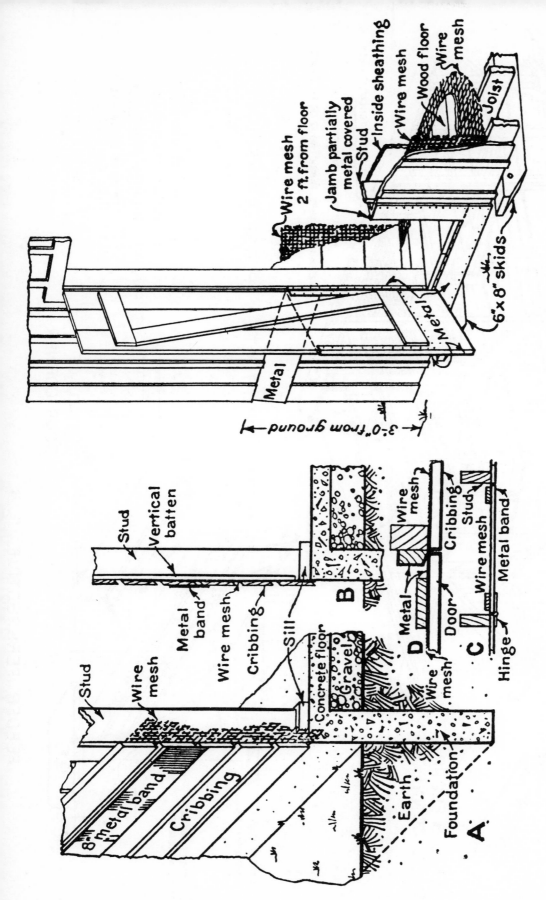

Rat proofing corn crib and portable granary. Left. Granary with concrete floor rat proofed by using wire netting around crib to height of 2 ft. or more from top of foundation. Strip of galvanized iron 8 in. wide is fastened above wire netting. Rats are unable to get a footing on smooth metal and cannot climb over it. A, Section through wall; B, Section through door, which is made of cribbing on vertical battens; C, Plan of door; D, Enlarged detail of jamb at closing side of door. Right. Wire mesh is used on sides of granary and under wood floor.

427

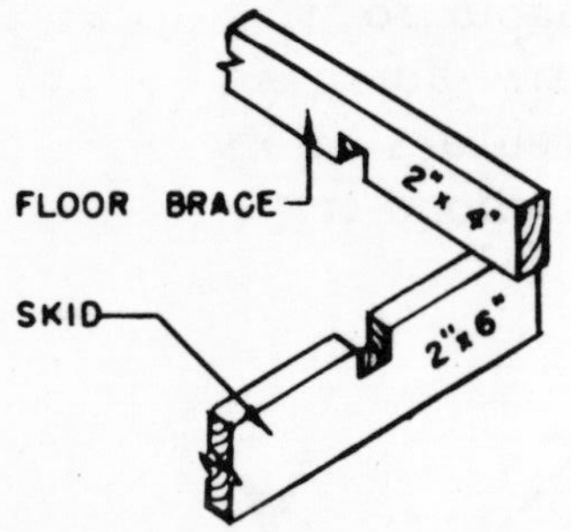

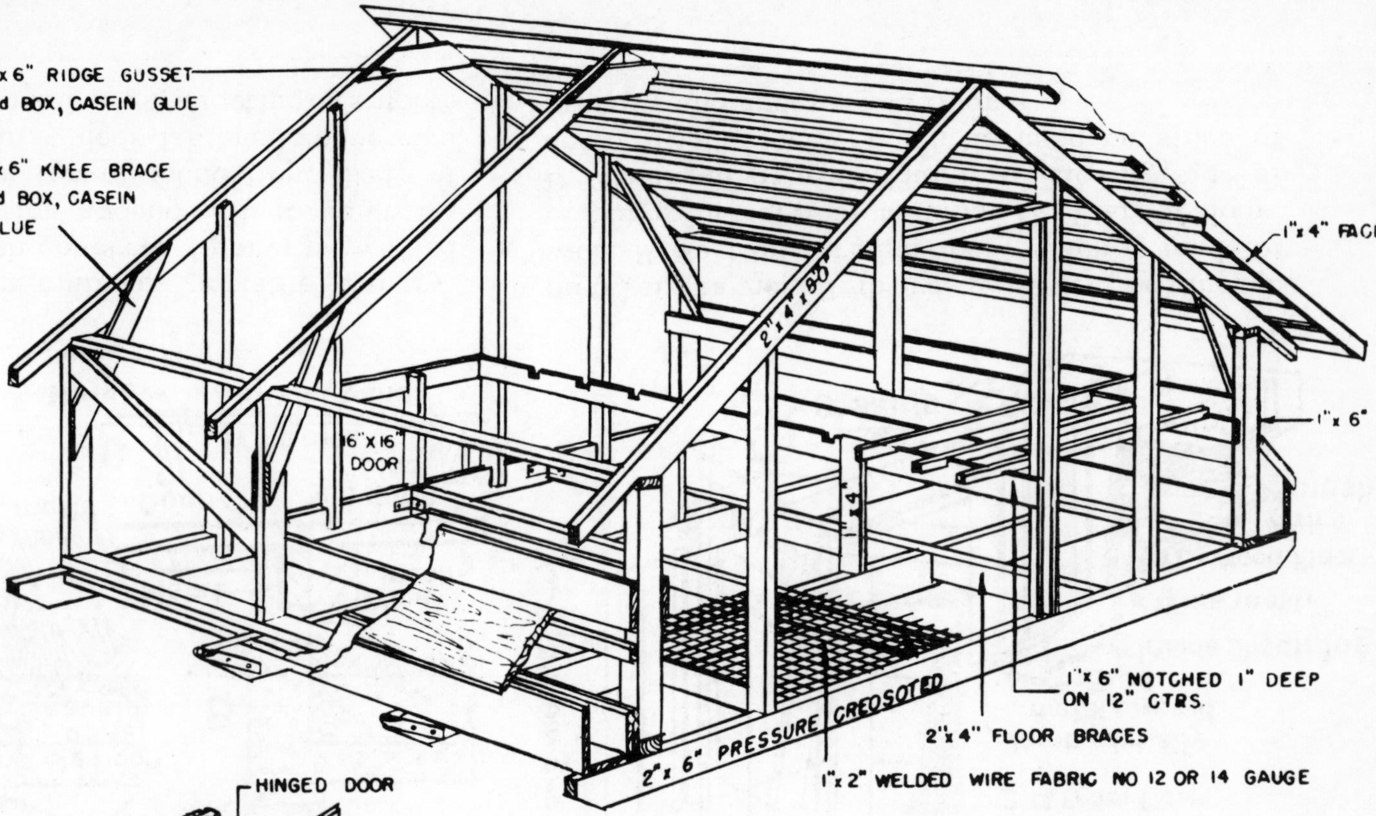

CONSTRUCTION PERSPECTIVE

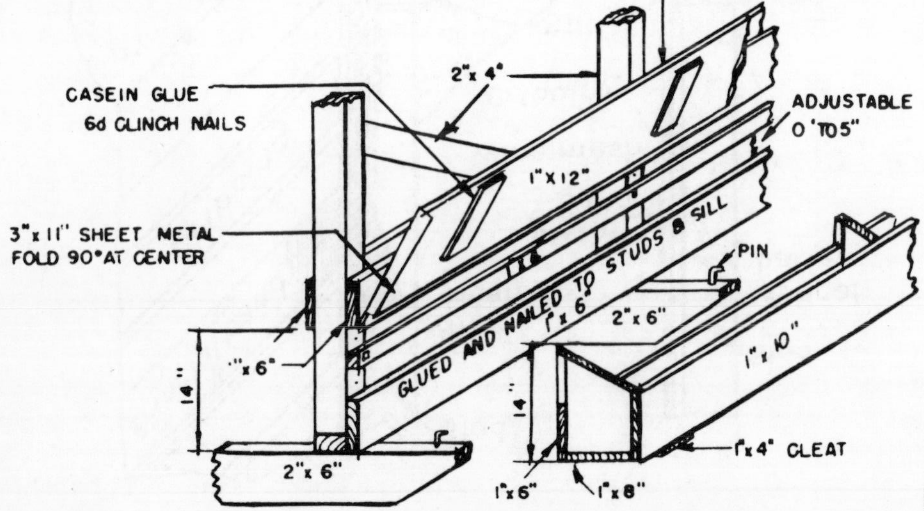

RANGE SHELTER
(From Midwest
College Plan
Service)

1"x 4" FACIA

1" 6"

1"x 6" NOTCHED 1" DEEP
ON 12" CTRS.

2"x 4" FLOOR BRACES

1"x 2" WELDED WIRE FABRIC NO 12 OR 14 GAUGE

2"x 6" PRESSURE CREOSOTED

2"x 4" 16"O.C.

16"x16"
DOOR

1"x 6" RIDGE GUSSET
7d BOX, CASEIN GLUE

1"x 6" KNEE BRACE
7d BOX, CASEIN
GLUE

DETAIL OF
DOOR CORNER

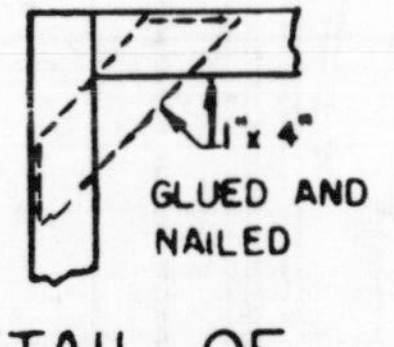

1"x 4"

GLUED AND
NAILED

HINGED DOOR

ADJUSTABLE
0'TO 5"

SILL

PIN

1"x 0"

1"x 4" CLEAT

1"x 12"

2"x 6"

GLUED AND NAILED TO STUDS @ 1"x 6"

1"x 8"

1"x 6"

2"x 4"

1"

4"

2"x 6"

"x 6"

CASEIN GLUE
6d CLINCH NAILS

3"x11" SHEET METAL
FOLD 90°AT CENTER

FEEDER PERSPECTIVE

SKID & FLOOR
BRACE CONNECTION

2"x 4"

2"x 6"

FLOOR BRACE

SKID

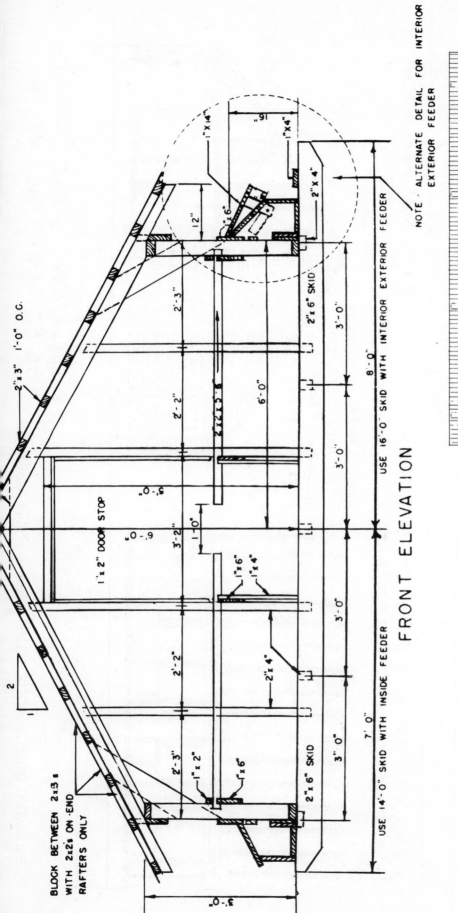

FRONT ELEVATION

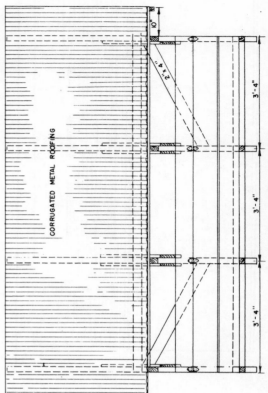

SIDE ELEVATION

Note: Cover front, back and sides down to feeder with 18 gauge 1 in. mesh poultry netting

RANGE SHELTER—front and side elevations showing constructional details

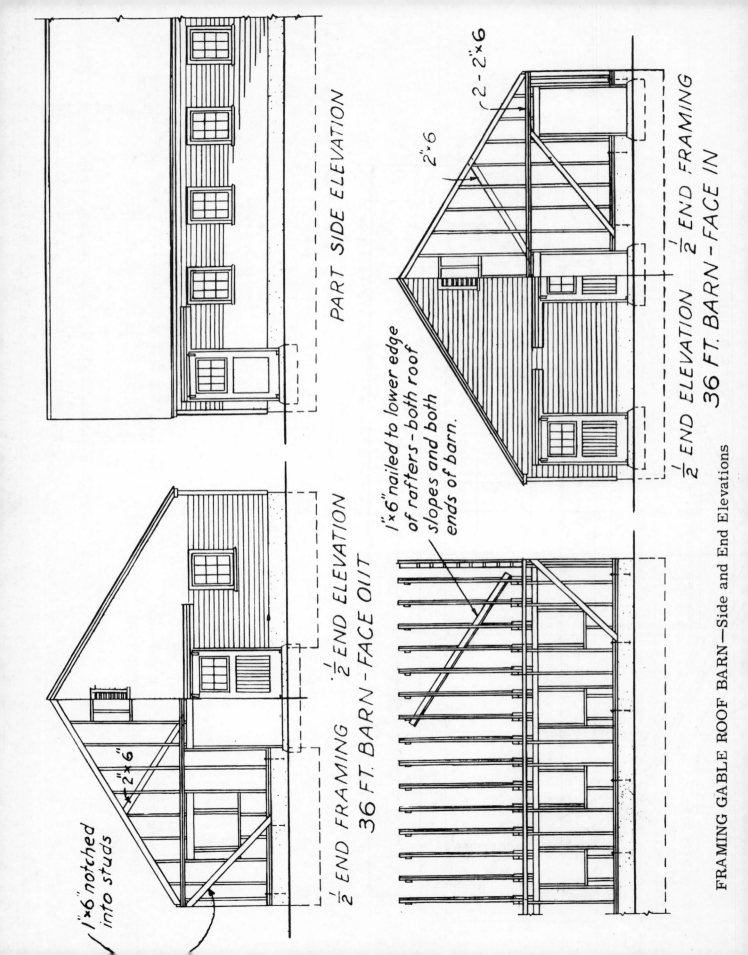

PART SIDE ELEVATION

½ END ELEVATION
½ END FRAMING 36 FT. BARN - FACE OUT

1"×6" notched into studs

2"×6"

1"×6" nailed to lower edge of rafters - both roof slopes and both ends of barn.

2-2"×6

2"×6

½ END ELEVATION
½ END FRAMING 36 FT. BARN - FACE IN

FRAMING GABLE ROOF BARN—Side and End Elevations

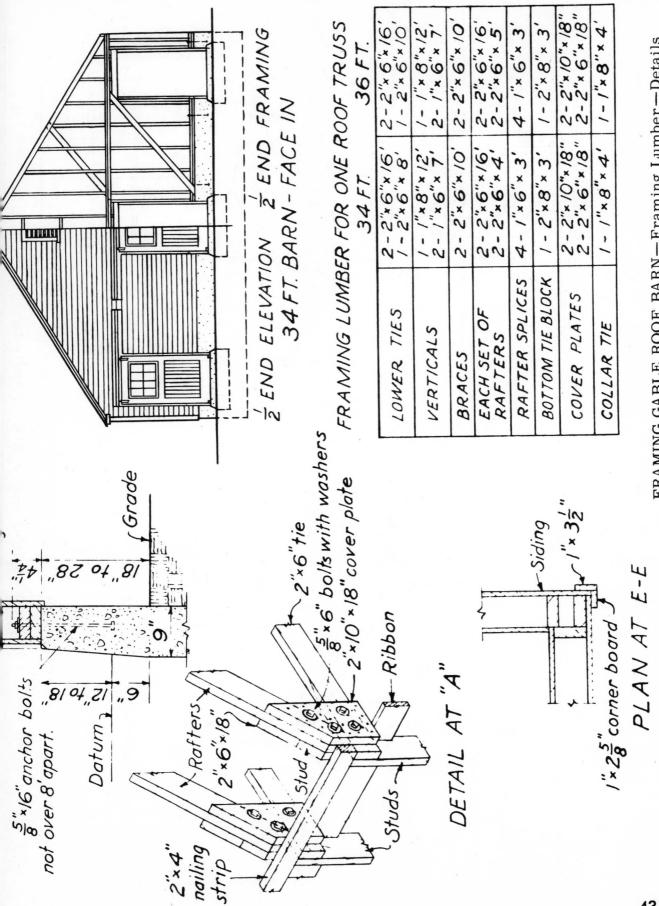

FRAMING LUMBER FOR ONE ROOF TRUSS

	34 FT.	36 FT.
LOWER TIES	2-2"×6"×16' 1-2"×6"×8'	2-2"×6"×16' 1-2"×6"×10'
VERTICALS	1-1"×8"×12' 2-1"×6"×7'	1-1"×8"×12' 2-1"×6"×7'
BRACES	2-2"×6"×10'	2-2"×6"×10'
EACH SET OF RAFTERS	2-2"×6"×16' 2-2"×6"×4'	2-2"×6"×16' 2-2"×6"×5'
RAFTER SPLICES	4-1"×6"×3'	4-1"×6"×3'
BOTTOM TIE BLOCK	1-2"×8"×3'	1-2"×8"×3'
COVER PLATES	2-2"×10"×18" 2-2"×6"×18"	2-2"×10"×18" 2-2"×6"×18"
COLLAR TIE	1-1"×8"×4'	1-1"×8"×4'

½ END ELEVATION ½ END FRAMING
34 FT. BARN - FACE IN

⅝"×16" anchor bolts not over 8' apart.

Grade

Datum

18" to 28"

4½"

6"

12" to 18"

6"

2"×4" nailing strip

Rafters 2"×6"×18'

Stud

Studs

2"×6" tie

⅝"×6" bolts with washers

2"×10"×18" cover plate

Ribbon

DETAIL AT "A"

Siding

1"×3½"

1"×2⅝" corner board

PLAN AT E-E

FRAMING GABLE ROOF BARN—Framing Lumber—Details

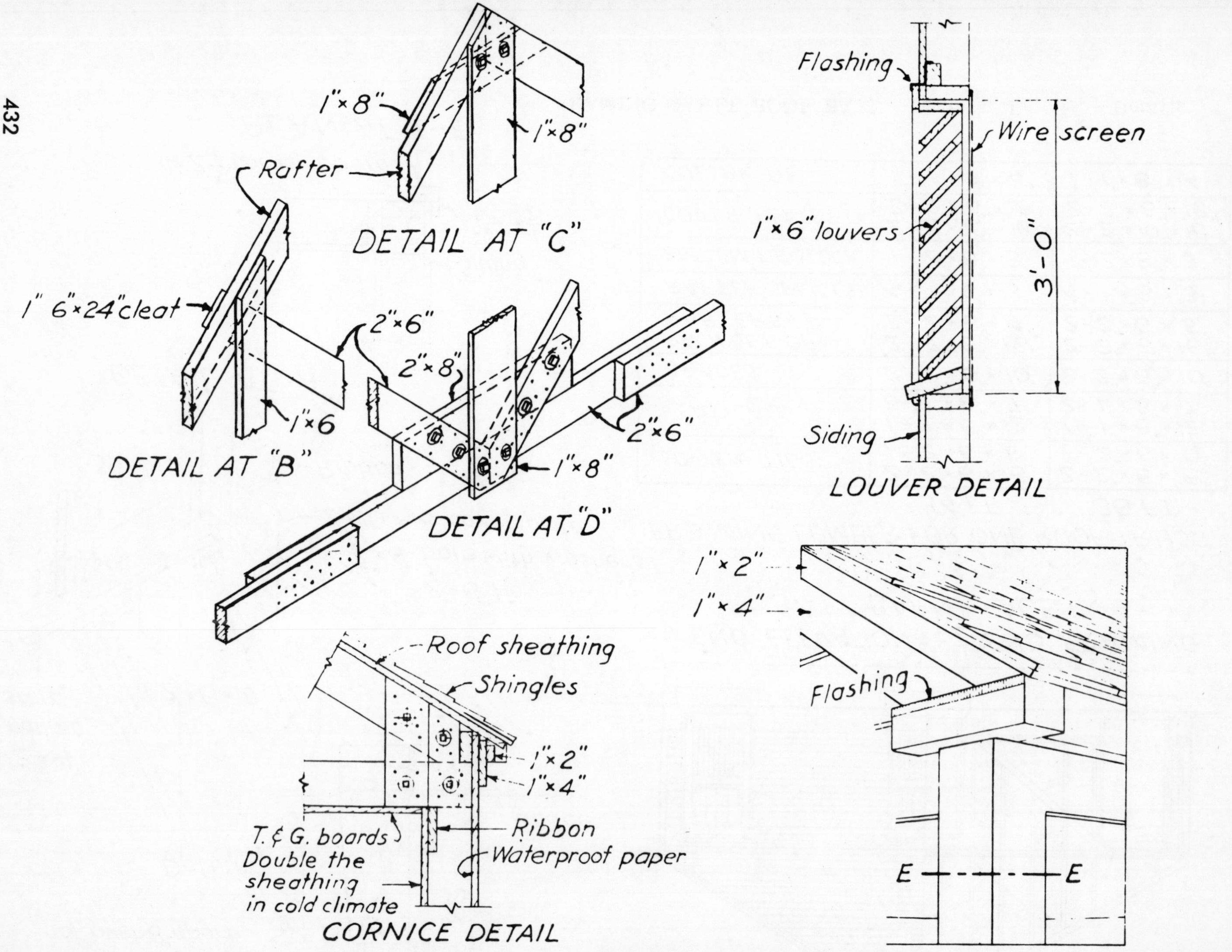

LOUVER DETAIL

Wire screen

3'-0"

Flashing

1"x 6" louvers

Siding

Flashing

1"x 2"

1"x 4"

E ———— E

DETAIL AT "C"

1"x 8"

1"x 8"

Rafter

2"x 6"

1"x 8"

DETAIL AT "D"

2"x 6"

2"x 8"

1"x 6"

DETAIL AT "B"

1" 6"x 24" cleat

Roof sheathing

Shingles

1"x 2"

1"x 4"

Ribbon

Waterproof paper

T.& G. boards

Double the
sheathing
in cold climate

CORNICE DETAIL

FRAMING GABLE ROOF BARN—Details

432

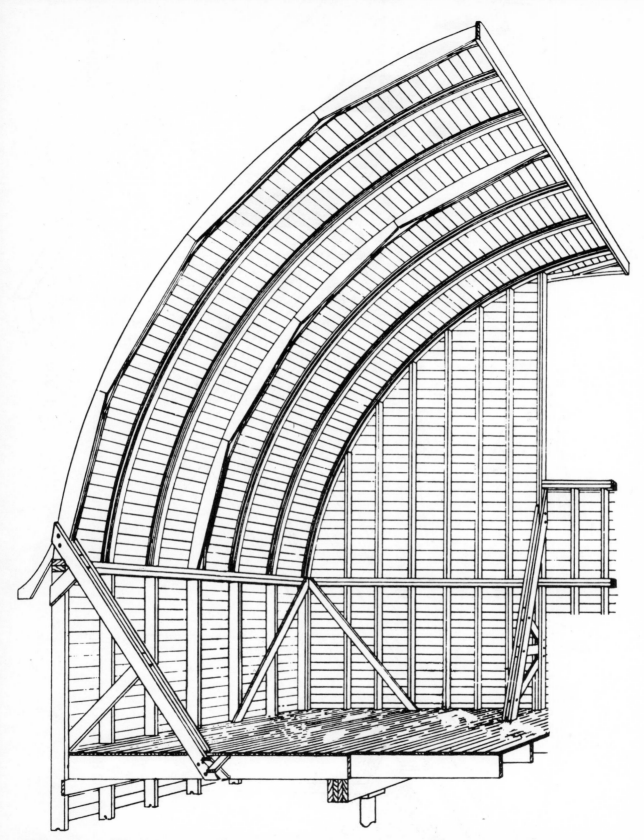

GOTHIC BARN ROOF DETAILS--Interior Perspective Showing Combinations of
Bent and Sawed Rafters. To be Used on Barns Not over 34 Ft. Wide.

433

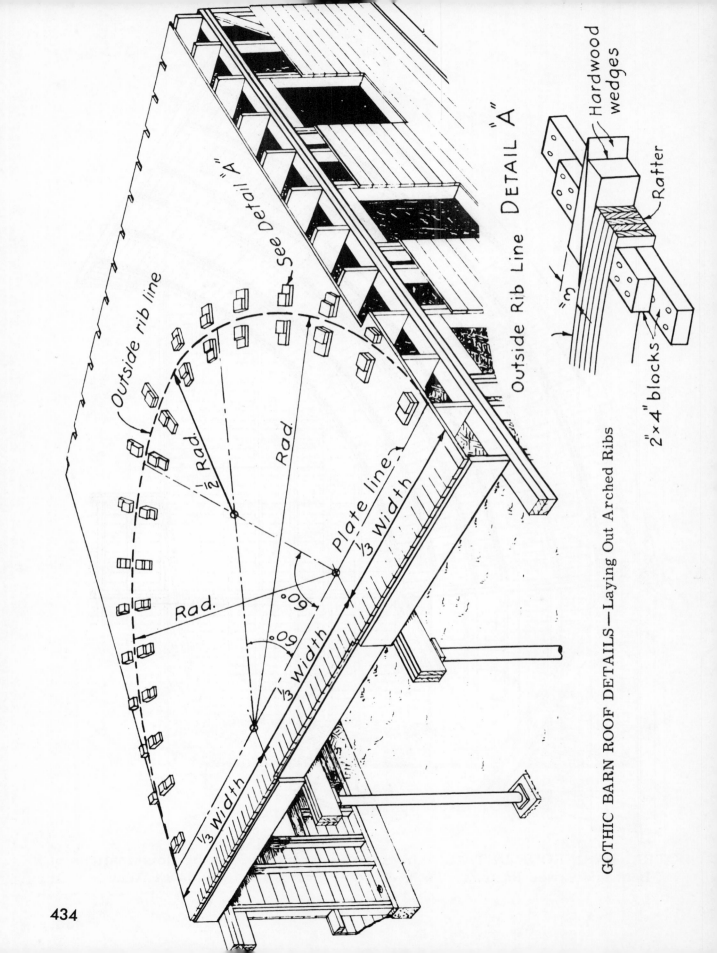

Outside rib line

See Detail "A"

½ Rad.

Rad.

Rad.

Rad.

60°

60°

Plate line

⅓ Width

⅓ Width

⅓ Width

⅓ Width

Hardwood wedges

Rafter

Outside Rib Line   DETAIL "A"

≡ 3

2×4" blocks

GOTHIC BARN ROOF DETAILS—Laying Out Arched Ribs

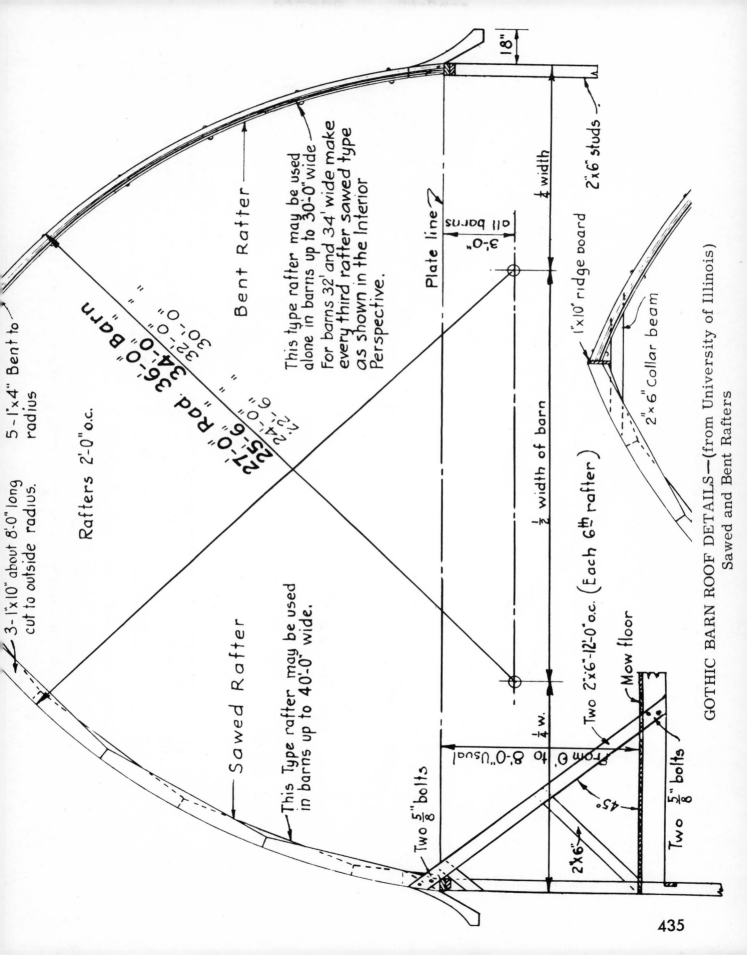

18"

2×6" studs

¼ width

Plate line

all barns
3'-0"

1×10" ridge board

2×6" Collar beam

Bent Rafter

This type rafter may be used
alone in barns up to 30'-0" wide.
For barns 32' and 34' wide make
every third rafter sawed type
as shown in the Interior
Perspective.

5 – 1"×4" Bent to
radius

Rafters 2'-0" o.c.

30'-0"
32'-0"
34'-0"
36'-0"
25'-6"
27'-0" Rad. 36'-0" Barn

3 – 1"×10" about 8'-0" long
cut to outside radius.

Sawed Rafter

This Type rafter may be used
in barns up to 40'-0" wide.

½ width of barn

¼ w.

From 6'-0" to 8'-0" Usual

Two ⅝" bolts

2×6"

45°

Mow floor

Two 2"×6"–12'-0" o.c. (Each 6th rafter)

Two ⅝" bolts

GOTHIC BARN ROOF DETAILS—(from University of Illinois)
Sawed and Bent Rafters

435

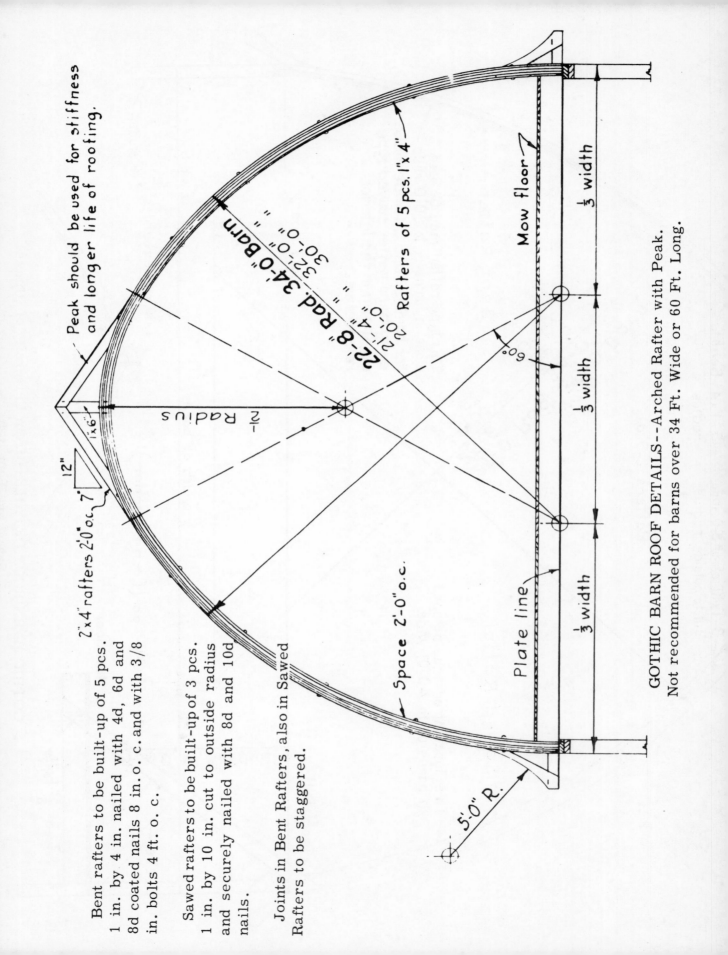

Peak should be used for stiffness and longer life of roofing.

2"x4" rafters 2'-0" o.c.

12" / 7"

1"x6"

22'-8" Rad 34'-0" barn

2½ Radius

21'-4" 32'-0"
20'-0" 30'-0"

Rafters of 5 pcs. 1"x 4"

Mow floor

60°

⅓ width

⅓ width

⅓ width

Plate line

Space 2'-0" o.c.

5'-0" R.

Bent rafters to be built-up of 5 pcs. 1 in. by 4 in. nailed with 4d, 6d and 8d coated nails 8 in. o. c. and with 3/8 in. bolts 4 ft. o. c.

Sawed rafters to be built-up of 3 pcs. 1 in. by 10 in. cut to outside radius and securely nailed with 8d and 10d nails.

Joints in Bent Rafters, also in Sawed Rafters to be staggered.

GOTHIC BARN ROOF DETAILS--Arched Rafter with Peak. Not recommended for barns over 34 Ft. Wide or 60 Ft. Long.

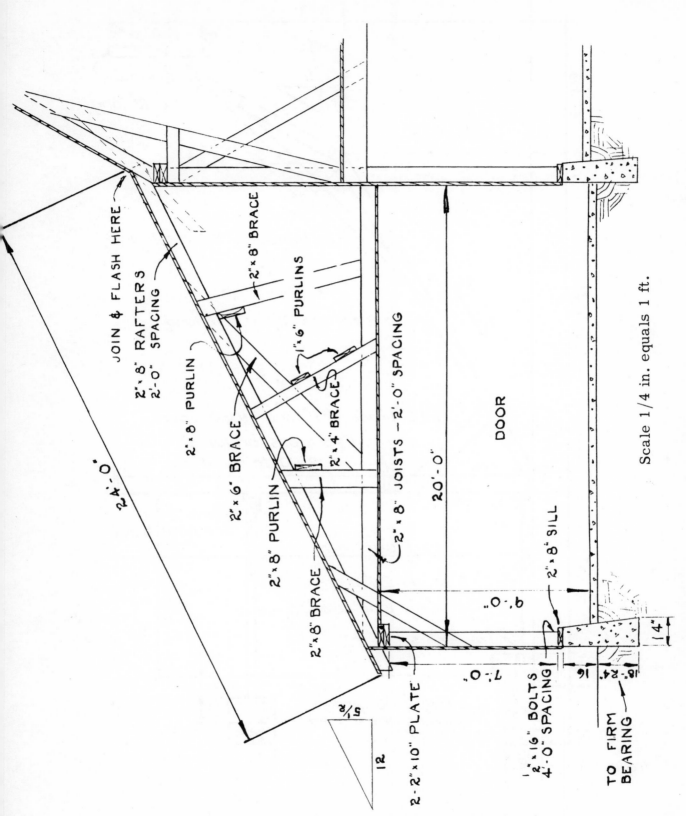

20 FOOT SHED WITH TRUSSED ROOF (from University of Illinois)

Scale 1/4 in. equals 1 ft.

437

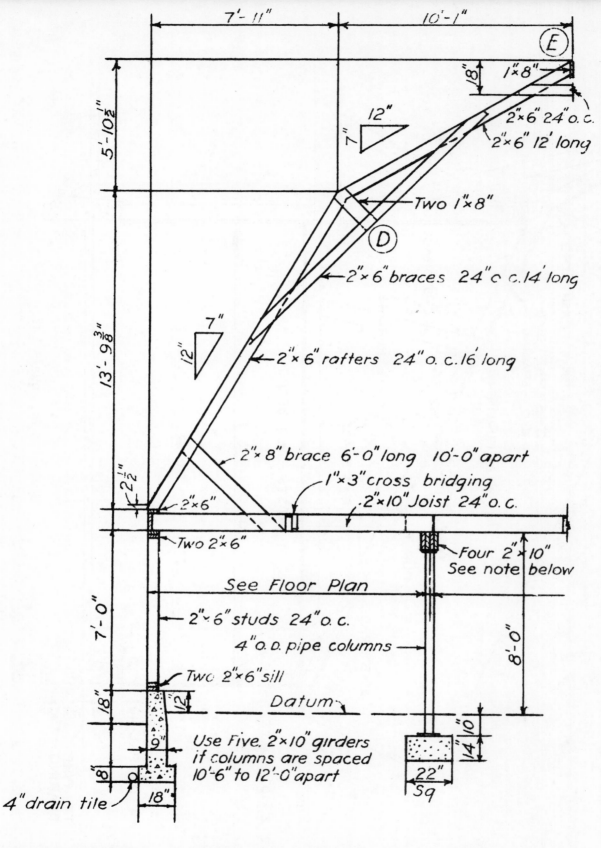

BRACED RAFTER FRAMING—36 ft. Barn—Loose hay .78 tons per lineal foot.

W-4. Perspective drawing, 24 ft. x 36 ft. pole-frame machine shed.

POLE-FRAME CONSTRUCTION

Pole-frame construction for farm buildings, particularly one-story buildings, has a number of advantages. The construction job is easy and it usually requires less high-priced material than regular frame construction. The foundation and framing are completed in one operation; the poles replace the main framing, foundation and most of the bracing required in regular frame construction.

Treated poles suitable for use in pole-frame construction are readily available from lumber yards in most localities. Poles cut from home wood-

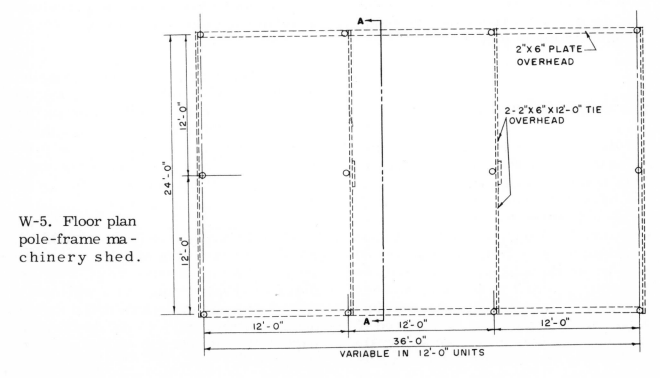

W-5. Floor plan pole-frame machinery shed.

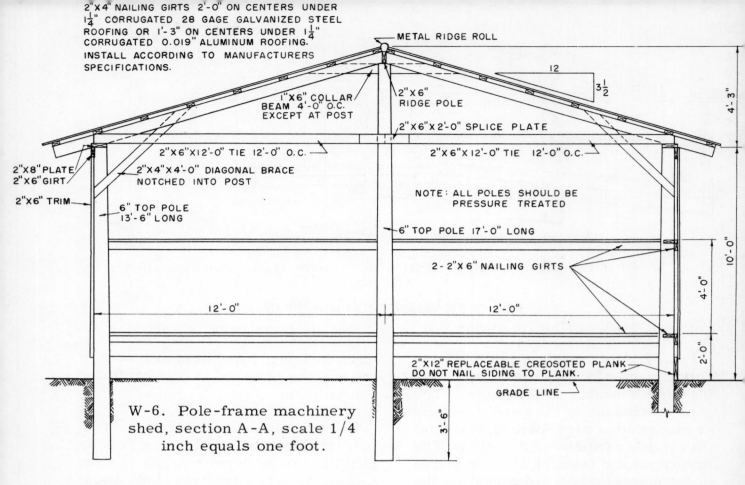

2"X 4" NAILING GIRTS 2'-0" ON CENTERS UNDER
1¼" CORRUGATED 28 GAGE GALVANIZED STEEL
ROOFING OR 1'-3" ON CENTERS UNDER 1¼"
CORRUGATED 0.019" ALUMINUM ROOFING.
INSTALL ACCORDING TO MANUFACTURERS
SPECIFICATIONS.

METAL RIDGE ROLL

12

3½

4'-3"

1"X6" COLLAR
BEAM 4'-0" O.C.
EXCEPT AT POST

2"X6"
RIDGE POLE

2"X6"X2'-0" SPLICE PLATE

2"X8"PLATE
2"X6"GIRT

2"X6"X12'-0" TIE 12'-0" O.C.

2"X6"X12'-0" TIE 12'-0" O.C.

2"X4"X4'-0" DIAGONAL BRACE
NOTCHED INTO POST

2"X6" TRIM

NOTE: ALL POLES SHOULD BE
PRESSURE TREATED

6" TOP POLE
13'-6" LONG

6" TOP POLE 17'-0" LONG

10'-0"

2-2"X6" NAILING GIRTS

4'-0"

12'-0"

12'-0"

2'-0"

2"X12" REPLACEABLE CREOSOTED PLANK
DO NOT NAIL SIDING TO PLANK.

GRADE LINE

W-6. Pole-frame machinery
shed, section A-A, scale 1/4
inch equals one foot.

3'-6"

lots are also suitable, if treated so they will last. About the only woods that do not need treating are osage orange and black locust.

TREATING HOME-CUT POLES

Poles to be treated are preferably cut in the spring while the sap is rising. This makes peeling the bark easier. The bark, both outer and inner, should be peeled off the entire pole. If there isn't time for doing this, the bark should be peeled at least from the portion that is to be set in the ground and about two feet above. Small knots and branches should be trimmed flush. After trimming, the posts should be allowed to season until very dry. This usually takes two to four months in the summer

and six to eight months in the winter. Posts won't soak up the "preserving" solution properly if they are green or wet.

A number of preserving solutions are available. Pentachlorophenol is one that has recently been brought to the attention of farmers and is available in most localities. Instructions furnished by the manufacturer of the preserving solution should be followed carefully.

After treating, the posts should be piled for seasoning and let dry until they can be handled easily. Put the stack of treated poles in a well ventilated spot and keep them out of direct sunlight since some woods check when exposed to sunlight and untreated wood is exposed.

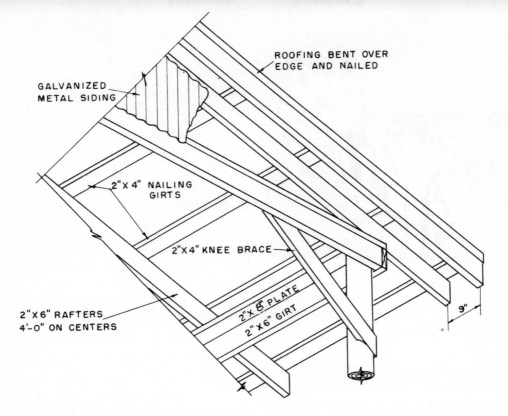

ROOFING BENT OVER
EDGE AND NAILED

GALVANIZED
METAL SIDING

2"x 4" NAILING
GIRTS

2"X4" KNEE BRACE

2"x 6" PLATE

2"x 6" GIRT

2"x 6" RAFTERS
4'-0" ON CENTERS

9"

W-7. Details showing construction of machinery shed at corner. Drawings from Mid-West Plan No. 74127.

CONSTRUCTING MACHINERY SHED

Constructional details on a practical pole-frame shed for machinery, 24 x 36 feet in size, drawing W-4, are given in Figs. W-5 and W-7.

ORDER OF CONSTRUCTION

1. Stake out location where building is to be erected. This should be on a well-drained site, particularly if dirt floor will be used.

2. Set poles. These should be placed in the ground a minimum of three and a half feet.

3. Level and nail plate onto top end of posts and nail on girt.

4. Fasten top cross ties in place onto posts; then, nail rafters to poles. Rafters should rest on plates and should not be notched.

5. Level and nail on center and bottom nailing girts.

6. Toenail remaining rafters in place.

7. Put on roof-nailing girts, then corrugated roofing, following manufacturer's specifications.

8. Nail on metal siding.

441

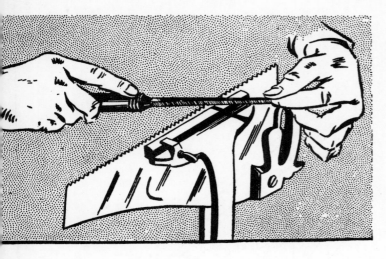

W-8. How to hold file when sharpening handsaw.

SHARPENING HAND SAWS

There are two general types of hand-saws — crosscut for cutting across the grain of wood and rip for cutting with the grain of wood. See Fig. W-10. The difference in the two saws is in the shape of the teeth. A crosscut saw has the teeth filed straight across the saw at right angle to the blade that cut like chisels.

JOINTING SAW TEETH

If the teeth of a saw are uneven or incorrectly shaped, the top edges must be filed down to the same level before sharpening. This is called jointing.

Place the saw in a clamp. Use a regular saw clamp as shown in Fig. W-8, if available. If not, you can fit the saw between two boards in a wood vise. Run a mill file lightly back and forth the length of the blade, or use a regular saw jointer, if one is at hand.

A bright light arranged so the light falls on the teeth will enable you to determine which points have been touched by the file.

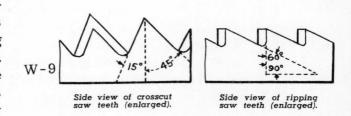

W-9

Side view of crosscut saw teeth (enlarged).

Side view of ripping saw teeth (enlarged).

W-10

Looking from back of saw. Shows how teeth, when set, extend beyond edge of blade.

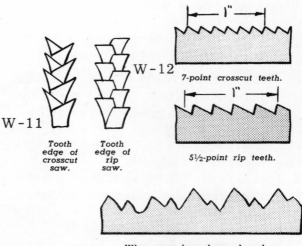

W-11

Tooth edge of crosscut saw.

Tooth edge of rip saw.

W-12

7-point crosscut teeth.

5½-point rip teeth.

W-13

When saws have been abused so the teeth are shaped like the ones shown in these drawings they need retoothing at the factory.

442

SHAPING SAW TEETH

For best results gullets or recesses between saw teeth must be of equal depth. The fronts and backs of all teeth must have the proper shape and angle (see W-9) and the teeth must be uniform in size.

To shape the teeth on a saw, either rip or crosscut, that has been jointed down considerably, place the saw in the clamp, with the handle at the right. The bottoms of the gullets should be 1/8 inch above the jaws of the clamp; allowing more of the teeth to project will cause the file to chatter and screech and dull the file quickly.

Use a slim-taper, triangular-shaped file, which suits or fits between the teeth. The following table indicates the length of file needed; the length automatically taking care of the size of the file.

5, 6-point crosscut saw, use 7 inch file
5, 5 1/2, 6-point rip saw, use 7 inch file
7, 8, 9-point crosscut saw, use 6-inch file
7-point rip saw, use 6-inch file
9, 10-point crosscut saw, use 5 1/2-inch file
10, 11, 12-point crosscut saw, use 4 1/2-inch file

To determine the point of a saw, where the figure is not given on the blade, count the number of tooth points to the inch, measuring one inch from the point of any tooth, as illustrated in Fig. W-12. In most rip saws, 6 points

and coarser, the teeth at the point are finer than the teeth in the balance of the blade; therefore in measuring rip saw teeth be sure to take the regular teeth at the butt of the blade close to the handle.

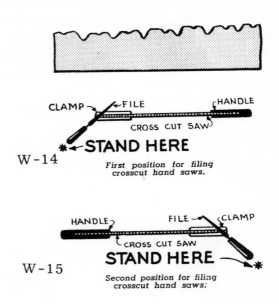

W-14

First position for filing crosscut hand saws.

W-15

Second position for filing crosscut hand saws.

Place the file well down in the gullet or space between the teeth, and file straight across the saw at right angle to the blade. Use long, even strokes; cut only on the forward stroke and raise the file each time on the return stroke. If the teeth are of unequal size press the file against the teeth having the largest tops, until you reach the center of the flat surface made by jointing. Then, move the file to the next gullet, and file until the balance of the top disappears and the tooth has been brought to a point. Keep in mind that the teeth must be all alike in size and shape to cut equal amounts of wood and make the saw operate smoothly. When all the teeth have been properly shaped and jointed you're ready to set them.

The teeth of a hand saw should be set before sharpening to avoid injuring the cutting edges with the set.

SETTING SAW TEETH

The purpose of setting saw teeth, that is, springing over the upper part of each tooth, one to the right, the next to the left, the entire length of the saw edge, Fig. W-11, is to make the saw

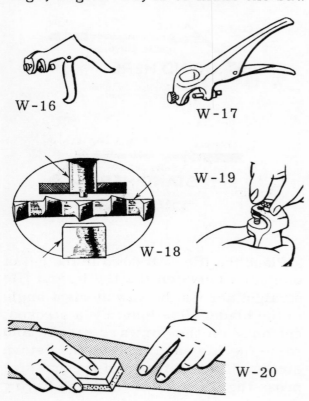

W-16

W-17

W-19

W-18

W-20

cut a kerf slightly wider than the thickness of the blade, to give clearance and prevent friction which would cause the saw to bind and be hard to pull.

In setting a handsaw, a pin punch and hammer are sometimes used, but the usual practice is to use a set as shown in Figs. W-16 or 17. Saw sets are preferable as they can be adjusted to

bend each tooth at the proper place and just the right amount.

In starting out with a saw set, first determine the number of teeth per inch of your saw, and set the anvil pointer of the set to the same number, Fig. W-19. Next, adjust the gauge screw under plunger, so saw blade passes easily between end of screw and anvil.

Starting at one end, SET EACH ALTERNATE TOOTH by pressing lever. The direction of set is correct when thin cutting edges of teeth are bent outward. Continue until you reach the end of the saw in the vise and set remaining alternate teeth in the opposite direction.

In setting teeth, particular care must be taken to see that the set is regular. It must be the same width from end to end of the blade, otherwise the saw will not cut true; it will run out of line and the cut will be "snaky."

FILING CROSSCUT HAND SAWS

Place the saw in the filing clamp with the handle at the right and the bottom of the gullets 1/8 inch above the jaws of the clamp. A way to tell which teeth have been filed is to smoke them slightly with a lighted candle before starting out. This will make it easy to see the fresh file cuts.

Stand at the position as shown in Fig. W-14. Start at the unhandled end of the saw. Pick out the first tooth that is set toward you. Place the file in the gullet to the left of this tooth. Hold the file handle toward the left, letting it find its own bearing against the teeth it touches. While filing hold the file level, do not allow it to tip upward or downward, and be sure the file sets down well into the gullet. The file should cut only on the push stroke. It files the tooth to the left and the tooth to the right at the same time. Proceed slowly. Better still, practice on an old saw of no value, if you have one, until you get the knack of handling the file.

Observe the shape and bevel of the unused teeth near the handle end of a saw. If these teeth are shaped as they were when the saw left the factory, they will serve as a guide.

File each tooth until you cut away one-half of the flat top, or smoked portion you made as a guide, then lift the file from the gullet. Skip the next gullet toward the handle. Repeat the filing operation on the two teeth the file now touches, being careful to file at the same angle as before. Continue this way, placing the file in every second gullet, until you reach the handle end of the saw.

Study Fig. W-15, before you proceed further. Turn the saw around in the clamp with the handle to the left. Take the position shown. Place the file in the gullet to the right of the first tooth set toward you—this is the first of the gullets you skipped when filing the other side of the saw. Turn the file handle to the desired angle toward the right. Now file until you cut away the other half of the flat top made on

the teeth as a guide, and the teeth are sharpened to a point. Continue this, placing the file in every second gullet, until you reach the handle.

FILING HAND RIP SAWS

With but one difference, rip saws are filed like crosscut saws. They are filed with the file held STRAIGHT ACROSS the saw, at a right angle to the blade.

Place saw in clamp with handle toward the right. Start at the opposite end. Place the file in the gullet to the left of the first tooth toward you. Continue placing file in every SECOND GULLET and filing straight across. Remember that the points, not the edges, do the cutting. When the handle of the saw is reached, turn the saw around in the clamp. Start at the unhandled end again, placing the file in the first gullet skipped when filing from the other side. Continue to file every second gullet until handle-end of saw is reached.

FINISHING WITH AN OILSTONE

After completing the filing job, it's a good idea to lay the saw flat on a bench and run an oilstone very gently over the sides of the teeth, Fig. W-20. This will correct small inaccuracies in setting, remove any burrs or wire edge that may be present, and make the saw cut more smoothly. The same treatment will usually help a saw that "runs."

INDEX

448 PRACTICAL CARPENTRY